**HEMES
AND
HEMOPROTEINS**

*Proceedings of the Third Colloquium of the
Johnson Research Foundation of the University of Pennsylvania
Philadelphia, April 16 and 17, 1966*

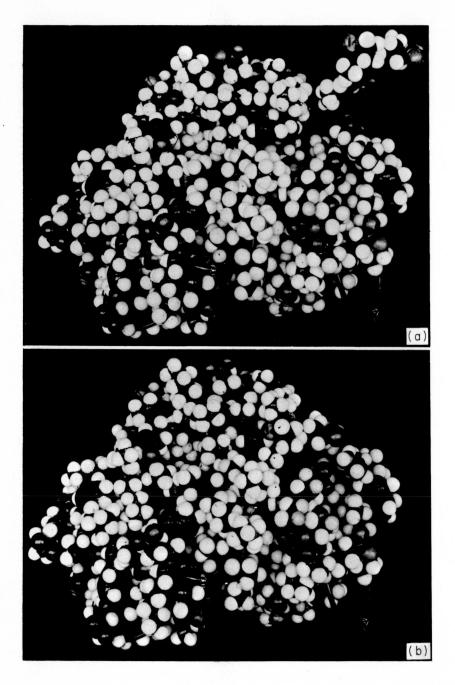

A space-filling model of sperm whale myoglobin, showing (a) the nonpolar pocket left by the removal of the heme, and (b) the intact molecule with the heme propionic acid groups forming part of the polar surface.

# HEMES
# AND
# HEMOPROTEINS

EDITED BY

BRITTON CHANCE     RONALD W. ESTABROOK

TAKASHI YONETANI

JOHNSON RESEARCH FOUNDATION, SCHOOL OF MEDICINE
UNIVERSITY OF PENNSYLVANIA, PHILADELPHIA, PENNSYLVANIA

ACADEMIC PRESS · NEW YORK · LONDON · 1966

163390

ACADEMIC PRESS INC.
111 Fifth Avenue, New York, New York 10003

United Kingdom Edition published by
ACADEMIC PRESS INC. (LONDON) LTD.
Berkeley Square House, London W.1

LIBRARY OF CONGRESS CATALOG CARD NUMBER:  66-29873

PRINTED IN THE UNITED STATES OF AMERICA

# Participants

ALAN D. ADLER, *Department of Biology, University of Pennsylvania, Philadelphia, Pennsylvania*

J. O. ALBEN, *Department of Physiological Chemistry, Johns Hopkins University School of Medicine, Baltimore, Maryland*

JACK BARRETT, *Laboratory of Chemical Biodynamics, Lawrence Radiation Laboratory, University of California, Berkeley, California*

HELMUT BEINERT, *Institute for Enzyme Research, University of Wisconsin, Madison, Wisconsin*

DEREK S. BENDALL, *Johnson Research Foundation, University of Pennsylvania School of Medicine, Philadelphia, Pennsylvania*

WALTER D. BONNER, JR., *Johnson Research Foundation, University of Pennsylvania School of Medicine, Philadelphia, Pennsylvania*

ARTHUR S. BRILL, *Department of Molecular Biophysics, Yale University, New Haven, Connecticut*

GEORGE F. CAMERON, *New England Institute for Medical Research, Ridgefield, Connecticut*

WINSLOW S. CAUGHEY, *Department of Physiological Chemistry, Johns Hopkins University School of Medicine, Baltimore, Maryland*

BRITTON CHANCE, *Johnson Research Foundation, University of Pennsylvania School of Medicine, Philadelphia, Pennsylvania*

MILDRED COHN, *Johnson Research Foundation, University of Pennsylvania School of Medicine, Philadelphia, Pennsylvania*

GEORG CZERLINSKI, *Johnson Research Foundation, University of Pennsylvania School of Medicine, Philadelphia, Pennsylvania*

DON DEVAULT, *Johnson Research Foundation, University of Pennsylvania School of Medicine, Philadelphia, Pennsylvania*

DAVID L. DRABKIN, *Department of Biochemistry, Division of Graduate Medicine, University of Pennsylvania School of Medicine, Philadelphia, Pennsylvania*

WILLIAM A. EATON, *Department of Chemistry, University of Pennsylvania, Philadelphia, Pennsylvania*

ANDERS EHRENBERG, *Biokemiska Institutionen, Medicinska Nobel-institutet, Karolinska Institutets, Stockholm, Sweden*

WILLIARD B. ELLIOTT, *Department of Biochemistry, School of Medicine, State University of New York at Buffalo, Buffalo, New York*

RONALD W. ESTABROOK, *Johnson Research Foundation, University of Pennsylvania School of Medicine, Philadelphia, Pennsylvania*

THOMAS L. FABRY, *IBM Watson Laboratory, Columbia University, New York, New York*

TORGEIR FLATMARK, *Department of Biochemistry, University of California at San Diego, La Jolla, California*

PHILIP GEORGE, *Department of Chemistry, University of Pennsylvania, Philadelphia, Pennsylvania*

QUENTIN H. GIBSON, *Department of Biochemistry and Molecular Biology, Cornell University, Ithaca, New York*

MARTIN GOUTERMAN, *Conant Chemical Laboratory, Harvard University, Cambridge, Massachusetts*

FRANK N. R. GURD, *Department of Biochemistry, Indiana University School of Medicine, Indianapolis, Indiana*

GORDON A. HAMILTON, *Frick Chemical Laboratory, Princeton University, Princeton, New Jersey*

GEORGE I. H. HANANIA, *Department of Biochemistry, American University, Beirut, Lebanon*

HENRY A. HARBURY, *Department of Biochemistry, Yale University, New Haven, Connecticut*

GEORGE P. HESS, *Department of Chemistry, Cornell University, Ithaca, New York*

J. L. HOARD, *Department of Chemistry, Cornell University, Ithaca, New York*

ROBIN M. HOCHSTRASSER, *Laboratory for Research on the Structure of Matter, University of Pennsylvania, Philadelphia, Pennsylvania*

MARTIN D. KAMEN, *Department of Chemistry, University of California at San Diego, La Jolla, California*

JOAN KEILIN, *Department of Veterinary Clinical Studies, School of Veterinary Medicine, University of Cambridge, Cambridge, England*

Tsoo E. KING, *Laboratory for Respiratory Enzymology, School of Science, Oregon State University, Corvallis, Oregon*

ARTHUR KOWALSKY, *Johnson Research Foundation, University of Pennsylvania School of Medicine, Philadelphia, Pennsylvania*

GEORGE LANG, *Physics Department, Carnegie Institute of Technology, Pittsburgh, Pennsylvania*

M. RUDOLF LEMBERG, *Department of Biochemistry, Institute of Medical Research, The Royal North Shore Hospital, Sydney, Australia*

EMANUEL MARGOLIASH, *Department of Molecular Biology, Abbott Laboratories, North Chicago, Illinois*

SINISA L. MARIČIĆ, *Johnson Research Foundation, University of Pennsylvania School of Medicine, University of Pennsylvania, Philadelphia, Pennsylvania*

ALBERT S. MILDVAN, *Johnson Research Foundation, University of Pennsylvania School of Medicine, Philadelphia, Pennsylvania*

RHONA MIRSKY, *Department of Chemistry, University of Pennsylvania, Philadelphia, Pennsylvania*

MARTIN MORRISON, *Medical Research Institute, City of Hope Medical Center, Duarte, California*

THOMAS H. MOSS, *Department of Chemistry, University of California at San Diego, La Jolla, California*

PETER NICHOLLS, *Department of Biochemistry, State University of New York at Buffalo, Buffalo, New York*

CHRISTOPHER L. NOBBS, *Medical Research Council, Laboratory of Molecular Biology, Cambridge, England*

GRAHAM PALMER, *Biophysics Research Division, Institute of Science and Technology, University of Michigan, Ann Arbor, Michigan*

ABEL SCHEJTER, *Department of Biochemistry, Tel-Aviv University, Tel Aviv, Israel*

HEINZ SCHLEYER, *Johnson Research Foundation, University of Pennsylvania School of Medicine, Philadelphia, Pennsylvania*

GREGORY R. SCHONBAUM, *Department of Biochemistry, University of Alberta, Edmonton, Alberta, Canada*

JULIUS SCHULTZ, *Department of Biological Chemistry, Hahnemann Medical College, Philadelphia, Pennsylvania*

REINHARD SEYFFERT, *Max Planck-Institut fur Zellchemie, Munchen, Germany*

VICTOR E. SHASHOUA, *Department of Biology, Massachusetts Institute of Technology, Cambridge, Massachusetts*

E. C. SLATER, *Laboratory of Biochemistry, University of Amsterdam, Amsterdam, The Netherlands*

LUCILE SMITH, *Biochemistry Department, Dartmouth Medical School, Hanover, New Hampshire*

PHILLIP STRITTMATTER, *Department of Biological Chemistry, Washington University School of Medicine, St. Louis, Missouri*

P. A. TRAYLOR, *Department of Chemistry, University of California at San Diego, La Jolla, California*

PETER URNES, *Department of Chemistry, Harvard University, Cambridge, Massachusetts*

DAN W. URRY, *Institute for Biomedical Research, Education and Research Foundation, American Medical Association, Chicago, Illinois*

WALTER W. WAINIO, *Department of Physiology and Biochemistry, Rutgers — The State University, New Brunswick, New Jersey*

JUI H. WANG, *Department of Chemistry, Yale University, New Haven, Connecticut*

HERMAN C. WATSON, *Medical Research Council, Laboratory of Molecular Biology, Cambridge, England*

R. J. P. WILLIAMS, *Inorganic Chemistry Laboratory and Wadham College, Oxford University, Oxford, England*

I. YAMAZAKI, *Biophysics Division, Research Institute of Applied Electricity, Hokkaido University, Sapporo, Japan*

TAKASHI YONETANI, *Johnson Research Foundation, University of Pennsylvania School of Medicine, Philadelphia, Pennsylvania*

F. C. YONG, *Science Research Institute, Oregon State University, Corvallis, Oregon*

MICHAEL ZERNER, *Conant Chemical Laboratory, Harvard University, Cambridge, Massachusetts*

# Preface

During the last decade, studies on hemoproteins have served as the foundation for our understanding and knowledge of the molecular structure of enzymes. The establishment by X-ray crystallography of the tertiary structure of myoglobin and hemoglobin, the determination of the primary sequence of cytochrome *c* from 28 different species, and experiments designed to measure and compare the reactivity of proteins in the crystalline and soluble states now permit the answering of penetrating questions concerning the mechanism of action of enzymes.

On the sixteenth and seventeenth of April, 1966, crystallographers, theoreticians, physical chemists, and biochemists convened in the library of the Johnson Research Foundation of the University of Pennsylvania to discuss recent developments in the study of hemes and hemoproteins. The colloquium was organized to honor M. R. Lemberg, H. Theorell, D. Drabkin, and D. Goddard, and especially to celebrate two landmarks in the study of hemoproteins — the late David Keilin's book on cell respiration and cytochrome ("Cell Respiration and Cytochrome," Cambridge Univ. Press, London and New York, 1966), and the fortieth anniversary of the studies by R. Hill and H. F. Holden on the resolution of hemoglobin [*Biochem. J. 20*, 1326 (1926)].

Starting from a consideration of the chemistry of heme and its binding proteins, the colloquium was primarily devoted to the interaction of the protein-bound heme with ligands. Formal presentations and discussions revealed both the current trends of research and the present status of experimental techniques for studying the environment of the active site and its influence on the reactivity of hemoproteins. The present volume is the result of these proceedings. The contributions of the theoreticians, in an attempt to better define and interpret the biochemists' observations, set the goals to be achieved in the future. The overwhelming efforts expended so far in furthering our knowledge of hemoproteins and the high percentage of successful results encourage an intensification of these efforts in the future. The present volume is an attempt to synthesize the many facets of heme and hemoprotein chemistry, displaying the interchange of current ideas upon which to build in the future.

The task of compiling and organizing the proceedings of a colloquium is a formidable undertaking. The skill and perseverance of Mrs. Chance, Mrs. Pilkanis, Mrs. Palmer, and Mrs. Fischer are gratefully acknowledged. In addition we wish to acknowledge the cooperation and patience of the staff of Academic Press.

THE EDITORS

September 29, 1966

# Table of Contents

## STRUCTURE AND REACTIVITY OF MYOGLOBIN AND HEMOGLOBIN

### III. Ligand Binding to Myoglobin and Hemoglobin: R. J. P. Williams, Chairman

### IV. Intermolecular Interactions of Crystalline and Soluble Myoglobin and Hemoglobin: P. George, Chairman

# STRUCTURE AND REACTIVITY OF HEMATIN ENZYMES: CATALASES, PEROXIDASES, CYTOCHROMES, AND OXIDASES

## V. Structure and Reactivity of Hydro-Peroxidases: B. Chance, Chairman

## VII. Ligand Binding and Reaction Mechanisms of Oxidases: J. H. Wang, Chairman

## VIII. Kinetics of Electron Transfer Reactions in Cytochrome $c$: T. Yonetani, Chairman

# THEORETICAL INTERPRETATIONS

# CHEMISTRY OF HEMES AND HEMOPROTEINS

# OPENING REMARKS

Occasionally, there is a very appropriate moment for a Colloquium. It has seemed to me that, this year, the upsurge of experimentation on a number of aspects of hemoprotein study has progressed to a point which merits special consideration. While we are several years "post-myoglobin", the application of the crystallographic technique to a number of other proteins presages our eventual knowledge of the detailed structure of many important enzymes. At the same time, the development of incisive physical methods has proceeded apace: optical techniques have reached new levels of sensitivity and rapidity; electron spin and nuclear magnetic resonance, volume magnetic susceptibility and optical rotatory dispersion, and now Mössbauer studies, have been added to provide definitive information on atomic and electronic properties of the heme. Kinetic studies by the stopped, accelerated, and continuous flow methods are supplemented with fast photolysis techniques, most recently employing the Q-switched laser. And last, but by no means least, the chemist's approach to the study of the nature of hemoprotein compounds and the reactions of the active sites with various ligands continues to progress rapidly. Preparative enzymology may reveal hemoproteins with unusual properties for detailed study; examples are hemoglobin M and cytochrome c peroxidase.

However, perhaps the most compelling reason to hold a Heme Colloquium at this time is that our good friend and colleague from Australia, Professor M. R. Lemberg, has come to the Johnson Foundation for a few months. He has devoted his life to hemoproteins and is a symbol of vigor and productivity in this field. This small colloquium is dedicated to his interest and honor.

Britton Chance

# INTRODUCTORY REMARKS

## Rudolf Lemberg

It is a great pleasure for me to preside over this symposium together with my old friend, Dr. Drabkin, and our gracious host, Dr. Chance, whom I thank for his all too kind introductory words. This is following the 1959 Canberra and the 1964 Amherst symposia as the third symposium especially devoted to hemoproteins. I do not wish to delay the beginning of this very rich intellectual meal which the organizers have prepared for us, but I feel I ought to add a note of sadness and one of gladness; sadness that the beloved master of many of us David Keilin, is no longer with us, and gladness that Joan Keilin, now a research worker of high repute in her own right, is present. I also wish to welcome the other visitors, many old friends and some new.

Now without further delay I ask our first chairman, Professor Slater, to begin proceedings.

# I.

# Structure and Reactions of Heme
## E. C. Slater, Chairman

# STEREOCHEMISTRY OF PORPHYRINS[*]

J. L. Hoard

Cornell University
Ithaca, New York

A diagram of the porphine skeleton, the essential core of any porphyrin molecule, is given in Fig. 1. No double bonds are indicated; the patterns of delocalized $\Pi$-bonding in porphine and the porphyrins, as subsequently evaluated with the aid of the structural data, are not easily represented by any combination of classical formulae. A number of important porphyrins are simply derived from deuteroporphyrin-IX, the convenient trivial name for 1,3,5,8-tetramethylporphyrin-6,7-dipropionic acid. Replacement in a porphyrin of the two central hydrogen atoms attached to nitrogen by a divalent metal atom, or by ClFe(III), $CH_3OFe(III)$, etc., yields a metalloporphyrin; the metal atom, to which the four nitrogen atoms are then complexed, assumes a coordination number of 4,5,6 ... as determined by the number of axial ligands. Of little or no direct biological significance is the synthetic $\alpha$, $\beta$, $\gamma$, $\delta$-tetraphenylporphine (abbreviated as TPP) and its metal derivatives, but structural studies of these materials have provided some quite important information.

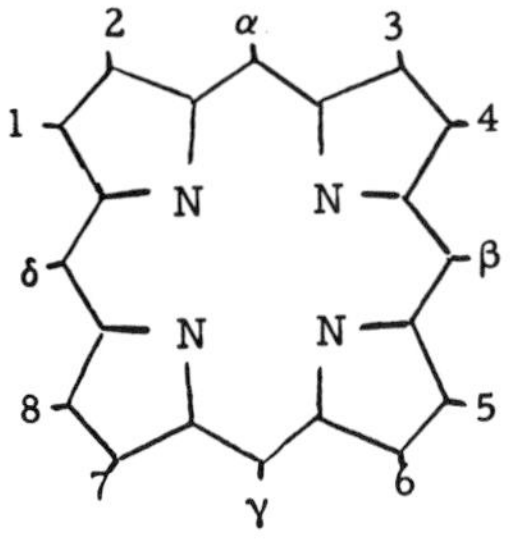

Fig. 1. Diagram of the porphine skeleton.

Note that in Table I

$C_\alpha \cdots C_\delta$ become $C_m$

$C_1 \cdots C_8$ become $C_b$

Unnumbered carbon atoms (pyrrole $\alpha$ carbons) become $C_a$.

[*]Supported by PHS Grant GM 09370 and NSF Grant G-23470, and by the Advanced Research Projects Agency under Contract No. SD-68 with Cornell University.

The principal obstacle to rapid progress in elucidating porphyrin structure has proved to be the reluctance of these materials, especially those of prime biological interest, to furnish single crystals suitable for X-ray diffraction analysis. Typically, the crystals either are much too small or, when large enough, are subject to internal packing disorder that may vary markedly both in kind and in degree. Crystalline disorder often is so extensive as to preclude structure determination; in more favorable cases the nature of the disorder must be identified and its importance assessed, else the structural results may be definitely misleading (vide infra). In four of the five structural studies for which we can report reliable stereochemical data, it was necessary to evaluate the role of crystalline disorder.

Stereochemistry of the porphine core in porphyrins. The structural investigations that contribute significantly to the understanding of the stereochemical characteristics of the essential porphine skeleton in porphyrins are first discussed. Our published (1) structure determination for triclinic crystals of nickel (II) 2,4-diacetyldeuteroporphyrin-IX dimethyl ester (abbreviated as NiDeut)* furnishes, we judge, the most accurate set of bond parameters that have been obtained for a metalloporphyrin. The accuracy of the determination, nevertheless, does not suffice to establish the reality of subtle variations in the bond parameters of the porphine skeleton that one would expect to be produced by the diverse chemical nature and asymmetric substitution pattern of the side-chains. Bond distances and angles in the porphine skeleton, averaged in agreement with the four-fold symmetry of $C_{4v}$ (or, effectively, of $D_{4h}$), are listed in Table II along with analogous (but generally less accurate) data for some other porphyrins. Such averaging is justified by the fact that no experimentally determined bond parameter departs sufficiently from the average for the type, when compared with the calculated standard error,

*Abbreviated terminology for porphyrins:

| Abbreviation | Compound |
|---|---|
| NiDeut | Nickel(II) 2,4-diacetyldeuteroporphyrin-IX dimethyl ester |
| CuTTP | Copper(II) tetraphenylporphine |
| PdTTP | Palladium(II) tetraphenylporphine |
| ClHem | Chlorohemin |
| MeOFeMeso | Methoxyiron(III) mesoporphyrin-IX dimethyl ester |
| tet-TTP | Tetraphenylporphine--in tetragonal crystals |
| trc-TTP | Tetraphenylporphine-- in triclinic crystals |
| (H₂OFeOH)TTP | Aquohydroxyiron(III) tetraphenylporphine |

to attain probable significance; standard deviations are 0.007 Å for Ni-N, ~ 0.010 Å for C-N and C-C bond lengths, and range from 0.35 to 0.75° for bond angles. The averaging of the data reported in Table I reduces the number of distinct structural classes of carbon atoms in the porphine skeleton to just three -- as one might expect for an isolated porphine molecule (cf., Fig. 1); the three classes are methine carbon, designated $C_m$ in Table I, and pyrrole carbons, $C_a$ and $C_b$, which correspond to the $\alpha$ and $\beta$ carbons of a free pyrrole molecule.

Apart from that of NiDeut, the tetragonal structure type reported by Fleischer et al. (2) for two isomorphous metal derivatives of tetraphenylporphine, CuTPP and PdTPP, affords the one additional example of a crystalline arrangement known to be utilized without packing disorder by a metalloporphyrin.

TABLE I

Averaged Bond Data for the Central Skeleton in Porphyrin

| | Distances, Å | | | | | |
|---|---|---|---|---|---|---|
| | M-N | $N-C_a$ | $C_a-C_b$ | $C_b-C_b$ | $C_m-C_a$ | Ref. |
| NiDeut | 1.960 | 1.383 | 1.446 | 1.350 | 1.375 | (1) |
| CuTPP | 1.981 | 1.385 | 1.449 | 1.337 | 1.369 | (2) |
| PdTPP | 2.009 | 1.373 | 1.436 | 1.346 | 1.400 | (2) |
| ClHem | 2.062 | 1.384 | 1.449 | 1.337 | 1.378 | (13) |
| MeOFeMeso | 2.073 | 1.395 | 1.466 | 1.368 | 1.377 | (12) |
| tet-TPP | 2.054* | 1.350 | 1.438 | 1.362 | 1.403 | (8) |
| trc-TPP | 2.065* | 1.370 | 1.442 | 1.351 | 1.400 | (9) |
| Porphine | 2.051* | 1.366 | 1.442 | 1.342 | 1.386 | (10) |
| ($H_2$OFeOH)YPP | 2.049 | 1.383 | 1.445 | 1.378 | 1.395 | (14) |

| | Bond Angles, Deg. | | | | | |
|---|---|---|---|---|---|---|
| | $C_a-NC_a$ | $NC_aC_b$ | $C_aC_b-C_b$ | $NC_a-C_m$ | $C_aC_m-C_a$ | Ref. |
| NiDeut | 104.4 | 110.0 | 106.8 | 125.3 | 123.9 | (1) |
| CuTPP | 107.8 | 107.9 | 108.1 | 127.3 | 123.1 | (2) |
| PdTPP | 106.4 | 109.5 | 107.3 | 124.9 | 125.0 | (2) |
| ClHem | 106.1 | 109.4 | 107.6 | 124.9 | 125.9 | (13) |
| MeOFeMeso | 107.0 | 109.1 | 107.4 | 125.9 | 124.1 | (12) |
| tet-TPP | 108.9 | 108.7 | 106.9 | 126.1 | 125.2 | (8) |
| trc-TPP | 107.7 | 108.8 | 107.4 | 126.2 | 125.6 | (9) |
| Porphine | 107.8 | 108.5 | 107.5 | 125.5 | 126.8 | (10) |
| ($H_2$OFeOH)TPP | 105.5 | 110.8 | 106.6 | 125.9 | | (14) |

*
 Ct.-N distance (Ct. = center of skeleton).

11

The accuracy of the structure determination for CuTPP approaches that attained for NiDeut, and one notes that corresponding C-C and C-N distances (Table I) within the porphine skeletons of these materials are in generally close agreement.

Table II presents bond orders for the porphine skeleton in the NiDeut molecule as evaluated by the somewhat different approaches that have used experimentally determined bond lengths to this end. The MO bond orders were read from bond order vs. bond length curves constructed by Lofthus (3) with the aid of molecular orbital theory; orders of 1 and 2 correspond to the respective bond lengths of 1.543 and 1.335 Å for C-C links and to 1.474 and 1.274 Å for C-N links. The $\pi$-bond orders in the fourth column were computed following Cruickshank and Sparks (4); $\pi$-bond orders of 0 and 1 for C-C links correspond, respectively, to a pure $\pi$-bond of 1.48 Å length between two trigonally hybridized carbon atoms and a standard double bond of 1.335 Å length. Simple enumeration of the classical Kekulé-type formulae gives the double bond characters in the fifth column.

The data listed in Table II suggest a less general delocalization of $\pi$-bonding than any of the published theoretical treatments (5-7) of the porphine skeleton would lead one to expect. The close approach of the $C_b-C_b$ bond distance to the double bond value should be viewed in context with the observed shortening of the $C_a-C_b$ distance from the pure $\sigma$ bond ($sp^2$ hybridization) value of 1.48 Å; this latter provides the more sensitive test for delocalization of $\pi$-bonding. It does not appear (Table II) that C-C and $N-C_a$ bond lengths vary largely from one metalloporphyrin to another. Interest in small variations of this sort is currently dwarfed by a number of striking stereochemical phenomena that remain to be presented.

TABLE II

Bond Orders in the Porphine Skeleton

| Bond Type | Length, Å | MO Bond Order | $\pi$-Bond Order | Kekulé Approx. |
|---|---|---|---|---|
| $N-C_a$ | 1.383 | 1.39 | 0.2[*] | 1/4 |
| $C_a-C_b$ | 1.446 | 1.40 | 0.18 | 1/4 |
| $C_b-C_b$ | 1.350 | 1.92 | 0.88 | 3/4 |
| $C_m-C_a$ | 1.375 | 1.81 | 0.67 | 1/2 |

[*]

This estimate corresponds to 1.42 Å for the length of a trigonally hybridized C-N $\sigma$-bond and 1.274 Å for a C=N double bond. See text.

From our earliest structure determination (8) for the tetragonal modification of crystalline tetraphenylporphine (tet-
TPP) -- or equally from the essentially isomorphous CuTPP structure (2) -- we concluded that the porphine moiety, as compared
with an aromatic hydrocarbon of the benzene series, is quite
susceptible to significant folding, ruffling, or doming when
subjected to moderate stressing. Thus, the TPP (or CuTPP)
molecule in the crystal is markedly ruffled in agreement with
the point group $S_4$ or 4; methine carbon atoms of $\alpha$ and $\gamma$ type
(Fig. 1) lie nearly 0.40 Å above the mean skeletal plane, those
of $\beta$ and $\delta$ type the same distance below. Further, the pattern
of anisotropic thermal vibrations (8) strongly supports the
conclusion that deformation normal to the mean plane requires
only comparatively modest stresses; there would seem, indeed,
to be quite general agreement on this point (1,2,8-10).
Although complete planarity of the porphine skeleton as the
equilibrium configuration has not been objectively demonstrated
for any porphyrin molecule, the observed deviations from planarity in crystals are generally smaller (1,9,12,13) than in the
cited instances. In crystalline porphine (10), the quasi-$S_4$
ruffling of the skeleton would seem quite trivial, both practically and theoretically, were it not objectively significant in
terms of the assigned accuracy with which atomic positions were
determined.

The comparative ease of deformation of the porphine skeleton would seem to arise (1,8) as follows: (I) A planar configuration, unlike the case of a benzenoid hydrocarbon, cannot
be expected to minimize the angular strains in the pattern of
$\sigma$-bonding, whereas a moderately ruffled or domed configuration
would do so. (II) The significant part of the delocalized $\pi$-
bonding favoring a planar configuration (individual pyrrole
rings should be planar in any case) is confined to the meander-
ing band or sixteen-membered ring comprising methine carbon,
$C_a$ carbon, and nitrogen atoms (Fig. 1); the capacity of $\pi$-bond-
ing to enforce planarity is surely more limited than in the
benzene series. The standard expectation is that II will dom-
inate, but one should recognize that observations on the isolated molecule are required to prove or disprove the matter.
Configurational adaptibility of the skeleton to environmental
stresses is to be expected in any case.

In the structural arrangement briefly reported by Silvers
and Tulinsky (9) for the triclinic form of tetraphenylporphine
(trc-TPP), the central pair of hydrogen atoms in the molecule
are attached to a diagonally opposed pair of nitrogen atoms
(Fig. 1). The separation of this pair of nitrogen atoms is
0.14 Å greater than that of the other diagonally opposed pair
that do not carry hydrogen atoms. The mean radius of the central "hole" i.e., the average distance of a nitrogen atom from

the center of the molecule (Ct.-N) is 2.065 Å.  In <u>tet</u>-TPP (8) or, equally, in porphine (10) the hydrogen atoms are handled quite differently.  Fourier difference synthesis gave unambiguous resolution of the central hydrogen atoms as four half-atom peaks each in just the right position to be bonded to a nitrogen atom.  This observation, as pointed out by Webb and Fleischer (10), suggests that the two protons must occupy statistically the four half-atom positions; a nuclear magnetic resonance study (11) of TPP in solution supports this interpretation.  One may add that the frequency of the interchange is apparently comparable, at least, with that of vibrations involving the nitrogen atoms.

In our NiDeut paper (1) it was pointed out that the radius of the central hole, Ct.-N, is from 0.05 to 0.10 Å larger in a porphyrin or metalloporphyrin than it is in the analogous phthalocyanine or metal derivative thereof.  A combination of two factors was seen to account for most of this difference in metric:  The distance of methine carbon or of the corresponding nitrogen in the phthalocyanines from the center of the molecule appears to approach constancy at 3.40 $\pm$ 0.02 Å, but the ring bond angle at methine carbon (Fig. 1) in the porphyrins is consistently about 125° whereas that at nitrogen in the phthalocyanines is ∼117°.  The geometrical relations are shown in the superposition diagram of Fig. 2.  Inasmuch as approximate theory is all too likely to take just the same form for porphyrins and phthalocyanines, it is of some importance to recognize that these classes of materials differ structurally to a degree that gives rise to quite real differences in properties.  Thus, the chloroiron (III) derivative of phthalocyanine differs from the analogous chlorohemin in spin state (12).

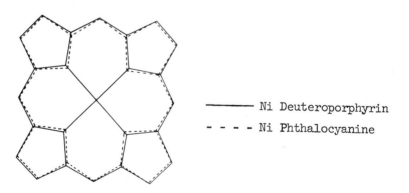

———— Ni Deuteroporphyrin

- - - - Ni Phthalocyanine

<u>Figure 2.</u>  Superposition diagram of the inner skeletons of the NiDeut and nickel phthalocyanine molecules.

The coordination group in metalloporphyrins. The radius of the central hole, Ct.-N, is 2.054 Å in tet-TPP, and it averages 2.051 Å in porphine and 2.065 Å in trc-TPP. Consequently, one concludes that a value of 2.05-2.06 Å for Ct.-N is characteristic of the neutral unsubstituted porphine moiety in a porphyrin, and that this is likely to be exceeded only for the mono- or di-protonated cationic species. In no metalloporphyrin thus far studied has the Ct.-N distance exceeded 2.02 Å; for metal-nitrogen bond distances larger than 2.01 Å, the metal atom is observed to lie out-of-plane from the four nitrogen atoms (vide infra). In the Ni(II), Cu(II), and Pd(II) derivatives, with M-N distances ranging from 1.960 to 2.009 Å (Table I), the metal atom is accurately centered among the four nitrogens.

Much of the information outlined earlier is utilized in the extensive discussion, especially of the coordination group, that appears in our paper (12) on the crystalline structure and molecular stereochemistry of methoxyiron(III) mesoporphyrin-IX dimethyl ester (abbreviated as MeOFeMeso). It was necessary to identify and to take into account an interesting type of packing disorder in the crystal that, as it turned out, did not seriously affect the accuracy with which the bond parameters of the central coordination group were determined.

The geometry of the five-coordinate square-pyramidal coordination group in the MeOFeMeso molecule is displayed in Fig. 3. The iron atom lies 0.455 Å out-of-plane from the nitrogen atoms and, indeed, some 0.490 Å from the mean plane of the porphine skeleton; this latter is somewhat domed, with the iron atom at the top, even though the molecules of the porphyrin fit back to back in the crystal. The Fe-N and Fe-O bond lengths of 2.073 and 1.842, respectively, carry standard errors of 0.006 and 0.004 Å. The shortness of the Fe-O bond for a high-spin sextet Fe(III) complex is ascribable to features of the five-coordinate geometry: the non-bonding or closed shell repulsions between oxygen and the nitrogen ligands are much smaller than in a normal octahedral complex and, more important, the electron density associated with the electron in the $d_z2$ orbital of the high-spin iron atom can be largely accommodated in the lobe pointing away from the methoxy ligand.

Allowing for the difference in Fe-Cl and Fe-OMe bond lengths, Fig. 2 serves almost equally well to describe the five-coordinate group reported by Koenig (13) in his admirable study of chlorohemin (i.e., chloroiron(III) protoporphyrin-IX). Packing disorder in the crystal was somewhat more serious for chlorohemin than for MeOFeMeso, and Koenig's bond parameters carry larger standard deviations than do ours. The iron atom is 0.475 Å out-of-plane from the nitrogen atoms in chlorohemin, and an Fe-N bond length of 2.062 Å is obtained.

15

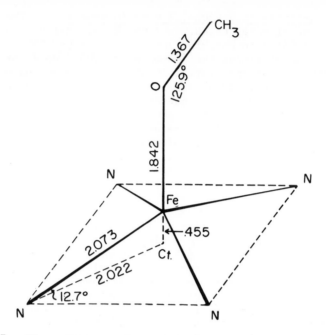

<u>Figure 3</u>. The square-pyramidal five-coordination group in the molecule of methoxyiron (III) mesoporphyrin-IX dimethyl ester.

Consideration of the structural parameters of the MeOFe-Meso coordination group, in conjunction with a wealth of background material from more general studies, led us to propose (12) the following hypothesis in respect to the stereochemical behavior of high-spin (quintet and sextet) iron porphyrins. A substantial displacement (>0.30 Å) of the iron atom from the plane of the four nitrogen atoms to which it is bonded is a normal structural property of all high-spin iron porphyrins. It is based upon the premise that the electronic structure of high-spin Fe$^{+++}$ gives this ion too large an effective size to allow it to be accommodated in the plane of the nitrogen atoms, and, <u>a fortiori</u>, that the same principle must apply to the still larger high-spin Fe$^{++}$. Ferroheme, chlorohemin, and MeO-FeMeso are familiar examples of high-spin ferrous and ferric porphyrins (12).

When this hypothesis was first put forward (at the Gordon Conference on "Metals and Metal Binding in Biology" in July, 1964), it was recognized that the structure determination reported by Fleischer <u>et al</u>. (2) for the high-spin aquohydroxy-iron(III) tetraphenylporphine (to be written as (H$_2$OFeOH)TPP)

16

rather spoke against our proposal. It was pointed out at the Conference that the structure analysis had ignored quite convincing evidence for disorder in the crystal. To resolve the problem, we have recently utilized the experimental data of Fleischer et al. (ADI Document 7869) for $(H_2OFeOH)TPP$ to demonstrate that such disorder does indeed characterize the crystalline arrangement, and that the iron atom lies nearly 0.40 Å out-of-plane from the nitrogen. A paper (14) describing this work was presented at the ACS "Symposium on Biologically Significant Coordination Compounds", Pittsburgh, March 28-31, 1966, and is slated for early publication.

The nature of the $(H_2OFeOH)TPP$ crystal structure is briefly as follows. The structural framework of the tetragonal crystal is essentially determined by the packing of the tetraphenylporphine moieties, and the central coordination group of each molecule is given virtually unrestricted opportunity to assume its preferred configuration -- to the degree, indeed, that the polar sequence $H_2O$-Fe-OH within the octahedral coordination group may equally well be aligned parallel or antiparallel with the four-fold axis. Although the experimental data are of quite satisfactory quality, the completely ordered structure proposed by Fleischer et al. does not refine properly; it leads rather to such large apparent thermal motions of the iron atoms along the four-fold axes as to preclude altogether (2) the use of the standard techniques of anisotropic refinement.

Inasmuch as there is no dimensional restriction on the use of a mixture of parallel and anti-parallel orientations of the polar coordination groups, and it is further evident that a statistically random (1:1) mixture is conducive both to kinetic simplicity during crystallization and to a stabilizing entropy of mixing, we have reanalyzed the data in terms of just such a disordered structure. The model which leads to the same answer by any and all variations of the usual refinement. procedures is sufficiently described by specifying the statistically averaged molecule of $C_{4h}$-4/m symmetry in the space group I4/m. All atoms of the porphine skeleton, the four phenyl carbon atoms attached to methine carbons, and the four terminal carbon atoms of phenyl groups lie in the symmetry plane at $z$ = 0, and the planes of the phenyl groups are parallel to the tetragonal $c$ axis. Half-atoms of iron lie on the $c$ axis at $\pm z$ and oxygen atoms on the $c$-axis at $\pm z'$ (half-atoms of oxygen from $H_2O$ and OH on the same side of the iron atom turn out not to be resolvable from one another).

Full-matrix least-squares refinement of the statistical model leads to a conventional R of 0.100 in the isotropic case, to 0.073 with anisotropic refinement; both refinements check out very satisfactorily against final difference syntheses and give, by objective criteria, essentially the same quantitative description of the structure. An $\underline{R}$ of 0.17 was reported by Fleischer et al. (2).

Bond parameters within the porphine skeleton and the phenyl groups are in good agreement with the data from other studies given in Table II. The corresponding parameters given by Fleischer et al. (2) are internally consistent in terms of the estimated standard deviations cited by them, but the new results represent a striking improvement. Thus, the six phenyl C-C bond lengths from the earlier study range from 1.30 to 1.44 Å, average to 1.385 Å, and carry an e.s.d. for an individual bond length of 0.06 Å; the three independent phenyl C-C bond lengths from the study now reported range from 1.38 to 1.41 Å, average to 1.395 Å, and carry an e.s.d. for an individual bond length of 0.013 Å.

In Fig. 4 the statistically averaged model is represented in the manner recommended by Johnson (15). The resolution of the two half-atoms of iron is made evident, as is, equally, the lack of resolution of any other pair of half-atoms. The size and shape of each ellipsoid is quantitatively indicative of the thermal motion of the associated atom, half-atom, or pair of un-resolved half-atoms, as the case may be; the probability that the center of the vibrating entity lies on or within the asso-ciated ellipsoid is 0.65 as a time average. Inasmuch as the apparent thermal motions of atoms (unresolved half-atoms, in principle) in the porphine skeleton of the statistically aver-aged molecule are not much larger parallel to the $\underline{c}$ axis than they are in the perpendicular mirror plane, one concludes both that the model is a very good approximation and that the por-phine skeleton of an individual molecule in the crystal does not depart significantly from planarity.

In the coordination group of the statistically averaged molecule, the iron half-atom is formally displaced 0.384 ± 0.005 Å from the plane of the nitrogen atoms, and is thus 0.77 Å away from its mirror image. It seems more probable that not that (mathematical) overlap of these two half-atoms in the refinement procedures gives the 0.77 Å separation as a minimum value. This view finds some support in the observation that the shorter (2.19 Å) of the two Fe-O bond distances is about 0.10 Å longer than is anticipated for octahedrally coor-dinated high-spin $Fe^{+++}$ to $H_2O$ or, especially, to $OH^-$. One then notes that the much larger of the two Fe-O separations at 2.96 Å corresponds only to a weak interaction with a neutral water molecule, but to a quite favorable electrostatic inter-action of $Fe^{+++}$ with $OH^-$. It would seem that the shorter 2.19 Å distance needs to be assigned to the $Fe-OH_2$ bond in order to account for the stability of the coordination group

18

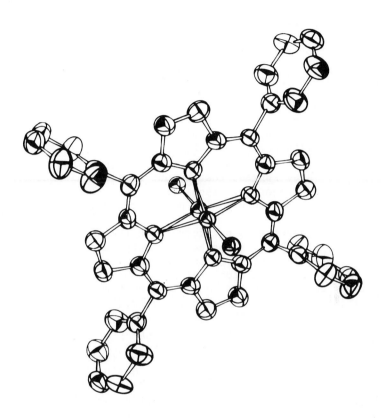

Figure 4. Diagram of the statistically averaged $(H_2FeOH)TPP$ molecule. Note the clear resolution of the half-atoms of iron.

toward loss of water in ordinary circumstances, e.g., from the loosely packed crystals. This assignment gains appeal if one notes that the electron in the $\underline{d}_{z^2}$ orbital of $Fe^{+++}$ must have a stronger repulsive interaction with the charged $OH^-$ than with the neutral $H_2O$. It is plausible, consequently, to associate the 2.19 and 2.96 Å distances with the respective $Fe-OH_2$ and $Fe-OH^-$ bonds, and thus arrive at a model that suggests why the six-coordination group may be stable toward loss of water and transformation into a highly polar five-coordination group analogous to that in the MeOFeMeso molecule.

Although our resolution of the problem of crystalline disorder is, we believe, surely correct, it would be idle to pretend that accurate Fe-O bond lengths have been obtained.

The out-of-plane displacement of the iron atom in sperm whale metmyoglobin, reported by Kendrew (16) as greater than 0.25 Å, presumably represented a conservative estimate that took into account both the low resolution of the structure determination and the novelty of the phenomenon. All of the published structural data thus far reported for high-spin iron porphyrins, although limited as yet to Fe(III) derivatives, are in agreement with our stereochemical hypothesis (12) as stated above. According to M. Gouterman (17), recent theoretical calculations also suggest that an out-of-plane displacement of the high-spin iron atom is required for stability of the por-phyrin whether the coordination number be four, five, or six.

A second hypothesis put forward in the MeOFeMeso paper (12) deals with the anticipated stereochemical behavior of six-coordinate low-spin iron in a porphyrin. It was suggested that the low-spin iron atom, Fe(II) or Fe(III), must be nearly or exactly centered in the mean plane of the nitrogen atoms, and that all bond distances should be $\gtrsim 0.10$ Å shorter than those corresponding to the high-spin complex. This suggestion, indeed, is merely an extension to the porphyrins of principles generally obeyed by coordination complexes involving the more usual ligands (i.e., molecular oxygen not included) with which the inorganic chemist commonly deals. One would then expect that transformation of an iron porphyrin from the high-spin to the low-spin state -- accomplished, let us say, by the intro-duction of a sixth ligand (either by addition or by substitu-tion) that has a sufficiently strong interaction with the iron atom -- should be accompanied by non-trivial movements of the iron atom and its ligands relative to one another. In addition to a general tightening up of all bonds, one would expect also to find the iron atom centered nearly or exactly among the four nitrogen atoms of the porphine skeleton.

The preceding analysis leads to the expectation that the reversible oxygenation of myoglobin or hemoglobin, a process marked by a reversible high-spin to low-spin transition, should involve non-trivial alterations in the detailed configuration and dimensions of the coordination group as specified above. One then asks whether stereochemical alterations at and con-tiguous to a heme center may not, in the case of hemoglobin, require cooperative movements (translations and rotations of groups) in the protein framework that are propagated in some degree as far as one or more neighboring heme centers. We put this question in the attempt to find some tenable (even if

20

highly tenuous) starting point for a mechanism that must ulti-
mately account for the cooperative nature of reversible oxygenation in hemoglobin and for the large accompanying movements
of the hemes (18) relative to one another. Stereochemical alterations at one heme center, of course, could do no more than
trigger the overall mechanism.

Having specified the stereochemical changes in the coordination group of an iron porphyrin that we expect to accompany
transition from the high-spin to the low-spin state, we must
now point out that recent X-ray diffraction studies of ferrimyoglobin (metmyoglobin) azide (19), deoxymyoglobin (20), and
oxymyoglobin (21) speak against any substantial difference in
the position of the iron atom relative to the mean plane of
the heme as this appears in the several proteins. But we must
also point out that these analyses utilize experimental data
of intrinsically very low resolution and, further, that they
employ a highly specialized form of Fourier difference synthesis that does not involve the individual refinement of complex
phases for each of the related structures. Although the analytical procedures should be most sensitive to a shift in the
coordinates of the iron atom in the unit cell as between a
high-spin myoglobin and its low-spin derivative, there is, in
fact, no a priori requirement that the coordinates of the iron
atom should shift appreciably; indeed, one may expect that a
variety of movements in the flexible unanchored heme will
account for most of the stereochemical alterations in the central coordination group. It is the positions of the lighter
atoms (N,C,O) in the central portion of the heme that need to
be determined with an objective accuracy quite substantially
higher than has yet been achieved in the structure analyses of
the proteins if one is to use these data for direct assessment
of the dimensional changes that accompany the transition from
high- to low-spin. The qualitative successes of the analytical
procedures are undeniable, but their quantitative significance,
in our judgment, should be viewed with reserve. It is quite
difficult to see how a molecule of oxygen can approach closely
enough to the iron atom for more than trivial interaction if
the iron atom remains some 0.40 Å out-of-plane away from the
oxygen ligand. It is difficult also to appreciate the necessity for transition to the low-spin state if the coordination
group is to ignore the usual concomitant advantages that accrue
from a general tightening up of configuration; such shorter
distances bespeak the stronger interactions that are needed to
compensate for the energy expended in the pairing of spins.

One should, of course, determine structure for low-spin iron porphyrins, both ferrous and ferric, in order to see whether the octahedral coordination group does in fact assume the tight iron-in-plane configuration specified earlier as expected for the low-spin or "strong field" case. We now have sources for several such materials; there are problems of recrystallization, but we hope to get single crystals suitable for X-ray analysis from some, at least, of the preparations received.

Fleischer et al. (2) report X-ray data (ADI Document 7869) and a structure derived therefrom for tetragonal crystals of a presumed diaquozinc(II) tetraphenylporphine, $Zn(OH_2)_2TPP$, in which the octahedral coordination group has the required symmetry of the point group $C_{4h}$. We have now shown (22) that the X-ray data are in rather better agreement with the monoaquo formula, $Zn(OH_2)TPP$, and a disordered structure in which the polar square-pyramidal coordination group has equal probability for parallel or anti-parallel orientation along the tetragonal c axis; the statistically averaged model is quite similar to that described earlier for $(H_2OFeOH)TPP$. The purely mathematical (as distinguished from the physical) aspects of the crystallographic evidence can be handled on either model -- the consequence of quite inadequate experimental data along the critical c axis of the crystal -- but the physical interpretation of the derived thermal parameters is straightforward only for the disordered structure.

All supplementary evidence, moreover, supports the disordered model. The reported experimental density (2), 1.31 g/cc, agrees with that calculated, 1.315 g/cc, for the monoaquo formula, not with the 1.35 g/cc calculated for the diaquo case. The $Zn-OH_2$ distance of 2.20 Å given by our analysis corresponds to a real, if somewhat weak, bond, whereas the 2.45 Å given by the original study does not enable one to assign any obvious structural role to the water molecules.

The fact that anhydrous ZnTPP is reported (2) to crystallize in what are evidently low density crystalline forms (of undetermined structures) rather than in the compact arrangement assumed by CuTPP and PdTPP suggests that, as in the case of high-spin iron, the metal ion is too large or is otherwise unadapted for accommodation in the plane of the nitrogen atoms. This may account for the formation of $Zn(OH_2)TPP$ in preference to $Zn(OH_2)_2TPP$ and the observed displacement, 0.20 Å, of the zinc atom from the plane of the nitrogens in $Zn(OH_2)TPP$. A structure investigation now in hand for crystals of a Zn(II) derivative of α, β, γ, δ-tetra(p-pyridinyl) porphine is expected to shed light on this matter.

## Summary

The crystalline structures and molecular stereochemistries of several porphyrins have been determined by analysis of the three-dimensional X-ray diffraction data afforded by single crystals. The porphine core of porphyrins is shown to be a relatively flexible entity that may be significantly ruffled, folded, or domed as demanded by environmental stresses; this flexibility is seen to derive from a unique combination of $\sigma-\pi$ and $\pi$-bonding as evaluated from measured bond distances and angles. Non-trivial structural differences as between the inner skeletons of analogous porphyrins and phthalocyanine derivatives are apparent. Centering of the metal atom in the porphine skeleton is observed for those metalloporphyrins in which the complexing bond length is $< 2.01$ Å. Rather convincing evidence is presented that, independently of coordination number, a substantial displacement ($\gtrsim 0.35$ Å) of the iron atom from the plane of the porphine nitrogen atoms is a normal structural property of all high-spin iron porphyrins. Shorter bond lengths by 0.10 Å and centering of the iron atom in the porphine skeleton are anticipated for six-coordinate low-spin iron porphyrins.

## References

1.  Hamor, T. A., W. S. Caughey, and J. L. Hoard. J. Am. Chem. Soc., 87, 2305 (1965).

2.  Fleischer, E. G., C. K. Miller, and L. E. Webb. J. Am. Chem. Soc., 86, 2342 (1964); 85, 1353 (1963).

3.  Lofthus, A. Mol. Phys., 2, 367 (1959).

4.  Cruickshank, D. W. J., and R. A. Sparks. Proc. Roy. Soc. (London) A, 258, 270 (1960); D. W. J. Cruickshank, Tetrahedron, 17, 155 (1962).

5.  Longuet-Higgins, H. C., C. W. Rector, and J. R. Platt. J. Chem. Phys., 18, 1174 (1950).

6.  Kobayashi, H. J. Chem. Phys., 30, 1373 (1959).

7.  Gouterman, M., G. Wagniere, and L. C. Snyder. J. Mol. Spectry., 11, 108 (1963).

8.  Hamor, M. J., T. A. Hamor, and J. L. Hoard. J. Am. Chem. Soc., 86, 1938 (1964); 85, 2334 (1963).

9.  Silvers, S., and A. Tulinsky. J. Am. Chem. Soc., 86, 927 (1964).

10. Webb, L. E., and E. B. Fleischer. J. Chem. Phys., 43, 3100 (1965); J. Am. Chem. Soc., 87, 667 (1965).

11. Becker, E. D., R. B. Bradley, and J. C. Watson. J. Am. Chem. Soc., $\underline{83}$, 3743 (1961).

12. Hoard, J. L., M. J. Hamor, T. A. Hamor, and W. S. Caughey. J. Am. Chem. Soc., $\underline{87}$, 2312 (1965).

13. Koenig, D. F. Acta Cryst., $\underline{18}$, 663 (1965).

14. Glick, M. D., G. H. Cohen, and J. L. Hoard, in preparation.

15. Johnson, C. K. In ORTEP, A Fortran Thermal-Ellipsoid Plot Program for Crystal-Structure Illustrations, Oak Ridge National Laboratory, ORNL-3794 (1965).

16. Kendrew, J. C. Science, $\underline{139}$, 1259 (1963).

17. Gouterman, M. This volume, p. 589.

18. Muirhead, H., and M. F. Perutz. Nature, $\underline{199}$, 633 (1963).

19. Stryer, L., J. C. Kendrew, and H. C. Watson. J. Mol. Biol., $\underline{8}$, 96 (1964).

20. Nobbs, C. L., H. C. Watson, and J. C. Kendrew. Nature, $\underline{209}$, 339 (1966).

21. Chance, B., and H. C. Watson. This volume, p. 149.

22. Glick, M. D., G. H. Cohen, and J. L. Hoard. ACS Symposium on "Coordination Compounds of Biological Interest", Pittsburgh, March 28-31, 1966.

## DISCUSSION

Watson: In protein structure work, the resolution achieved is at best only 1.5 Å, whereas the small-molecule crystallographer can do very much better. We have not, therefore, attempted to define the detailed configuration of any single group in the protein, but have rather tried to fit the detailed data provided by conventional crystallography to our cruder observations on the whole protein. We hope that by putting together both types of structural data, it will be possible to attempt a detailed interpretation of the mode of action of the protein.

Hoard: I can fully subscribe to Dr. Watson's quite reserved statement on the problems of mutual interest.

ON THE STRUCTURE AND REACTIONS OF
HEME a AND CYTOCHROME c OXIDASE*

Winslow S. Caughey[‡], J. Lyndal York,
Sue McCoy, and Donald P. Hollis

Department of Physiological Chemistry
The Johns Hopkins University School of Medicine,
Baltimore, Maryland, 21205

In this paper recent findings on the isolation and structure of the green heme of beef heart muscle are reported, and
reactions of the heme and of cytochrome c oxidase with molecular oxygen are considered.

Warburg and Gewitz (1) reported the first isolation of
hemin a from beef heart muscle in 1951, and by 1961 sufficient
evidence had accumulated from the combined efforts of many
investigators to enable Lemberg (2) in a fine review to suggest many features of its structure. More recently Lynen and
coworkers (3,4) suggested an interesting biosynthetic pathway
and structure for the long alkyl group known to be in the molecule, as well as additional evidence for the presence of a
vinyl group, to give the total structure shown in Fig. 1.
Somewhat earlier, studies of isolation methods, structures,
and reactions of a-type hemes from heart muscle were initiated
in our laboratory (5,7). These investigations have now been
extended and the structure examined in somewhat greater detail.

Isolation of the heme from beef heart muscle. The difficulties we and others(2,3,4) had encountered in attempts to
prepare demonstrably pure hemin a in good yields by following
isolation procedures similar to those employed by Warburg and
Gewitz (1), or more recent modifications, prompted us to seek
a new isolation procedure. We sought a method for separating
the lipid and heme components cleanly and conveniently, which
would also provide a low-spin $Fe^{++}$ complex suitable for use in
nuclear magnetic resonance (NMR) spectroscopy.

The isolation procedure developed is outline in Scheme 1
where the product is an $Fe^{++}$ complex with one pyridine ligand
(pyridine heme a) (5). In this way a product of high purity

*This work was supported by U.S. PHS Research Grant HE-06-79.

‡Lederle Medical Faculty Award Scholar.

SCHEME 1

## ISOLATION OF PYRIDINE HEME a

4 KG BEEF HEART MUSCLE MINCE
1. Wash with 8 l distilled water at 4°C; repeat once.
2. Wash with 4 l 80 percent acetone for 10 min.
3. Wash with 7 l chloroform for 15 min.

WASHED MINCE
1. Extract with 3 l chloroform-pyridine (2:1,v/v) for 1 hr; repeat twice.

CRUDE HEME EXTRACT
1. Reduce volume to 200 ml under vacuum at 40°C.
2. Store overnight at 4°C.
3. Filter and concentrate to 60 ml under vacuum at 40°C.
4. "Freeze out" lipids at -30°C by adding 10 ml water; repeat three times.
5. Filter combined supernatants and evaporate to dryness under vacuum at 40°C.

CRUDE HEMES
1. Chromatograph on celite wet with upper phase of mixture of pyridine-chloroform-0.1 per-cent aqueous sodium bicarbonate-isooctane (30:15:15:2, v/v) at 22± 1° C. Elute with lower phase.

HEME a ELUATE FRACTION
1. Neutralize bicarbonate with 1N acetic acid.
2. Wash with 1/2 volume water; repeat twice.
3. Evaporate to dryness under vacuum at 40°C.
4. Dissolve residue in 1 ml pyridine and precipitate with 8 ml isooctane (overnight at -20°C).
5. Dry the precipitate in constant weight under vacuum at 65°C.

100 MG PYRIDINE HEME a

free from lipids and other hemes and chromatographically homogeneous can be obtained conveniently in high yield (estimated
to be greater than 95 per cent). Alternatively, if the eluate
fraction from the chromatography is not washed with dilute
acetic acid, the product obtained in similar yield is the disodium salt of the hematin (disodium hydroxohemin a). These
yields may be compared with yields obtained by other workers
of 210 mg porphyrin a from 65 kg heart muscle (6) and 1.0 g
"cytohemin" from 253 kg heart muscle (4).

Evidence for the structure of heme a. The quantitative as
well as qualitative determination of substituent groups in a
product that had been isolated in essentially 100 per cent yield
was considered important in view of the possibility that two
slightly different a-type hemes are present in cytochrome
oxidase -- one associated with "cytochrome a", the other with
"cytochrome a₃".

The number and relative positions of many of the periph-
eral substituent groups depicted in Fig. 1 have been supported
by NMR and infrared spectra. Three ring-bound methyl groups
are indicated at positions 1,3, and 5. Three such methyls are
indeed found in the NMR spectra as are four meso protons, one
for each of the $\alpha,\beta,\gamma$ and $\delta$ positions (5,7,8). One vinyl group
has been detected quantitatively in the near infrared where in
chloroform solution a terminal methylene band at 1620 m$\mu$
($a_m$, 0.33) was found (7,8). A vinyl group and its reduction

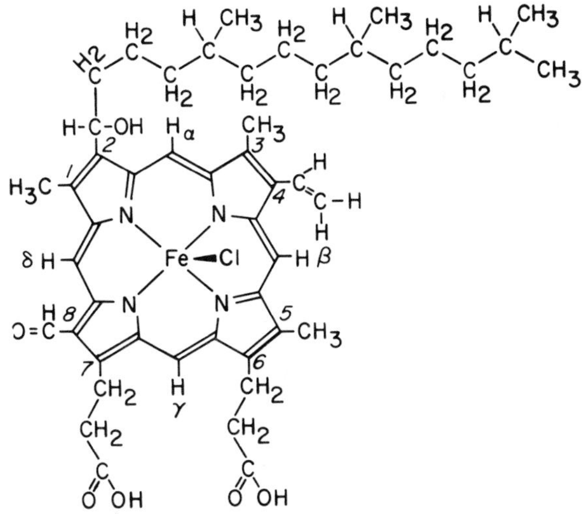

Figure 1. Structure of Chlorohemin a, proposed by Lynen and
coworkers (3,4).

product (i.e., an ethyl group) have been observed in the NMR spectra as well (9). Lynen and coworkers also concluded that a vinyl group was present on the basis of the identification of methylethylmaleimide among the chromic acid oxidation products of their hydrogenated hemin a chloride (3). We had also isolated methylethylmaleimide following oxidation of a hydrogenated product from pyridine heme a in yields as high as 25 percent. The yields were nevertheless too low to provide the quantitative evidence required for establishing the presence of one vinyl per molecule of heme a. One formyl group was observed quantitatively in the infrared where for chloroform solutions carbonyl and carbon-hydrogen stretching frequencies are at 1667 and 2746 $cm^{-1}$, respectively (5,7,8). In NMR spectra one formyl proton is observed at characteristically low field (8). The presence of the two propionic acid groups is consistent with, but not as clearly established by, the NMR and (IR) spectra. However the preparations of the disodium salt of the hemin and dimethyl esters of the metal-free porphyrin derivatives does provide clear evidence for the propionic acid groups.

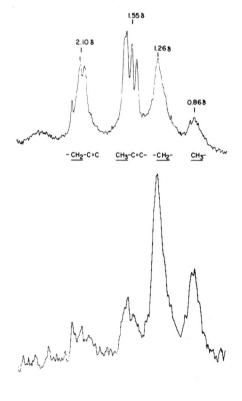

Figure 2. 100Mc NMR spectra in pyridine-d$_5$ for the 0-3 - Region. Upper trace: dipyridine heme a. Lower trace: Derivative obtained upon hydrogenation of pyridine heme a in ethyl acetate with Pd on CaCO$_3$.

Our findings do not support the assignment of a 1-hydroxy
-5,9, 13-trimethyltetradecyl group at the 2-position as shown
in Fig. 1.    NMR spectra for the alkyl proton region were found
to differ in several important respects from the expected
spectra for such a group (Fig. 2).    The general assignment of
protons in the 0.9 region to terminal methyl groups, in the
1.3 region to saturated methylenes, in the 1.5 region to methyl
groups on unsaturated carbons, and in the region around 2.1 to
unsaturated methylenes, as shown in Fig. 1, can be made.    As a
specific check on these assignments deuteroporphyrin IX dimethyl
ester with a 1-hydroxy-5,9,13-trimethyltetradecyl substituent
was prepared and its NMR spectrum found to have the chemical
shifts and relative areas expected for four saturated methyl
and nine saturated methylene groups.    The NMR spectra of the
alkyl region of heme a can be reasonably interpreted in terms
of chemical shifts and integrated intensities as resulting from
structures I, II, III, or IV, which include (a) two methyl
groups adjacent to double bonds, (b) a terminal saturated methyl
(the broadening observed suggests several adjacent methylenes),
(c) three saturated methylenes, and (d) four methylenes adjacent
to double bonds.    These structures contain only 16 carbons in
the skeleton.    Elemental analyses conform equally well, or
somewhat better, to a 16-carbon than to a 17-carbon chain
(Table 1).    However, these data do not rigorously exclude a
17-carbon chain for which the data of Lynen and coworkers provided strong support.

$$\text{(I)  Ring} \rangle\!\!-\!\! \underset{\underset{OX}{|}}{CH}\!-\!CH_2\!-\!CH_2\!-\!\underset{\underset{CH_3}{|}}{C}\!=\!CH\!-\!CH_2\!-\!CH_2\!-\!\underset{\underset{CH_3}{|}}{C}\!=\!CH\!-\!CH_2\!-\!CH_2\!-\!CH_2\!-\!CH_2\!-\!CH_3$$

$$\text{(II)  Ring} \rangle\!\!-\!\! \underset{\underset{OX}{|}}{CH}\!-\!CH_2\!-\!CH_2\!-\!CH_2\!-\!\underset{\underset{CH_3}{|}}{C}\!=\!CH\!-\!CH_2\!-\!CH_2\!-\!\underset{\underset{CH_3}{|}}{C}\!=\!CH\!-\!CH_2\!-\!CH_2\!-\!CH_2\!-\!CH_3$$

$$\text{(III)  Ring} \rangle\!\!-\!\! \underset{\underset{OX}{|}}{CH}\!-\!CH_2\!-\!CH_2\!-\!CH\!=\!\underset{\underset{CH_3}{|}}{C}\!-\!CH_2\!-\!CH_2\!-\!CH\!=\!\underset{\underset{CH_3}{|}}{C}\!-\!CH_2\!-\!CH_2\!-\!CH_2\!-\!CH_2\!-\!CH_3$$

$$\text{(IV)  Ring} \rangle\!\!-\!\! \underset{\underset{OX}{|}}{CH}\!-\!CH_2\!-\!CH_2\!-\!CH\!=\!\underset{\underset{CH_3}{|}}{C}\!-\!CH_2\!-\!CH_2\!-\!CH_2\!-\!\underset{\underset{CH_3}{|}}{C}\!=\!CH\!-\!CH_2\!-\!CH_2\!-\!CH_2\!-\!CH_3$$

29

TABLE I

## Elemental Analyses for Heme a Derivatives

| | $\%C$ | $\%H$ | $\%N$ | $\%Fe$ |
|---|---|---|---|---|
| Pyridine Heme a: | | | | |
| Found (5) | 65.60 | 7.09 | 7.64 | 4.94 |
| Calcd. $C_{59}H_{71}N_6O_{10}Fe$ | 65.61 | 6.63 | 7.78 | 5.17 |
| " $C_{60}H_{73}N_6O_{10}Fe$ | 65.87 | 6.73 | 7.68 | 5.10 |
| | | | | |
| Hydroxohemin a, Na$_2$salt: | | | | |
| Found | 61.03 | 6.71 | 6.55 | |
| Calcd. $C_{54}H_{65}O_{11}Fe$ | 61.07 | 6.17 | 6.60 | |
| " $C_{55}H_{66}N_5O_{11}Fe$ | 61.39 | 6.28 | 6.51 | |
| | | | | |
| Chlorohemin a: | | | | |
| Found (this work) | 65.55 | 6.59 | 6.57 | 6.56 |
| " (Warburg, et al.(13)) | 64.47 | 6.79 | 6.50 | 6.42 |
| " (Grassl, et al. (4)) | 65.75 | 6.60 | 5.65 | 6.06 |
| Calcd. $C_{48}H_{56}N_4O_6FeCl$ | 65.79 | 6.44 | 6.39, | 6.37 |
| " $C_{49}H_{58}N_4O_6FeCl$ | 66.10 | 6.57 | 6.29 | 6.27 |
| | | | | |
| Porphyrin a dimethyl ester: | | | | |
| Found | 73.56 | 7.91 | 6.39 | |
| Calcd. $C_{50}N_{62}N_4O_6$ | 73.68 | 7.67 | 6.87 | |
| " $C_{51}N_{64}N_4O_6$ | 63.88 | 7.78 | 6.76 | |

Thus, with the NMR data available, uncertainties in the integrated intensity values are too great to permit a choice between I, II, III, IV or structures with an additional carbon (particularly if the added carbon were present as an unsaturated methylene), nor can a choice be made between I,II,III, or IV or a mixture of such structures. Indeed, certain solvent effects on these spectra could be interpreted as resulting from the presence of a mixture of two components with subtle differences in the structure of the alkyl side chains. The postulation of such a mixture would be one way to accomodate our findings with those of Lynen and coworkers. Because their degradation products were obtained in rather low yields from the hemin which was, in turn, obtained from heart in much lower yields than was our product, it is not unreasonable to suggest their maleimides could have arisen from but one component in a mixture of a-type hemins.

The unsaturation in the alkyl side chain (two double bonds) has also been demonstrated by quantitative reduction (catalytic dehydrogenation) and is consistent with characteristic carbon-hydrogen stretching frequencies, with the incorporation of

chloride into the chain, and with the observation that yields
of long chain degradation products from chromic acid oxidations
are less than 1 percent with pyridine heme a and about 25 percent with hydrogenated heme a.

The structure of heme a is found to differ from that of
Fig. 1 in another important respect, namely, an amino sugar-
like moiety is apparently attached to the long alkyl chain (9,10).
The presence of an hexosamine grouping in heme a is supported by
elemental analyses, infrared spectra, solubility characteristics,
and other evidence. A hexosamine would reasonably be in a pyra-
nose form and attached via a glycosidic linkage to the 1-carbon
of the long alkyl group. The "amino sugar" was cleaved during
conversions of heme a to porphyrin a. Also, refluxing a solution
of heme a and sodium chloride in acetic acid yielded a chlorohemin with elemental analyses and visible absorption characteristics comparable to those found for hemin a chloride by Warburg
and Gewitz (1) and by Lynen and coworkers (3,4), where clearly
no amino sugar moiety can be present (Fig. 3). The "X" of I,
II, III, and IV thus represents a group of composition $C_6H_{11}NO_4$
for which structural details are incomplete. In our porphyrin
a dimethyl ester preparations, where -O-X has been cleaved, we
have failed to detect an $\alpha$ OH group in the infrared region
where such groups are readily found with compounds known to
have $\alpha$ OH groups (7,8). Elemental analyses indicated the presence of six oxygens. These and other findings can be rationalized in terms of cyclic ether formation (e.g., an oxygen
bridging the 1 and 5 carbons of the chain) under acidic conditions which prevail during the iron removal step.

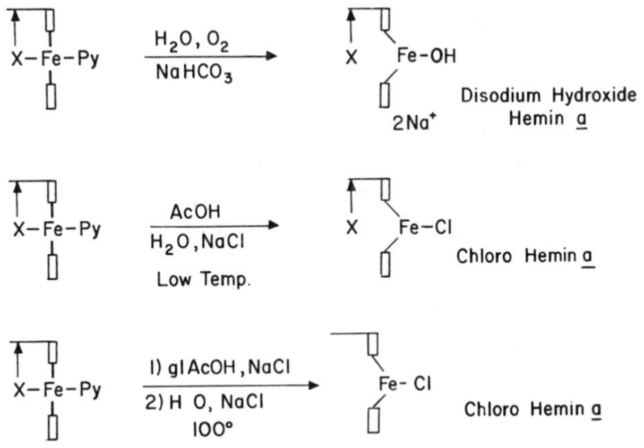

Figure 3. Reactions of pyridine heme a.

Reactions of heme a and cytochrome c oxidase. It has been of interest to consider the manner in which the unique structural features of heme a could contribute importantly to its natural function. Recognition of the presence of an unsaturated side chain with an amino sugar-like group attached in heme a clarifies the interpretation of several aspects of heme a chemistry and also stimulates speculation of possible roles for these groups in cytochrome c oxidase function.

Differences in the reactivity of heme a and protoheme are particularly marked. Dipyridine protoheme undergoes autoxidation far more readily than does pyridine heme a (5,11). This could be related to differences in redox potential, but as pointed out earlier, the rate of overall oxidation of these hemes can be influenced by the slow rates of ligand dissociation, as well as by rates of steps involving oxygen reduction (11) per se. Thus, pyridine is dissociated thermally from the solid pyridine heme a under vacuum at a reasonable rate only at temperatues in excess of $100^{\circ}$, whereas pyridine is lost from the dipyridine protoheme at a very rapid rate at $50^{\circ}$. Evidence for solid monopyridine monoxy hemes has been obtained with both hemes (Fig. 4). Thus, when solid pyridine heme a is heated under vacuum at $145^{\circ}$ followed by exposure of the solid to air, an overall weight change precisely that expected for the loss of one pyridine and pick-up of one $O_2$ molecule is found.

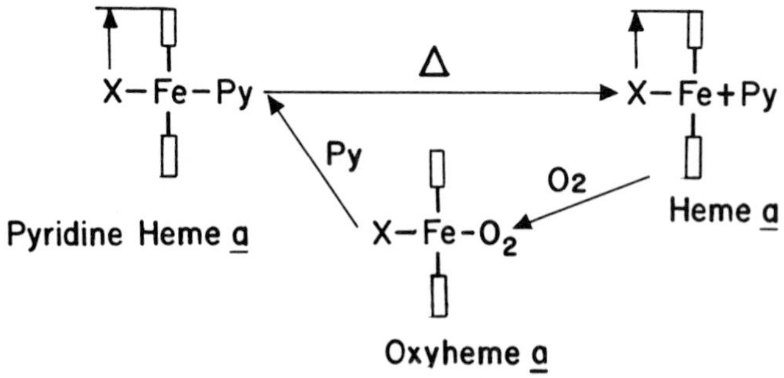

Figure 4. Thermal dissociation of pyridine from solid pyridine heme a, followed by oxygen uptake.

Evidence for the reversible oxygenation of pyridine heme a in aqueous pyridine solutions was discussed earlier (5) (Fig. 5), an observation not yet seen with protoheme. Several observations are in accord with a low rate of displacement of "X" as a ligand to iron. In the final step of the isolation of pyridine heme a, excess pyridine is removed from the sample by heating to constant weight under vacuum to give a product which can be reasonably assumed to have one pyridine ligand and the amino group of the sugar as a second ligand.

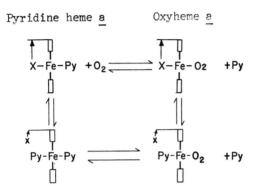

Pyridine heme a          Oxyheme a

$X-Fe-Py + O_2 \rightleftharpoons X-Fe-O_2 + Py$

$Py-Fe-Py \rightleftharpoons Py-Fe-O_2 + Py$

Dipyridine heme a     Pyridineoxy heme a

Figure 5.  Possible reactions of pyridine heme a with oxygen in solution.

The slow changes in visible absorption and in NMR spectra that are observed when pyridine heme a is dissolved in pyridine of high purity are consistent with a slow displacement of "X" as a ligand by a second pyridine ligand (Fig. 6). Further examination of these and related observations show promise of providing important new insight into the mechanistic details of the reaction of these hemes with molecular oxygen.

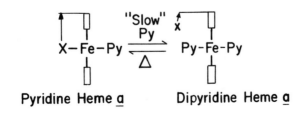

$X-Fe-Py \underset{\Delta}{\overset{\text{"Slow"}\ Py}{\rightleftharpoons}} Py-Fe-Py$

Pyridine Heme a          Dipyridine Heme a

Figure 6.  Reversible reaction of pyridine heme a with pyridine.

While heme $\underline{a}$ can be rather inert toward autoxidation, oxygen reduction by cytochrome $\underline{c}$ oxidase is extremely rapid. A most important contribution to the rapid rate, and particularly to the reduction of $O_2$ to the level of water, undoubtedly follows from the fact, only recently clear, that the reduced oxidase can readily supply four reducing equivalents--one from each heme $\underline{a}$ and one from each copper atom (14,15) (see equation below).

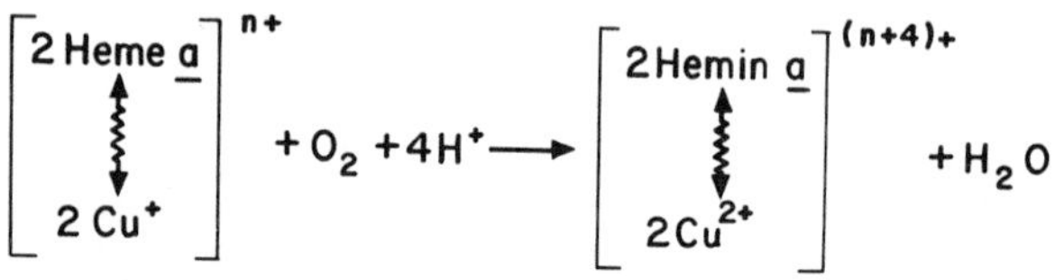

$$\begin{bmatrix} 2\,\text{Heme}\;\underline{a} \\ \updownarrow \\ 2\,Cu^{+} \end{bmatrix}^{n+} + O_2 + 4H^{+} \longrightarrow \begin{bmatrix} 2\,\text{Hemin}\;\underline{a} \\ \updownarrow \\ 2\,Cu^{2+} \end{bmatrix}^{(n+4)+} + H_2O$$

With $O_2$ binding at a heme $Fe^{++}$ and three electrons readily available to the iron upon demand, the mechanistically simple picture for the rapid reduction and protonation of oxygen shown in Fig. 7 can be operative (11). Complete reduction of the oxidase by cytochrome $\underline{c}$ would return the iron site to $Fe^{++}$ status with water as a ligand, if any. Several lines of evidence support the notion of a requirement of the simultaneous, or rapidly consecutive, transfer of four electrons to oxygen for the rapid reduction of $O_2$ to water. Very recent kinetic studies have shown the participation of more than one heme in the autoxidation of dipyridine hemes (15). Four reduction equivalents (i.e., four copper atoms) are also present at sites where oxygen is reduced to water in copper enzymes (14,16). Now with evidence for an amino sugar-like grouping directly

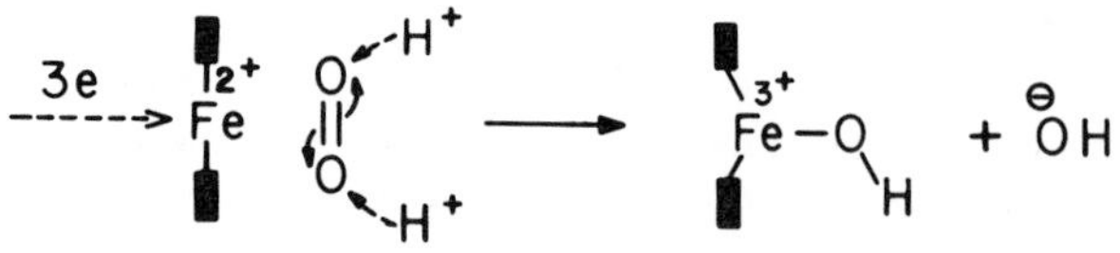

Figure 7. A schematic representation for oxygen reduction by reduced cytochrome $\underline{c}$ oxidase via rapidly consecutive or simultaneous transfer of four electrons to $O_2$. Each oxygen atom also accepts a proton from the aqueous environment to form two hydroxyls, one of which remains as a ligand to iron and the other passes into the external medium. In this scheme neither oxygen atom dissociates from the locus of the iron atom before the oxygen atom has become reduced to the water oxidation level.

bound to the porphyrin structure, it is tempting to speculate that this group serves as a ligand to iron or to copper, or as a bridging ligand facilitating electron-transfer among copper and heme moieties. The presence of the unsaturated side chain and the amino sugar moieties also provides more intriguing possibilities for direct chemical mechanism whereby oxygen reduction is coupled to phosphorylation.

## References

1. Warburg, O., and H. S. Gewitz.  Z Physiol Chem., $\underline{288}$, (1951).

2. Lemberg, R.  In Advances in Enzymology (F.F. Nord, ed.), Vol. 2³, Interscience Publishers, Inc., New York, 1961, p. 265.

3. Grassl, M., U. Coy, R. Seyffert, and F. Lynen.  Biochem. z., $\underline{337}$, ³5 (196³).

4. Grassl, M., U. Coy, R. Seyffert, and F. Lynen.  Biochem. z., $\underline{3³8}$, 771 (196³).

5. Caughey, W. S., and J. L. York.  J. Biol. Chem., 2³7, PC2414 (1962).

6. Morell, D. B., J. Barrett, and P. S. Clezy.  Biochem. J., $\underline{78}$, 79³ (1961).

7. York, J. L. and W. S. Caughey.  Abstracts of Papers, 145th Meeting, American Chemical Society, New York, p. 46C (196³).

8. Caughey, W. S., J. O. Alben, W. Y. Fugimoto, and J. L. York.  J. Org. Chem., in press.

9. Caughey, W. S., S. McCoy, and J. L. York.  Federation Proc., $\underline{25}$, 647 (1966).

10. Caughey, W. S.  In Oxidases and Related Redox Systems (T. E. King, H. S. Mason, and M. Morrison, eds.), Vol. I, John Wiley and Sons, Inc., New York, 1965, p. 110.

11. Caughey, W. S., J. O. Alben, and C. A. Beaudreau.  In Oxidases and Related Redox Systems (T. E. King., H. S. Mason, and M. Morrison, eds.), Vol. I, John Wiley and Sons, Inc., New York, 1965, p. 97.

12. Warburg, O., H. S. Gewitz, and W. Völker.  Z. Naturforsch., $\underline{106}$, 541 (1955).

13. In Oxidases and Related Redox Systems (T. E. King, H. S. Mason, and M. Morrison, eds.), Vol. II, John Wiley and Sons, Inc., New York, 1965, p. 539.

14. Frieden, E., S. Osaki, and H. Kobayashi.  In Oxygen (New York Heart Association, ed.), Little, Brown, and Co., Boston 1965, p. 213.

15. Couen, I. A., and W. S. Caughey, Abstracts of Papers, 151st Meeting, American Chemical Society, Pittsburgh, H 105, (1966).

16. Caughey, W. S. In Oxidases and Related Redox Systems (T. E. King, H. S. Mason, and M. Morrison, eds.), Vol I, John Wiley and Sons, Inc., New York, 1965, p. 235.

# THE CHEMICAL STRUCTURE OF HEME a[*]

M. Rudolf Lemberg[‡]

Department of Biochemistry, Institute of Medical Research
The Royal North Shore Hospital
Sydney, Australia

The structure of seven of the eight side chains of porphyrin a and also the relative position of all eight side chains have been established by work of schools in Germany, in this country, in Canada, Italy, and Australia. In 1959, a structure had been suggested by myself and my coworkers (1) which left only the nature of two side chains undefined. Lynen and his fellow-workers (2) then found that the group in position 4 was vinyl, not substituted vinyl, as had been postulated by Warburg and by Piatteli.

Lemberg et al.,
1959

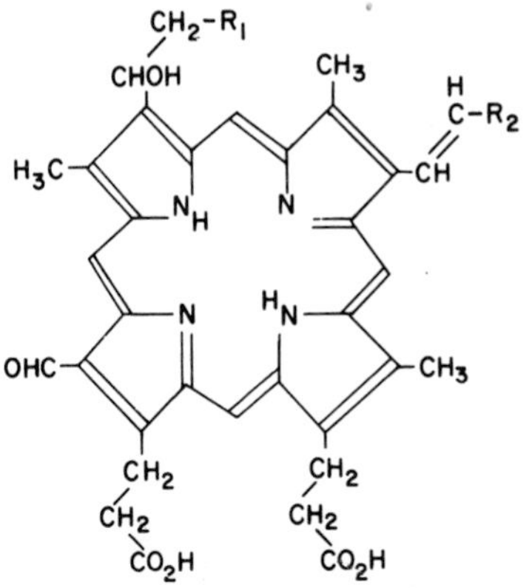

Lynen et al.,
1963

$$R_1 = -[CH_2-CH_2-\overset{CH_3}{CH}-CH_2]_3 H$$
$$R_2 = H$$

[*]Supported by grants from USPHS and National Health and Research council of Australia.

[‡]Present address: Johnson Research Foundation, University of Pennsylvania, Philadelphia, Pa.

37

Therefore, our discussion will only be concerned with the structure of the side chain in position 2. Clezy and Barrett (3), in my laboratory, have shown that this side chain is linked to the porphyrin ring by a -CH(OH)-group. This conclusion was based on the chromatographic behavior of the porphyrin a ester in the Chu, Green, and Chu (4) method, the increase of $R_F$ by treatment with acetic anhydride in pyridine, and the dehydration of the side chain to -CH=CH·R, or oxidation to -CO-CH₂R, with the expected alteration of the absorption spectra. Lynen and co-workers (5) then established that the side chain 2 in catalytically hydrogenated porphyrin a is a saturated $C_{17}H_{35}$ alkyl group with three hydrogenated isoprene groups and have assumed the side chain in porphyrin as indicated in Fig. 1. Our analyses of hemin a (Table 1) agree closely with those of Lynen and his group, but not so well with those of Warburg whose crystalline hemin a contained about 10 percent of protohemin. These analyses agree moderately well with the Lynen formula, but would even better fit a formula with 4 hydrogen atoms less, and/or one (but not two) oxygen atoms more. The side chain established by Lynen and co-workers is that of the hydrogenated porphyrin, and in addition to the α-hydroxyl group, other groups in the $C_{17}$ side chain may have been reduced in the catalytic hydrogenation.

TABLE I

Analyses of Hemin a

|  | C | H | N | Fe | Cl |
|---|---|---|---|---|---|
| Warburg and Gewitz (1951) | 64.47 | 6.79 | 6.50 | 6.42 | 4.20 |
| Lemberg, Clezy and Barrett (1959) | 65.41 | 6.56 | - | 5.90 | 3.75 |
| Lynen et al. (1963) | 65.75 | 6.60 | 5.65 | 6.06 | - |

There are two sets of experimental data which are difficult to explain on the basis of the Lynen formula (cf. my recent review (6)). In the first place porphyrin aα can be reversibly converted by aqueous hydrochloric acid into a spectroscopically quite similar porphyrin, aβ , which has a far lower HCl-number (3 as against 15). The two porphyrins do not appear to differ in their basic pK in detergent solution (J. N. Phillips, personal communication). The difference must therefore be due to the more hydrophilic character of porphyrin aβ . Clezy and Barrett have established that the difference resides in the side chain 2 (3). Addition of water to an isolated double bond

38

in the long alkyl side chain may be the cause of this more hydrophilic character of aβ , although some objections against this explanation have been raised by Clezy and Barrett.

Secondly, the supposed "acetylation" of porphyrin a is accompanied by a 2 mμ shift of the absorption bands to the blue, which is reversed by hydrolysis. A similar shift has been found by Morrison (7) for the hemochrome. No such shift is found on acetylation of other α-hydroxyl-porphyrins, e.g., hematoporphyrin. We are now investigating whether acetic anhydride really acetylates. The reaction may conceivably be the closure of a furane or pyrane ring with an unsaturated bond of the side chain, or with an enolic hydroxyl in a similar position (Fig. 2).

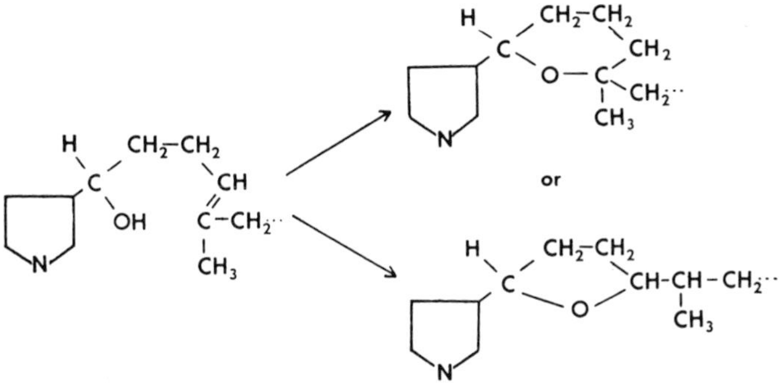

Figure 2. Ring closure on acetylation of porphyrin a.

Thirdly, the Lynen structure postulates three asymmetric carbon atoms. So far, no optical activity has been found. One may understand why the α-CHOH group does not cause it, being in conjugation with the formyl group in position 8 through the porphyrin ring, as shown in the following scheme for the enolization of the α-hydroxyl group:

R·CHOH·C·C=C·C=C·C·C·CHO $\rightleftharpoons$ RC(OH)=C·C=C·C=C·C=CHOH

However the two $R_1CH(CH_3)R_2$ groups should cause optical activity.

39

Thus far, I have discussed only the nature of hemin a obtained from heart muscle or purified oxidase preparations by elution with acetone containing 0.4 N HCl. The hemin is eluted at room temperature in 15 min. Any linkage broken by such treatment would have to be labile. Caughey (8) has suggested that by this treatment an aminosugar is removed which is still present in the heme a (or better hemochrome a) extracted by his method using pyridine and chloroform. In a comparison of the pyridine hemochrome obtained by dissolving our hemin a in pure pyridine with Caughey's, we have been unable to discover differences in the absorption spectra (Table II) or in the behavior of aqueous pyridine solution toward oxygenation and evacuations (Table III) (9).

TABLE II

Lemberg and Caughey

Absorption Spectra of Hemochromes a in Pyridine
and Aqueous Pyridine

|  | $\alpha$ | Min | $\beta$ | $\gamma$ |
|---|---|---|---|---|
| 1) Hemin a in 100 percent pyridine | 583 m$\mu$ | 548 m$\mu$ | 530 m$\mu$ | 429 m$\mu$ |
| R | 1.0 | 0.30–0.36 | 0.36–0.40 | 5.0–5.4 |
| 2) Hemin a in 20 percent pyridine-0.1 N NaOH + $Na_2S_2O_4$ | 587 m$\mu$ | 540 m$\mu$ | None | 430.5 m$\mu$ |
| R | 1.0 | 0.30–0.46 | -- | 4.8–4.95 |

TABLE III

Comparison of Behavior of Caughey and Lemberg Hemochromes a
in 80 percent Aqueous Pyridine - 20 percent Water

|  |  | Caughey | Lemberg |
|---|---|---|---|
| $\epsilon_\alpha$ : | before evacuation | 1 | 1 |
|  | 1 hr after evacuation | 1.67 | 1.73 |
|  | + $Na_2S_2O_4$ | 1.77 | 1.82 |

Caughey has recently adduced further evidence (10) for the presence of an aminosugar in his compound. However, it will be essential to distinguish between three possibilities: 1) that the aminosugar is present as an impurity; 2) that it is bound to the heme-iron only in hemochrome fashion (if so, heme a would still be as defined by us and by Lynen's group); 3) that it is bound by covalent linkage to the $C_{17}$ side chain possibly through

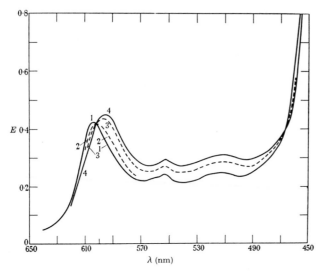

Figure 3. Modification of cytochrome oxidase at pH 9.5.
Time after addition of alkali:
1) 8 min          3) 120 min
2) 30 min         4) 180 min

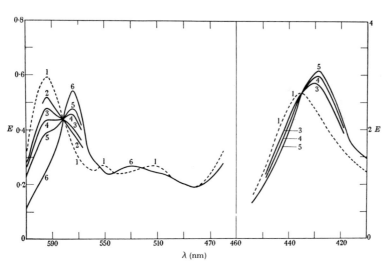

Figure 4. Denaturation of cytochrome oxidase at pH 12.5 with
Schiff base formation.
Time after addition of 1 N NaOH:
1) 1 min          3) 20 min          5) 80 min
2) 8 min          4) 40 min          6) 240 min

41

a glycosidic linkage to the α-hydroxyl, as well as to the heme-iron. The latter raises stereochemical difficulties, at least as far as 2-aminosugars are concerned. It would appear less likely that the linkage is from this α-hydroxyl by ether linkage to another sugar hydroxyl, though perhaps not impossible on account of the semienolic character of the α-hydroxyl. If the third assumption is correct, we face a puzzling nomenclature problem: the compound would still be a semi-hemochrome, to which no nitrogen free heme a would fully correspond.

Finally, so far nobody has adduced valid evidence for the presence of two different hemes a which might correspond to the two cytochromes a and a₃. The aα - aβ isomerism was a red herring whose ghost we have laid ourselves. On the contrary, there is a great deal of evidence that the two cytochromes differ in the way in which heme a is bound to the protein. The differences, both those between the two cytochromes and those between the cytochromes and synthetic heme a-proteins, disappear when the protein is modified by high pH, urea, or some ionic detergents, without (Fig. 3) or with (Fig. 4) the linkage of the formyl group to an ε-amino group of protein lysine which occurs at high alkalinity (11).

For our later discussions of the role of heme a in the oxidase, it will be useful to keep in mind that the large hydrophobic alkyl group which gives lipophilic character to the molecule is further increased in size by attachment of phospholipid, and secondly, that the formyl group in the intact oxidase is far less reactive than in the free heme a compounds or porphyrin a. Spectroscopic evidence shows that it does, for example, not react with sodium bisulphite, and little if at all with other usual formyl reagents (12). Schiff base formation, which takes place with other proteins at pH 9.5, requires a much higher pH with cytochrome oxidase. However, this may rather be due to the greater degree of conformational change in the protein necessary to bring a lysine ε-amino group into a suitable position, and this brings us to the heme a protein interaction which will be discussed later.

## References

1. Lemberg, R., P. Clezy, and J. Barrett. In Haematin Enzymes (J. E. Falk, R. Lemberg, and R. K. Morton, eds.), Pergamon Press, New York, 1961, p. 350, 357.

2. Grassl, M., G. Augsburg, Y. Coy, and F. Lynen. Biochem. Z., 337, 35 (1963).

3. Clezy, P., and J. Barrett. Biochem. J., 78, 798 (1961).

4. Chu, T. C., A. A. Green, and E. J. Chu. J. Bio. Chem., 190, 643 (1951).

5. Grassl, M., U. Coy, and F. Lynen. Biochem. Z., 338, 771 (1963).

6. Lemberg, R. Revs Pure and Applied Chem. (Australia), 15, 125 (1965).

7. Morrison, M. In Haematin Enzymes (J. E. Falk, R. Lemberg, and R. K. Morton, eds), Pergamon Press, New York, 1961, p. 358.

8. Caughey, W. S., and J. L. York. J. Biol. Chem., 237, PC 2414 (1962).

9. Lemberg, R. Biochem. Z., 338, 97 (1963).

10. Caughey, W. S., S. U. Coy, and J. L. York. Federation Proc., 25, 2586 (1966).

11. Lemberg, R., and T. B. G. Pilger. Proc. Roy. Soc. (London) B, 159, 429, 436 (1963).

12. Takemori, S., I. Sekuzu, and K. Okunuki. J. Biochem. (Tokyo), 48, 569 (1960).

# THE SIDE CHAIN OF CYTOHEMIN

Reinhard Seyffert, Marianne Grassl and Feodor Lynen

Max Planck-Institut für Zellchemie,
München und Chemisches Laboratorium der Universität München,
Institut für Biochemie
Germany

Many investigators have contributed to the present know-ledge of the structure of cytohemin (hemin a); their work has been reviewed in detail by Lemberg (1) in 1961 and more recently by Falk (2). The chemical structure and physical measurements of heme a have been dealt with at this symposium.

In 1959 Clezy and Barrett (3) and Lemberg et al. (4) proposed a partial formula for cytohemin (I) summarizing the facts known about the structure at that time. In Formula I the groups $R_1$ and $R_2$ stand for saturated alkyl chains which together consist of 13 to 16 carbon atoms. The presence of additional carbon atoms was indicated by elemental analysis on crystallized cytohemin (5,6), the resorcinol melt (5) and determinations of the molecular weight (cf.(1)). Prior to this investigation, the nature of these chains remained unclear.

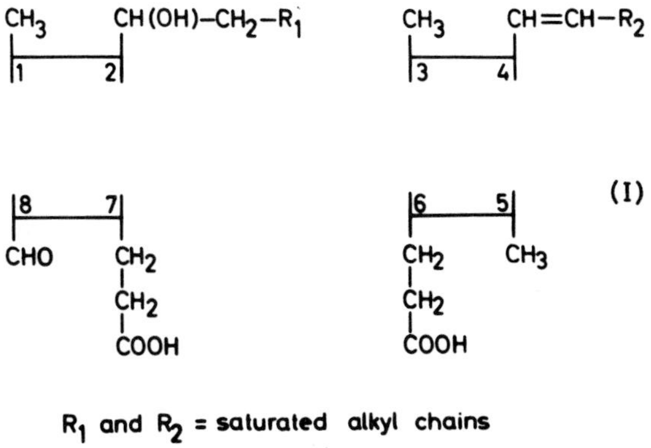

$R_1$ and $R_2$ = saturated alkyl chains

Figure 1. Partial formula for cytohemin (I) (1959).

Kiese, Kurz and Thofern (7) reported the interesting finding that a protohemin-requiring mutant strain of Staphylococcus aureus (Micrococcus pyogenes) lacked both proto- and cytohemin. After growing on a protohemin-containing culture medium, however, the mutant strain contained cytohemin in the same concentration as the parent strain. Therefore, protohemin became a likely precursor in the biosynthetic pathway leading to cytohemin.

In considering these facts and the established features of cytohemin, Lynen and Grassl (8) proposed the following pathway for the biosynthesis of cytohemin (Fig. 2): protohemin (II) is alkylated by farnesyl-pyrophosphate (III) or another allyl-pyrophosphate at the vinyl group in position 2, and the intermediate carbonium ion is attacked by an OH-group. In subsequent reactions the side chain is reduced and the methyl group in position 8 is oxidized to the formyl state resulting in the formation of cytohemin (IV). The presence of an $\alpha$ - hydroxy group was indicated by work of Clezy and Barrett (9).

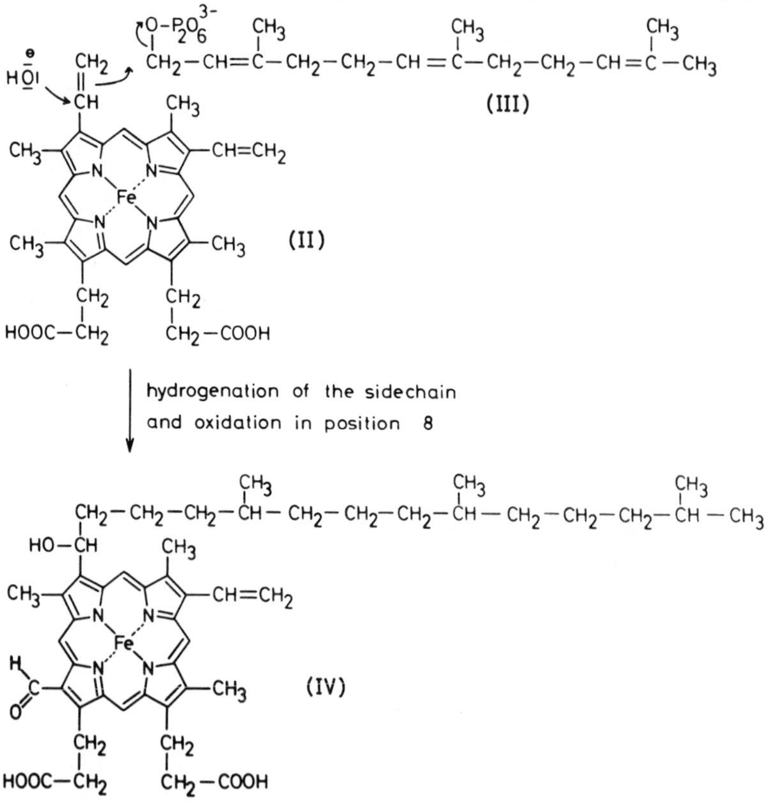

$$O-P_2O_6^{3-}$$

$$CH_2-CH=C-CH_2-CH_2-CH=C-CH_2-CH_2-CH=C-CH_3$$

(III)

(II)

hydrogenation of the sidechain
and oxidation in position 8

$$CH_2-CH_2-CH_2-CH-CH_2-CH_2-CH_2-CH-CH_2-CH_2-CH_2-CH-CH_3$$

(IV)

Figure 2. Hypothetical pathway for the biosynthesis of cytohemin.

46

The theory that the alkylation takes place at the vinyl group
in position 2 is in agreement with results of the same investigators (10): this vinyl group was found to be more electro-
negative than that in position 4.  In Lemberg's formula (I),
therefore, $R_1$ and $R_2$ should be hexahydrofarnesyl and hydrogen,
respectively.

The Carbon Skeleton of the Side Chain. To obtain evidence
for our proposal, cytohemin was isolated from beef heart and
degraded to maleimides (11) as shown in the following scheme:

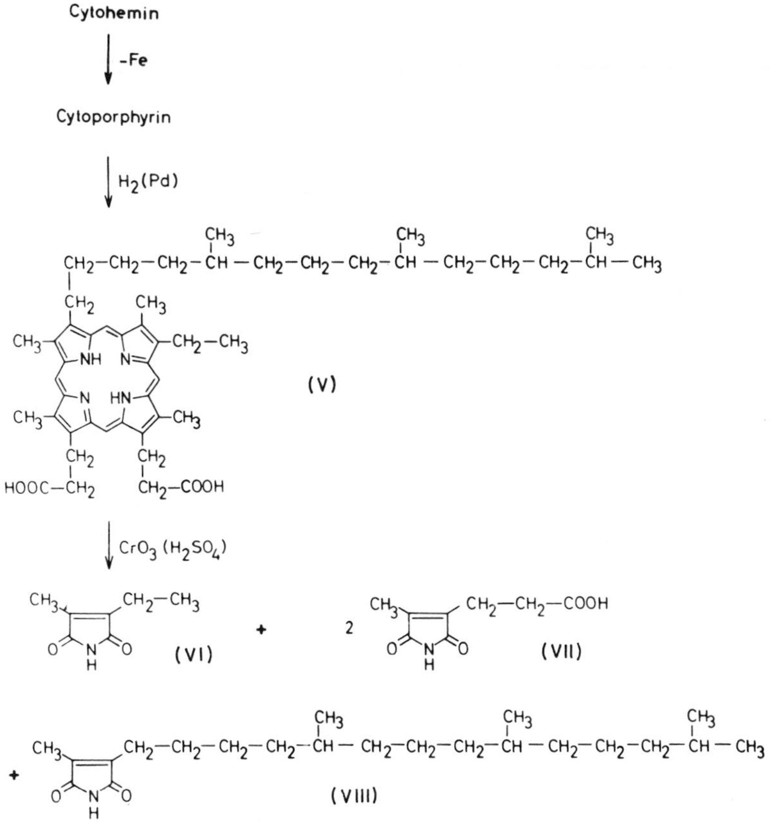

Figure 3.  Scheme for the oxidative degradation of cytohemin to
maleimides.

Cytohemin was converted into cytoporphyrin and the cytoporphyrin hydrogenated with palladium catalyst in formic acid.  By
this treatment, the vinyl, formyl, and $\alpha$-hydroxy groups were

converted into saturated hydrocarbon groups and thus protected against chromic acid oxidation. Oxidation of the reduced cyto-porphyrin (V) with chromic acid then gave methyl-ethyl-maleimide (VI), hematinic acid (VII), and a lipophilic methyl-alkyl-maleimide. The latter should be identical with methyl-5,9,13-tri-methyltetradecyl-maleimide (VIII), according to our proposal. Methyl-ethyl-maleimide and hematinic acid isolated from the reaction mixture were identified by comparison with authentic compounds.

To prove the structure of the lipophilic maleimide, the expected methyl-5,9,13-trimethyltetradecyl-maleimide was syn-thesized and characterized by infra-red spectroscopy, ultra-violet spectroscopy, elemental analysis, mass spectrometry, and gas-liquid chromatography. Moreover, methyl-alkyl-maleimides

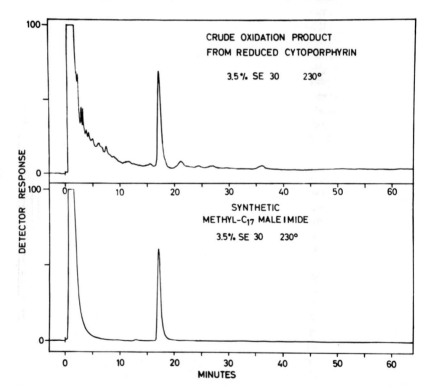

Figure 4. Gas-liquid chromatography of the crude oxidation pro-duct from reduced cytoporphyrin, and of authentic methyl-5,9, 13-trimethyltetradecyl-maleimide (1.5 µg). Conditions: 3.5 percent SE-30 on 80/100 mesh silanized Chromosorb W-AW, HMDS-treated, 2.5 m X 1/8"; 25 ml He/min; 230° column temperature, flame, ionization detector.

with ethyl-, tetrahydrogeranyl-, lauryl-, and hexadecyl- side
chains were synthesized, and their behavior in gas-liquid chromatography was studied with respect to chain length and branching (11, and unpublished results).

The degradation product from reduced cytoporphyrin was
compared with methyl-5,9,13-trimethyltetradecyl-maleimide by
means of thin-layer chromatography, infra-red spectroscopy, gas-
liquid chromatography on polar and non-polar columns, and mass
spectrometry. The compounds were identical in all respects (11).
The gas chromatograms of the crude oxidation product and of the
synthetic compound on an SE-30-column are shown in Fig. 4. The
same pattern was obtained on a polar FFAP column (FFAP = modified
carbowax) and on other columns. The best evidence, however, for
the identity of the degradation product with the synthetic compound was given by mass spectrometry (Figure 5).

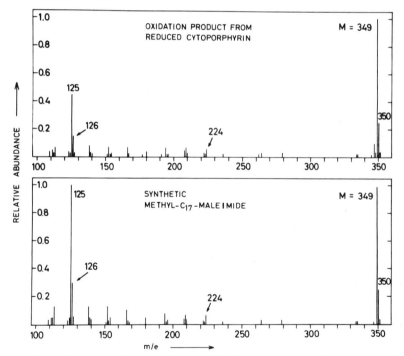

Figure 5. Mass spectra of the oxidation product from reduced
cytoporphyrin (0.67 mg) and authentic methyl-5,9,13-trimethyl-
tetradecyl-maleimide (0.88 mg). Both compounds were purified
by thin-layer chromatography before running the mass spectra.
For conditions, cf. ref. (11). In the spectrum of the oxidation product, the ion current was constant only above m/e = 170.

In the diagrams, the range from m/e = 100 to m/e = 360 is shown, indicating that the distribution of the peaks is the same with the exception of minor impurities. During the run of the oxidation product, the ion current below m/e = 170 was not constant, so the peak height cannot be compared quantitatively in this range.

If protohemin is alkylated by allyl-pyrophosphates other than farnesyl-pyrophosphate, e.g., geranyl-PP or geranyl-geranyl-PP, cytohemins with C-12 and C-22 side chains would be formed. However, there were no indications of such cytohemins in our experiments with beef heart cytohemin.

To look for cytohemins with different chain lengths, cytohemin was also isolated from Baker's yeast and degraded to maleimides as described above (Fig. 3). The isolation procedure is shown in Table 1.

TABLE I

Isolation of Cytohemin from Yeast

| Procedure | Cytohemin $\mu$Mol per Kg yeast* | Purity* | Yield* | References |
|---|---|---|---|---|
| Extraction with Me-et-ketone/$CH_3$CN/HCl | 3.6 | – | 100°/o | (12) |
| 2 Extractions with Acetone/HCl | 3.1 | 3.8°/o | 86°/o | modified from (13) |
| Washing on $Al_2O_3$-column | 2.5 | 20°/o | 69°/o | modified from (13) |
| Partition chromatography on Celite | 1.7 | 85°/o | 47°/o | (14) |

*mean values

The hemin was extracted from Baker's yeast by shaking pressed yeast with glass beads in an organic solvent mixture according to Barrett (12), and was then purified by a combination of methods from several investigators. Cytohemin of 80-93 percent purity was obtained by this procedure. After chromic acid oxidation of the reduced cytoporphyrin, the analysis via gas-liquid chromatography demonstrated that the maleimides were methyl-ethyl-maleimide (VI) and methyl-5,9,13-trimethyltetradecyl-maleimide (VIII), thus indicating the alkylation of protohemin by farnesyl-pyrophosphate. As in the experiments with beef heart, only a C-17 side chain was found. Side chains of C-12 and C-22 were not found in amounts greater than 3 percent of the C-17 chain.

## Discussion

The experiments described provide clear evidence for the carbon skeleton of the side chain of cytohemins from beef heart and yeast. This indicates that farnesyl-pyrophosphate is involved in the biosynthesis of cytohemin by alkylating the vinyl group of protohemin. Thus, the recognized ability of allyl-pyrophosphates to alkylate double bonds (15,16) can be extended to the class of hemin compounds. The alkyl side chains of other hemins, such as cryptohemin $a$ (17) and perhaps hemin $a_2$ (18), are very likely synthesized in the same manner.

## References

1. Lemberg, R. Advan. Enzymol., $\underline{23}$, 265 (1961).

2. Falk, J. E. Porphyrins and Metalloporphyrins, BBA Library Vol. 2, Elsevier Publ. Co., Amsterdam, 1964, p. 97.

3. Clezy, P.S. and J. Barrett. Biochim. Biophys. Acta, $\underline{33}$, 584, (1959).

4. Lemberg, R., P. S. Clezy, and J. Barrett. In Proc. Haematin Enzyme Symposium, Canberra, 1959 (J. E. Falk, R. Lemberg, and R. K. Morton, eds.), Pergamon Press, London, 1961, p. 344.

5. Warburg, O., H. S. Gewitz, and W. Völker. Z. Naturforsch., $\underline{10b}$, 541 (1955).

6. Warburg, O. and H. S. Gewitz. Hoppe-Seylers Z. Physiol. Chem., $\underline{288}$, 1 (1951).

7. Kiese, M., H. Kurz, and E. Thofern. Biochem. Z., $\underline{330}$, 541 (1958).

8. Grassl, M., G. Augsburg, U. Coy, and F. Lynen. Biochem. Z., $\underline{337}$, 35 (1963).

9. Clezy, P. S., and J. Barrett. Biochem. J., $\underline{78}$, 798 (1961).

10. Barrett, J., and P. S. Clezy. Nature, $\underline{184}$, 1988 (1959).

11. Grassl, M., U. Coy, R. Seyffert, and F. Lynen. Biochem. Z., $\underline{338}$, 771 (1963).

12. Barrett, J. Biochim. Biophys. Acta, $\underline{54}$, 580 (1961).

13. Kiese, M., and H. Kurz. Biochem. Z., _325_, 299 (1954).

14. Caughey, W. S., and J. L. York. J Biol. Chem., _237_, PC 2414 (1962).

15. Lynen, F., B. W. Agranoff, H. Eggerer, U. Henning, and E. M. Möslein. Angew. Chem., _71_, 657 (1959).

16. Lynen, F. In Ciba Foundation Symposium on Quinones in Electron Transport (G. E. W. Wolstenholme and C. M. O'Connor, eds.), Churchill, London, 1961, p. 244.

17. Parker, M. J. Biochim Biophys. Acta, _35_, 496 (1959).

18. Barrett, J. Biochem. J., _64_, 626 (1956).

# STRUCTURE OF HEME a

## DISCUSSION

**Slater:** All are in agreement about seven of the side chains of heme a, so we need only discuss the eighth, namely that in position 2. There are four points: 1) Is the long side chain saturated or unsaturated? 2) Is it $C_{16}$ or $C_{17}$? 3) Is the oxygen in hydroxyl or ether? 4) What is the amino sugar-like moiety that Dr. Caughey brought forward? With respect to the first question, it does seem to me that Dr. Caughey's evidence is very impressively in favor of unsaturation. Dr. Lemberg also agrees that this fits his data. Perhaps I should ask Dr. Seyffert if the Munich group have any evidence that would exclude there being unsaturation in the side chain?

**Seyffert:** No, because we have not dealt with functional groups or unsaturation in the side chain in position 2. In our degradation procedure, all unsaturated groups were removed by hydrogenation.

**Morrison:** Warburg's group did a quantitative study of the catalytic hydrogenation of heme a (1). They concluded that the formyl and vinyl groups alone accounted for the hydrogen uptake.

**Caughey:** On catalytic hydrogenation, uptake corresponding to three double bonds has been detected, one for the vinyl group, leaving the remaining two for the long alkyl group. Unsaturation was also detected in the carbon-hydrogen stretching region of the infra-red.

**Slater:** On the question of $C_{16}$ vs. $C_{17}$, Dr. Caughey brought forth evidence that his NMR data fit better a $C_{16}$ side chain. But there is very strong chemical evidence from the Munich group in favor of $C_{17}$. Wouldn't you agree, Dr. Caughey?

**Caughey:** I would agree that they presented very strong evidence for their structure; we cannot, however, accomodate our NMR data to this. For example, a terminal isopropyl group in the chain is not indicated. We have prepared a porphyrin with a 1-hydroxy-5,9,13-trimethyltetradecyl substituent for which the NMR spectrum was inconsistent with the NMR spectrum for heme a where unsaturation was clearly evident and a terminal isopropyl group was not clearly evident.

Slater:  There is also the evidence of the biosynthetic pathway brought forward by the Munich group.

Seyffert:  From our mass spectra of the oxidation product and the synthetic methyl-5,9,13-trimethyltetradecyl-maleimide, we have strong evidence for a terminal isopropyl group in the side chain.

In the range from m/e = 40 to m/e = 120, the observed distribution of peaks which result from direct cleavage and from rearrangement products from the methyl end of the side chain is the same for both compounds.

$$CH_3 \quad\quad\quad\quad CH_2-CH_2-CH_2-CH_2-\overset{\overset{\displaystyle CH_3}{|}}{CH}-CH_2-CH_2-CH_2\dagger\overset{\overset{\displaystyle CH_3}{|}}{CH}\dagger CH_2 \dagger CH_2 \dagger CH_2 \dagger \overset{\overset{\displaystyle CH_3}{|}}{CH}-CH_3$$

Further evidence for a terminal isopropyl group is given by gas-liquid chromatography.  We have studied in detail the retention behavior of branched and unbranched methyl-alkyl-maleimides by plotting the log retention time vs. carbon number of the alkyl chain, after the method of A. T. James (2) (cf. also Murray (3,4)).  These data are in agreement with three methyl groups.

Caughey:  Possibly the only way to resolve the apparent discrepancy in structures is for a mixture of hemes to be present. The maleimide oxidation products were obtained in very small yield by the Munich group; particularly small when referred to the total heme a content in the muscle.  Could you estimate the actual percentage yield of your oxidation product?

Seyffert:  Yes.  The actual yield of methyl-ethyl-maleimide is 25-30 percent related to reduced cytoporphyrin, and that of methyl-5,9,13-trimethyltetradecyl-maleimide is 7-10 percent. The lower yield of the lipophylic maleimide is due to an incomplete reduction of the long alkyl side chain, since it is very difficult to achieve the complete reduction of cytoporphyrin to a mesoporphyrin-like compound.  We think that this may be due to a tetrahydropyrane ring structure, which was also discussed by Dr. Lemberg and Dr. Caughey.  (See fig. 1)

Slater:  This brings us naturally to the next point, hydroxyl or ether oxygen.

Lemberg:  There is much to be said for the presence of the pyrane ring in porphyrin a itself, but does this adequately

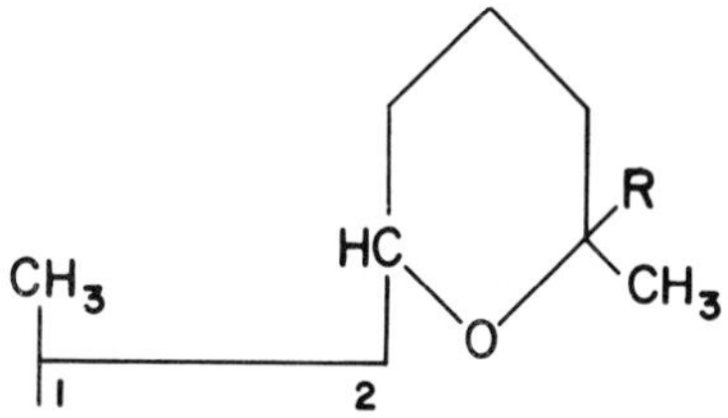

Figure 1. (Seyffert) Tetrahydropyrane ring structure.

explain the behavior of porphyrin a in the Chu and Chu chromatography with kerosene-propanol (5). The $R_f$ of porphyrin a
was 0.26, similar to that of other $\alpha$-hydroxylalkyl porphyrins,
while that after acetylation was 0.62 (6). Perhaps Dr. Barrett
would report on our experience with porphyrin a.

Barrett: The rate of acetylation of porphyrin a is slow compared with that of other side chains having a primary or
secondary alcohol group on the $\alpha$-carbon of a side chain or a
tertiary alcohol group in the nucleus. This low rate is not
contingent on the presence of a formyl group, since porphyrin
a acid (with COOH instead of CHO) shows a similar difficulty
of acetylation. It is unlikely to be due to displacement of
a hexosamine, since the same difficulty of acetylation is
found with the material treated with 17 percent HCl.

Regarding the $\alpha \leftrightarrows \beta$ conversion, we early considered the
possibility of involving hydration of a double bond in the
alkyl side chain, but this alone could not account for the
marked lowering of the Willstatter number of porphyrin a and
porphyrin a alcohol on conversion to the $\beta$ form. Hydroxylation may occur with a concomitant change in the configuration
of the alkyl side chain, particularly if there is at least one
other double bond in the chain.

Morrison: If you believe that the different isolation procedures yield different products, as Dr. Caughey has indicated
(7), then some of the discrepancies are readily attributable
to this factor. We have attempted to evaluate the two isolation procedures, and could not show any difference in products
isolated between the pyridine-chloroform and the acidified-
acetone extraction procedures. The isolated products were
evaluated both in terms of molecular weight and of chromatographic mobility in two types of chromatographic systems. One
chromatographic system reflected solubility characteristics,
and the other reflected differences in the size of the compounds. I have consistently pointed out that the chromatographic mobility and spectral properties of heme a could not

be accounted for by an hydroxyl alkyl side chain (8), and am delighted that there now seems to be agreement on this point.

Slater: So neither Dr. Lemberg nor Dr. Morrison finds any evidence for the extra component.

Lemberg: We have found no differences in spectrum and autoxidation behavior between hemochrome produced according to Caughey and that produced from our hemin a (9).

Morrison: Dr. M. Grinstein of Buenos Aires has recently spent some time in our laboratory, and we have used his procedure (10) to make porphyrin a. When a chloroform solution of the chromatographically purified porphyrin a ester was evaporated to dryness, a green form of the porphyrin a was obtained. In the green form, the No. 1 band in the 600 mμ region shifts out to about 655 mμ and is greatly intensified. The No. 3 band is decreased tremendously and in some cases appears only as a small shoulder. Preparations of the porphyrin a in this green form, when compared with porphyrin a in its usual or red form show a great decrease in the absorption in the infrared due to formyl groups with a concomitant increase in the acetal regions of absorption, suggesting that an intra or inter molecular acetal had been formed by the porphyrin a molecule. Now this conversion of the red porphyrin a to the green form of porphyrin a takes place whether the porphyrin a was derived from the crude heart-muscle preparation itself or from a purified cytochrome c oxidase preparation, suggesting that it was not some miscellaneous contaminant which was causing the conversion of the red porphyrin a to the green porphyrin a. If the green porphyrin a is taken into methanol-sulfuric acid in the same proportions used for the esterification of the porphyrin and the spectral changes are recorded as a function of time, it has been noted that the No. 1 band decreases as a function of time for the first 4 hours in a rather linear manner and the No. 3 band increases at the same time and a new band appears in the region of 590 mμ. Now if you allowed this porphyrin a to stand in the methanol-sulfuric acid for 24 hours or thereabouts and then treat it as you would the porphyrin after esterification, the chloroform solution that you finally wash free of sulfuric acid and methanol has the spectrum of porphyrin a as usually described.

Lemberg: We have repeatedly observed the green color of solid porphyrin a on glass surfaces and when adsorbed to filter paper, and also observed a strong band in the red part of the spectrum in chloroform solutions. By the simple process of dissolving in neutral acetone, the red porphyrin a is immediately restored.

The shift of band I of the neutral porphyrin and its marked intensity increase are difficult to explain on the basis of semiacetal formation. Stereochemically, the model shows that intramolecular semiacetal formation of the formyl in 8 with hydroxyls in positions 1 and 5 or 6 of the side chain 2 is impossible, and in positions 9 and 10 unlikely.

The phenomenon is more plausibly explained as due to an allylic shift of double bonds between the formyl in 8 and the α hydroxyl in side chain 2 as indicated in Fig. 4 of my paper (9).

King: Regardless of whether hematin a contains an extra component, as suggested by some workers, or not, the molecule should be optically active. Indeed, the problem of optical activity or, rather, inactivity, is a serious obstacle to settling the chemical structure of hematin a. In collaboration with Dr. J. A. Schellman, we carefully measured the optical rotation of hematin a in aqueous solution at pH 7.4 from 200 mμ to 590 mμ. No indication of optical activity was observed. Under these conditions, the molar rotation must be smaller than $500^{\circ}$ in the whole wavelength covered; by contrast, the oxidized form of cytochrome oxidase showed an amplitude of $150,000^{\circ}$ in the Soret region. A question which I want to ask is whether anyone has determined the molecular weight of hematin a in aqueous solution?

Lemberg: The molecular weight as defined by the formula is in good agreement with that obtained by Cu titration of the free porphyrin, as well as the molecular extinction data, in comparison with other porphyrins.

King: I do not mean the molecular weight calculated from elementary analysis which gives, of course, the minimum or monomeric molecular weight; I meant to ask if any direct, physical measurement had been made. I would visualize the optical inactivity of hematin a to be due to dimerization in aqueous solution. If dimerization or polymerization occurs in such a way that one molecule is the mirror image of the other, then the dimer becomes optically symmetrical. In addition to the asymmetric carbon atoms in hematin a, the iron in protoheme, at least, does not lie exactly on the plane of the porphyrin, as judged from X-ray studies of heme in myoglobin and hemoglobin (although I am not sure whether iron in free protohematin solution is on the same plane of the porphyrin). At any rate, protohematin in aqueous solution is also optically inactive. I am inclined to think that when apomyoglobin or apohemoglobin react with protohematin, the latter is depolymerized.

Morrison: I think Dr. Gibson will point out that in certain solvents you may be sure that protoheme is a monomer.

Gibson: It is certainly more nearly monomeric in some than in others.

Morrison: In the proper solvent, such as pyridine, most of the heme is monomeric; in this solvent, we could not detect any rotation for heme a.

King: But is there any direct, physical measurement of the molecular weight of either protoheme (protohematin) or heme a (hematin a) in aqueous solution in the absence of pyridine? That pyridine forms a ligand with the iron just as apoproteins do remains to be investigated. Therefore, it may not be relevant that pyridine hemochromogen is monomeric. Moreover, I am not even sure how conclusive the evidence is for pyridine hemochromogen of heme a existing truly in monomeric form. Likewise I do not think its molecular weight(s) has been determined by direct, physical methods.

Slater: Dr. Lemberg has a question which he would like to direct to Dr. Caughey.

Lemberg: I still have difficulty in accepting Dr. Caughey's evidence for an amino sugar as bridge between the a-hydroxyl of side chain 2 and the heme iron. For stereochemical reasons, the bridge cannot be glycosidic for any 2-amino sugar. One would have to assume either a non-glycosidic bridge, or a glycosidic bridge to position 5 of the chain, or an unknown 5- or 6-amino sugar. None of these assumptions appears attractive, for a number of reasons.

Caughey: May I reemphasize our earlier statement that structural details for the amino sugar-like group are incomplete. Nor has the position of this grouping on the alkyl chain been established. We fully agree with Dr. Lemberg that stereochemical arguments preclude the bridging of certain groups between the alkyl chain and iron. Other structures we consider quite reasonable do permit such bridging.

Slater: Dr. Caughey should have an opportunity to answer a rather important question about oxygen in the side chain.

Caughey: The question was, I believe, is there or is there not a hydroxyl present in native heme a? If present, physical evidence should be obtainable. Dr. York and I reported earlier our inability to detect an infrared band characteristic of a hydroxyl on carbon $\alpha$ to a porphyrin ring (11).

<u>Lemberg</u>:  Some physical evidence is available from the chroma-
tography of porphyrin ester in the Chu and Chu procedure.  We
are at present investigating whether or not the product of
treatment with acetic anhydride in pyridine contains acetyl or
not.

<u>Ehrenberg</u>:  Dr. Yonetani and I have some preliminary data on
the paramagnetic susceptibility of heme <u>a</u>.  Heme <u>a</u> at 1.25 mM,
prepared according to the method of Lemberg and dissolved in
0.1 M phosphate buffer, pH 7, in the presence of 1 percent
Emasol, was found to have a magnetic susceptibility of 6200
($\pm$ 250) x 10$^{-6}$ cgs emu in the oxidized state.  In the reduced
state, its magnetic susceptibility drifted from 9400 to 6600
x 10$^{-6}$ cgs emu during about 30 minutes under anaerobic conditions.  It was observed that the light absorption of heme <u>a</u>
did not obey Beer's law under these conditions, indicating the
aggregation of heme <u>a</u> which made it difficult to interpret the
susceptibility data.

## References

1.  Warburg, O., and H. S. Gewitz.  Z. Physiol. Chem., <u>288</u>, 1
    (1951).

2.  James, A. T.  In <u>Methods of Biochemical Analysis</u>, <u>Vol. 8</u>
    (D. Glick, ed.), <u>Interscience Publishers</u>, New York, 1960,
    p. 1.

3.  Murray, K. E.  Aust. J. Chem., <u>12</u>, 657 (1959).

4.  Murray, K. E.  Aust. J. Chem., <u>15</u>, 510 (1962).

5.  Chu, T. C., A. G. Green, and E. V. Chu.  J. Biol. Chem.,
    <u>190</u>, 643 (1951).

6.  Barrett, J.  Nature, <u>183</u>, 1185 (1959).

7.  Caughey, W. S.  In <u>Oxidases and Related Redox Systems</u> (T.
    E. King, H. S. Mason, and M. Morrison, eds.), John Wiley
    and Sons, New York, 1965, p. 109.

8.  Morrison, M. and E. H. Stotz.  J. Biol. Chem., <u>228</u>, 123
    (1957) and Morrison, M., J. Connelly, J. Petix, and E. H.
    Stotz.  J. Biol. Chem., <u>235</u>, 1202 (1960).

9.  Lemberg, R.  This volume, p. 41.

10. Grinstein, M.  J. Biol. Chem., <u>167</u>, 515 (1947).

11. York, J. L., and W. S. Caughey.  Abstract, Am. Chem. Soc.
    145th Meeting, New York, 1963, p. 46C.

## II.

## Reactions of Heme with Proteins
### M. Kamen, Chairman

# STRUCTURAL INTERACTIONS OF HEME WITH PROTEIN

H. C. Watson

Medical Research Council Laboratory of Molecular Biology
Hills Road, Cambridge, England

X-ray data suggest that, with minor variations, the configuration of the polypeptide chain first discovered in sperm whale myoglobin (1) is probably a characteristic feature of all vertebrate myoglobins and hemoglobins (2,3). At the present time the structure of only one hemoprotein is known in detail and in this contribution I shall be concerned mainly with the interaction of the heme with protein as found in sperm whale myoglobin. Reference will, however, be made to the sequence data available for other hemoproteins when the combined chemical and structural information indicates the presence or absence of a basic structural feature of the interaction of the heme with the protein.

The general nature of the heme environment. In sperm whale myoglobin the polypeptide chain is folded so that the interior of the molecule is almost exclusively filled with hydrophobic groups (4,5). Cut deeply into this hydrophobic interior is a cleft into which fits the heme (see frontispiece). The orientation of the heme group is such that the ordered vinyl groups are buried in the hydrophobic interior and the carboxyl groups of the propionic acids form part of the polar surface of the molecule (see frontispiece).

The configuration of the heme. The porphrin ring system is not planar but slightly concave towards the iron atom's sixth coordination position. The heme iron occupies a position at least $\cdot 3$ Å from the best porphrin plane in all the heme derivatives so far studied in full detail (6,7,8). The direction of the displacement of the iron is along the heme normal towards the covalently linked epsilon nitrogen atom of histidine residue (F8)[*]. The distance between the peak centers of the iron and the ligand in the calculated electron density distributions is $2.1 \pm \cdot 2(5)$ Å.

[*]The system of labelling the amino acid residues is as defined in an earlier publication (9).

Hydrogen bonds to the heme. The two propionic acid side
chains are both hydrogen bonded to amino acid side chains in
sperm whale myoglobin.   In onecase the bond is to the nitrogen atom of the guanidinium group of arginine (CD3) while the
other is bonded to the epsilon nitrogen atom of a histidine
residue (FG3).   These residues cannot be important in stabilizing the heme, however, since in other globin chains (see
ref. 10) the residues cited are often replaced by amino acids
with hydrocarbon side chains.

The ligand bonded to the heme iron often forms a hydrogen
bond to the epsilon nitrogen atom of the so-called "distal"
histidine (E7).   This histidine is an invariant feature of all
normal vertebrate globin chains, but since there is no ligand
at the sixth coordination position in reduced myoglobin (8),
we must conclude that this bonding arrangement is also not
essential for stabilizing the interaction of the heme and protein.

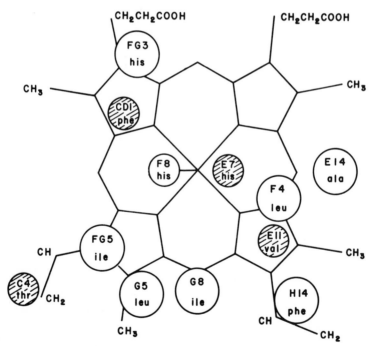

Figure 1.  Surroundings of the heme group in sperm whale myoglobin.  Blank circles represent amino acids on the side of the
heme nearest the covalently linked histidine; shaded circles
represent amino acids on the ligand binding side of the heme.

Hydrophobic bonding between heme and protein. Twelve
amino acid side chains fall within van der Waals contact distance of the porphrin ring (Fig. 1). Two of these residues,
the heme-linked and distal histidines, appear to have special
physiological importance since they are two of the nine remaining invariant globin residues (5). Of the remaining ten residues, three are in contact with the surrounding medium and
seven are completely buried within the molecule. With the
exception of the invariant threonine (C4), whose hydroxyl group
bonds to a main chain carbonyl, all internal residues are
strictly non-polar.

Table 1 shows all the amino acid replacements so far reported for the heme contact residues (5). Although sidechains
in equivalent structural positions vary markedly in size and
shape, the internal residues remain consistently non-polar.

TABLE I

Replacements among amino acids in contact with the heme group

|  | Residue | Observed |
|---|---|---|
| (a) special function | E7 | His |
|  | F8 | His |
| (b) in contact also with surface | E14 | Gly,Ala,Ser,Asp,Glu |
|  | F4 | Leu |
|  | FG3 | His,Leu |
| (c) no contact with surface | C4 | Thr |
|  | CD1 | Phe |
|  | E11 | Val,Ile |
|  | FG5 | Val,Ile |
|  | G5 | Leu, Phe |
|  | G8 | Val, Ile, Leu |
|  | H14 | Val, Phe |

## Discussion

From the description given for the heme environment in
myoglobin it would appear that the forces stabilizing the interaction of the heme with protein are mainly hydrophobic in nature.
This suggests therefore that the globin chain does not stabilize
the heme binding, but rather that the interaction of the heme
with globin stabilizes the molecule as a whole. This hypothesis
is supported by the fact that globin from sperm whale myoglobin
exhibits considerably different optical rotary dispersion
properties from those of the native protein (11).

## References

1. Bodo, G., H. M. Dintzis, J. C. Kendrew, and H. W. Wycoff. Proc. Roy. Soc. (London) A, 253, 70 (1959).

2. Kendrew, J. C. Science, 139, 1259 (1963).

3. Perutz, M. F. Science, 140, 863 (1963).

4. Kendrew, J. C. Brookhaven Symposium in Biology, No. 15, 216 (1962).

5. Perutz, M. F., J. C. Kendrew, and H. C. Watson. J. Mol. Biol., 13, 669 (1965).

6. Kendrew, J. C., R. E. Dickerson, B. E. Strandberg, R. G. Hart, D. R. Davies, D. C. Phillips, and J. C. Shore. Nature, 185, 422 (1960).

7. Stryer, L., J. C. Kendrew, and H. C. Watson. J. Mol. Biol., 8, 96 (1964).

8. Nobbs, C. L., H. C. Watson, and J. C. Kendrew. Nature, 209, 339 (1966).

9. Kendrew, J. C., H. C. Watson, B. C. Strandberg, R. E. Dickerson, D. C. Phillips, and J. C. Shore. Nature, 190, 663 (1961).

10. Perutz, M. F. J. Mol. Biol., 13, 646 (1965).

11. Harrison, S. C., and E. R. Blout. J. Biol. Chem., 238, 2016 (1965).

# KINETICS OF HEME-GLOBIN INTERACTIONS*

Quentin H. Gibson

Department of Biochemistry and Molecular Biology
Cornell University, Ithaca, New York

and

Eraldo Antonini

Istituto di Chimica Biologica, Citta Universitaria
Roma, Italy

The favorable combination of qualities possessed by hemo-globins, of which their availability in large quantities is not the least important, has permitted the accumulation of a body of detailed information about them with correlations between structure and function in a degree of detail approached for few other groups of proteins. The long perspective of hemoglobin chemistry includes many "firsts" among which are the resolution of hemoglobin into native globin and heme, the reconstitution of hemoglobin, and the preparation of synthetic heme-globin complexes and heme porphyrin complexes, all of which were reported by Hill and Holden (1) in a single paper, published exactly forty years ago. This paper attempts to review briefly some of the developments which have stemmed from Hill and Holden's pioneer work, with special reference to the kinetics of the heme-globin interaction.

Rate of the Protohematin-Globin Reaction. Hill and Holden (1) noted that this reaction was "rapid" in terms of test-tube mixing, and their observation was confirmed quanti-tatively by Gibson and Antonini (2), who added that the reac-tion was strongly biphasic, about 20 percent taking place in 0.15 sec, whereas 15 sec was required for 90 percent comple-tion, and, by varying the concentrations of hematin and glo-bin, showed that the rate was determined more by the behavior of the hematin than by the globin. Shack and Clark (3) have shown that hematin in aqueous solutions is polydisperse with particle weights ranging up to 50-100,000, and it seemed that the depolymerization reactions were probably limiting.

*This work was supported by USPHS GM 14276.

Combination of Carboxyheme with Globin. The sharp spectrum and high extinction coefficient of carboxyheme, coupled with the 1:1 stoichiometry for Fe and CO reported by Hill (4) suggest that this compound is predominantly monomeric in solution or at worst, a monomer-dimer mixture with a fair proportion of monomer, so that its reaction with globin might be expected to reflect more nearly the kinetic possibilities of the protein-heme interaction. Experiment showed that the reaction between carboxyheme and globin was not only very fast (Fig. 1), but also had two stages. It was analyzed in terms of the scheme:

$$\text{Heme} + \text{globin} \underset{k_2}{\overset{k_1}{\rightleftharpoons}} \text{heme-globin complex} \qquad (1)$$

$$\text{Heme-globin complex} \overset{k_3}{\rightleftharpoons} \text{Hemoglobin} \qquad (2)$$

where $k_1$ was of the order of $5 \times 10^8$ $M^{-1}sec^{-1}$, and $k_3$ about 350/sec at room temperature. The scheme also accounted satisfactorily for the marked temperature dependence of the overall reaction (apparent activation energy of 11-12 kcal), which was largely attributed to $k_3$.

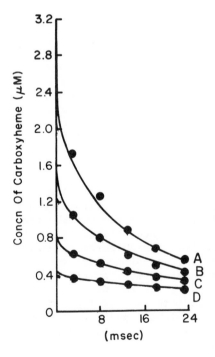

Figure 1. Combination of carboxyheme with human hemoglobin globin. Four concentrations of carboxyheme and globin were used, giving concentrations after mixing of: A, 3.2 µM; B, 1.64 µM; C, 0.84 µM; D, 0.43 µM. The reagents were dissolved in borate buffer, pH 9.1, equilibrated with a partial pressure of 200 mm CO in nitrogen. The observations are shown as points; the continuous lines were computed from Eqns. (1) and (2) by numerical methods. Values of the constants used in obtaining the continuous lines were:

$$k_1 = 4.75 \times 10^8 \ M^{-1}sec^{-1}$$
$$k_2 = 1750 \ sec^{-1}$$
$$k_3 = 375 \ sec^{-1}$$

The effect of varying the concentration of CO was also examined; there was no influence on the rate of the reaction. Obviously, therefore, heme CO could react directly with globin without requiring free heme as an intermediate. Other heme derivatives were also able to react with globin, and the ferrous cyanide compounds were given special attention. Monocyanide heme reacted in much the same way as carboxyheme, but dicyanide heme did not react directly. In this case the cyanide concentration influenced the rate of the reaction by competition with globin for monocyanide heme (Figs. 2A and B), and the results required detailed treatment taking into account the rate of dissociation of dicyanide heme as well as the reaction of monocyanide heme with globin. As Fig. 2B shows, quite good agreement was obtained between theory and experiment. Fuller details are given in (2). These experiments indicate that it is apparently necessary to have one side of the heme molecule free if reconstitution of hemoglobin is to take place.

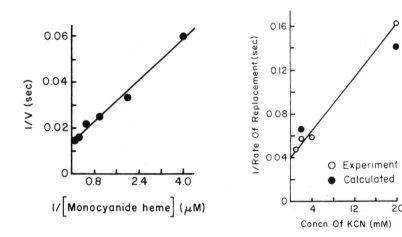

Figure 2. A. Combination of monocyanide heme with hemoglobin globin. The plot shows the reciprocal of the pseudo first order velocity constant calculated over the period 3-8 msec after mixing against the reciprocal of the concentration of monocyanide heme present immediately after mixing. Observations were made at 435 m$\mu$; light path length, 2 cm; borate buffer, pH 9.1; 20° C. Values: $k_2/k_1$ = 0.88 $\mu M^{-1}$; $k_3$ = 90 sec$^{-1}$.

B. Formation of cyanide hemoglobin from mixtures of dicyanide heme and hemoglobin globin reacting in the presence of various concentrations of cyanide. The ordinate gives the reciprocal of the observed velocity constant measured over the period 3-8 msec after mixing. Initial concentrations: dicyanide heme, 6 $\mu M$; hemoglobin globin, 10 $\mu M$ dissolved in borate buffer, pH 9.1. Observations made at 440 m$\mu$; light path length, 2 cm.

Combination of Deutero-, Meso-, and Hematohemes with
Globin. Experiments parallel to those with protoheme (2) have
also been carried out by Gibson and Antonini (5) using the CO
compounds of the various hemes. The results reproduced in
Table I show that mesoheme does not differ greatly from protoheme; deuteroheme combines somewhat more slowly, while hematoheme reacts a great deal less readily still, and dimethyl-
deuterohemedisulfonate does not react at all. Analysis of the
experimental results was performed within the framework of the
scheme of Eqns (1) and (2), but in the later work a systematic
analysis of the data using a digital computer was attempted,
and a series of experiments with up to ten different concentrations of heme and globin was carried out with each heme.
It was anticipated that the computer would select the best
values of the three rate constants, and print them out together
with their standard errors. The event turned out somewhat differently, with the computer finding more than one set of "best"
values depending on the priming values supplied to it. After
some investigation it was decided that (a) a good fit to the
experimental results was obtained with any large value of $k_1$,
provided that a correspondingly large value of $k_2$ was selected,
and (b) that the multiple minima were due to inhomogeneity of
the data and corresponded to situations where there was a
close fit to one set of data points, while others were relatively
neglected with alternations between the points fitted and the
points neglected. The most likely cause of the heterogeneity
appeared to be changes in the reactivity of the heme solutions
during the course of the rather lengthy experiments.

One other point deserves mention: in the experiments with
hemin the reaction was followed over a range of wavelengths in
the Soret region, and it was found that in the neighborhood of
the isosbestic points there were significant differences in
the time course of the reaction which were attributed to the
spectrophotometric contribution of the intermediate postulated
in the scheme of Eqns (1) and (2).

Combination of Porphyrin with Globin. It is natural to
consider whether or not the presence of iron in a porphyrin
has a material effect upon its interaction with globin. This
question has been examined by Gibson (6) who found that there
was little spectrophotometric difference between free monomeric
porphyrin and porphyrin-globin, but was able to follow the
reaction by using changes in fluorescence quenching which
accompany it. The results were closely parallel to those with
the corresponding hematins, and the rate constants derived
from the appropriate kinetic analysis were similar (Table I).
The analogy extended further to cover the apparent energy of
activation, and, in all respects which could be examined, the
reactions appeared essentially the same; thus no role need be
ascribed to the iron atom in determining heme binding.

TABLE I

## Rates of Reaction of Porphyrin and Hemes with Native Globin

The column headed $t_{50}$ gives the time for half-completion of the change in fluorescence in a mixture of $2.5 \times 10^{-6}$ M porphyrin with 1 equivalent of globin in 0.05 M borate buffer, pH 9.1, 22°.

The rate constants in the remaining columns refer to the scheme:

$$d \underset{k_2}{\overset{k_1}{\rightleftharpoons}} 2m\!:\!m \; + \; g \underset{k_4}{\overset{k_3}{\rightleftharpoons}} complex\!:\!complex \overset{k_5}{\longrightarrow} mg$$

in which $\underline{d}$ = concentration of porphyrin dimer, $\underline{m}$ = concentration of porphyrin monomer, $\underline{g}$ = concentration of globin, mg = concentration of porphyrin-globin compound. Figures for CO-hemes are taken from Gibson and Antonini.

| | $t_{50}$ | $10^6 \times k_2/k_1$ | $10^{-6} \times k_3$ | $k_4$ | $k_5$ |
|---|---|---|---|---|---|
| | msec | M | $M^{-1} sec^{-1}$ | $sec^{-1}$ | |
| **Porphyrins** | | | | | |
| Proto- | 21 | 4 | 45* | 190* | 105 |
| Meso- | 35 | 6 | 16* | 120* | 190 |
| Hemato- | 130 | 2 | 6 | 20 | 30 |
| **CO-hemes** | | | | | |
| Proto- | | | 50* | 1800* | 370 |
| Meso- | | | 5* | 160* | 200 |
| Hemato- | | | 1 | 50 | 40 |

*These values are minima only; larger values in the same ratio are also possible.

General Discussion of Results on Heme and Porphyrin Binding. Although the kinetic results are, of course, adequately described in terms of Eqns (1) and (2), it is legitimate to speculate on the chemical changes which determine them. The very rapid first step of combination between heme and globin is little more than an order of magnitude less in rate than would be expected in a diffusion controlled reaction where the protein is treated as providing a hemispherical sink region within which any heme molecule will interact, according to the treatment of Alberty and Hammes (7). Binding at this preliminary stage may be due to the formation of hydrophobic bonds between the porphyrin ring system and a corresponding area in the globin molecule. Since the detailed analysis of the myoglobin and hemoglobin molecules by X-ray methods carried out by Perutz and Kendrew and their co-workers (see for example ref. 8) has shown that the hydrophobic residues of both free and ligand bound hemoglobins lie buried within the protein, such a suggestion would require a major difference in conformation between globin and hemoglobin. There is ample reason to suppose such a difference may, in fact, exist. Thus, hemoglobins are readily crystallized: globin crystals have never been prepared; hemoglobins withstand heating to 50° or more: globin denatures rapidly at temperatures above 17°. The suggestion that an hydrophobic area is exposed in globin is in good agreement with the low specificity of binding. Not only are hemes and porphyrins readily taken up, but large hydrophobic organic molecules such as bromthymol blue react rapidly with globin (9), and can promote its polymerization also, as judged by ultracentrifuge experiments (E. Antonini, unpublished experiments). The plausibility of such a model is supported by analogy with the behavior of bovine serum albumin with hemin and 1-anilinonaphthalene sulfonate (ANS). Some years ago Weber (10) suggested that this dye was bound to hydrophobic regions within a fold of the albumin molecule, and in a series of elegant experiments has since substantiated his earlier proposal. In kinetic experiments using a stopped flow apparatus it was possible to follow the adsorption of the dye, (second order constant $8 \times 10^8$ $M^{-1}sec^{-1}$ at 20°), and its displacement either by octanoate (first-order rate 20/sec), or by hemin, which is much more firmly held by BSA than is ANS. Similar observations were also made with native globin, where hemin can again readily displace, or at least quench the fluorescence of, adsorbed ANS (G. Weber and Q. H. Gibson, unpublished experiments). The globin–ANS reaction has been investigated in detail by Stryer (11) who has demonstrated a stoichiometry similar to that of hemin.

The importance of hydrophobic bonding in heme binding by globin is further illustrated by considering the effects of change in structure of the heme. Thus, three hemes are effectively bound: proto-, meso-, and deuteroheme, in that order; they have in the appropriate positions two vinyl, two ethyl and two H groups. Although deuteroheme is less firmly bound than the first two, the difference is not large. When, however, the vinyl groups are replaced by the hydroxyethyl groups of hematoheme, binding occurs less readily and the product is markedly less stable (12).

The second step in hemoglobin re-formation, described by $k_3$, may tentatively be identified with the folding of the peptide chain around the heme group, following (2). This process is only slightly reversible under ordinary circumstances and in free hemoglobin appears not to occur at all.

72

Polymerization of $\alpha\beta$ Subunits. The description of the heme binding process so far given has been in terms of a subunit of molecular weight 16,000 containing a single heme. Ultracentrifuge studies have shown, however, that the mean molecular weight in solutions of globin is somewhat more than twice this (13) so that the predominant species is probably the $\alpha\beta$ dimer. If so, it would be expected that during the process of combination with heme a series of intermediates would be formed: thus writing G for the globin subunit, and H for hematin molecule the minimum reactions would be:

$$GG + H \rightleftharpoons HGG \tag{3}$$

$$HGG + H \rightleftharpoons HGGH \tag{4}$$

Practical attempts to detect intermediates of the form HGG have been uniformly unsuccessful (14). The approaches have included fluorescence titrations, as well as kinetic spectro-fluorimetry using both the natural tryptophan fluorescence and induced fluorescence following binding of ANS. The expectation was that, in view of the quenching radius of the heme molecule (15), a species such as HGG would be almost entirely without fluorescence; thus, if significant amounts of such a species were formed during heme binding, fluorescence and spectrophotometric titrations would show a breakdown in correlation. In kinetic experiments using an amount of heme insufficient to saturate the globin, an "overshoot" in fluorescence quenching would be expected but was not observed. These negative experiments suggest that the binding of a second molecule of heme by HGG is easier than the binding of the first so that HGG remains a minority species throughout.

Except in rather dilute ( $1 \times 10^{-5}$ M) solutions, many hemoglobins are predominantly tetrameric, and so, if heme binding occurs to $\alpha\beta$ dimers, a further step corresponding to joining up of the paired subunits might be expected. In this case, too, evidence of intermediates has been sought in ultracentrifuge experiments, following sedimentation with light of various wavelengths. The conclusion has been (14) that no large amounts of any intermediates occur, the solutions containing only $H_4G_4$ and $G_2$ units, without species such as $G_4H_2$ or $G_4H_3$, within the limits of precision of the measurements. It appears that the complete hemoglobin molecule is more stable than its intermediates.

Exchange of Hemes Between Hemoglobins. In a few special cases it is possible to follow the transfer of heme from one protein to another. Thus Rossi-Fanelli and Antonini (16) mixed apomyoglobin with protoferrihemoglobin and observed that at neutral pH there was a transfer of hematin from hemoglobin to myoglobin with a rate constant of the order of $10^{-4}$/sec ($t_{50}$ about 2 hr) at room temperature.

If this figure is combined with an overall apparent rate constant of $7 \times 10^7 M^{-1} sec^{-1}$ for the "on" reaction, an equilibrium constant of $10^{-12}$ M is indicated, which agrees reasonably with the values obtained by Banerjee (17,18). Thus, although an exchange reaction may sometimes give misleadingly low apparent rates, the measurements of (16) were probably of the correct order of magnitude.

Experiments were next carried out in which various combinations of hemes and hemoglobins were mixed together, and the spectra of the mixtures recorded at intervals. Although apparently simple, such experiments offer difficulties of interpretation because of the large number of spectrophotometrically distinct species, and because of the possibility of side reactions. The procedure finally adopted was to work with dilute solutions of hemoglobins and hemes, giving a peak absorbance in the Soret region of less than 1/cm and to add successive portions of heme solution to the hemoglobin, recording the spectrum repeatedly after each addition to be sure that no further change was taking place. The results of some 70 experiments carried out at room temperature in 0.05 M phosphate buffer pH 7.4, and in 0.05 M borate buffer pH 9.1 fall into a consistent pattern which may be summarized as follows: replacement reactions occur with ferrihemoglobins and with liganded hemoglobins (CO), but not with ferrohemoglobins. Protoheme can replace meso-, deutero-or hematohematin; mesohematin can replace deutero- or hematohematins; and deuterohematin can replace hematohematin. If a reaction occurs at all, it is effectively complete within 30 sec under the conditions specified. If no measurable change was seen in one hour, the result was defined as "no reaction".

The results with the synthetic hemoglobins obviously differ widely from those reported by Rossi Fanelli and Antonini (14), especially in rate, and this difference was sharpened when stopped flow experiments were performed. In the first of these, high concentrations of hematins and hemoglobins were used, and the rates of the displacement reactions were similar to those for the combination of hematins with globin at comparable concentrations.

On using more dilute solutions the rates were increased, becoming absolutely higher in spite of the dilution. Further, when the reaction was followed at different wavelengths, the apparent rate varied significantly (Fig. 3). Such a result is impossible if the replacement reaction proceeds with the formation of a free heme binding site as intermediate, since the concentration of such free sites must always be small. It follows that the sum of bound hemes and of free hemes is constant, so that a single composite extinction coefficient, together with one concentration term, can describe all the changes.

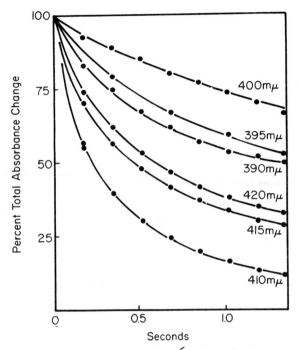

Figure 3. The reaction of 2.5 x 10$^{-6}$ M deuterohemoglobin with 2.5 x 10$^{-6}$ M protohematin followed at different wavelengths. The ordinate shows the percent of the total reaction completed at the time shown. The isosbestic point was at 405 mμ; at shorter wavelengths the overall change was an increase in absorbance. Stopped flow apparatus 2 cm light path, 0.05 M borate buffer, pH 9.1, 20°.

The results of Fig. 3 do not conform to such a scheme, but require the formation of some intermediate species. An obvious proposal is that the deuterohemoglobin picks up a molecule of protohemin to form an intermediate within which exchange at the primary binding site occurs. This idea seems to be supported by the results of experiments with deuterohemoglobin and protoporphyrin (Fig. 4). In this experiment changes in porphyrin fluorescence were followed, and may be explained by supposing that during the first few tens of milliseconds after mixing, protoporphyrin is being taken up by deuterohemoglobin, with resultant quenching of fluorescence by the heme. Exchange follows with the formation of stable porphyrin globin and release of deuterohematin into the solution, accompanied by an increase of fluorescence output.

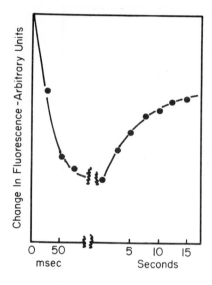

Figure 4. The reaction of 2.5 x 10⁻⁶ M deuterohemoglobin with 2.5 x 10⁻⁶ M protoporphyrin IX followed by fluorescence spectrophotometry. The first part of the record is represented upon an extended time-scale to show the development of fluorescence quenching. Excitation was at 405 mµ and fluorescence was observed with Corning filter No. 3085 in a stopped flow apparatus. Other conditions as for Fig. 3.

These experiments were necessarily performed using hemoglobins with unnatural hemes, and need not, therefore, be pertinent to the behavior of protohemoglobin. Indeed, it may be that differences in the binding of the heme associated with alterations either in subunit folding, or in the relations of the subunits one with another, are important in determining such properties as the change in n as between protohemoglobin on the one hand, and deutero- and mesohemoglobins on the other.

Finally, it should be remembered that globin is much less stable than the hemoglobin, and although a rather good recovery of the molecular properties is possible (13), there must always be a greater risk of inhomogeneity in reconstituted than in natural preparations.

## References

1.  Hill, R., and H. F. Holden. Biochem. J., 20, 1326 (1926).

2.  Gibson, Q. H., and E. Antonini. Biochem. J., 77, 328 (1960).

3.  Shack, J., and W. M. Clark. J. Biol. Chem., 71, 143 (1947).

4.  Hill, R. Proc. Roy. Soc. (London) B, 100, 419 (1926).

5.  Gibson, Q. H., and E. Antonini. J. Biol. Chem., 238, 1384 (1963).

6. Gibson, Q. H. J. Biol. Chem., 239, 3282 (1964).

7. Alberty, R. A., and G. G. Hammes. J. Phys. Chem., 62, 154 (1958).

8. Perutz, M. F. J. Mol. Biol., 13, 646 (1965).

9. Antonini, E., J. Wyman, A. Rossi-Fanelli, and A. Caputo. J. Biol. Chem., 237, 2773 (1962).

10. Weber, G., and D. J. R. Laurence. Biochem. J., 56, xxxl (1954).

11. Stryer, L. J. Mol. Biol., 13, 482 (1965).

12. Rossi-Fanelli, A., and E. Antonini. Arch. Biochem. Biophys., 77, 478 (1958).

13. Rossi-Fanelli, A., E. Antonini, and A. Caputo. Biochim. Biophys. Acta, 28, 221 (1958).

14. Antonini, E., and Q. H. Gibson. Acta Biol. et Med. Germ. Suppl. III, 26 (1964).

15. Weber, G., and F. J. W. Teale. Trans. Faraday Soc., 54, 640 (1958).

16. Rossi-Fanelli, A., and E. Antonini. J. Biol. Chem., 235 PC$_4$ (1960).

17. Banerjee, R. Biochim. Biophys. Acta, 64, 368 (1962).

18. Banerjee, R. Biochim. Biophys. Acta, 64, 385 (1962).

## DISCUSSION

Adler: What evidence have you that, during the kinetic phase of the reaction, the hemes bind only at the active site? Can the heme bind at another site or in another manner than that observed in the final equilibrium state of heme and protein?

Gibson: In this specific case, one cannot say where binding occurs as a result of kinetic work. What I have been doing is raising a pyramid of interpretive guesswork which really is based on the X-ray structural knowledge.

George: Is it clear, experimentally, in which step of this two-step mechanism for the combination of the heme, the iron-nitrogen bond is made?

Gibson: We suggest that it is, in fact, in the first step, certainly in the case of carboxyhemoglobin, because most of the spectrophotometric change is associated with the rapid phase.

Schonbaum: Is there any effect of $D_2O$ on $k_3$?

Gibson: This has not been examined.

Strittmatter: Part of the data which I will present tomorrow deals with the binding of various heme analogs to apo-cytochrome $b_5$. It is certainly in agreement with the mechanism Dr. Gibson assumes; they similarly single out the hematoheme analog, which alone forms a less stable protein complex that is readily dissociated by heme and by denaturing conditions.

Gibson: I may say that the stability of the different synthetic hemoglobins changes progressively. Thermal stability, for example: you can heat protoheme hotter than you can heat meso- and deutero-heme, and certainly a lot hotter than hematoheme.

Strittmatter: Have you used any other metals in your porphyrin analog?

Gibson: No, I have used no metals other than iron.

Strittmatter: Cobalt and manganese derivatives of protoporphyrin IX bind equally well to apo-cytochrome $b_5$, so the metal is a requirement but the species may be varied.

# STRUCTURAL INTERACTIONS OF HEME a AND PROTEIN*

M. Rudolf Lemberg

Department of Biochemistry, Institute of Medical Research
The Royal North Shore Hospital
Sydney, Australia

There are at least three types of heme a proteins. The first is represented by cytochrome a. This does not react with CO and cyanide and has a relatively high $\alpha$-band, causing the $\gamma/\alpha$ ratio to be even lower than in cytochrome c (3 as compared to 4) (1,2). It has a half-time of reduction by dithionite (1-5mM) of about 20 secs (3). This makes possible a study of its differential spectrum (ferrous minus ferric) which shows maxima at 604 and 444 mµ (4,5) that are different from those of the "cytochrome a" of Horie and Morrison (600 and 439 mµ)(6).

Cytochrome $a_3$ represents the second type of heme a protein. It reacts with CO and cyanide, has a low $\alpha$-band, and therefore, a high $\gamma/\alpha$ ratio of >8, or in the differential spectrum as high as 25. It resembles free heme a in detergent solution (7,8) rather than hemochromes a or other hemoproteins a. As with free heme a, CO shifts the $\alpha$-band toward the blue (to 590 mµ)(2)(Table I). Reduction by dithionite is more than 10 times slower than that of cytochrome a (3). There is other evidence which supports that cytochrome $a_3$ is more high-spin than cytochrome a, although so far only a trace of the charge transfer band in the red (about 635 mµ distinct in some other hemoproteins a) has been discovered in ferric cytochrome oxidase (a and $a_3$). Perhaps this is combined with the Cu band at 830 mµ.

Thirdly, there is a large class of heme a proteins which have a low $\gamma/\alpha$ ratio, but differ from cytochrome a by their ability to react with CO and cyanide, with CO shifting the absorption band to the red (9). They resemble the imidazole

*This work was supported by grants from the National Institutes of Health and the National Health and Medical Research Council of Australia.

‡Present address: Johnson Research Foundation, University of Pennsylvania, Philadelphia, Pennsylvania.

TABLE I

Shift of $\alpha$-band of Ferroheme a Compounds by CO

| | Fe$^{++}$ | | | FeCO | | |
|---|---|---|---|---|---|---|
| | $\alpha(\lambda)$ | $\gamma(\lambda)$ | $R\frac{\varepsilon\gamma}{\varepsilon}\alpha$ | $\alpha(\lambda)$ | $\gamma(\lambda)$ | $\Delta\lambda\alpha$ |
| Heme a | 600 | 410 | 5.5 | 602 | 425 | +2 |
| Heme a −cholate | 603 | 437 | 8.8 | 602 | 427 | −1 |
| Heme a −Emasol 4130 | 605 | 438 | 7.0 | 597 | 426 | −8 |
| Heme a −pyridine | 587 | 430 | 3.8 | 592 | 429 | +5 |
| Heme a −4−methyl imidazole | 594 | 441 | 3.3 | 605 | 435 | +11 |
| Heme a −globin | 595 | 442 | 4.2 | 603 | 432 | +8 |
| Cytochrome a | 604 | 445 | 4.5 | --- | --- | --- |
| Cytochrome $a_3$ | 604 | 444 | 10 | 589 | 430 | −15 |
| Cytochrome $a_1$ | 589 | 442 | -- | 593 | 427 | +4 |

hemochrome. To this class belong the hemoproteins a synthesized with globin, horse−radish apoperoxidase, and even with
serum albumins; also those present in mildly modified cytochrome oxidase (10); and the cytochrome $a_1$ of Acetobacter
Pasteurianum.

Thus, it appears likely that we have an open linkage
involving only one protein nitrogen in cytochrome $a_3$, but a
firm linkage to two protein nitrogens in cytochrome a similar
to that present in most cytochromes c. Both are altered by
alteration of the protein conformation to the third type, in
which still two nitrogens can be attached to the heme iron,
but one so loosely that CO can replace it, as it does in the
imidazole or pyridine hemochromes.

The synthetic heme a globin does not combine reversibly
with oxygen, and the heme a apoperoxidase is an extremely weak
peroxidase (9). In contrast with the protoheme compounds, a−
peroxidase has more high−spin character than the hemoglobin a,
to judge from the height of the 635 m$\mu$ absorption bands of the
ferrihemoproteins.

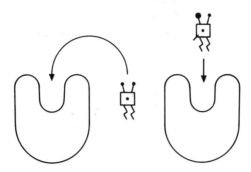

<u>Figure 1.</u>  Combination of protoheme and heme <u>a</u> with proteins.

Fig. 1 is somewhat fanciful, but will make my point clear.
We know that in myoglobin the protoheme, represented here as a
kind of double-headed frog, jumps into the protein pool head
first, with its hydrophilic legs (the carboxyl groups) stick-
ing out and the hydrophobic edge wedged between the hydrophobic protein side chains (Kendrew (11)).  This, according to
Wang (12), is the basis for the reversible oxygenation (although admittedly unstable, hemato- and copro-hemoglobins are
apparently also able to combine reversibly with oxygen)(13).
The heme <u>a</u> frog has no hydrophobic edge, and moreover its
large hydrophobic head will prevent it entering the protein
pool head first.  Thus, it will enter feet first, immersing
the hydrophilic carboxyl groups and the formyl group in the
pool.  This may enhance the suitability of heme <u>a</u> as the
prosthetic group of an oxidase, although we have primitive
protoheme oxidases in cytochromes <u>o</u>, and perhaps also in peroxidases reacting with certain substrates.  The picture may
also explain the relative inactivity of the formyl side chain
in the oxidase, with the role of the formyl being mainly the
increase of the oxidation-reduction potential.

## References

1.  Yonetani, T.  J. Biol. Chem., <u>235</u>, 845 (1960).

2.  Lemberg, R., T. B. G. Pilger, N. Newton, and T. Clarke.
    Proc. Roy. Soc. (London) B, <u>159</u>, 405 (1964).

3.  Lemberg, R., and M. V. Gilmour.  Unpublished experiments.

4.  Lemberg, R., and J. T. Stanbury.  Unpublished experiments.

5.  Vanneste, W. H.  Biochemistry, <u>5</u>, 1838 (1966).

6. Horie, S., and M. Morrison. J. Biol. Chem., 239, 1438 (1964).

7. Lemberg, R., N. Newton, and J. E. O'Hagan. Proc. Roy. Soc. (London) B, 155, 356 (1961).

8. Horie, S. J. Biochem., 57, 147 (1965).

9. Lemberg, R., D. B. Morell, N. Newton, and J. E. O'Hagan. Proc. Roy. Soc. (London) B, 155, 339 (1962).

10. Lemberg, R., and T. B. G. Pilger. Proc. Roy. Soc. (London) B, 159, 436 (1964).

11. Kendrew, J. C. Science, 139, 1259 (1965).

12. Wang, J. H. In Haematin Enzymes (J. E. Falk, R. Lemberg, and R. K. Morton, eds.), Pergamon Press, New York, 1961, p. 98.

13. O'Hagan, J. E. Biochem. J., 74, 417 (1960).

# INTERACTIONS OF HEME a WITH POLYAMINO ACIDS AND PROTEINS[*]

Tsoo E. King, F. C. Yong, and S. Takemori[‡]

Laboratory for Respiratory Enzymology and
Department of Chemistry, Oregon State University
Corvallis, Oregon

X-ray analysis is probably the only reliable method to
determine the particular amino acids (of the protein moiety)
which coordinate with the iron in hemoproteins.  By this means
histidine has been found with certainty to constitute the
linkage in myoglobin and in hemoglobin (1,2).  However, the
X-ray method is not applicable to the study of cytochrome oxidase at present.  Investigation of the interactions of hematin
a with synthetic polypeptides as well as with those proteins
of known composition may shed some light on the problem of
coordination.  This paper reports on an investigation of this
kind together with some tentative inferences derived therefrom.

Hematin a was prepared from soluble cytochrome oxidase
(3).  The native globin was isolated from freshly prepared
crystalline bovine oxyhemoglobin (4).  The "nativeness" of the
isolated globin was ascertained by the reconstitution technique
(4).  Four samples of poly-L-lysine, other poly-L-amino acids,
and crystalline protohematin were procured from Mann Research
Laboratories.  Poly-L-histidine with a molecular weight of
8,000 was a product of the biophysics department of the
Weizmann Institute.

Concentrations of hematin a and protohematin were determined by the alkaline pyridine hemochromogen methods and millimolar absorbance indices of 27.4 at 587 m$\mu$(3) and 34.4 at
556 m$\mu$ (5), respectively, were used.  Spectrophotometric measurement was conducted at room temperature in a cuvette with
an optical path of 1 cm in a Cary spectrophotometer.

[*]This work was supported by grants from the National Science
Foundation, the Public Health Service, the American Heart Association, and the Life Insurance Medical Research Fund.

[‡]Present address:  Department of Chemistry, Faculty of Science,
University of Kanazawa, Kanazawa, Japan.

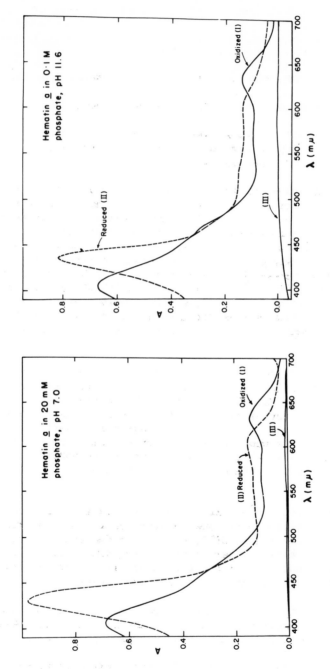

Figure 1.  Absorption spectra of hematin a at pH 7.0.  The final concentration was 14.5 μM hematin a in 20 mM phosphate buffer.  Curve I, oxidized; II, dithionite reduced (5-10 minute reduction); III, base line.

Figure 2.  Absorption spectra of hematin a at pH 11.6.  The final concentration was 14.8 μM hematin a in 0.1 M phosphate buffer.  Curve I, oxidized; II, dithionite reduced (5-10 minutes reduction); III, base line.

84

Figs. 1 and 2 illustrate the absorption spectra of free hematin a isolated from purified cytochrome oxidase, according to the method described previously (3), in neutral and alkaline media. In phosphate buffer, pH 7.0, both the $\alpha$ and $\gamma$ bands were relatively broad and centered at 633 and 406 m$\mu$, respectively. Upon reduction, the Soret band showed a pronounced hyperchromicity and a red shift to 430 m$\mu$; the $\alpha$-band became less distinct. Hematin a at pH 11.6 exhibited a broad $\alpha$-peak centered at approximately 633 m$\mu$ and $\gamma$-peak at 405 m$\mu$. Dithionite reduction further widened the $\alpha$-band but sharpened the Soret peak to 436 m$\mu$. Heme a* (the reduced form) was not stable as witnessed by the decrease of the absorbance on standing. A decrease of as much as 10 percent in the Soret region was observed in 30 min.

The absorption characteristics of hematin a changed upon the addition of poly-L-lysine in either neutral or alkaline media. As shown in Fig. 3, maxima at 400 and 630 m$\mu$ were formed in a neutral medium. After reduction with dithionite, the spectrum exhibited a broad band at 580 m$\mu$ and no distinct Soret maximum.

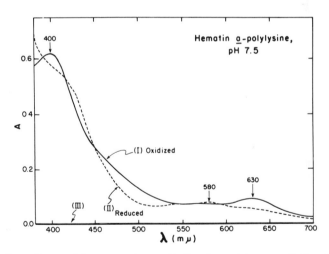

Figure 3. Absorption spectra of the hematin a-polylysine complex in neutral medium. The final concentration was 3.8 $\mu$M polylysine and 17 $\mu$M hematin a, pH 7.5. Curves I, oxidized; II, dithionite reduced; and III, the base line.

*The terms protohematin and hematin a refer to their oxidized state, and protoheme and heme a to the reduced state. When in general description the oxidation state is not a point of significance, hematin and heme are used interchangeably.

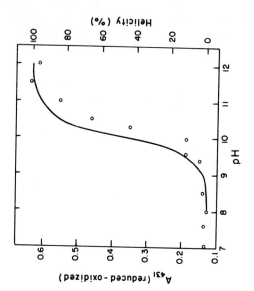

Figure 5. Comparison of the pH profiles of helicity of polylysine and the Soret maxima of the difference spectra of the heme a–polylysine complex. The solid line represents the helicity of polylysine in percentage from ref. 6; circles, the absorbance of Soret maxima at 431 mμ of the difference spectra (reduced minus oxidized samples). The pH values for the absorbance were measured at 22°, while those for the helicity were measured at 25°.

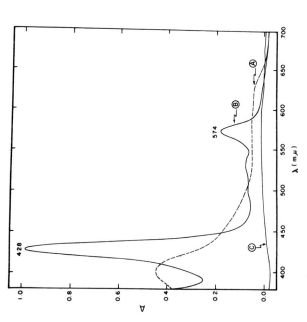

Figure 4. Absorption spectra of the hematin a–polylysine complex in alkaline medium. The final concentration was 6.5 μM polylysine and 9.2 μM hematin, pH 11.6. Curve A, oxidized; B, Dithionite reduced; C, base line.

86

In alkaline buffer, hematin a reacted with polylysine to give a greenish color with broad absorption maxima centered at 633 and 407 mµ. The color became wine red after reduction; the distinct absorption maxima were at 574 and 428 mµ as shown in Fig. 4. Further treatment of the reduced sample with carbon monoxide shifted the $\alpha$ and $\gamma$ maxima to 584 and 424 mµ, respectively. The $\beta$-band became discernible.

The effect of pH on the spectral characteristics of the complex was investigated. Fig. 5, depicting a pH profile with respect to the absorbance of the Soret maximum, shows that the absorbance approximates the helicity of polylysine. The displacement of less than 0.5 pH unit may be apparent rather than genuine because the experimental points on the original curve (6) of the helicity are somewhat scattered, and the precision of the rotational determination may not be high. The binding constant of the complex, although not accurately calculated, appears to be very high as judged from the titration curve shown in Fig. 6.

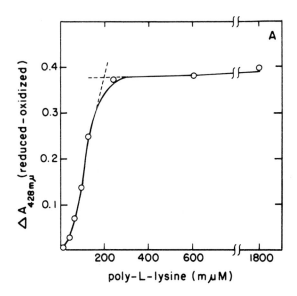

Figure 6. Stoichiometry of the hematin a-polylysine complex at pH 10.6. The heme a at a final concentration of 13.9 µM was spectrophotometrically titrated with polylysine (degree of polymerization, 480) as indicated.

Borohydride reaction with the hematine a-polylysine complex at pH 11.6 caused the blue shifts of both the $\alpha$ and $\gamma$
bands. The reduced form showed distinct maxima at 558 and
418 mµ and a shoulder at 523 mµ as shown in Fig. 7. The spectrum of the carbon monoxide compound of the borohydride-reacted
complex was also different from that of the complex not subjected to the borohydride reaction. The hematin of the
borohydride-reacted complex was not extractable by acid-acetone.
Iron analysis revealed that the hematin was "fixed" to the
protein moiety. This property was not shared by the protohematin-polylysine complex nor by the polylysine complex of
hematin a which had been reacted with borohydride prior to the
reaction with the polyamino acid.

Hematin a did not react with L-histidine, L-lysine, L-
glutamic acid, L-aspartic acid, L-proline, L-alanine, poly-L-
glutamic acid, poly-L-proline, and protamine in either neutral
or alkaline media under the conditions similar to those used
for polylysine (for less than 2 mg nitrogenous compound per **ml.**)

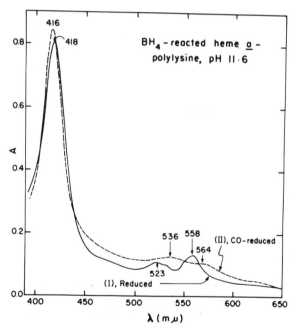

Figure 7. Absorption spectra of the borohydride-reacted heme a-
polylysine complex. Curves I, dithionite reduced; II, dithionite reduced and subsequently treated with carbon monoxide. The
system containing 13.5 µM hematin a and 4.8 µM polylysine in 0.1
M phosphate buffer, pH 11.6, was treated with a slight excess
(based on heme) of sodium borohydride at 0° for 3 hours.

However, the spectra of heme a in the presence of 5 percent lysine (but not other free amino acids tested including also L-methionine and L-tryosine) at pH 11.6 closely resembled those of the heme a-polylysine complex at the same pH. This observation indicates that the binding constant of heme a with monomeric lysine is many orders smaller than that with polylysine.

Although polysarcosine, poly-L-tyrosine, and poly-L-histidine reacted with hematin a, the reaction differed from that with polylysine. The behavior of polyhistidine toward hematin a was interesting but complicated. This polyamino acid is insoluble in aqueous media at pH higher than 5.8 even in the absence of phosphate. At pH 5.7, the oxidized form of the complex showed maxima at 594 and 423 mμ. Upon dithionite reduction turbidity developed, but the maxima were distinguishable at 592, 562 and 423 mμ with a shoulder at approximately 442 mμ. The reduced form appeared very rapidly autoxidizable. After adjustment of the system in the oxidized form to pH 11.6, a green precipitate was formed which was dissolved in dimethylsulfoxide (DMSO), but the solution did not exhibit a distinct α-band in the oxidized form (Fig. 8); by contrast, hematin a alone in this solvent showed clear maxima (Fig. 9).

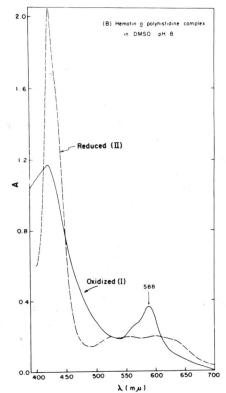

Figure 8. Absorption spectra of the hematin a-polyhistidine complex in dimethylsulfoxide. The system containing 16.7 μM hematin and 140 μM polyhistidine in 10 mM phosphate buffer was adjusted to pH 11.6. The precipitate formed was separated and then dissolved in dimethylsulfoxide. The solution gave apparent pH 8. Subsequently, 0.01 ml aqueous dithionite was added to the system (3 ml) and the reduced spectrum was thus obtained.
———— oxidized
- - - - reduced

89

Upon addition of aqueous dithionite, absorption maxima appeared at 588, 523, and 421 mμ. Free heme a in DMSO showed maxima at 583 and 432 mμ (cf. Fig. 9).

With respect to absorption maxima, behavior exhibited by the reaction of hematin a with polylysine at pH 11.6 was the same with serum albumin, native globin (from hemoglobin), and histone (7). Both spectral properties and borohydride reduction were completely different when protohematin was used instead of hematin a. Moreover, the spectral behavior of the protohematin complexes greatly depended upon the age of the protohematin solution used.

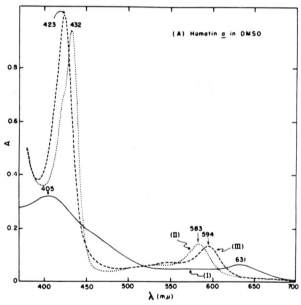

Figure 9. Absorption spectra of hematin a in dimethylsulfoxide. The final concentration of hematin a was 9.3 μM. Curves I, oxidized; II, dithionite reduced; III, dithionite reduced and subsequently treated with carbon monoxide.

From the data presented here (cf. 8,9), together with the behavior of cytochrome oxidase described previously in publications by this laboratory (3) and also by others (10-12), a number of salient points may be deduced. Here it suffices to point out a striking resemblance between these hematin a complexes of polylysine and of proteins with high lysine content (as well as monomeric lysine at high concentrations) on one hand and cytochrome oxidase in alkaline media on the other.

Although absorbance indices differ, the positions of the band maxima of the complexes of polylysine, albumin, globin, and histone are practically the same as those of cytochrome oxidase at pH 11.6 in the oxidized, the reduced, the carbon-monoxide reduced, the borohydride-treated, and the borohydride-treated followed by carbon monoxide-reduced forms. Moreover, after borohydride treatment the heme a in the complexes or in cytochrome oxidase is acid-acetone nonextractable.

These characteristics are not exhibited when hematin **a** is replaced by protohematin. It is thus tempting to conclude that at least one lysine residue of cytochrome oxidase coordinates with the heme iron at pH 11.6* and another forms a Schiff base with the formyl group on the porphyrin nucleus. These properties are compatible with the high lysine content in cytochrome oxidase recently reported (14). Needless to say, any conclusion based on inference or correlation is at best only indirect and tentative. Moreover, using spectral behavior with respect to the absorption maxima as a means for the identification of the nature of the ligand requires further justification. Likewise, whether the different absorption maxima exhibited by many protohematin-linked hemoproteins, for example, might be interpreted as the difference of the ligands remains to be studied. At present, molecular spectroscopy is not advanced enough either to interpret meaningfully or to predict accurately the fine structure of hemoprotein spectra.

A preliminary report on some facets of the work has appeared (15) and a fuller account of other observations pertaining to reactions of heme a and of protoheme will be reported elsewhere.

### Summary

Hematin ·a isolated from purified cytochrome oxidase reacts with poly-L-lysine both in acid and alkaline media. pH is a function for the appearance of the Soret peak at 428 mμ for the reduced form or 430-1 mμ for the difference spectrum, the reduced minus the oxidized. This type of the pH profile approximates the pH-dependent helicity variation of polylysine. Borohydride reaction of the heme a complex of polylysine (as well as of globin) renders the heme to be acid nonextractable.

---

*It seems to be fairly certain (3, see also 13) that with respect to the spectral characteristics and binding with ligands (such as carbon monoxide [ref. 11]), there is no difference between cytochromes a and $a_3$ at pH 11.6.

The interaction has also been studied between hematin a (as well as protohematin) and a number of other poly-L-amino acids, free amino acids and several proteins. From the data presented here together with the behavior of cytochrome oxidase described previously (3), it is tentatively concluded that at least one lysine residue of cytochrome oxidase coordinates with the heme iron at pH 11.6 and another forms a Schiff base with formyl group on the prophyrin nucleus. The justification and reservation for the conclusion has been pointed out.

## References

1.  Kendrew, J. C., H. C. Watson, B. E. Strandberg, R. E. Dickerson, D. C. Phillips, and V. C. Shore. Nature, 190, 666 (1961).

2.  Perutz, M. F., M. G. Rossmann, A. F. Cullis, H. Muirhead, G. Will, and A. C. T. North. Nature, 185, 416 (1960).

3.  Takemori, S., and T. E. King. J. Biol. Chem., 240, 504 (1965).

4.  Rossi-Fanelli, A., E. Antonini, and A. Caputo. Biochim. Biophys. Acta, 30, 608 (1958).

5.  Falk, J. E. In Porphyrins and Metalloporphyrins, BBA Library No. 2, Elsevier Publishing Co., Amsterdam, 1964, 240.

6.  Applequist, J., and P. Dotty. In Polyamino Acids, Polypeptides and Proteins (M. Stahmann, ed.), University of Wisconsin Press, Madison, Wisconsin, 1962, p. 161.

7.  Johns, E. W. Biochem. J., 92, 55 (1964).

8.  Kiese, M., and H. Kurtz. Biochem. Z., 330, 117 (1958).

9.  Morrell, D. B., J. Barrett, P. Clezy, and R. Lemberg. In Hematin Enzymes (J. E. Falk, R. Lemberg, and R. K. Morton, eds.), Pergamon Press, London, 1961, p. 320.

10. Keilin, D. Proc. Roy. Soc. (London) B, 98, 312 (1925).

11. Lemberg, R. Proc. Roy. Soc. (London) B, 159, 429 (1964).

12. Orii, Y., and K. Okunuki. J. Biochem. (Tokyo), 55, 37 (1964).

13. Lemberg, R., and G. E. Mansley. Biochim. Biophys. Acta, 96, 187 (1965).

14. Matsubara, H., Y. Orii, and K. Okunuki. Biochim. Biophys. Acta, 97, 61 (1965).

15. King, T. E., F. C. Yong, and S. Takemori. Biochem. Biophys. Research Comm., 22, 658 (1966).

MAGNETO-OPTICAL ROTATION SPECTRA OF
HEMOGLOBIN AND ITS DERIVATIVES

Victor E. Shashoua

Department of Biology, Massachusetts Institute of Technology
Cambridge, Massachusetts

## Introduction

Many investigations of the physical properties of hemoglobin and its derivatives have been reported in defining its
biological activity. These include the absorption spectral
studies of Drabkin (1), the electron spin resonance studies
of Gordy and Rexroad (2), the magnetic susceptibility measurements of Pauling and Coryell (3), and more recently the magnetic circular dichroism measurements of Schooley, Bunnenberg
and Djerassi (4). In this laboratory we have been studying
the application of the technique of magneto-optical rotation
(MOR) spectroscopy (5) in an attempt to experimentally define
the fundamental relationships of MOR spectra to molecular
structural parameters. Hemoglobin and its derivatives were
found to be among the group of substances with pronounced
magnetic rotations and were, therefore, quite suitable for
MOR studies.

In magneto-optical rotation spectroscopy, a magnetic
field is used to induce optical rotations (Faraday effect) in
a substance. Measurements of the variation of the induced
magnetic rotation as a function of wavelength gives an MOR
spectrum. In the optical absorption band region of a substance, the MOR spectrum shows anomalous rotatory dispersion
features (6) which may be useful for characterizing certain
aspects of molecular structure. This paper describes the MOR
spectra of hemoglobin, methemoglobin and their complexes with
various ligands. In the course of these measurements, the
natural optical activity of the products was also obtained to
give their optical rotatory dispersion (ORD) spectra.

## Experimental Methods

MOR Measurements. The MOR spectra were determined in the
MOR spectropolarimeter previously described (7). The freshly
prepared solutions were studied at a 5,000 gauss magnetic
field under an atmosphere of nitrogen. The apparatus used was
an automatic solvent compensating instrument (sensitivity
+.001 in the visible), which has two opposed magnetic fields,
one for solution and one for solvent. This has one disadvantage in that it cannot compensate for the solvent molecules
displaced by the solute in the solution compartment. As
pointed out earlier (8,9), this deficiency only becomes important when the Verdet constant of the solute is of the same
order of magnitude as for the solvent. As shown in Fig. 1
for some of the hemoglobin data, this correction becomes quite
important All the data of this paper have been corrected for
solvent rotation. Here, a plot of the specific magnetic rotation $[\alpha]sp$, as defined by Equation 1, is given as a function
of wavelength:

$$[\alpha]sp = \frac{\theta}{\ell\,c} \frac{10,000}{H} \qquad (1)$$

where $\theta$ is the measured angle of rotation in degrees, $\ell$
is the path length in decimeters, c is the concentration in
g /ml  and H is the magnetic field in gauss.

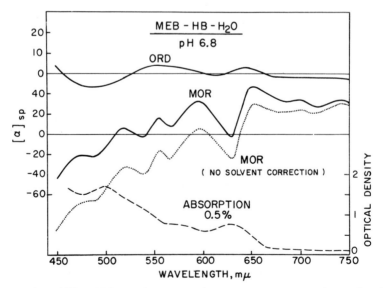

Figure 1. MOR, ORD, and absorption spectra of methemoglobin,
showing the effect of solvent correction on the MOR data.

The data are normalized to a standard magnetic field of 10,000 gauss; the reported $[\alpha]_{sp}$ values constitute the sum of the positive and negative components of the observed type III MOR spectra as shown later (by $\triangle$ in Fig. 4), and the solutions were measured in a 1 cm. cell at $10^{\circ}C$. in a phosphate buffer at pH 6.8, the isoelectric point of hemoglobin. The natural optical activities (ORD spectra) were obtained in the absence of magnetic field for the solutions at the concentration levels shown in the absorption spectra of the figures; and these were subtracted from the measured sum of natural activity and induced magnetic rotations to give the MOR spectra. The additivity of magnetic rotation and optical activity was established in a separate experiment for regions outside absorption bands with poly- $\gamma$-benzyl-L-glutamate by finding that the same absolute value of magnetic rotation is obtained when the applied field is reversed to give a rotation in the opposite sense as the natural optical rotation.

Materials. The bovine hemoglobin samples were commercial grade materials obtained from Sigma Chemical Company, St. Louis, Missouri. These were converted to hemoglobin by reduction of 0.25 percent solutions in pH 6.8 with formamidine sulfinic acid (10). The reduction was carried out with a slow stream of nitrogen bubbling through the solutions.

Methemoglobin was prepared from the commercially available crystalline bovine hemoglobin by oxidation with potassium ferricyanide, using equal mixtures of 1 percent solutions of the reactants at pH 6.8. The solutions were then dialyzed and lyophilized to give the solid methemoglobin.

One sample of fresh horse hemoglobin[*] prepared was from whole blood using the method of Steinhardt and Zaiser (11). This was isolated as the oxyhemoglobin derivative and studied at pH 6.8. Fig. 2A shows the MOR and ORD spectra of the sample at the visible region of the spectrum. A comparison of this with the results for the corresponding commercial sample (Fig. 3C and Table I) shows an over-all similarity in the spectra, indicating the validity of the measurements for the different sources of material. The larger specific magnetic rotation for the fresh sample, however, may be attributable to either a species difference (bovine vs. horse) or to some "inactive" material diluting the commercial grade samples.

The various derivaties of hemoglobin were prepared by bubbling the appropriate gas ($O_2$, or CO) into the solutions of freshly reduced hemoglobin for about one hour at $10^{\circ}C$.

[*] This sample was supplied by Dr. C. P. Malone of the E. I. duPont de Nemours and Co., Inc.

The concentrations were chosen to provide solutions appropriate
for the spectral studies. The methemoglobin derivatives
(CN and F) were obtained by mixing equal amounts of 0.5 percent
sodium salt solutions (i.e., a large excess) of the anions at
pH 6.8 with the appropriate concentrations of hemoglobin suitable for MOR measurements. The hydroxide derivative was prepared by dissolving methemoglobin in a pH 10 phosphate buffer.
In each case, the published absorption spectra (1) were used
to confirm the formation of a product.

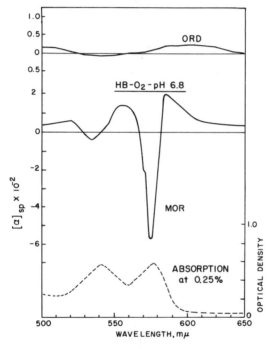

Figure 2. MOR, ORD,
and absorption spec-
tra of horse hemo-
globin (freshly
isolated sample).

## Results and Discussion

Each of the four active sites of hemoglobin (12) contains
a porphyrin nucleus with a central iron atom. The structure
can be represented as an octahedral complex with four nitrogen
ligands, a globin in the fifth position and a substituent lig-
and at the sixth position. Tables I and II and Figs. 3 to 6
summarize the MOR and ORD measurements for the various ligands
studied at the indicated absorption wavelengths. The natural
optical activity (ORD spectra) of these molecules is generally
quite small and similar to the results reported by Beychok and

Blout (13) for the 450-650 mμ region. The MOR spectra, however, exhibit distinct anomalous rotatory dispersion features
which are easily measured in the spectropolarimeter. The MOR
spectra were all type III (6), with a negative rotation peak
coinciding with the absorption maxima of the compounds. It is
interesting to note that the specific magnetic rotations for
the hemoglobin data are about one order of magnitude less than
the results for cytochrome c (14,15) with essentially the same
porphyrin chromophore and ferrous iron substituent in the molecule. The present knowledge of MOR spectroscopy cannot yet
explain the significance of such differences. Perhaps the
protein envelope around the cytochrome c molecule or the assy-
metry in the ligand fields about the hemoglobin molecule have
some influence on the magnetic rotation.

   <u>Relationship to Ligand Field</u>.  Table I and Fig. 3 show
the MOR spectral data on hemoglobin and its derivatives.

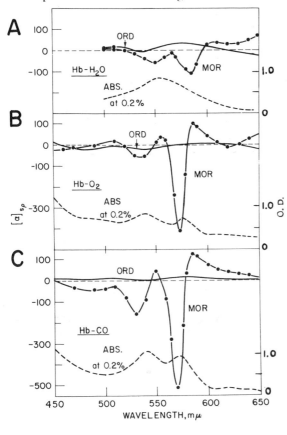

Figure 3. Magne-
to-optical rota-
tion spectra of
hemoglobin and
its derivatives.
A, Aquo-ferro-
hemoglobin
B, Oxyferrohemo-
globin
C, Carboxyferro-
hemoglobin

The magnitude of the specific magnetic rotation of the bovine hemoglobin shows about a four-fold change from 150 to 650 for replacement of water with carbon monoxide as ligand, at the 560 mμ region of the spectrum. The oxyhemoglobin data are at an intermediate range with a value of 510 for the 564 mμ absorption band. A comparison of these results with published magnetic susceptibility data shows no obvious relationship to the paramagnetism of the samples (see Table I). The results, however, seem to follow the known ligand fields of the substituents--a large magnetic rotation corresponding to a large ligand field.

In Table II and Figs. 4 to 6, a similar study for various substituted methemoglobins suggests a relationship to the spin state of the hemoprotein. These data, however, are more complicated since the four-absorption-band system (high spin) for the visible absorption region of methemoglobin reduces to the

TABLE I

MOR Spectral Data for Hemoglobin

pH = 6.8, $10^{\circ}$ C

| Ligand | Absorpt. Maxima mμ | MOR Data[a] | | | | Magnetic Moment B.M.[d] | No. un-paired Electrons |
|--------|--------------------|-------------|--------|-------------|--------|-------------------------|-------------------------|
| | | $\frac{\lambda 1}{m\mu}$ | $[\alpha]sp$ | $\frac{\lambda 2}{m\mu}$ | $[\alpha]sp$ | | |
| $H_2O$[b] | 554 | 550 | 45 | 585 | 150 | 4.9 | 4 |
| $O_2$[b] | 540 | 538 | 100 | 574 | 510 | 0 | 0 |
| $CO$[b] | 540 572 | 530 | 210 | 570 | 650 | 0 | 0 |
| $O_2$[c] | 542 577 | 535 | 118 | 576 | 785 | 0 | 0 |

(a) The $[\alpha]sp$ values of the MOR data are the sum of the positive and negative components of the type-3 MOR spectra, as illustrated by $\triangle$ in Fig. 4.

(b) Commercial grade bovine hemoglobin.

(c) Fresh horse hemoglobin data.

(d) Data obtained from Ref. 16.

two-band system for methemoglobin cyanide (low spin). Nevertheless, if we compare the peak heights as defined by $\triangle$ in Fig. 4, for what may be assumed as equivalent absorption bands in the molecules, then a correlation between the magnitude of the magnetic rotation and the spin state of the methemoglobin derivative is observed. Thus for the series of type III MOR spectra (6) a large magnetic rotation appears to correspond to compounds with low spin and a small magnetic rotation is observed for high spin compounds. In Table II, band III methemoglobin derivatives with the ligands $H_2O$, OH, F have small magnetic rotations whereas the cyanide derivative has a large magnetic rotation corresponding to the low spin state.

TABLE II

MOR Spectral Data for Methemoglobin pH 6.8, $10^{\circ}$ C

| Ligand | Band I $\dfrac{\lambda 1}{m\mu}$ $[\alpha]sp$ | | Band II $\dfrac{\lambda 2}{m\mu}$ $[\alpha]sp$ | | Band III $\dfrac{\lambda 3}{m\mu}$ $[\alpha]sp$ | | Band IV $\dfrac{\lambda 4}{m\mu}$ $[\alpha]sp$ | | M.M.[a] B.M. | Unp. El. |
|---|---|---|---|---|---|---|---|---|---|---|
| $H_2O$ | 630 | 50 | 567 | 36 | 540 | 20 | 500 | 28 | 5.20 | (4) |
| F | 606 | 95 | --- | -- | 550 | 30 | 485 | 38 | 5.92 | 4 |
| OH[b] | 607 | 32 | 575 | 95 | 538 | 38 | --- | -- | 4.47 | 4 |
| CN | --- | -- | 565 | 470 | 540 | 129 | --- | -- | 2.5 | 1 |

(a) The magnetic moment data were obtained from Refs. 16, 17, 18.

(b) This was studied at pH 10.

Note: All the $[\alpha]sp$ data reported here are the peak height data, which include positive, as well as the negative, portions of the MOR measurements at the given absorption band (see Fig. 5).

Relationship to magnetic susceptibility. The initial objective in the MOR studies of the hemoglobins was to find out experimentally whether there are any observable correlations with the magnetic properties of these substances. As shown in Tables I and II for both the hemoglobin and methemoglobin derivatives, a high magnetic rotation seems to correspond to substances with a low magnetic moment. For example, a fourfold increase in the specific magnetic rotation of hemoglobin occurs when water is substituted by cyanide as the ligand.

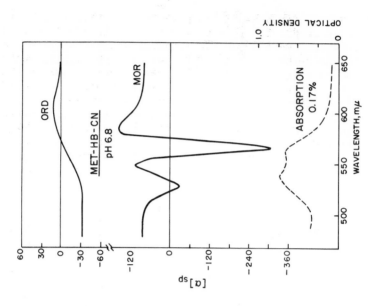

Figure 5. MOR, ORD, and absorption spectra of methemoglobin cyanide at pH 6.8, 10° C

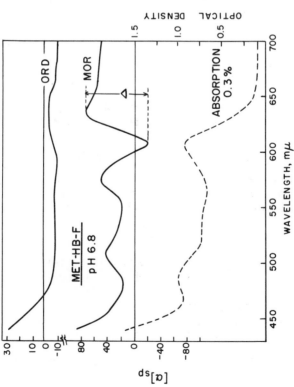

Figure 4. MOR, ORD, and absorption spectra of methemoglobin fluoride at pH 6.8, 10° C, △ peak height data used for comparison of results.

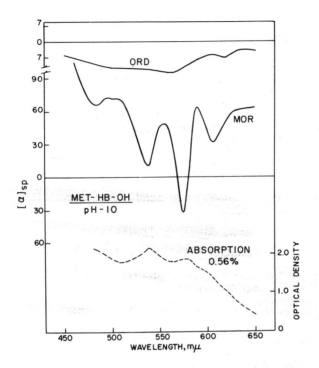

Figure 6. MOR, ORD, and absorption spectra of methemoglobin hydroxide at pH 10, 10° C.

Similarly in the methemoglobin series a decrease in the magnetic susceptibility from 5.2 (17) to 2.5 (18) accompanies an increase by a cyanide ligand. These results suggest a correlation with the spin state of the hemoprotein.

## Summary

A study of the magneto-optical rotation (MOR) spectra of hemoglobin, methemoglobin and their derivatives was carried out at the visible absorption region of the molecules. The specific magnetic rotations of hemoglobins and methemoglobins substituted with groups such as $H_2O$, $O_2$, CO, CN, F and OH were found to suggest some relationships with the ligand fields of the substituents and also a possible correlation with the spin states of the molecules; high spin states corresponding to low magnetic rotational strength.

# References

1. Drabkin, D. L.   In Haematin Enzymes (J. E. Falk, R. Lemberg, and R. K. Morton, eds.), Pergamon Press, London, 1961, p. 142.

2. Gordy, W., and H. N. Rexroad.  In Free Radicals in Biological Systems (M. S. Bloo, ed.), Academic Press, New York, 1961, p. 263.

3. Pauling, L., and C. D. Coryell.  Proc. Natl. Acad. Sci., 22, 210 (1936).

4. Schooley, D. A., E. Bunnenberg, and C. Djerassi.  Proc. Natl. Acad. Sci., 53, 579 (1965).

5. Shashoua, V. E.  J. Am. Chem. Soc., 82, 5505 (1960).

6. Shashoua, V. E.  J. Am. Chem. Soc., 86, 2109 (1964).

7. Forsythe, J. G., R. Kieselbach, D. J. Troy, and V. E. Shashoua.  J. of Applied Optics, in press.

8. Briat, B., M. Billardon, and J. Badoz.  Compt. Rendu Acad. Sci., t. 256, 3440 (1963).

9. Shashoua, V. E.  J. Am. Chem. Soc., 87, 4044 (1965).

10. Shashoua, V. E.  Biochemistry, 3, 1719 (1964).

11. Steinhardt, J., and E. Zaiser.  J. Am. Chem. Soc., 75, 1599 (1953).

12. Cullis, A. F., H. Muirhead, M. F. Perutz, M. G. Rossman, and A, C. T. North.  Proc. Roy. Soc. (London), A 265, 161 (1962).

13. Beychok, S., and E. R. Blout.  J. Mol. Biol., 3, 769 (1961).

14. Shashoua, V. E.  Nature, 203, 972 (1964).

15. Shashoua, V. E.  Arch. Biochem. Biophys., 111, 550 (1965).

16. Coryell, C. D., F. Slitt, and L. Pauling.  J. Am. Chem. Soc., 198, 33 (1952).

17. Keilin, D.  Proc. Roy. Soc. (London), B 113, 393 (1933).

18. Keilin, D., and E. F. Hartree.  Biochem. J., 49, 88 (1951).

HEME a LINKAGES

DISCUSSION

Morrison:   I should like to mention some work which Dr. Estabrook tells me has been completely forgotten, concerning the
linkage of the heme to the apo-protein of cytochrome c oxidase.
In our procedure, we made an acetone powder of a purified cytochrome c oxidase, and then measured the heme extract at $-10^\circ$
with acidified acetone as a function of time.  We found that
we got a biphasic curve, clearly showing that there are probably two types of linkage to the heme.  This indicates that the
heme a was linked to the apoprotein of cytochrome oxidase in
two different ways, and these linkages were consequently
cleaved differentially by the acidified acetone (1). The amount
of heme a which was rapidly extractable was about equal to
that which was extracted more slowly.  These data lend further
support to the hypothesis that cytochrome c oxidase has the
heme prosthetic group in two different protein environments,
one corresponding to cytochrome $a_3$ and the other to cytochrome
a.  One might further speculate that the rapidly extracted heme
corresponds to the more loosely bound cytochrome $a_3$, while the
heme which is more difficult to extract might correspond to
cytochrome a.

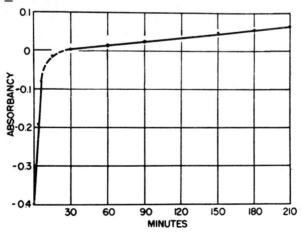

Figure 1.  (Morrison)  Extraction of heme prosthetic group of
cytochrome c oxidase.  The heme was extracted from a purified
cytochrome c oxidase by acidified acetone at $-10^\circ$ C, and heme
extracted was determined spectrophotometrically (1).

That the ability to extract the heme prosthetic group reflects more than the simple solubilization of the heme is further pointed out by our studies employing the chloroform pyridine extraction procedure of Caughey. Heme a is very soluble in this solvent; but heme a cannot be extracted from a dehydrated cytochrome c oxidase preparation. If water is added back to the protein, the heme a can then be extracted satisfactorily.

King: I do not think that Dr. Morrison's comment on the non-extractibility of heme a from his acetone powder of cytochrome oxidase has relevance to our experiments on the "fixation" of heme a on apocytochrome oxidase protein or on polylysine. I do not need to bother you with figures, but I can tell you that heme a in cytochrome oxidase after the borohydride reaction at pH 11.6 can no longer be extracted by acid-acetone (2). Under the same conditions but without the borohydride reaction, the heme a is freely extractable to the acid-acetone almost quantitatively. This is equally true for the heme a--polylysine complex, as detailed in the text (3) and in one of our recent papers (4). Thus we conclude that a non-protonated $\epsilon$-amino group of lysine residue forms a Schiff base in alkaline pH with the formyl side chain of the porphyrin. Borohydride hydrogenates the Schiff base to form a stable covalent bond, and therefore the heme a is no longer acid-acetone soluble or, as we say, the heme is "fixed" to the protein or to the polylysine molecule. Protohematin does not share this property.

Yong: I should like to add to Dr. King's data that the poly-histidine--heme a complex in the reduced form was highly "auto-oxidizable", both in aqueous solution and in DMSO.

Lemberg: Of all proteins, cytochrome oxidase requires most severe denaturation before it can form a Schiff base by condensation of the formyl group of the heme with an $\epsilon$-amino group of lysine residues. In most other proteins, this can be done at a pH of about 9.5; in cytochrome oxidase, a pH of 12.5 is required with unaltered cytochrome oxidase with an absorption band of 418-419 m$\mu$ in the ferric form (5) and a slightly lower pH (11.5) in an oxidase which has been kept at low temperature for a long time and shows this band at 423 m$\mu$ (Lemberg and Stanburg, unpublished results).

King: Our study of the effect of alkali on cytochrome oxidase (2) uses "good" soluble cytochrome oxidase preparation; pH 11.6 is sufficient to demonstrate the effect. We have also studied the spectral change at different pH values. A pH profile has also been published. The pH curve is rather sharp and pH 11.6 is maximal for the absorbance at 574 m$\mu$ with the reference wavelength of 630 m$\mu$. I must add that our pH data are referred to at room temperature $(23-25°)$. Furthermore, we have also used cytochrome oxidase in the particulate form, i.e., the Keilin-Hartree preparation. The result is virtually the same. However, even in the system of poly-L-lysine, pH 9.5 does not completely do the job as detailed in our paper (3).

Professor Lemberg, are you implying that the particular amino acid (of the cytochrome oxidase protein) which coordinates with heme a iron is different at neutral pH from that at pH 11.6? In other words, is there a change of a ligand due to pH? If so, either free heme a or some intermediates should occur during the pH change. Do you agree?

Lemberg: No. The greater sensitivity of the 423 mμ $Fe^{3+}$, slightly altered, oxidase to high pH may be entirely due to a conformational change, making the aldimine formation easier. Spectroscopically, free hematin a formation can be demonstrated only at a pH of about 13-13.5, i.e., higher than that necessary for Schiff base formation. But it might, of course, be present in smaller concentrations even at lower pH.

Ehrenberg: In collaboration with Dr. Blauer of Jerusalem, we have studied the compound formed between poly-L-lysine and protoheme, in the pH range where poly-L-lysine has formed a helix, but where all the amino groups are not discharged. In this region we form a protoheme-poly-L-lysine compound very similar to cytochrome c in spectra and magnetic properties. Then we have determined the molecular weight of this complex, and found it to fit best with the structure in which there are three helices with the hemes inserted between the helices. This model fits with the number of lysine residues per heme and the molecular weight of the whole complex, and shows how the heme can fit in between the helices of a protein and how they can be bound with two nitrogen groups from each of them.

Lemberg: We must not forget that, in the particular instance of the porphyrin-heme a compound of Dr. King, hemes a are bound to the protein not only by linkages of heme-iron to the protein but also be covalent linkages between the formyl side chains of heme a and the amino groups of the polylysine.

Yong: I should like to show two slides which indicate how a fresh preparation of protohematin and an aged one interact quite differently with poly-L-lysine. The first slide (Fig. 2) shows a fresh preparation of protohematin after reacting with poly-L-lisine at pH 11.6. The oxidized spectrum agrees with that of Dr. Blauer's data. The reduced form showed absorption maxima at 557, 528, and 432 mμ. Upon passing CO, the maxima

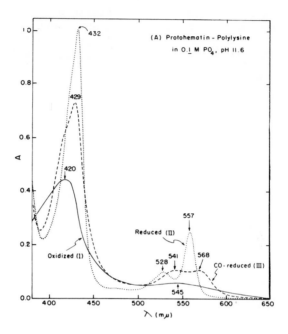

Figure 2. Protohematin-polylysine complex at pH 11.6. The system contained 5.3 µM freshly prepared protohematin and 3.6 µM poly-L-lysine (mol. wt. 74,000) in 0.1 M phosphate buffer, pH 11.6. (I) oxidized; (II) reduced; and (III) reduced, subsequently saturated with carbon monoxide.

shifted to 568, 541, and 429 mµ. Note that the absorbance of the Soret band of the CO-spectrum was lower than that of the reduced form.

With an aged preparation, as shown in Fig. 3, there was a blue shift of the absorption maxima in the Soret region. The γ-maxima for the oxidized form was at 391 mµ, the reduced at 424 mµ, and the CO-reduced at 418 mµ. These experiments were performed with the same concentration of protohematin solution. You will notice that the extinction of the reduced form was about half that of the fresh preparation. In contrast, the absorbance of the CO-reduced γ-peak became greater than that of the reduced.

Ehrenberg: Our preparation was "fresh", in the context of Dr. Yong's comment.

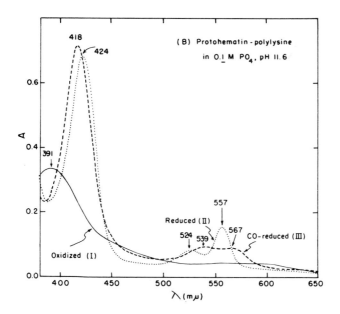

Figure 3. Aged protohematin-polylysine complex at pH 11.6.
The system was the same as in Fig. 2, except that an aged
solution of protohematin was used.


Harbury: I might mention that we have prepared polylysyl derivatives of the heme octapeptide from horse heart cytochrome c,
using the α-amino group of the heme peptide as initiator of an
N-carboxyanhydride polymerization. A derivative containing an
average of 80 lysine residues per mole was found to remain a
hemochrome to values of pH as low as 7. The ORD curves resemble those for the simpler heme peptide systems which we have
described, and, as might be expected, differ markedly from the
dispersion patterns for complexes obtained upon mixing polylysine with free heme.

## References

1. Stotz, E. H., M. Morrison, and G. Marinetti. In Enzymes:
   Units of Biological Structure and Function (O. H. Gaebler,
   ed.), Academic Press, Inc., New York, 1956, p. 401.

2. Takemori, S., and T. E. King. J. Biol. Chem. 240, 504 (1965).

3. King, T. E., F. C. Yong, and S. Takemori. This vol., p. 83.

4. King, T. E., F. C. Yong, and S. Takemori. Biochem. Biophys.
   Res. Comm., 22, 658 (1966).

5. Lemberg, R. Proc. Roy. Soc. (London), B 159 429 (1964).

GENERAL DISCUSSION

Chance:  What are the forces that might retain the heme in
place in the globin, and why does the heme stay there?

Watson:  In the myoglobin structure we find several salt bridges,
but many of these interactions are forced upon the molecule by
the packing arrangement within the crystal.  Where there is not
a very close interaction with a neighboring molecule, side chains
avoid making hydrogen bonds to neighbors.  From this and from
other evidence, we conclude that the protein as a whole is stabilized by the hydrophobic nature of the interior.  Now, if you
look at the heme group in myoglobin, you will find that it makes
very many hydrophobic interactions, 60 atom-to-atom contacts of
less than 4 Å units, and 150 of less than 4.3 Å.  Simple energy
calculations therefore show that these hydrophobic interactions
strongly stabilize the interaction of heme and globin chain.

Chance:  Does this suggest that the picture of the heme entering the slot of apo-myoglobin that you showed represents an
oversimplification?

Watson:  Yes.

Brill:  There are several experiments which bear upon the role
of carboxyl groups in the binding of porphyrins to protein.
Maehly (1) found that, when the proprionyl carboxyl groups of
protoporphyrin IX or protoheme are esterified, there is no
spectrophotometric indication of binding upon addition of these
to apo-horseradish peroxidase.  O'Hagan (2) and O'Hagan and
George (3) found that hemoglobins and myoglobins reconstituted
with hemes that lack carboxyl groups are relatively unstable.
Furthermore, O'Hagan (4) and Maehly (1) present evidence that
the proprionyl carboxyl groups are involved in the binding of
protoheme and protoporphyrin to serum albumin.  These facts
serve to temper one's viewpoint of the role of hydrophobic
interactions in protoporphyrin-protein binding.

Lemberg:  I want to call your attention to two observations
which I think belong here.  The one is that protoporphyrin
dimethyl ester is unable to combine with globin, while both
hematin ester and free porphyrin are.  The hydrophobic linkages are thus the most important ones, but in the absence of

the iron imidazole linkage, a linkage between porphyrin carboxyl and the globin is required to keep the porphyrin
combined (5).

The second observation refers to the old observation of
Sano (6) that in the instance of reconstruction of cytochrome
c from the apoprotein, the protoporphyrinogen rather than the
porphyrin is necessary for the combination.

Caughey: Changes in substituents at the 2 and 4 positions of
the heme have been noted to result in differences in rates of
reconstitution and also in the stabilities of reconstituted
proteins with an order vinyl, ethyl, and hydrogen. Possible
differences in interactions (steric or other) of the substituents per se with protein have been discussed. These substituents may also exert significantly different effects on the
strengths of interactions of the delocalized $\pi$-electron system of heme with the protein environment. The order of the
electron-withdrawing effect observed in several systems (e.g.,
ligand binding, porphyrin basicity) is vinyl>hydrogen>ethyl.
The order vinyl>ethyl>hydrogen is an order consistent with
"electron-donating" power and, therefore, consistent with the
order of donor effectiveness in the formation of donor-acceptor
interactions between heme and protein moieties.

## References

1. Maehley, A.C. Nature, 192, 630 (1961).

2. O'Hagan, J. Biochem. J., 74, 417 (1960).

3. O'Hagan, J. and P. George. Biochem. J., 74, 424 (1960).

4. O'Hagan, J. Nature, 184, 1808 (1959).

5. Asahura, T., S. Minikami, Y. Yonegama, and M. Yoshikawa.
   J. Biochem. (Tokyo), 56, 594 (1964).

6. Sano, S., N. Nanzyo, and C. Rimington. Biochem. J., 43,
   270 (1964).

# STRUCTURE AND REACTIVITY OF MYOGLOBIN
# AND HEMOGLOBIN

# III.
## Ligand Binding to Myoglobin and Hemoglobin
### R. J. P. Williams, Chairman

# MÖSSBAUER STUDIES OF HEMOGLOBIN

George Lang[*]
Physics Department, Carnegie Institute of Technology
Pittsburgh, Pennsylvania

and

Walter Marshall
Theoretical Physics Division, A. E. R. E.
Harwell, Didcot, Berks, England

## Introduction

Hemoglobin and its prosthetic group, heme, have been the objects of a number of recent Mössbauer spectrometry studies (1-5). Most of the original work has been concentrated upon measurement and interpretation of isomer shifts and quadrupole splittings. Fortunately, the low concentration of iron in hemoglobin (as distinct from heme compounds) makes possible also the observation of magnetic interactions in some compounds, and additional chemical information can be obtained.

The minimum iron-iron separation in the hemoglobin molecule is about 25 Angstroms, so that the electron spin systems are almost free of magnetic interaction. At sufficiently low temperature spin lattice interactions also are suppressed, so that the electron spin relaxation time becomes longer than the Larmor precession time of the nucleus. Under these conditions the structure of the magnetic hyperfine interaction between the nucleus and the unpaired atomic electrons may be discerned in the Mössbauer absorption spectrum of the iron, provided the ground electronic state is magnetic.

The technique of Mössbauer spectrometry has been discussed in two useful introductory books (6,7) and several review articles(8,9). We will therefore provide only the minimum background necessary to understand the meaning of the experimental data, and we confine ourselves to the case of $Fe^{57}$.

Fig. 1 shows the transformation, by electron capture, of 270 day $Co^{57}$ to an excited state of $Fe^{57}$, and the subsequent

*U. S. Air Force Office of Scientific Research Fellow during part of this work.

decay to the stable ground state of this nucleus. In 91 percent of the decays the nucleus reaches the 14.4 keV state,
which has a lifetime $\tau$ of about $1.4 \times 10^{-7}$ sec. The decay to
the ground state then proceeds via either gamma emission or
internal conversion, the ratio of occurrence being about 10 in
favor of the latter. Thus, on the average, for each $Co^{57}$ decay,
there are produced 0.09 gamma rays of 136 keV, 0.91 gamma rays
of 122 keV, 0.08 gamma rays of 14.4 keV, and 0.83 conversion
electrons. The energy width of the long lived 14.4 keV state
is $\hbar/\tau$ or $4.7 \times 10^{-9}$ eV. If the 14.4 keV gamma is permitted
to fall upon a $Fe^{57}$ nucleus in its ground state it can, under
proper conditions, be resonantly absorbed. The energy dependence of the absorption is very sharp, being just equal to the
excited state width specified above. Before the work of
Mössbauer it was thought that, since the nucleus is held in
place by rather weak Coulomb forces, recoil losses in emission
and absorption must always broaden this energy dependence.
Mössbauer's contribution was the demonstration that a nucleus
which is bound to a crystal lattice can have a significant
probability of recoil-free emission or absorption given by the
familiar Debye-Waller factor of X-ray diffraction. The recoil-
free fraction and its temperature dependence can in fact provide
information concerning the vibration spectrum of the molecule
and the crystal. Precise measurement of this quantity is
difficult and its interpretation is complex. We will not discuss it further in this paper.

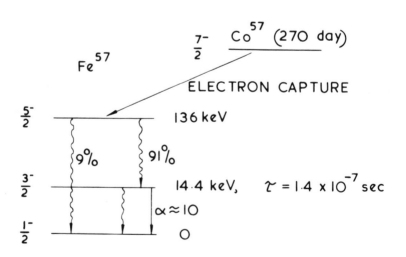

Figure 1. Decay scheme of $Co^{57}$.

In the diagram of Fig. 1 we have neglected the possible
interactions which can give rise to hyperfine structure in the
ground and 14.4 keV levels of $Fe^{57}$ nucleus. This hyperfine
structure, which we will discuss in more detail below, characterizes the chemical environment of the iron nucleus. The
method of studying it is in principle identical to optical
absorption spectrometry, i.e., one illuminates the sample by
means of a variable source of monoenergetic radiation and
observes the energy dependence of absorption. In most cases
the hyperfine splitting is greater than the energy level
widths, and a line structure is observed. One is then faced
with the usual spectroscopic problem of determining the energy
level positions from the experimentally determined energy differences. The energy level scheme, together with a knowledge
of the types of interactions which affect it, is then indicative of the electronic environment.

In doing Mössbauer spectrometry with $Fe^{57}$, a source of
$Co^{57}$ is used to provide the 14.4 keV radiation. In the proper
environment (in our case, diffused into Cr), this will emit a
single line free of hyperfine structure. The energy of the
radiation may be varied over the narrow range required by
utilizing the ordinary first order Doppler shift. If the
source is moved with velocity v, positive when approaching the
absorber, the gamma ray energy is given by

$$E\gamma = E_0 (1 + v/c) \tag{1}$$

where $E_0$ is the gamma energy of a source at rest. Data are
usually presented as counting rate in the detector plotted as
a function of the velocity of the source, positive velocity
corresponding to increased gamma energy. In this paper we will
occasionally specify energy in mm/sec, where we mean that it
is $v E_0/c$.

The simplest nuclear-electronic interaction results from
the change of nuclear charge radius upon excitation. It gives
rise to a shift in the absorption spectrum given by

$$\delta = K \left( \sum_s |\psi(o)|^2 - \sum_a |\psi(o)|^2 \right) \tag{2}$$

where $\sum_s |\psi(o)|^2$ is the electron density at the source nucleus,
and $\sum_a |\psi(o)|^2$ is the electron density at the absorber nucleus.
The constant K is approximately 0.5 mm $(a_0)^3$ sec$^{-1}$. The second
order Doppler shift, a relativistic effect, causes an additional spectrum shift which depends upon temperature. At low
temperatures the size of this effect is a function of the
phonon spectrum of the absorber. Fortunately it is small, and
for our purposes it is sufficient to assume it to be the same
for all materials and to have the effect of shifting the spectrum to the right with decreasing temperature by an amount of

$6 \times 10^{-4}$ mm/sec for each degree of temperature change.

The 14.4 keV excited state of $Fe^{57}$ has an electric quadrupole moment, which interacts with the electrostatic potential according to the Hamiltonian

$$H_Q = \frac{QV_{zz}}{4} \left[ I_z^2 - \frac{5}{4} + \frac{\eta}{3} (I_x^2 - I_y^2) \right] \; ; \eta = \frac{V_{xx} - V_{yy}}{V_{zz}} \quad (3)$$

where Q is the nuclear quadrupole moment, I is the nuclear spin, $V_{zz}$ is the second spatial derivative in the z direction of the electrostatic potential, and so forth. The field gradients are strongly influenced by asymmetric $\underline{d}$ electron charge distributions on the iron, and less strongly by more remote charges. Quadrupole interaction has the effect of splitting the excited nuclear state into two levels. Fig. 4A is an example of a situation in which only quadrupole and chemical shift are present. The former splits the absorption into two lines, separated by an energy ΔE, while the latter shifts the center of symmetry of the pattern.

The $Fe^{57}$ nucleus has a magnetic moment in both the ground and excited states. In the presence of a magnetic field $\underline{H}$ these states are split in accordance with the Hamiltonian

$$H_M = -g_N \beta_N \underline{I} \cdot \underline{H} \quad (4)$$

where $\beta_N$ is the nuclear magneton and $g_N$, the nuclear gyromagnetic ratio, has the values $+0.1806 \pm 0.0014$ and $-0.1033 \pm 0.0008$ in the ground and excited states, respectively (10). If there are unpaired electrons in the vicinity of the nucleus and if their spins are not being flipped too rapidly by spin-spin or spin-lattice interactions, they will give rise to various terms in the effective magnetic field. The magnetic Hamiltonian may then be written more explicitly as

$$H_M = 2 \, g_N \beta \beta_N \sum_k \frac{1}{r_k^3} \left[ \underline{l}_k \cdot \underline{I} + 3(\hat{\underline{r}}_k \, \underline{s}_k) \, (\hat{\underline{r}}_k \, \underline{I}) \right.$$
$$\left. -(\underline{s}_k \, \underline{I}) - K(\underline{s}_k \cdot I) \right] - g_N \beta_N \underline{I} \cdot \underline{H}_a \quad (5)$$

Here β is the electron magneton, $l_k$ is the orbital angular momentum of the kth electron, $s_k$ is its spin, and the summation is taken over all unpaired electrons. The first term represents the interaction of the nucleus with the electrons regarded as current loops, and the next two come from ordinary magnetic dipole-dipole interactions. The term involving $K$ results from the Fermi contact interaction, and takes account of two effects: (1) the inner core $\underline{s}$ electrons are polarized through exchange effects with the unpaired $3\underline{d}$ electrons; (2) in suitable symmetries the $\underline{d}$ electrons have a small amount of $\underline{s}$ character. The last term in the Hamiltonian allows for the direct effect of any externally applied field, $\underline{H}_a$.

It is possible to make some general predictions concerning the expected Mössbauer spectra in various types of chemical compounds. Table I shows the $\underline{d}$ electron energy level scheme of iron, the ordering corresponding to that deduced by Griffith for hemoglobin azide. The high spin ferrous material has charge asymmetry and large quadrupole interaction is expected. Since the spin is integral, all degeneracy could be lifted by the crystalline environment. Thus, magnetic hyperfine interaction is possible, but is not assured. The low spin ferrous ion has cubic symmetry in its charge distribution, so that no contribution is expected to the quadrupole interaction. The high spin ferric ion, with spherical charge distribution, should have no quadrupole interaction. The spherical distribution of spin and the absence of orbital angular momentum should cause all terms of the Hamiltonian (5) to vanish except the Fermi contact term. The low spin ferric complex is a very interesting case. The single hole in the lower triplet should cause quadrupole interactions, and the half integral spin guarantees a magnetic ground state, in which all of the interaction terms of (5) must be present. It must be borne in mind that the considerations of this paragraph involve only lowest order effects; they will be subject to some modifications when some of the more subtle bonding effects are taken into account.

TABLE I

Occupation of the Iron d Orbitals

in Several Prototypal Situations

| STATE: | FERROUS | | FERRIC | |
|---|---|---|---|---|
| SPIN: | 2 | 0 | 5/2 | 1/2 |
| $E_4$, $x^2-y^2$ | ↑ | | ↑ | |
| $E_3$, $3z^2-r^2$ | ↑ | | ↑ | |
| $E_2$, zy | ↑ | ↑↓ | ↑ | ↑ |
| $E_1$, zx | ↑ | ↑↓ | ↑ | ↑↓ |
| 0, xy | ↑↓ | ↑↓ | ↑ | ↑↓ |

## Experimental Procedure

In order to determine the Mössbauer absorption spectrum, the absorber material under study is interposed between the monochromatic gamma source and a proportional counter detector. The counting rate in the detector is then determined as a function of source velocity, hence, as a function of gamma ray energy (for details, see refs. 5-7).

Because hemoglobin contains only 0.3 percent iron, enrichment is essential for the observation of the broad paramagnetic spectra. Enrichment to about 50 percent in $Fe^{57}$ was obtained by injection of enriched iron citrate into iron-deficient rats. Hemoglobin was extracted from the rat blood by standard methods, and the various compounds were made. Their composition was verified spectrophotometrically before and after the Mössbauer measurements, and only freshly prepared samples were used. A typical sample consisted of about 1 ml of solution which was about 5 mM in heme iron. This was placed in a lucite holder so that the gamma rays had to traverse about 3/16 inch of solution. Measurements were made at dry ice, liquid nitrogen, helium, and pumped helium (about 1.2 percent) temperatures.

## Experimental Results

The observed Mössbauer absorption spectra are shown in Figs. 2 to 9. The ordinates in the absorption spectra are given in millions of counts, and the percentage of this which is attributable to background is indicated in the captions. The background percentage is an estimate and has an uncertainty of about ± 10 percent of the maximum count. In order to conserve space, the spectra are sometimes stacked two to a figure; in these cases they are labeled, and a separate labeled ordinate scale is provided for each. The velocity (i.e., energy) scale is relative to the center of symmetry of a metallic iron absorber.

The spectrum of oxygenated red cells at $4^{\circ}K$ is shown in Fig. 3. No difference has been observed between the spectra of cells and those of refined oxyhemoglobin solution. The cells were used as a conveniently concentrated form of hemoglobin for the observation of the spectrum in an applied magnetic field.

There is a general tendency, most pronounced in HiCN (Figs. 8 and 9), for the magnetic structure to disappear at high temperatures. HiCN also has the best resolved low temperature magnetic hyperfine structure. In the first specimens the line at zero velocity was much stronger, and the presence of ferrocyanide or ferricyanide was suspected. (potassium ferricyanide is introduced in the chemical processing and later

120

removed by dialysis.) A contamination of only a few percent
of the inorganic iron is detectable, for its spectrum remains
narrow at low temperature, while the ferric hemoglobin absorption becomes wide and shallow. Dialysis time was lengthened
until the spectrum was independent of it, and the spectrum
shown is believed to be entirely attributable to hemoglobin iron.

The low temperature hemoglobin azide spectrum is shown in
Fig. 7. Three different samples were measured and the spectrum
is thought to be free of inorganic iron contamination. Three
different hemoglobin fluoride samples were investigated and the
data are believed to be free of effects of non-hemoglobin iron.
Fig. 5 demonstrates the great simplication of the HiF spectrum
which is achieved upon application of an external magnetic field.

Hemoglobin Nitric Oxide. The low temperature spectra of
HbNO are shown in Fig. 2. As the temperature is raised to $195^{\circ}K$,
one observes a spectrum which is similar in general appearance,
but has less distinct detail. Because NO contains an odd number
of electrons this compound must display magnetic properties.
The electronic structure has been discussed by Griffith (11).
He points out the possibility of some spin transfer to the iron,
but in his analysis, which assumes the spin to be on the NO,
covalent mixing enters only in its effect in splitting the
orbitals of the NO molecule. Because a large hyperfine structure
is observed in the Mössbauer absorption spectrum, we must assume
very strong covalent bonding and a large spin transfer. Indeed,
the bonding is so strong that the distinction between ferrous
and ferric forms of the iron ion becomes significantly blurred.
This last conclusion is of particular interest in view of the
recent suggestion (12) that some hemoglobin compounds previously
assumed ferrous, do indeed contain ferric ions.

In HbNO, the g value is very near to that of a free spin
(13). This implies that the $\pi$ antibonding orbitals of the NO
are well separated in energy. If the NO were located above
the iron and perpendicular to the heme plane, these orbitals
would be, in first approximation, degenerate. Hence we regard
this structure as unlikely and first consider the alternative
symmetric arrangement in which NO is parallel to the heme plane
and its atoms are equidistant from the iron. This structure and
the pertinent orbitals are shown in Fig. 10. A further assumption is that the only covalent bonding of importance is that
between the $\pi_z$ antibonding orbital of NO (this would be
$(N_z - O_z)/\sqrt{2}$ of Fig. 11)and the $d_{yz}$ orbital of the iron. The
$\pi_x$ antibonding orbital is of course orthogonal to the iron $\underline{d}$
orbitals, and is unchanged in energy. The interaction between
the antibonding $\pi_z$ and the $d_{yz}$ will produce a pair of levels

which straddle $\pi_x$ in energy as shown in the figure. When the three electrons are placed in this level scheme, we are forced to put the unpaired one in $\pi_x$; this is unsatisfactory because it implies that the unpaired spin remains remote from the iron nucleus, contradicting the experimental observation. We conclude that our supposed structure is unsatisfactory and that the actual arrangement must be one of lower symmetry, in which the axis of the NO molecule is at an intermediate angle to the porphyrin plane. For this situation, both the $\pi$ antibonding orbitals of the NO bond with the $\underline{d}$ orbitals of Fe so that the unpaired electon is in an orbital (say a combination of $\pi_x$ and $\underline{d}$) in which it has a large probability of being near the Fe nucleus. Neither the ferric assignment, $(d_{zy})^1 (\pi)^2$, nor the ferrous assignment, $(d_{zy})^2 (\pi)^1$, is an accurate description of this situation. The former would imply hyperfine interaction comparable in strength to that of HiCN, and the latter would imply negligible hyperfine interaction. The strength of the hyperfine interaction appears in fact to be intermediate, about half that of HiCN. This discussion is oversimplified in the sense that in strongly covalent materials it is necessary to allow for the effects of electrons outside the particular interacting orbitals under immediate consideration.

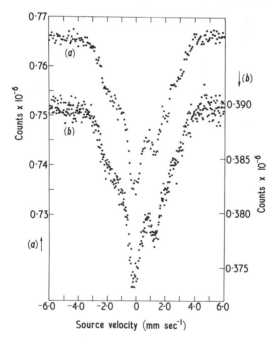

Figure 2. Mössbauer absorption spectrum of hemoglobin nitric oxide at (a) 4°K(background 40 percent), and (b) 1.2°K (background 35 percent).

The g value of HbNO (isotropic with magnitude 2.03) indicates that the orbital angular momentum in this compound is very effectively quenched, and thus the spin is well isolated from interaction with molecule vibrational modes. The observed persistence of the hyperfine interaction in the Mössbauer spectrum to high temperature is therefore an expected result. The detailed shape of the HbNO spectrum depends in a complicated way upon the spatial distribution of the unpaired spin. At this point we make no attempt to solve this much more difficult problem.

Oxyhemoglobin. This material shows simple quadrupole splitting at all temperatures with a slight temperature dependence. The values of the splitting are 1.89 mm/sec, 2.19 mm/sec, and 2.24 mm/sec at dry ice, liquid nitrogen, and liquid helium temperatures, respectively. (Each value has an uncertainty of $\pm$ 0.05 mm/sec.) Magnetic susceptibility measurements indicate S = 0 for this compound, immediately ruling out the structure in which $O_2$ stands perpendicular to the heme plane.

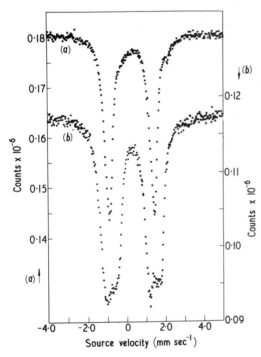

Figure 3. Mössbauer absorption spectrum of oxygenated red cells at 4°K in (a) zero applied field (background 30 percent), and (b) a field of 30 kilogauss applied perpendicular to the gamma ray path (background 30 percent).

For the parallel symmetric arrangement we again refer to Fig. 10, the only difference from NO being the addition of another electron. This would put two in $\pi_x$, giving a diamagnetic compound. At the same time, the effective number of electrons in $d_{yz}$ is reduced from 2 to 2 $b^2$, where the relative bonding orbital is $\alpha \pi_z + b d_{yz}$. If the energies of $\pi_z$ were initially about equal, $b^2$ could be near to 1/2. Such a value would imply that the quadrupole interaction of the d electrons would be characteristic of a single hole in $d_{yz}$. This would make the prinicipal electric field gradient negative, with a quadrupole splitting of the same size as is seen in the high spin ferrous compounds, i.e., about 3 mm/sec. It is in rough agreement with the observed splitting, 2.2 mm/sec at $4^O$K. The Mössbauer spectrum of oxyhemoglobin in a magnetic field, Fig. 4B, enables one to deduce the sign of the field gradient. It is found to be negative, in agreement with our model. As in the case of HbNO, neither ferrous nor ferric assignment is completely satisfactory for this material.

An interesting feature of the $HbO_2$ Mössbauer spectra is the temperature dependence of $\Delta E$. This implies the existence of low lying excited states (15) which have appreciable occupation at $195^O$K. It is difficult to believe that these states represent electronic excitation, for this would almost certainly give rise to paramagnetism, in contradiction to susceptibility measurements. It is possible that the reduction of $\Delta E$ is caused by a rotation of the $O_2$ molecule, but we can at present neither defend nor refute this speculation.

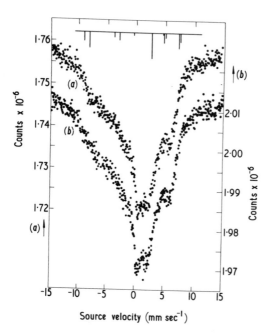

Source velocity (mm sec$^{-1}$)

Figure 4. Mössbauer absorption spectrum of hemoglobin fluoride at a) $4^O$K, background 40 percent, and b) $1.2^O$K, background 40 percent. Line spectrum calculated for the low temperature approximation; valid at both $4^O$ and $1.2^O$ K. No parameters are free, all having been determined from the spectra of Fig. 5. The lack of sharp lines in the observed spectrum is attributed to spin relaxation.

Hemoglobin Fluoride. At low temperatures HiF, with spin
5/2, exhibits the complicated magnetically split structure seen
in Fig. 4. The magnetic effect is found to persist up to 195°
K, in keeping with the fact that the L = 0 state of the ion
implies isolation of the spin from the lattice vibrations.
The application of a magnetic field simplifies the spectrum
(Fig. 5) and provides the key to its interpretation. The simplification results from the fact that the applied field tends
to fix the electron spin direction, hence the effective field
which acts on the nucleus, and the situation corresponds to
ordinary Zeeman effect. In zero applied field the problem is
the more difficult one of combining nuclear and electronic
angular momenta to make states of definite total angular momentum. The predicted line spectra of Fig. 5 result from a
detailed treatment which involves two parameters. In making
the fit the constant, 2D, of the spin Hamiltonian is found to
be 14 cm$^{-1}$, a result which is consistent with ESR data (16).
The other parameter is $K$ of Eq. (5), whose value is found to

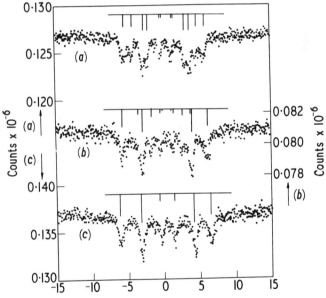

Source velocity (mm sec$^{-1}$)

Figure 5. Mössbauer absorption spectra of hemoglobin fluoride
in a magnetic field at right angles to the gamma ray beam of
(a) 7.5 kg; (b) 15 kg; (c) 30 kg. Background 25 percent in
each case. In the calculation of the three line spectra above,
only two adjustable parameters are involved: the crystal field
constant, 2D, of the spin Hamiltonian is found to be ~14 cm$^{-1}$,
and the contact interaction, $K$, is found to be 0.35.

be 0.35. The predicted line spectrum of Fig. 4 is then found, using no additional parameters. The discrepancy between theory and experiment in Fig. 4 is of the type which is expected from electron spin relaxation effects. This mechanism would result in a spectrum which is blurred and compressed on the velocity scale, and would give rise to an additional line at a position corresponding to zero magnetic interaction.

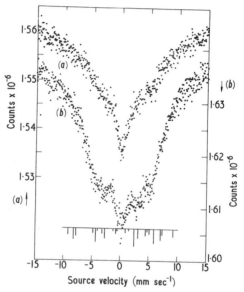

Figure 6. Mössbauer absorption spectrum of hemoglobin fluoride at (a) 195°K (background 40 percent), and (b) 77° K (background 40 percent). The line spectrum is to be compared with the 77°K data. In calculating it no parameters are free, all having been determined from the spectra of Fig. 5. The lack of sharp lines in the observed spectrum is attributed to spin relaxation.


Hemoglobin Azide. The absorption spectrum of HiN$_3$ at 1.2° K is shown in Fig. 7, together with a predicted line spectrum. The data at 4° are similar to those shown, while the 77° result is much narrower. At 195° a quadrupole split spectrum appears, with a slight asymmetry caused by residual magnetic effects. ESR measurements (16,17) on this spin 1/2 material have been interpreted (18) in terms of expansion coefficients which describe the electronic wave function in the presence of spin-orbit coupling. If we assume the value $K$ = 0.35 which was found for HiF, this provides the information necessary to determine the Mössbauer spectrum. We regard the agreement with experiment as shown in Fig. 7 as good, considering the sensitivity of the results to small changes in the coefficients.

The calculation indicates a high temperature $\Delta E$ of 2.7 mm/sec, compared with the observed value of 2.3 mm/sec. A difference of this magnitude could easily be caused by the direct action of extra-ionic charges. The quenching of magnetic interaction at high temperature is an expected result because this ion has non-zero orbital angular momentum, and spin-orbit interaction serves to couple the spins to molecular vibrations.

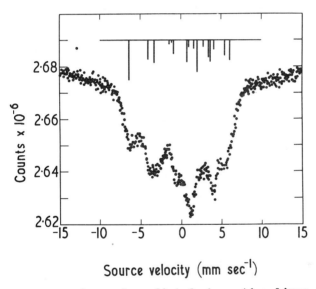

Source velocity (mm sec$^{-1}$)

Figure 7. Comparison of predicted absorption lines and the 1.2°K hemoglobin azide data. The theory contains no degree of freedom, all parameters having been determined from the g values. The breadth of the observed absorption lines is attributed to spin relaxation.

Hemoglobin Cyanide. Like $HiN_3$, this material has a low-spin ferric ion with $S = 1/2$. The 1.2° data and a predicted line spectrum are shown in Fig. 8. The 4° spectrum is similar; at 77° an asymmetric quadrupole split pair appear, and at 195° all trace of magnetic interaction has disappeared. No ESR data are available for this compound, so the fit of Fig. 8 has been obtained by adjusting the two expansion coefficients mentioned in the section on $HiN_3$. We regard the result as significant, for the two coefficients are essentially determined by matching

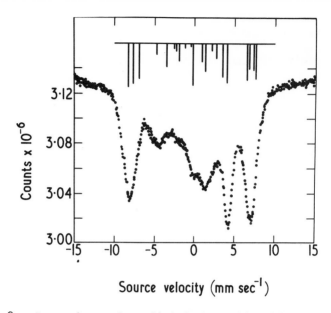

**Source velocity (mm sec$^{-1}$)**

Figure 8. Comparison of predicted absorption lines and the
1.2 °K hemoglobin cyanide data. Two free parameters, which
are coefficients in the electronic wave function, are used.
Their best values are found to be in the neighborhood of those
determined for the azide complex. The breadth of the observed
absorption is attributed to spin relaxation.


to the outer lines of the spectrum, and any correspondence with
interior lines lends credence to the theory. The predicted
quadrupole splitting of 2.15 mm/sec is to be compared with the
195°K result of 1.4 mm/sec. This discrepancy is rather large,
but conceivably could be caused by charges outside the ferric
ion. Assuming that our theory is correct, the Mössbauer results enable the prediction of $\underline{g}$ values, of 0.92, 1.99, and
3.33 in the x,y, and z directions, respectively.

From the ESR results (with which the present results con-
cur) on HiN$_3$ the electronic orbital levels are yz, zx, and xy
in descending order with separations 2.26 $\xi$, and 2.19 $\xi$, res-
spectively. Here $\xi$ is the spin-orbit coupling constant. From
the Mössbauer results the HiCN level order is found to be the
same, but with energy separations 1.01 $\xi$ and 2.28 $\xi$, respectively.
The HiCN complex therefore exhibits less asymmetry within the
porphyrin plane.

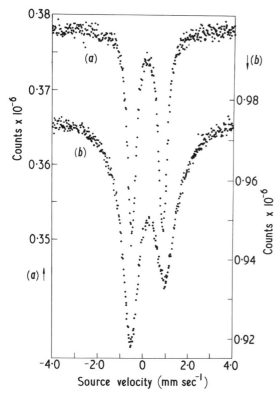

Figure 9. Mössbauer absorption spectrum of hemoglobin cyanide at (a) 195°K (background 50 percent), and (b) 77°K (background 50 percent).

## Summary

Through hyperfine interactions with the $Fe^{57}$ nucleus, electrons associated with the chemical bonds affect the Mössbauer absorption spectrum of iron compounds. An interpretation of the absorption spectrum can provide information on the electronic arrangement, hence on the near environment of the iron. The change of nuclear charge radius upon excitation gives rise to an energy shift in the absorption spectrum which is a measure of the electron density at the nucleus. Asymmetries in the electronic charge distribution give rise to interaction with the quadrupole moment of the nucleus, resulting in spectra containing two absorption maxima. In the case of paramagnetic compounds, magnetic hyperfine interactions between the nucleus and the electrons may sometimes be observed.

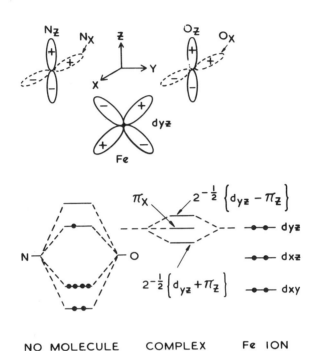

NO MOLECULE    COMPLEX    Fe ION

Figure 10. Energy levels of the hemoglobin-nitric oxide complex. The diagram is schematic and applies only to the symmetrical attachment of the NO molecule. It is shown in the text that the Mössbauer data require covalent bonding in $\pi_x$ as well as $\pi_y$, and hence imply a situation of lower symmetry. The data for oxyhemoglobin are, however, not inconsistent with a structure of the type depicted above.

An essential requirement is that the electron spin relaxation time be at least of the order of the nuclear Larmor period, since shorter relaxation times tend to cause an averaging out of the interaction. The large spacing between iron atoms in hemoglobin results in small electronic spin-spin relaxation, and at low temperatures almost all paramagnetic hemoglobin compounds exhibit the broad spectra characteristic of magnetic interaction. Interpretation of the spectra provides information, similar to that provided by ESR measurements, on the ordering and separation of electronic levels. Several hemoglobin compounds have been discussed to indicate the method of interpretation and the information which it provides.

## Acknowledgements

It is a pleasure to thank G. Newman and G. Bunguay for producing the enriched rat blood and for advice and help in the preparation of hemoglobin compounds. Without their help and the cooperation of R. J. P. O'Brien, who made available to us the facilities of the Nuffield Department of Clinical Biochemistry, University of Oxford, most of this work would have been impossible. We are indebted to R. J. P. Williams for advice on hemoglobin chemistry and structure. We are grateful also to M. F. Perutz and J. D. Kendrew for their encouragement and for several helpful discussions. For their willingness to share their equipment and techniques, and for their advice on all facets of this work, we are greatly indebted to the Harwell Mössbauer Group: T. Cranshaw, C. Johnson, and M. Ridout. It is a pleasure to thank L. Becker for help in taking the experimental data. Finally, one of us (George Lang) wishes to thank the U. S. Air Force Office of Scientific Research for support during the first part of this work and E. Bretscher of the Harwell Nuclear Physics Division for his continuing encouragement and hospitality.

## References

1. Gonser, U., R. W. Grant, and J. Kregzde. App. Phys. Lett., 3, 189 (1963).

2. Gonser, U., R. W. Grant, and J. Kregzde. Science, 143, 680 (1964).

3. Karger, W. Berichte der Bunsen Gesellschaft, 68, 793 (1964).

4. Bearden, Alan J., Thomas H. Moss, Winslow S. Caughey, and A. Beardreau. Proc. Nat. Acad. Sce., 53, 1246 (1965).

5. Lang, G., and Walter Marshall. Proc. Phys. Soc. London, 87, 3 (1966).

6. The Mössbauer Effect (H. Frauenfelder, ed.), W. A. Benjamin, Inc., New York, 1962.

7. Mossbauer Effect: Principles and Applications (G. K. Wertheim, ed.), Academic Press, Inc., New York, 1964.

8. Gol'danskii, V. I. In The Mössbauer Effect and Its Applications in Chemistry, (Consultants Bureau 1964).

9. Muir, A. J., Jr., and K. J. Ando. In Mössbauer Effect Data Index, North American Aviation, Inc., 1964, p.

10. Preston, R. S., S. S. Hanna, and J. Heberle. Phys. Rev., 128, 2207 (1962).

11. Griffith, J. S.  Proc. Roy. Soc. A., 235, 23 (1956).

12. Weiss, J. J. Nature, 202, 83 (1964).

13. Sancier, K. M., G. Freeman, and J. S. Mills.  Science, 137, 752 (1962).

14. Hartree, E. F.  Ann. Repts. Prog. Chem., 43, 287 (1946).

15. Lang, L. G., S. DeBenedetti, and R. I. Ingalls.  J. Phys. Soc.  Japan, 17, Supp. B-1, 131 (1962).

16. Gibson, J. F., D. J. E. Ingram, and D. Schonland.  Disc. Faraday Soc., 26, 72 (1958).

17. Gibson, J. F., and D. J. E. Ingram.  Nature, 178, 905 (1957).

18. Griffith, J. S.  Nature, 180, 30 (1957).

## DISCUSSION

Ehrenberg: I would like to point out the importance of defining the compounds actually studied by the Mössbauer technique.
Most work is done at low temperatures on frozen solutions or
lyophilized samples. From ESR work we know that, in many cases,
we do not have the same compound under these conditions as we
have in solution. We have found cases of this for myoglobin,
hemoglobin, and catalase. In every case in which it is possible, the sample used for Mössbauer studies should also be examined by ESR and/or light absorption under the same conditions.

There have been some discrepancies reported in the data
on ferrihemoglobin and ferrimyoglobin hydroxide compounds in
frozen solutions. I have recently made some experiments based
on this topic. When ferrihemoglobin is titrated with NaOH and
then the sample is frozen and observed in a spectroscope, the
light absorption at about 630 mμ decreases gradually as would
have been expected from the pK of the transition from the aquo
to the hydroxyl form. The same was observed in the presence
of glycine buffer. With borate buffer, the 630 mμ band persisted to 1 or 2 units higher pH values in the frozen states, as
compared with solutions at room temperature. This is, perhaps,
what Keilin and Hartree observed (1). The actual compound and
its spin state observed in frozen solutions are hence sometimes
critically dependent on salts and small molecules present in
the solution. Another example is that of catalase + $NH_3$ (2)
in which no compound is observed in solution at room temperature, but a complete formation of a catalase-$NH_3$ compound takes
place upon freezing of the sample.

Lang: This is true; I certainly agree that it would be very
good to have ESR, magnetic susceptibility, Mössbauer, and
optical data all on the same sample and over the same temperature range. I can only say that, in cases where we have frozen
compounds down to 4°, then remelted and refrozen them we have
not seen any difference in the Mössbauer spectrum. It appears
that nothing serious that is irreversible has occurred, but
that is about as strong a statement as I can make. We can say
that the samples were, in general, very concentrated solutions
from which almost certainly some precipitation must have occurred on freezing; as a matter of fact, some of them showed evidence of precipitation in the ultra-filtration. However, we

are forced to have these solutions rather concentrated in order to get some signal from them.

Williams: I think we can settle this without debate, because we have measured the absorption spectra of quite a number of the compounds of hemoglobin before and after Mössbauer determinations. The spectra are as you would expect. We do not have EPR data, except for one or two of the compounds.

Chance: The point is not so much whether irreversible changes have occurred, but whether you have the same species at lower temperatures as at higher temperatures.

Moss: The first quick point I want to make is that the isomer shift measured for oxyhemoglobin also supports Lang's proposal that the bond involves considerable delocalization of iron d-electrons. The shift is similar to that observed by Bearden, Caughey, Beaudreau and myself for Fe(II) bispyridine heme compounds (3), where there is also electron delocalization to the extent that the "valence" of the iron is not very meaningful.

The main thing I want to discuss, however, is the problem suggested by the Mössbauer spectrum obtained for acid methemoglobin at pH 6. Specifically, I cannot help but be struck by the similarity of the acid methemoglobin and the methemoglobin-azide spectra. Both have the wide (2.0 and 2.3 mm/sec, respectively) quadrupole splitting, with similar isomer shifts. More important, the magnetic broadening and splitting of the quadrupole lines have approximately the same temperature dependence, indicating very similar spin-lattice relaxation times. The hyperfine patterns obtained in the two cases have the same form. The relaxation times appear quite fast at 195° K, which is more characteristic of the low-spin Fe(III) than of the high-spin form. The similarity of the hyperfine patterns indicates very similar electronic configurations.

Even more striking is the fact that the Mössbauer spectrum of the acid methemoglobin is so different from that of the high-spin methemoglobin-fluoride. The quadrupole splitting and the dependence and form of the magnetic splitting of the fluoride are all completely different from that of the acid methemoglobin. This is in contrast to ESR measurements, which give very similar g-values for the acid methemoglobin and the methemoglobin-fluoride.

The suggestion I am obviously getting at is that the methemoglobin-azide and acid methemoglobin observed in Lang's experiments actually were similar low-spin forms. The "magnetic" observations of these proteins have been made, in general, under widely differing chemical and thermal conditions. If the ligand bonded to the iron can be, as Caughey suggests (4) something which varies in degree from a water molecule to a hydroxyl ion, depending on effects as far away from the iron as the distal nitrogen of the distal imidazole, it would not be surprising if a low-spin hydroxyl state were sometimes stabilized in methemoglobin due to experimental conditions not normally well defined. This could be the case in Lang's experiment.

I cannot agree with the interpretation that the wide quadrupole splitting is due to covalent distortion of the high-spin ion. Such distortion ought to be more pronounced in the reduced iron carbonmonoxyl derivative, where the iron would be a more effective $\pi$-donor. Yet the quadrupole splitting of the carbonmonoxy form is much less that that seen for Lang's acid methemoglobin. Moreover, any such distortion ought to change the ESR signal appreciably. Yet the methemoglobin fluoride and high-spin acid methemoglobin give very similar $g = 6$ values. I think that the answer must be that for some reason the ion seen by Lang's Mössbauer studies was not the same high-spin ion measured in previous ESR experiments, but a low-spin form. It might not be an hydroxide in the simplest sense observed optically in high pH solution, but still a low-spin form.

Related to this problem is the observation of the Mössbauer spectrum at pH 9. If the simple idea of mixed spin states as thermal equilibria of high and low spins were adopted, one would expect the Mössbauer spectrum to show two pairs of lines, with temperature-dependent relative intensities. Instead, only a single pair of lines is observed. Just as we ought to specify more accurately the nature of the "water" or "hydroxyl ion" bound to the iron, we ought to specify more accurately the relaxation times and the extent of the system in which we infer thermal mixtures. The Mössbauer spectra illustrate this necessity.

Williams: I have quite a lot of evidence obtained in collaboration with Johnson at Harwell to support this point. The interesting thing is that the hydroxide mixed spin form of hemoglobin is crucially different from the hydrated form. The Mössbauer behavior of the hydroxide is in agreement with temperature dependence of ESR data. It is true that the hydrate has some similarities with the azide and the hydroxide.

The Mössbauer data are as follows. We have prepared two derivatives of rat hemoglobin--one (A) at pH 6.0 and the second (B) at pH 9.0. (A) has the spectrum of Fe(III) aquo-hemoglobin

as exactly as we can measure both before and after the whole
series of Mössbauer spectra have been taken. (B) has the spectrum of Fe(III) hydroxy-hemoglobin when tested in the same way.
(A) and (B) have different but not very different Mössbauer
spectra at all high temperatures, e.g., at solid carbon di-
oxide:

|       | Isomer shift | Quadrupole splitting |
|-------|--------------|----------------------|
| (A)   | 0.18         | 2.05                 |
| (B)   | 0.15         | 1.80                 |

However the spectra at low temperature ($4.2°$ K) are very different, and they are differently temperature and magnetic field
dependent. Finally their spectra in a high magnetic field at
low temperature are entirely different. The hydroxide alone
is now very closely related to the azide, which, like the hydroxide, is supposed to be low spin at low temperature. Thus
we are convinced that the aquo-complex has not become the hydroxide through ionization at low temperatures. The spin state
of the aquo complex at these temperatures is not certain and
it is not yet permissable to argue from Mössbauer data, especially isomer shift and quadrupole splittings, that it is
definitely in either spin state. We know that high spin (hemin)
and low spin (hemoglobin cyanide) have almost identical isomer
shifts. We also know that very large quadrupole splittings
can occur in either spin state. Theory does not exclude either
possibility. Finally, it would appear that the relaxation times
for the hemoglobin Fe(III) compounds fall in the sequence:

$$CN^- > N_3^- \gtrless OH^- > H_2O > F^-.$$

Dr. C. Johnson, myself, and our collaborators will publish a
long series of experiments on all the compounds as soon as the
data make sense, but for the moment we prefer to warn against
naive conclusions.

Lang: To sum up what has been said, I agree that on the basis
of Mössbauer spectra alone, one would say that acid methemoglobin is a low-spin ferric compound, while on the basis of ESR
spectra alone, one would say it was a high-spin ferric compound with a large D-value. I do not know how the two different impressions of this compound can be rationalized at present.
Marshall and I (5) have attempted to explain the $4°$ K Mössbauer
data in terms of a very large cylindrically symmetric distortion of the 3d shell (S = 5/2). This would not change the
predicted ESR signal, since $g_\perp$ = 6 already corresponds to the
large D approximation, and making this term of the spin Hamiltonian yet larger would only improve the approximation. It
may be that the large distortion can supply the spin-lattice

interaction necessary to account for the Mössbauer data. At present, this is mere speculation, but I know of no other model which is consistent with all available data.

With respect to the methemoglobin hydroxide, I would say the following. A recent Mössbauer measurement of this compound by Johnson, Williams and coworkers (R. J. P. Williams, personal communication) at Harwell confirms the general features found by Marshall and me (5). The only difference is consistent with the assumption that a small amount of non-heme $Fe^{57}$ (less than 5 percent) was present in the original sample. The Mössbauer data are consistent with an S = 1/2 assumption, even to a fair no-parameter fit to the $4°$ K data, based on published g-values (6). This is analogous to the treatment of hemoglobin azide by Marshall and me (5). The highest temperature at which Mössbauer data are available is $195°$ K. Since the thermal spin mixture assumptions are based on room temperature susceptibility, there is no essential conflict between the two results.

I would like to inject here a note of caution. When the spectra are broadened by a factor of 20 or so at low temperatures, they become proportionately weak. More concentrated (e.g., non-protein) compounds will, in general, not experience this modification. Thus, one must guard against the relative amplification of the artifact. This is particularly relevant with regard to reconstituted protein samples.

Williams: I believe one comment is in order here: it is known from the ESR data of Ehrenberg that relaxation times are different for a compound such as the hemoglobin fluoride vs. a compound such as the hydrate. Relaxation time and differences in quadrupole moment will, I think, show the reason why Mössbauer spectra may be very different for two compounds of the same spin state. The problem then is, what causes differences in relaxation behavior? Is it small percentages of other spin forms, or is it due to the thermal motion of the protons of $H_2O$?

### References

1. Keilin, D., and E. F. Hartree. Nature, 164, 254 (1949).

2. Ehrenberg, A., and R. W. Estabrook. Acta Chem. Scand., in press.

3. Bearden, A. J., T. H. Moss, W. S. Caughey, and C. A. Beaudreau. Proc. Natl. Acad. Sci., 53, 1246 (1965).

4.  Caughey, W. S., J. L. York, S. McCoy, and D. P. Hollis. This volume, p. 25.

5.  Lang, G., and W. Marshall. Proc. Phys. Soc., 87, 3 (1966).

6.  Gibson, J. F., D. J. E. Ingram, and D. Schonland. Disc. Faraday Soc., 26, 72 (1958).

# CARBONYL STRETCHING FREQUENCIES AND CARBON MONOXIDE BINDING IN RED BLOOD CELLS, HEMOGLOBINS, AND HEMES[*]

J. O. Alben

Department of Physiological Chemistry
The Ohio State University, College of Medicine
Columbus, Ohio

W. S. Caughey[‡]

The Johns Hopkins University School of Medicine
Baltimore, Maryland

Carbonyl stretching frequencies ($v_{CO}$) serve as a sensitive measure of bonding in heme carbonyls and in metal carbonyl compounds generally. Thus in pyridinecarbonylhemes, $v_{CO}$ values increase, and strengths of CO binding to Fe decrease, with increasingly electron-withdrawing substituents either on the porphyrin ring, or on the pyridine ligand trans to the CO. The pyridinecarbonyl of protoheme dimethyl ester exhibited an absorption maximum at 1977 $cm^{-1}$ whereas the mesoheme, which binds CO more strongly, and the 2,4-diacetyl deuteroheme, which binds CO less strongly, gave $v_{CO}$ values of 1973 and 1984 $cm^{-1}$, respectively (1) when the spectra were determined as bromoform solutions, 0.1 M in pyridine. These results can be considered most simply in terms of the valence bond formalism where structures I and II both can be considered to contribute to the bonding:

$$-\text{Fe}-\text{C}\equiv\text{O} \longleftrightarrow -\text{Fe}=\text{C}=\text{O}$$
$$\text{I} \qquad\qquad \text{II}$$

The weaker the Fe-C bond, the less II will contribute and the greater will be the bond order and stretching frequency of the CO bond. These findings suggested the potential merit of comparing $v_{CO}$ values for hemoproteins as an independent and direct method for the determination of strengths of carbonyl binding.

[*]This work was supported by United States Public Health Service Research Grants Nos. HE-06079 and GM-11067.

[‡]Lederle Medical Faculty Award Scholar

Wang, Nakahara and Fleischer (2) reported rather broad carbonyl stretching bands for pyridinecarbonylprotoheme and for carbonylhemoglobin, both in KBr discs. In both cases they found the bands at 1970 $cm^{-1}$ and concluded, quite reasonably, that the nature of the bonding in heme and hemeprotein were identical. That this should be the case was surprising in view of the differences we had noted among the variously substituted heme carbonyls in solution. As hemoglobin pressed into KBr discs was likely to contain altered protein, it was desirable to re-examine these findings by solution spectra. We are now able to report carbonyl stretching frequencies for carbon monoxide bound to hemoglobin within the red blood cell as well as with a purified hemoglobin precipitate.

Careful matching of reference and sample cells with oxygenated and carbonyl preparations, respectively, has permitted the measurement of a difference spectrum of the carbonyl band. A Perkin-Elmer Model 521 infrared spectrometer equipped with demountable cells with $CaF_2$ windows and a 0.05 mm path length was used. Normal human hemoglobin was purified on DEAE cellulose and then precipitated from 70 percent saturated ammonium sulfate. Normal human red blood cells from freshly drawn blood were exposed to oxygen or carbon monoxide and packed by centrifugation. In both preparations a single carbonyl band with a half band width of about 8 $cm^{-1}$ was obtained. The absorption maxima were at 1951.5 $cm^{-1}$ for the cells and at 1951.9 $cm^{-1}$ for the hemoglobin precipitate. Frequencies were corrected to the water vapor absorption at 1918.05 $cm^{-1}$.

These data reveal no significant differences between CO bonding in the isolated hemoglobin precipitate and in the intact red blood cell, whereas there is a marked shift (26 $cm^{-1}$) to lower frequencies in the hemoglobin compared with the pyridinecarbonylprotoheme. The stronger Fe-C bonding in the hemoglobin undoubtedly reflects, among other factors, a difference in the effects of histidine and pyridine as ligands trans to the CO ligand.

A frequency of 1951 $cm^{-1}$ can be considered to denote an extremely strong Fe-C bond where structure II will make a considerable contribution. The observation of a single carbonyl band of narrow band width is strong evidence that CO must be bound to each of the four hemes in an identical manner. If the enthalpies of CO binding are thus the same at each heme, enthalpy differences cannot be invoked to explain the sigmoid saturation curve. These findings therefore provide experimental support for the interpretations of heme-heme interactions which assume equivalent strengths of binding at all four sites (3,4).

These investigations are being extended to include hemoglobins from other sources as well as other hemeproteins. Through collaboration with Drs. Samuel W. Boyer IV and Peter Hathaway, it has been possible for us to examine carbonyl absorptions with hemoglobins in red cells from human cord blood and from lamb and sheep (A and B cells) as well as solutions of sheep hemoglobins A, B, and C. The carbonyl absorption maxima are found near 1951 $cm^{-1}$ in each case, although marked differences in oxygen affinities have been found. The amino acid sequences for these hemoglobins vary widely except in the immediate vicinity of the heme. Indeed, the similarities of the heme environments are even more rigorously defined by the constancy of the carbonyl absorption frequencies.

## References

1.  Caughey, W. S., J. O. Alben, and C. A. Beaudreau. In Oxidases and Related Redox Systems (T. E. King, H. S. Mason, and M. Morrison, eds.), John Wiley and Sons, Inc., New York, 1965, p. 97.

2.  Wang, J. H., A. Nakahahara, and E. B. Fleischer. J. Am. Chem. Soc., 80, 1109 (1958).

3.  Wyman, J. Adv. Protein Chemistry, 19, 223 (1964).

4.  Vodrážka, Z., and J. Čejka. Coll. Czech. Chem. Commun., 30, 316 (1965).

# STRUCTURE AND LIGAND BINDING OF DEOXYMYOGLOBIN

## C. L. Nobbs[*]

Medical Research Council, Laboratory of Molecular Biology
Cambridge, England

The crystallographic studies of sperm whale metmyoglobin by Kendrew et al. (1) have revealed completely the tertiary structure of this protein. Recently a start has been made on the crystallographic investigation of the physiologically active deoxymyoglobin (2), and of the manner in which ligands bind to it in the vicinity of the heme group (3). These studies have utilized the fact of crystal isomorphism of the ferrous forms of myoglobin with metmyoglobin, and the technique of the difference Fourier synthesis.

With the detailed structural knowledge of myoglobin now at hand, analysis of the kinetics and mechanism of protein-ligand binding at the atomic level can be approached with increased confidence. With this in mind, I wish to bring forward three points which seem particularly appropriate to the subject of this Colloquium. These concern the resolving power of the crystallographic methods, the relationship of the structures of deoxymoglobin in crystal and solution, and the basic structure relationships in the neighborhood of the ligand binding sites.

Resolving power of the crystallographic technique. The production of a Fourier map of a crystal structure involves the summation of a three-dimensional Fourier series, each term of which includes the amplitude and phase of a particular X-ray spectral spot. Each of these spots carries spectral information from a set of parallel reflecting planes within the crystal, each set having a mutual separation of $d_i$. As more and more X-ray reflections are included in the Fourier series, corresponding to ever decreasing values of $d_i$, the greater (theoretically) becomes the resolution of the Fourier map. If X-ray data has been collected for a complete set of X-ray reflections down to a corresponding inter-planar spacing of $d_{min}$, then the limit of

[*]Royal Society Stothert Research Fellow

the resolution in the Fourier map is given by (4): $d_{lim}=0.61d_{min}$. As the resolution increases, the peaks in the Fourier map corresponding to the presence of electron density become higher above the background and sharper in outline. Even so, in a structure like metmyoglobin, which contains over 1,000 atoms, all of which are vibrating thermally, a considerable difficulty exists in placing each atom accurately in the structure, even when atomic resolution has been attained. At the present stage of the refinement of metmyoglobin, the mean standard deviation in the atomic co-ordinates is approximately 0.2 Å: but by utilizing stereochemical knowledge of rigid groups, e.g., histidine, the co-ordinate accuracy can be considerably improved for these groups.

However, as X-ray data is collected to increasingly higher resolution, the effect of errors from most sources, e.g., isomorphism, phase indeterminancy, increase also (5). Present experience indicates that the optimal value of $d_{min}$ is between 2.8 and 2.0 Å, which provides a practical limitation to the attainable resolution. This order of accuracy is considerably less than that obtained for the structures of small organic molecules. The crystal structures of porphyrin derivatives studied by Koenig (6) and Hoard et al. (7) will continue to provide the most accurate information available on the structure of the porphyrin moiety. As has been pointed out (8), the structure of the porphyrin in metmyoglobin is compatible with these data.

However, changes in the electron density distribution between two isomorphous crystal structures can be observed and measured beyond the limit of resolution ($d_{lim}$) expressed above. For example, we believe that in the difference Fourier between metmyoglobin and deoxymyoglobin using data for reflections corresponding to interplanar spacings greater than 2.8 Å, a movement of the heme iron atom of 0.1 Å would have been visible. Similarly, a rotation of a histidine residue about its $C_\beta-C_\gamma$ bond of 15° or about $C_\alpha-C_\beta$ of 5°, or a rotation of a leucine residue about $C_\beta-C_\gamma$ of 50° would have been visible in the Fourier maps. In fact, no such changes were seen.

Structure of deoxymyoglobin in solution. The problem of the relationship between the structure of myoglobin in crystal and in solution has been approached previously by Urnes (9) and Chance et al. (10). These studies have shown that the gross tertiary structure of the protein is maintained on dissolution, although relatively small and subtle changes in conformation may occur.

The most striking difference between the crystal structures of met- and deoxymyoglobin is the absence from the latter of the water molecule bound to the heme iron atom. (The
alternative suggestion, that in deoxymyoglobin this water molecule is present in the structure but is exchanging with water
of the bulk solvent water with a very low residence time at
the iron site, appears extremely unlikely from both crystallographic and steric considerations.) The other comparison of
immediate importance is that between deoxymyoglobin and deoxyhemoglobin, where we believe, from a comparison of spectral
and other properties, that the co-ordination of the iron atom
is the same in both compounds.

There is no firmly based evidence to suggest that the
state of the iron atom in solvated deoxymyoglobin and deoxyhemoglobin is different from that in the crystal. The only
evidence presented in favor of the existence of a water molecule co-ordinated to the iron atom of deoxyhemoglobin in solution was based on the observations of spectral changes induced
by drying the protein (11). Doubt has previously been cast on
the interpretation of these experiments (12). With the more
recently accumulated structural knowledge of hemoglobin and
myoglobin, the implications of dehydrating the protein can be
considered further.

Metmyoglobin in the crystal contained within it three
trapped water molecules (in addition to the heme-linked water)
which can be distinguished in Fourier maps, and it is also
surrounded by a partially ordered hydration shell. As Perutz
(13) has shown, the free energy loss due to the uncompensated
loss of any one of these molecules is of sufficient order of
magnitude to affect the system of very weak bonds that stabilizes the tertiary structure of the molecule. On drying, the
balanced spatial relationships between protein and water both
in the interior of the protein and at the surface will be disrupted, with the likely consequence of gross structural change.
Certainly the protein cannot function. One of the experiments
presented in favor of the presence of water bound to the heme
involved dessiccating a solution of deoxyhemoglobin in vacuo,
whereupon a compound was obtained which possessed a hemochromogen spectrum. Addition of water regenerated the deoxyhemoglobin. We would now consider that on drying, a slight col-
lapse of helix E had placed $N_\epsilon$ of histidine E7 in the previously unoccupied sixth co-ordination position of the iron.

Evidence against solvated deoxymyoglobin containing
heme-linked water may be summarized. Pauling (14) on theoretical grounds predicted that the ferroheme group in deoxymyoglobin and deoxyhemoglobin would not combine with water or

chloride or hydroxyl ions or similar groups under normal conditions. Reaction kinetic data indicate that deoxymyoglobin
reacts with ligands between $10^2$ and $10^3$ times faster than does
metmyoglobin (10,15), implying, in addition, that in metmyoglobin the removal of the water molecule constitutes the rate-
limiting step. Recently, NMR techniques have been applied to
solutions of hemoglobin and myoglobin derivatives to measure
the relaxation times of protons attached to water molecules in
the first co-ordination shell of the heme iron, and for which
either the protons themselves or the water molecules as a
whole exchange with the bulk solvent (16, S. Maricic, personal
communication). Although the results are at present tentative,
they appear to substantiate the crystallographic findings.

Deoxymyoglobin in solution undergoes a spectral change at
pH 13 which appears to represent the binding of an hydroxyl ion
at the water site. Perhaps it would be possible to compare
the nuclear quadrupole moments of these two forms and hence
measure the relative departure from octahedrality of the crystal field around the iron atom? This in turn may provide
information on the absence of the water molecule.

Ligand binding in proximity to the heme. The considerations of kinetics and exchange in the previous section raise
several issues concerning the size and accessibility of the
sites occupied by water and other ligands which bind to myoglobin in the vicinity of the heme.

There are two vacant sites (both hydrophobic) within the
myoglobin structure in the region of the heme group: (A)   On
the distal side of the heme and defined by the heme group and
residues B10 (Leu), B13 (Leu), B14 (Phe), C4 (Thr), CD1 (Phe),
E7 (His) and G8 (Ile); and (B)   One the proximal (histidine-
linked) side of the heme and defined by the heme, F4 (Leu),
F8 (His), G5 (Leu), H14 (Phe), and H18 (Ile). Neither of these
vacancies is occupied by water in deoxymyoglobin crystals, but
both can be occupied under certain conditions of ligand binding. Site A is that occupied by the ligands $CH_3CH_2NC$ (3), $O_2$
CO, $H_2S$, etc., while site B is occupied by xenon in the xenon
adducts of deoxymyoglobin (17) and metmyoglobin (18). (Site B
is also occupied by $HgI_3$ when it binds to metmyoglobin (19).)

The nature of the ligand binding at these two sites is
quite distinct. Whereas the ligands occupying site A are held
to the iron atom by direct chemical bonds, the xenon in site B
is held in the structure purely by van der Waals interactions
with surrounding groups, and especially with the heme. There
is no evidence that in deoxymyoglobin crystals xenon enters
site A, although experiments have been carried out up to a

xenon pressure of 2.5 atmospheres.

It appears that the xenon enters the molecule by way of a "gap" in the molecular surface between the heme group and amino acid residues F1 (Leu) and F4 (Leu), where its approach is short and relatively unobstructed. The rearrangement of residues surrounding the xenon appears to be minimal. However, consideration of the van der Waals dimensions of the residues surrounding the site A shows clearly that entry or exit of a water molecule or other ligand to this site must be accompanied by a pronounced movement of some of these residues. For example, the rotation of histidine E7 about its $C\alpha$-$C\beta$ bond, or the breathing of helix E can be envisaged (10).

In the crystal, intermolecular van der Waals contacts are also important in the region of ligand entry. These contacts occur between the original molecule and that related by a translation of one unit cell edge in the b-direction. Group E10 (Thr) has contacts with G17 (His) of this latter molecule of less than 4.0 Å, as does CAPR* with G17 (His), and CBPR with G17 (His) and H4 (Gln). On the other hand group PL has no such contacts less than 4.8 Å ( and only one less than 5.3 Å), and CD3 (Arg) none less than 6.2 Å. Thus even in the crystal, rotation of histidine E7 as suggested above could occur (moving the arginine CD3 sidechain in consequence) and alowing entry of the ligand. Although groups as large as ethyl isocyanide can diffuse into the crystal and occupy this site without distorting the crystal lattice, groups such as tertiary butyl isocyanide cannot. For example, the binding of imidazole to metmyoglobin is accompanied by an extension of the b-axial length (L. Stryer, personal communication), one interpretation of which is that residues E7 and CD3, and perhaps the group PL, have been forced away from their normal positions to accomodate the ligand.

A full understanding of the kinetics and mechanisms of ligand binding to myoglobin will require much further study, in which the use of both chemical and crystallographic methods will be necessary.

*For heme groups nomenclature, see ref. 18.

## Acknowledgements

I am indebted to Dr. H. C. Watson and Dr. J. C. Kendrew with whom I have collaborated closely, and to Professor B. Chance for helpful discussions.

## References

1. Kendrew, J. C., H. C. Watson, D. C. Phillips, et al., in preparation.

2. Nobbs, C. L., H. C. Watson, and J. C. Kendrew. Nature, 209, 339 (1966).

3. Nobbs, C. L. J. Mol. Biol., 13, 325 (1965).

4. Luzzati, V. Acta Cryst., 6, 142 (1953).

5. Crick, F. H. C., and B. Magdoff. Acta Cryst., 9, 901 (1956

6. Koenig, D. Acta Cryst., 18, 663 (1965).

7. Hamor, T. A., W. S. Caughey, and J. L. Hoard. J. Amer. Chem. Soc., 87, 2305 (1965); Hoard, J. L., M. J. Hamor, T. A. Hamor, and W. S. Caughey. J. Amer. Chem. Soc., 87, 2312 (1965).

8. Watson, H. C. This volume, p. 63.

9. Urnes, P. J. Gen. Physiol., 49, 75 (1965).

10. Chance, B., A. Ravilly, and N. Rumen. J. Mol. Biol., 17, 525 (1966).

11. Haurowitz, F. In Hemoglobin (F. W. J. Roughton and J. C. Kendrew, eds.), Butterworths, London, 1949, p. 53.

12. George, P., and R. J. Lyster. In Conference on Hemoglobin, Nat. Acad. Sci./Nat. Res. Council, Washington, 1958, p. 36.

13. Perutz, M. F. J. Mol. Biol., 13, 646 (1965).

14. Pauling, L. In Hemoglobin (F. W. J. Roughton and J. C. Kendrew, eds.), Butterworths, London, 1949, p. 57.

15. Millikan, G. A. Proc. Roy. Soc. (London), B, 120, 366 (1936).

16. Fabry, T. L., and H. A. Reich. Biochem. Biophys. Res. Comm., 22, 700 (1966).

17. Schoenborn, B. P., and C. L. Nobbs. In preparation.

18. Schoenborn, B. P., H. C. Watson, and J. C. Kendrew. Nature, 207, 28 (1965).

19. Kretsinger, R. In preparation.

# CRYSTALLOGRAPHIC STUDIES OF LIGAND BINDING ($CN^-$, $OH^-$, $F^-$)

## H. C. Watson and B. Chance[+]

Medical Research Council Laboratory of Molecular Biology
Hills Road, Cambridge, England

Crystallographic studies of various porphyrin derivatives have led to the suggestion that, in hemoproteins, the steric arrangement of the heme may change slightly as the spin state of the heme iron is altered (1). Since a change of this kind could be of central importance to our understanding of such phenomena as the cooperative association of oxygen with hemoglobin, we have attempted to test the validity of this concept by using the known structure of sperm whale myoglobin.

Two derivatives of myoglobin, the azide (2) and the deoxy (3), have so far been subjected to full three dimensional X-ray analyses. No significant differences in the heme arrangement or of the iron position have been found between these derivatives and the parent compound, metmyoglobin, even though the deoxymyoglobin study showed that the difference Fourier method can reveal structural differences of as little as 8 electrons out of a total of approximately 10,000 (4).

Met- and deoxymyoglobin are both high spin iron derivatives, but the azide complex is reported to be a mixture of both high and low spin state (5). Discrepancies of spin state according to ESR and Mossbauer data are discussed on p.133 f. The difference in the electron density between the azide and the met forms ought therefore to have indicated a structural rearrangement of the heme or of the protein had this occurred. It can be argued, however, that the steric alteration in the azide heme complex would be small and that a completely low spin iron derivative should be used to produce maximum effect. Oxymyoglobin is reported to have a zero spin heme iron, but crystals of this derivative are unstable and revert to metmyoglobin crystals when exposed to the conditions used in X-ray crystallography.

[+]Foreign Fellow, Churchill College, January-February, 1966; Present Address: Johnson Foundation, University of Pennsylvania, Philadelphia, Pennsylvania.

A series of experiments generally oriented towards a crystallographic study of the peroxide compound [to be reported
elsewhere (Chance and Watson, unpublished data)] has included
a study of the very low spin cyanide derivative. As controls
we have also studied, under the same experimental conditions,
the intermediate spin hydroxyl and the high spin fluoride derivatives.

Preparation of the myoglobin crystal derivatives. Crystals
of sperm whale myoglobin prepared by the method of Kendrew and
Parrish (6) were used to prepare the $CN^-$, $OH^-$, and $F^-$ derivatives as described below.

(a) Cyanide. Crystals were transferred from the crystal-
lising vial and immersed in a 3 M ammonium sulfate, 2 mM KCN
solution at pH 7.0. Within minutes the color of the crystals
changed from the original brown to pink. After allowing for
equilibration, crystals were mounted in thin-walled quartz
capillary tubes. Visual spectroscopic observation before and
after exposure to X-rays revealed no trace of the 630 mµ
absorption band characteristic of the original metmyoglobin
crystals.

(b) Hydroxide. Standard metmyoglobin crystals crack when
transferred directly to ammonium sulfate solutions adjusted to
pH 9.5 with NaOH. This difficulty was partly overcome by
transferring the crystals in several pH stages. Visual spectroscopic observation of the mounted crystals showed that the conversion from the met- to the hydroxide form was almost complete
at pH 8.9.

(c) Fluoride. The fluoride derivative was prepared by
allowing crystals to stand in 3 M ammonium sulfate, 0.18 M
NaF solution at pH 7.4. Under these conditions the 630 mµ
metmyoglobin absorption band had largely disappeared and was
replaced by the strong characteristic 610 mµ fluoride band.

Crystallographic procedure. The crystals were mounted as
described and oriented so that the h0ℓ section of the reciprocal lattice could be recorded with a precision type X-ray
diffraction camera. Using Cu $K_\alpha$ radiation from a rotating
anode X-ray tube it was necessary to expose each crystal for
approximately 10 hours to collect all the diffracted data to
spacings of 2.8 Å. Measurements of the lattice parameters
indicated that the $CN^-$, $OH^-$, and $F^-$ derivatives were all isomorphous with metmyoglobin crystals.

The myoglobin b axis projection is centered (6) and the
phases of the h0ℓ reflections are restricted to values of 0

and $\pi$. In calculating the electron density difference projections using equation (1)

$$\rho\,(x,y) = \sum_{h=-\infty}^{+\infty} \sum_{\ell=0}^{+\infty} 2(\underline{F_D} - \underline{F_P})\ \cos\,2\pi\ (hx + lz) \qquad (1)$$

we have assumed that the change in structure produced by ligand binding would be small and that the phases of the derivative reflections would be the same as those for the parent. For $(\underline{F_D} - F_P)$ we have therefore used $(\,|F_D - F_p|\,)\ \cos\,\alpha_p$, where $\underline{F_D}$ and $\overline{F_P}$ are the derivative and parent structure amplitudes and $\alpha_p$ is the phase of the parent reflection.

### Results

(a) <u>Control</u>. When measurements from the unmodified crystals were used as derivative intensities against the original native $\underline{hO\ell}$ data, the difference in electron density rarely exceeded 0.15 el. $\text{\AA}^{-3}$ (Fig. 1a). At 2.8 $\text{\AA}$ resolution this amounts to a change in structure of about one half a carbon atom.

(b) <u>Cyanide</u>. The difference in the projected electron densities between the cyanide and metmyoglobin derivatives is shown in Figure 1b. The most significant feature, a negative peak, represents the loss of one sulfate ion (2). Several peaks surround the sulfate position and could represent changes in the orientation of the distal imidazole. There are no density changes indicative of a heme iron movement, but the positive and negative density regions to the left and right of the heme group, as shown in Fig. 1b, could be interpreted in terms of a small movement of the porphyrin towards the iron. Regions of the Fourier map removed from the vicinity of the heme are relatively free from significant electron density peaks.

(c) <u>Hydroxide</u>. The electron density difference derived from the cyanide (Fig. 1b) and the hydroxide (Fig. 1c) reacted crystals show many common features. These two derivatives therefore share structural features which are not common to the native protein.

(d) <u>Fluoride</u>. The result obtained for the fluoride derivative (Fig. 1d) is the easiest of the three calculations to interpret. The addition of the negatively charged fluoride ion frees the sulfate bound to the distal imidazole and no other significant structural changes occur.

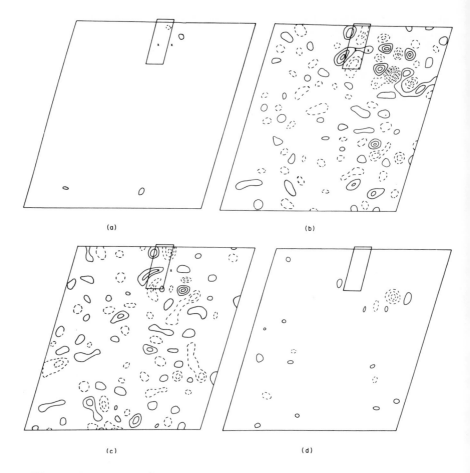

(a)          (b)

(c)          (d)

Figure 1. The h0ℓ electron density difference maps of (a) metmyoglobin pH 7.0 (b) cyanide myoglobin pH 7.0 (c) hydroxide myoglobin pH 9.5 (d) fluoride myoglobin pH 7.4. The contours are drawn at intervals of 0.15 el. $Å^{-3}$ (see text). The zero contour has been omitted and the negative contours are dashed. The projection of the heme is indicated in the top center of each map as also are the iron and heme ligand binding positions.

## Discussion

The results reported in this contribution are indicative rather than conclusive. The fluoride ion reacts with the protein in a manner that experience has led us to expect for a negatively charged ligand bound to a high spin ferric heme iron. The fact that this derivative behaves "normally" suggests that the electron density peaks appearing in the cyanide and hydroxide Fourier projections are truly indicative of structural changes.

The cyanide and hydroxide difference Fourier calculations shown in Fig. 1, although not identical, have many common features. We have investigated the effect of a gradual decrease in hydrogen ion concentration and have found that the features shown in Fig. 1c begin to appear at about pH 8 and become progressively more pronounced. We are convinced therefore that small changes in structure do occur as the pH is raised and that, in some respects, these changes are the same as those produced by reacting similar crystals with cyanide at pH 7.0.

For the three derivatives investigated there is no evidence of a change in the heme iron position relative to that in the parent compound. The positive and negative density regions about the heme in the cyanide calculation could be indicative of a small movement of the porphyrin towards the iron. This movement would be in agreement with the prediction that the heme should become more planar as the irons spin state is reduced (7). Similar positive and negative density regions are also present, however, in the hydroxide calculations (Fig. 1c).

From this work it is not possible to describe with confidence the detailed nature of the structural changes which do take place on formation of the cyanide and hydroxyl derivatives. In the absence of a structural investigation of the more physiologically important oxymyoglobin derivative, we feel that the results presented here would justify a full three dimensional investigation of the cyanide complex.

## References

1. Hoard, J. This volume, p. 9.

2. Stryer, L., J. C. Kendrew, and H. C. Watson. J. Mol. Biol., 8, 96 (1964).

3. Nobbs, C. L., H. C. Watson, and J. C. Kendrew. Nature, 209, 339 (1966).

4. Nobbs, C. This volume, p. 143.

5. This volume, Discussion after Lang, p. 133.

6. Kendrew, J. C., and R. G. Parrish. Proc. Roy. Soc. A., 238, 305 (1956).

7. Hoard, J., M. J. Hamor, and T. A. Hamor, and W. S. Caughey. J. Amer. Chem. Soc., 87, 2312 (1965).

DISCUSSION

**Hoard:**  I take it you grow these crystals in a solid state reaction.  Perhaps pertinent to this is the fact that we have observed many times that, when one has a very complicated complex with water of crystallization and one of the rather trivial waters is slowly lost, the quality of the data deteriorates rapidly during measurement; one gets out about the right structure, but one does not get good bond distances.  I suspect your method of growing crystals is not the best possible to get specimens.

**Watson:**  We obviously prefer to grow the crystals from solutions of a preformed compound.  We have done this for the azide and other derivatives but find no significant differences in electron density when we process the "soaked" against the "grown" X-ray diffraction data.  I think that this is one of those rare cases where going to a more complex system makes things perhaps easier to handle experimentally.

**Hoard:**  On the basis of this and of other statements made earlier in the day, I do question the whole procedure of using difference syntheses at this stage.  My first reaction is to disapprove entirely of carrying the method as far as the use of two-dimensional difference synthesis.

**Watson:**  You might disapprove of these methods, but the results obtained with the azide and deoxymyoglobin have proved that they do work.  I cannot think of a better justification for using any procedure.

**Williams:**  I think I am right in saying that the isocyanide compound is a low-spin compound.  Do you want to say anything about the position of the iron in this case?

**Nobbs:**  The study of the isocyanide derivative was done only in projection at 2.8 Å resolution and with this limitation there is no movement in the iron.  I think that you could probably detect a movement of about 0.1 Å or greater if it occurred.

Watson:  I would like you to think of the results I have presented as being indicative of a change in structure which is
similar in both cyanide and hydroxyl derivatives and not to
try to pin down the details of the structural change, even
though these preliminary results can be interpreted in terms
of a heme movement.  These derivatives are now obvious candidates for a full three dimensional X-ray investigation.

Williams:  Dr. Lang, have you any further comment on the Mössbauer data after seeing any of these structures?

Lang:  I would say that one would certainly see a difference
in the quadrupole splitting if one took out the water.  On the
other hand, I would not like to predict whether the water is
there or not, on the basis of the observed spectrum.

Nobbs:  May I infer then that the lack of the water molecule
in reduced myoglobin is agreed upon?

# PROTON RELAXATION MEASUREMENTS OF
## DISSOLVED AND CRYSTALLINE METHEMOGLOBIN AND METMYOGLOBIN[*]

S. Maričić[**], A. Ravilly and A. S. Mildvan[‡]

Johnson Research Foundation, University of Pennsylvania
Philadelphia, Pennsylvania

The proton relaxation technique has been used several times in attempts to study the accessibility of solvent molecules to hemes in various hemoproteins. The paper by Scheler (1) reviews the previous literature and draws attention to the care that is necessary in dealing with the results obtained at only one temperature. Pfeifer (2) has published a theoretical treatment of the problem of solvent accessibility to paramagnetic centers of macromolecules for the case in which only outer sphere relaxation mechanisms operate. That is, there are no solvent molecules in the first coordination sphere, or none of the ligands to the metal have exchangeable protons.

Experiments by Bernheim, Brown, Gutowsky and Woessner (3), Swift and Connick (4), and more recently by Luz and Meiboom (5) have shown that the relaxivities due to paramagnetic ions in aqueous solution are dependent on temperature. We have, therefore, undertaken a temperature study of proton magnetic relaxation rates in both solutions and suspensions of crystallites of metmyoglobin and methemoglobin.

The first object of this study was to define the experimental conditions which would permit meaningful comparison of data obtained from different species. Secondly, it was hoped that these experiments might yield information concerning the possible differences between the states of hemoproteins in solution vs. crystals. Thirdly, it was also felt that conclusions

*This work was supported in part by USPHS grants GM-12446, AM-09760, NSF grant GB-3453, and NSF grant GB-2482.

**Visiting Scientist under the Career Investigatorship Program of the American Heart Association while on leave of absence from the University Institute of Biology, Zagreb, Yugoslavia.

‡Established Investigator of the American Heart Association.

could be derived regarding various kinetic and structural details of ligand binding by hemoproteins.

## Experimental Methods

Sample preparation. The samples of hemoglobin were prepared from fresh horse blood. Methemoglobin was obtained by ferricyanide oxidation of oxyHb followed by dialysis against water, and was then equilibrated overnight in 0.1 phosphate buffer at pH=6.95.

Crystals of methemoglobin were grown in 1.6 M ammonium sulfate, pH=6.9, washed twice with ammonium sulfate solution to remove soluble hemoglobin. The crystals were finally suspended in 3.9 M ammonium sulfate, 0.1 M phosphate buffer, pH=6.95.

Myoglobin was prepared from horse heart muscle following the procedure of Theorell (6).

The crystals were obtained from an 80 percent saturated ammonium sulfate solution, washed twice and resuspended in the same solution, with 0.1 M phosphate buffer at pH=6.95. In order to obtain myoglobin solutions, the crystals were dialyzed against water followed by the equilibration of the resulting solution of metmyoglobin in the same buffer. The ammonium sulfate solutions were prepared from crystallized ammonium sulfate supplied by Mann Assay Labs which contained $1 \times 10^{-5}$ percent Fe.

The carbon monoxide compounds of both hemoproteins were prepared by reducing their met-forms with sodium dithionite, after which the solutions were saturated with CO. All solvents for these measurements were also saturated with carbon monoxide.

The concentrations of the samples were determined spectrophotometrically in the Soret region (at 409 m$\mu$ for metmyoglobin and at 405 m$\mu$ for methemoglobin).

Proton magnetic relaxation measurements. All the measurements were done at 24.3 MHz using a pulsed NMR instrument with a 180°-90° sequence to determine the null according to the Carr and Purcell method (7).

The temperature was kept constant to within half a degree with a Varian variable temperature accessory, probe, and variable temperature insert. The readings of the temperature were accurate to better than two degrees.

## Experimental Results

Fig. 1 summarizes all the measured values of $1/T_1$ corrected for the contribution due to the diamagnetic protein moiety. The reciprocal of the experimentally determined relaxation time of protons, i.e. $1/T_1^*$, is a sum of several reciprocal relaxation times, or relaxivities. As we are interested only in the paramagnetic contribution due to the heme-Fe in methemoproteins, we have to subtract the relaxivities due to other sources, including the protein itself and the solvent in the absence of paramagnetic species. We therefore have:

$$(1/T_1)_{mh} = [(1/T_1^*) - (1/T_1^o)]/C_{mh}$$

$$(1/T_1)_{pt} = [(1/T_1^*) - (1/T_1^o)] C_{pt}$$

$$(1/T_1)_p = (1/T_1)_{mh} - (1/T_1)_{pt}$$

The asterisk denotes the experimentally observed values for the solutions (or suspensions of crystals) and "o" refers to measurements of any particular solvent. $(1/T_1)_{mh}$ and $(1/T_1)_{pt}$ are relaxivities of methemoproteins (including their diamagnetic part of the protein) and of carbonmonoxyhemoproteins, respectively, normalized by their concentrations ($C_{mh}$, $C_{pt}$). $(1/T_1)_p$ is therefore a value determined entirely by the presence of the paramagnetic center in methemoproteins (normalized to unit concentration). $(1/T_1)_p$ is obtained by the assumption that $(1/T_1)_{pt}$ as measured on CO-hemoproteins equals the diamagnetic contribution for methemoproteins. The dimensions are $sec^{-1}M^{-1}l$, as indicated in the ordinate of graph 1. If our ordinates were multiplied by 55.5 (molarity of water) the dimensions ($sec^{-1}$) would agree with those in ref. 5. The coordination number "q", equals unity in our case.

The curve for methemoglobin solution in Fig. 1 is considered to be most reliably determined from measurements in neutral buffer for two different preparations, and by another set of measurements in 1 M ammonium sulfate solution. Similar scatter of data is observed for metmyoglobin curves, but the points are omitted for the sake of clarity. However, we experienced considerable difficulty in obtaining reproducibility with the CO-blanks for metmyoglobin (as distinct from COHb, which showed very good reproducibility between different sets of measurements). This means that the position of metmyoglobin curves in Fig. 1 along the ordinate, but not the general shape of the curves, is uncertain to within 100 $sec^{-1} M^{-1} l$.

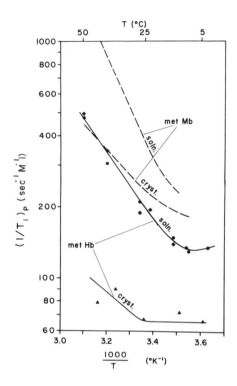

Figure 1. Paramagnetic contribution of methemoproteins to the longitudinal proton relaxation rates of water as a function of reciprocal temperature. For the curve of methemoglobin solution, the squares indicate measurements in buffered aqueous solution, while the circles refer to the values obtained with methemoglobin dissolved in 1 M ammonium sulfate solution. (See text for other details.)

The experimental points for methemoglobin crystals correspond to $(1/T_1)_{mh}$ − $(1/T_1)_{pt}$ for each pair of measurements at a given temperature. The curve drawn through these points is more reliable than is suggested by the scatter of the points because it was obtained as a difference from two smooth curves drawn through each set of data separately, i.e. for methemoglobin crystals and then for its blank, COHb-crystals. The diamagnetic blanks were found to be temperature independent, so that the low-temperature part of the methemoglobin-crystals curve in Fig. 1 is fairly certain.

TABLE I

| Origin | Frequency at which measured MHz | Temperature °C | $(1/T_1)_p$ $sec^{-1}M^{-1}l$ | Reference |
|--------|------|------|------|------|
| chironomus | 16 | 24 ± 1 | 1069 | 1 |
| human | 60 | | 250 ± 50 | 8 |
| | 60 | 28.8 | 238 | 9 |
| horse | 40 | 25 | 200 ± 20 | 10 |
| horse | 16 | 24 ± 1 | 335 | 1 |
| horse | 24.3 | 25 ± 1 | 200 ± 20 | present paper |

It is instructive to compare our data at 25° C with those available in the literature for methemoglobin solutions (see Table I). There is very good agreement for the vertebrate methemoglobin relaxivities bearing in mind that the experimental conditions are not strictly comparable for all of them. Our value of 200 ± 20 for horse methemoglobin agrees with the one obtained by Lumry et al. (10), while 335 $sec^{-1}M^{-1}l$ in Ref. 1 exceeds all other values for vertebrate methemoglobins.

TABLE II

| Origin | Frequency at which measured MHz | Temperature °C | $(1/T_1)_p$ $sec^{-1}M^{-1}l$ | Reference |
|--------|------|------|------|------|
| sperm whale | 60 | | 1400 ± 100 | 8 |
| whale | 40 | 25 | 1200 ± 100 | 10 |
| horse | 16 | 24 ± 1 | 730 | 1 |
| horse | 24.3 | 25 ± 1 | 380 | present paper |

Table II compares the relevant data for vertebrate metmyoglobin relaxivities. It seems that in this case there is a difference even between the two horse-myoglobin samples. Our figure appears to be too low; the reason for this is not clear at present.

No similar comparisons could be made for our results obtained with crystals as there is no such data in the literature to our knowledge.

## Discussion

Our main concern is to establish whether protons exchange from the paramagnetic site with those from bulk solvent. Luz and Meiboom (5) showed, in an incisive experiment with $Co^{++}$ and $Ni^{++}$ in a methanol-water mixture that there exist three temperature regions in a plot of $(1/T_1)_p$ vs the reciprocal of the absolute temperature. The three regions are characterized as follows:

a) Very slow exchange (two separate resonance lines observable by NMR) at low temperatures. The slope of the curve (straight line) is small and positive.

b) Chemical exchange-dominated region at intermediate temperatures, with a much larger but negative slope.

c) Very fast exchange at higher temperatures, with a (smaller) positive slope of the curve approaching a straight line.

For region (a), as pointed out by Pfeifer (2) the relaxivity would depend on parameters related to accessibility in the following way:

$$\text{relaxivity} \propto \mu_{eff}^2 \ \frac{\tau_s}{d^n} \tag{1}$$

Where:

$\mu_{eff}$ is the effective magnetic moment which often can be calculated from the temperature-dependent term of static susceptibility; $\tau_s$ is the electronic relaxation time of the paramagnetic center; d is the distance of closest possible approach of magnetic nuclei to the paramagnetic center outside the first coordination sphere, and n is an exponent which depends (for constant magnetic field) mainly on the diffusion coefficient of the solvent ($1 \leq n \leq 3$).

This means that the relaxivity, which in this temperature region is caused by the dipolar interaction of the paramagnetic center with protons outside the first coordination sphere, is inversely proportional to the distance of closest approach between the electron and nuclear magnetic dipole. However, the power of this dependence has no unique value for all systems.

$\tau_s$ may also differ in various hemoproteins and in the dissolved and crystalline state of a single hemoprotein. Although $\mu_{eff}$ is known for solutions of hemoproteins, it may differ in crystals.

The curves in Fig. 1 for metmyoglobin solution and crystals, and for methemoglobin solution, all have a region of negative slope. This fact clearly indicates that we have been measuring relaxivities in region (b), where exchange of protons between the first coordination sphere of iron and the bulk of solvent dominates the value of the relaxivity. In the case of methemoglobin crystals the data suggests the onset of the exchange-dominated region (b) only at the highest attainable temperatures.

We have not made measurements in the very-fast-exchange region (c) because of the instability of hemoproteins at high temperature. On the other hand, all of the curves (especially the methemoglobin data) closely approach the region of very slow exchange (a) at low temperatures. Although only a small portion of the curve in this region is observable (being limited by freezing), we may assume the values of the relaxivities around +5°C to be dominated by dipole-dipole relaxivities as given by Eqn. 1. These data can then be discussed in terms of possible (static) differences between crystals and solutions.

A gross comparison of the changes when going from solutions to crystals (see Fig. 1) reveals that the differences between the two states are greater for methemoglobin than for metmyoglobin. This is indicated particularly by a more extended region of dipole-dipole interaction (temperature region a ) in crystals of methemoglobin than in metmyoglobin. The crystal/solution difference in the relaxivities at around 5° C is also larger for methemoglobin, but as the data for metmyoglobin solution may be too low (see comparison in Table II), this conclusion is not certain.

The methemoglobin data of region (a) can be analyzed in terms of Eqn. 1. We assume, (although it has not been experimentally directly verified), that both the effective magnetic moments and the electron relaxation times for iron in methemoglobin are practically the same in solution and in crystals. We would, therefore, expect that the discussed difference in relaxivities ought to be accounted for by a change in the distance of closest approach (d in Eqn. 1) of bulk protons to

163

the paramagnetic center of the protein. From Eqn. 1, we may then write with s and c indicating solution and crystals respectively, and dip = dipolar:

$$\frac{(R_s \text{ dip})}{(R_c \text{ dip})} = R_{obs} = \frac{d_c^n}{d_s^n} \tag{2}$$

and

$$d_c^n = R_{obs} \times d_s^n \tag{3}$$

Since $1 \leq n \leq 3$,

$$d_c = R_{obs}^{1/3} \times d_s^{1/3} \quad \text{to} \quad d_c = R_{obs} \times d_s^3 \tag{4}$$

One would expect a difference in diffusion coefficient for the two states in view of the less mobile hydration shell in crystals as compared to solutions, but in what direction it would change for protons is difficult to predict with certainty.

If we assume that n does not change on going from solution to crystals (of methemoglobin) irrespective of its actual value (between 1 and 3), then

$$d_c \cong \left(\frac{132}{66}\right)^{1/n} \times d_s \tag{5}$$

Hence, d might increase by a factor of 1.26 to 2.0 on crystallization of methemoglobin.

More certain conclusions regarding the crystal/solution problem can be reached from the dynamic part of the data in Fig. 1 (region b). For methemoglobin the temperature of on-set of measurable exchange of protons is much higher for the crystals than for the solution. For met yoglobin, although the differences between solution and crystals are small in the region of slow exchange (a), the shapes of the two curves in the exchange dominated region (b) are quite different.

In order to discuss these observations quantitatively we made use of the following equation (4,5):

$$\frac{1}{T_1} - \frac{1}{T_{1A}} = \frac{pq}{T_{1M} + \tau_{M,}} \tag{6}$$

where: $1/T_{1A}$ is the relaxivity due to dipole-dipole interaction (derived from region a). $\tau_M$ is the residence time of the proton in the first coordination sphere; $T_{1M}$ is the spin-lattice relaxation time of the (magnetic) nucleus in the first coordination sphere; p is number of paramagnetic ions per solvent molecule, and q is the number of exchangeable protons in the first coordination sphere. (Hence pq is the mole fraction of water which is coordinated.)

Eqn. (6) is valid only for the (b) and (c) temperature regions, i.e., only if appreciable exchange of magnetic nuclei takes place between the first coordination sphere of the paramagnetic center and the bulk of solvent. On increasing the temperature above a certain value $\tau_M$ becomes short enough to overtake the dipolar relaxation mechanism of region (a) represented by Eqn. 1. In the (b) region $\tau_M$ is still much larger than $T_{1M}$ so that to a very good approximation the right-hand side of Eqn 2 equals $(pq)/\tau_m$, pq by definition being much smaller than unity.

In the very-fast-exchange region (c) $\tau_m$ becomes much smaller than $T_{1m}$, so that equation (6) could be approximated by $R = pq/T_{1M}$. Were this temperature range accessible for hemoproteins one could calculate the distance of the protons in the first coordination sphere from the paramagnetic center.

As shown in Fig. 1 the relaxivity is a function of temperature. This is introduced into Eqn. 6 because of the fact that $T_{1M}$ and $\tau_M$ are functions of temperature; $1/\tau_m$, the exchange rate, is a thermally activated process according to Arrhenius's law. We therefore approximate the higher temperature portions of our curves in Fig. 1 (region (b)) by straight lines, from which the kinetic parameters such as energy, heat and entropy of activation can be derived, and in addition the exchange rate $1/\tau_m$. We estimate the value of $1/T_{1A}$ at $+25^{\circ}C$ by extrapolation from the one at $+5^{\circ}C$. Although the extrapolation is based on limited data, it does not introduce serious error (cf. ref. 5). The calculated kinetic parameters are given in Table III.

With the exception of crystalline methemoglobin, the derived values in Table III are fairly certain. Shifts along the ordinate in Fig. 1, which may be possible for metmyoglobin solution (see comparison in Table II) are not expected to change substantially the shape of the exchange-determined portion of the curve. It is from this portion that the $\tau_m$ dependence on temperature has been derived.

We include in Table III the data for ferric ion in aqueous solution, which were given ($E_a$ and $1/\tau_m$) by Luz and Shulman (11). Let us first examine the last row for the rate-of-exchange values. The aqueous ferric ion has the fastest

## TABLE III

|  | $Fe^{3+}$ soln.[*] | metMb soln. | metHb cryst. | metHb soln. | metHb[**] cryst. |
|---|---|---|---|---|---|
| $E_a$ (kcal $M^{-1}$) | 12.1 | 10.0 | 4.8 | 6.6 | 3.7 |
| $\Delta H^{\ddagger}$ (kcal $M^{-1}$) | 11.5 | 9.4 | 4.2 | 6.0 | 3.0 |
| $\Delta S^{\ddagger}$ (cal deg$^{-1}$) | +9.5 | -7.8 | -27.3 | -21.3 | -34.0 |
| $\dfrac{1}{\tau_M}$ (sec$^{-1}$) | $2.6 \times 10^6$ | $1.4 \times 10^4$ | $5.7 \times 10^3$ | $5.6 \times 10^3$ | $1.9 \times 10^3$ |

**reference** temperature 25°C except for
** : 44°C (the extrapolated value for**
at 25°C is $1 \times 10^3$ sec$^{-1}$).
*data from Luz and Shulman, ref. 5.

rate of exchange. The corresponding data for $O^{17}$ as measured by Genser (12) are lower by three orders of magnitude. There- fore, Luz and Shulman concluded that the exchange mechanism in this case must be proton dissociation from the first co- ordination shell, and not exchange of water-molecules.

Since the values of $1/\tau_m$ for hemoproteins are comparable to those obtained from $O^{17}$ -relaxation measurements on ferric ion solutions, one is tempted to interpret the mechanism of exchange in our case as being due to exchange of whole water- molecules. A decision on this point must await measurements of the temperature dependence of $O^{17}$ -relaxivities with hemo- proteins. Attempts to distinguish between proton dissociation and water exchange mechanisms with the present experimental data must, therefore, be considered speculative.

At best, the observed rates give an upper limit to the rate of exchange of water into the coordination sphere of iron. The rates in Table III are much faster than the rates of azide binding observed experimentally by Chance et al. for metmyoglobin (13) and methemoglobin (14). If the rate of pro- ton exchange measured by NMR is equal to the rate of water ex- change, then the azide reaction is not limited by the release of the solvent ligand from the iron.

The unknown nature of the exchange makes less certain the detailed interpretation of all the derived kinetic parameters of Table III.

In crystals, the lower energy of activation (about half the value in solutions for both met-myoglobin and -hemoglobin), and the more negative entropy of activation suggest that the extra kinetic barrier to proton exchange in crystals as compared to solutions is indeed an entropy barrier, not an energy barrier. This tends to argue against a conformational change limiting the (proton) exchange which is seen by NMR. The latter hypothesis would require the unlikely assumption that the conformational change requires less energy of activation in the crystalline state than in solution. It seems more plausible to assume that in the crystal fewer pathways are available for (proton) exchange between the coordination shell of the iron and the bulk solvent.

While a transient conformation change appears unlikely in the transition state for proton exchange, the kinetic differences observed between hemoprotein solutions and hemoprotein crystals might be due to static differences in protein structure (13), and/or in protein hydration of the two states.

Thus, the fewer pathways available for proton exchange in the crystals may result from a more compact protein structure and/or from a more rigid hydration shell around the protein molecules. Both could cause steric occlusion of certain pathways for proton exchange.

These considerations are relevant whether we are observing exchange of protons or of whole water molecules. The physical transfer of a proton from the coordinate shell of iron to the bulk solvent is required for detection by relaxivity methods. Hence, freedom of reorientation of water molecules is necessary for exchange, and a more rigid hydration shell in the crystalline state might hinder this process.

That the effects are due to crystallinity rather than to the presence of ammonium sulfate is shown by the data on methemoglobin dissolved in 1 M ammonium sulfate (see Fig. 1). No change in rate is observed even though appreciable dissociation of hemoglobin into halves (15) may have occurred.

We are dealing with subtle effects and all that one may say presently is that the differences between the crystal and solution as observed by the proton magnetic relaxation technique imply that only small alterations, if any, take place in the molecular architecture of hemoproteins on crystalliztion.

Finally, inferences on the detailed structure at the sixth coordination site of iron in (met) hemoproteins can be made.

It is known that a large negative entropy of activation is characteristic of processes which create charge (such as ionizations) (16) and, thereby, orient solvent molecules. The positive entropy of activation for the established proton exchange in the case of $Fe^{+++}$ is of interest because there is no net creation of charge in this reaction (although it is difficult to predict the entropy of activation due to the incipient formation of $[Fe (H_2O)_5 OH]^{++}$ and a departing proton which is known to order water molecules by hydronium ion formation). By contrast, the negative $\Delta S^{\ddagger}$ - values for proton exchange in met hemoproteins suggest the possible participation of a reaction of the type:

$$[(L)_5 Fe (OH)]^{2+} \longrightarrow [(L)_5 Fe]^{3+} + OH^-, \text{ in which charge}$$
is created.

This implies that the structure of acid met-hemoproteins at the sixth ligand position might be A rather than B in Fig. 2. The structure depicted in B was proposed in ref. 17 for metmyoglobin and that in A in ref. 18 (for catalase). The two structures cannot be distinguished by the X-ray diffraction data. Of course, structure A is not a unique explanation of the negative $\Delta S^{\ddagger}$.

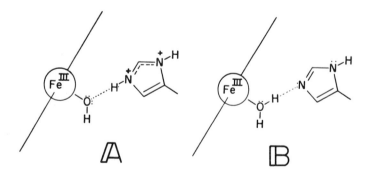

Figure 2. Alternative structures at the sixth coordination position of methemoproteins at neutral pH, which are discussed in the text.

A more direct test of this hypothesis might be made by measuring the chemical shifts of the bound water in hemoproteins. This might be accomplished directly or by measuring the transverse relaxation times of protons and of $^{17}O$ labelled water.

Moreover, such data might shed light on the nature of the structural differences between dissolved and crystalline hemoproteins, which are responsible for the observed kinetic differences.

## Summary

1) The effect of the bound iron in methemoglobin and metmyoglobin on the proton relaxation rate of the solvent, water, has been used to probe the environment of the paramagnetic center. The longitudinal proton relaxation rate $(1/T_1)$ of solutions and crystalline suspensions of methemoglobin and metmyoglobin has been measured at 24.3 MHz as a function of temperature between 0 and 45° C.

2) At low temperatures all four systems (methemoglobin solutions and crystals, metmyoglobin solutions and crystals) show a region of very slow exchange of protons between the bulk solvent and the coordination spere of iron. The slower relaxation rates observed for crystals as compared to solutions may be ascribed to a greater average distance of approach of protons to a region outside the first coordination shell of iron in the crystals.

3) At intermediate temperatures, all four systems show relaxation rates which are dominated by the rate of chemical exchange of protons (or water molecules) between the bulk solvent and the coordination sphere of iron. In this region the exchange is slower in crystals than in solution despite a lower energy of activation for proton exchange in the crystals. The additional barrier to proton exchange in the crystalline state is entropic. At 25°C the rates of proton exchange into the coordination shell of these methemoproteins in solution and in crystals are faster than the respective rates of azide binding previously reported by Chance. If the rate of proton exchange is equal to the rate of water exchange, then the azide reaction is not limited by the release of the solvent ligand from the iron.

## Acknowledgements

We are grateful to Professor Britton Chance for having inspired this study and for his keen interest in its progress, and to Professor Mildred Cohn who initiated the temperature study and provided critical comments and valuable advice throughout this work. Dr. Arthur Kowalsky's helpful criticism is greatly appreciated. We should like to thank Dr. N. Rumen, Mrs. A. Ravilly, and Mr. A. Achtert for their technical assistance.

## References

1. Scheler, W. Biochim. Biophys. Acta, 66, 424 (1963).

2. Pfeifer, H. Biochim. Biophys. Acta, 66, 434 (1963).

3. Bernheim, R. A., T. H. Brown, H. S. Gutowsky, and D. E. Woessner. J. Chem. Phys., 30, 950 (1959).

4. Swift, T. J., and R. E. Connick. J. Chem. Phys., 37, 308 (1962).

5. Luz, Z., and S. Meiboom. J. Chem. Phys., 40, 2686 (1964).

6. Theorell, H. Biochem. Z., 252, 1 (1932).

7. Carr, H. Y., and E. M. Purcell. Phys. Rev., 94, 630 (1954).

8. Kon, H., and N. Davidson. J. Mol. Biol., 1, 190 (1959).

9. Wishnia, A. J. Chem. Phys., 32, 871 (1960).

10. Lumry, R., H. Matsumiya, F. A. Bovey, and A. Kowalsky. J. Phys. Chem., 65, 837 (1961).

11. Luz, Z., and R. G. Shulman. J. Chem. Phys., 43, 3750 (1965).

12. Genser, E. E. Lawrence Radiation Laboratory Report UCRL 9846, University of California, Berkeley, California (1961).

13. Chance, B., A. Ravilly, and N. Rumen. Science, 150, 370 (1965).

14. Chance, B., and A. Ravilly. Federation Proc., 25, 648 (1966) Abstract No. 2593.

15. Rossi-Fanelli, A., E. Antonini, and A. Caputo. In Hemoglobin and Myoglobin, Adv. Prot. Chem., 19, 117 (1964).

16. Frost, A. A., and R. G. Pearson. In Kinetics and Mechanism, 2nd Edition, John Wiley and Sons, New York, 1961, pp. 142-147.

17. Stryer, L., J. C. Kendrew, and H. C. Watson. J. Mol. Biol., 8, 96 (1964).

18. Nicholls, P., and G. R. Schonbaum. In The Enzymes, 2nd Edition, (P. O. Boyer, H. A. Lardy, and K. Myrback, eds.), Vol. 8, Academic Press, New York, 1963, p. 209.

## DISCUSSION

Cohn: I just want to say that the work of Dr. Maricic on the proton relaxation rates is very preliminary. I think that the first step in the extension of this work should be to measure $T_2$, the spin-spin relaxation time, as well as $T_1$, the spin-lattice relaxation time, because some of the parameters which occur in $T_1$ and $T_2$ are the same and some are different. Together, these two types of measurement, I think, should yield a lot more information. Unfortunately, one of the limitations with proteins is the small temperature range available for this type of study, so that one cannot easily get the value of $T_{1M}$ in the case of proteins, from which the value of r, the distance between the iron and proton of water in the first coordination sphere, could be evaluated.

Fabry: I want to say a few words about the information which it is possible to get out of the measurement of proton relaxation rates of water. We have several parameters: the residence time of the water at the paramagnetic center ( $\tau_M$), a correlation time ( $\tau_c$) for the relaxation process, and some type of average of the distance of approach of the proton to the paramagnetic center. As Dr. Cohn said, in proteins we are limited in the Luz-Meiboom representation to the part of the curve which goes up with temperature, so you cannot get rid of $\tau_M$. We need a method to obtain $\tau_c$ which is equal to $\tau_s$ in this particular case. The part of the curve that Dr. Maricic has shown depends on $\tau_M$ and it also depends on $T_{1M}$ since $\tau_M$ should not be frequency dependent, and it turns out that the observed relaxation time in this region is also frequency dependent. All the frequency dependence must come from $T_{1M}$. So, from the frequency dependence you can get both an average for the distance of approach which is the most crucial value and also $\tau_c$ which should check with $\tau_s$ from ESR. We can obtain some estimate of the right frequency to use in spin echo experiments. If you estimate something like $10^{-10}$ for $\tau_s$, the frequency dependence will be between 0.5 and 10 mc. Most of the work on proteins has been done over 10 megacycles. As for the methodology, the best, and probably only, method to get meaningful interpretations is to do temperature dependence measurement, as Drs. Cohn and Maricic do, and from that, to decide qualitatively the importance of $\tau_M$. Now you have to take the temperature where the contribution of $\tau_M$ is the least, and from the frequency dependence at that temperature, you can get both $\tau_s$ and the average distance of approach. We are presently engaged in this type of measurement with Dr. S. H. Koenig, and it seems to work out.

Cohn: I think the information one can get from data on $T_1$ of the protons of water will be clarified if we consider the relationship

$$1/T_{1p} = \frac{1}{\tau_M + T_{1M}}$$

when $T_{1p}$ is the paramagnetic contribution to the relaxation time, $\tau_M$ is the residence time of the water protons in the first coordination sphere of the paramagnetic ion, and $T_{1M}$ is the relaxation time of the water protons in the first coordination sphere of the paramagnetic ion. In the temperature range where $\tau_M$ is so short as to be negligible, i.e., the rate of exchange of water protons between the first coordination sphere and the bulk water is very fast, $T_{1p}$, the measured value is equivalent to $T_{1M}$. Since $T_{1M}$ is a function of the distance between the paramagnetic ion and the proton and a correlation time, $\tau_c$ (for iron equivalent to $\tau_s$, the electron spin relaxation time), one could, in principle, determine this distance if one knew $\tau_s$. However, as Dr. Maricic has shown, in the temperature range in which one can work with myoglobin and hemoglobin, the exchange rate is sufficiently slow so that $\tau_M$ dominates the observed relaxation rate. In this range one can determine $\tau_M$, the reciprocal of the rate constant for the chemical exchange of the water protons between the first coordination sphere and the bulk water. However, as Dr. Fabry has said, at the highest temperatures, $T_{1M}$ is making some contribution, although $\tau_M$ dominates. This can be shown experimentally, as Dr. Fabry has pointed out, by studying the frequency dependence of $T_1$ since $\tau_M$ is independent of frequency and $T_{1M}$ is dependent on frequency in a limited frequency range. All I can say is that I wish Dr. Fabry luck in the interpretation of the frequency dependence measurements of $T_1$. We have studied the frequency dependence of $T_1$ for Mn-protein complexes and found that it cannot be described by the usual Bloembergen-Solomon equation derived for simple cases such as paramagnetic aquocations. However, these considerations should certainly not inhibit him from doing the experiments.

Fabry: In manganese, $\tau_s$ is much longer than in iron. Therefore, the correlation time $\tau_c$ which determines $T_{1M}$ ( $\frac{1}{\tau_c} = \frac{1}{\tau_r} + \frac{1}{\tau_s}$ ) depends predominantly on $\tau_r$ for manganese. In the case of iron, the story is much simpler because $\tau_c$ and so $T_{1M}$ depends only on $\tau_s$

# BINDING OF NITROGENOUS BASES TO MYOGLOBIN[*]

Joan Keilin

Department of Veterinary Clinical Studies
School of Veterinary Medicine
University of Cambridge, England

In 1925, Schumm (1) found that when myoglobin was treated with hydrazine, a 4-banded spectrum appeared in the visible region. This consisted of two stronger bands at 566 and 554 mμ and two weaker bands at 534 and 528 mμ. He also showed that this spectrum was given only by myoglobin and not by hemoglobin.

Bechtold, in 1935 (2), found that the same spectrum could be obtained using 2 percent v/v pyridine instead of hydrazine and that on shaking the solution with air the 4-banded spectrum reverted to that of oxymyoglobin. Higher concentrations of pyridine gave the usual spectrum of pyridine hemochromogen. Fig. 1 shows the 4-banded spectrum and its Soret band given by

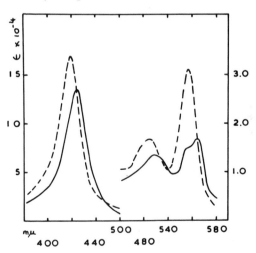

Figure 1. Effect of pyridine on myoglobin. ——— 4-banded spectrum and Soret band given by 6.6 percent v/v pyridine. — — — hemochromogen given by 20 percent v/v pyridine.

*This work was aided by USPHS Grant 5 ROI GM 11740.

173

dilute pyridine compared with the spectrum of myoglobin pyridine hemochromogen given by 20 percent v/v pyridine.

For Bechtold and his coworkers the interest of the 4-banded spectrum lay in what they considered to be its resemblance to cytochromes b and c. They believed that the cytochromes were derived from myoglobin (2,3,4) and suggested that cytochrome c as isolated in 1925 (5) was merely an artifact. As was to be expected, this theory aroused a lot of criticism: from Roche (6), Fischer and Gibian (7), Kiese and Kaeske (8), who reinvestigated the formation of the 4-banded spectrum, and from Gonella and Vanotti in 1943 (9), who made the first attempt to explain the nature of what had by then become known as the Bechtold spectrum.

Gonella and Vanotti regarded the 4-banded spectrum as a mixture of two hemochromogens with their α-bands at 565 and 554 mμ respectively. The first of these they visualised as a hybrid hemochromogen in which the heme Fe was coordinated with globin in position 5 and with a molecule of pyridine or hydrazine in position 6. The second hemochromogen they considered to be an "ordinary" hemochromogen formed by free heme present in the preparation. They suggested (I quote in translation) "that only part of the heme in muscle is chemically bound to globin while the other part is only adsorbed onto the muscle pigment". However, the view that free heme might be responsible for the second hemochromogen was dismissed by Theorell and de Duve (10), who obtained the 4-banded spectrum with recrystallised myoglobin.

For the sake of convenience let us call these twin hemochromogens A and B respectively, the α-band of A lying at about 565 mμ and that of B at about 554 mμ. The allocation of the β-bands will be considered later on.

In the present work all observations were first carried out with a Beck microspectroscope which was also used for observing low temperature spectra in the visible region. For these low temperature studies the solution was poured into a pyrex tybe with a flattened end, frozen in liquid $N_2$ and examined in the usual way. Sperm whale myoglobin (from Dr. Kendrew) and crystallised horse and donkey myoglobins were used, and all gave essentially the same results as did also crude muscle juice.

A survey of substances giving hemochromogens with free hemes showed that, in order to combine with the Fe of native myoglobin, certain steric requirements had to be met.

A 4-banded spectrum like that given by pyridine was obtained with nicotinic acid at pH 6 - 7 (Fig. 2) but substitution in the α or γ position of the pyridine ring as in picolinic acid or isonicotinic acid, prevented these substances

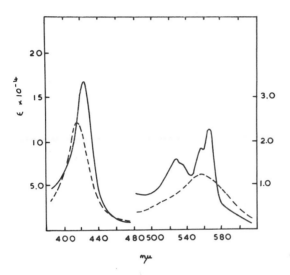

Figure 2. Absorption curves of myoglobin (— — —) and the
4-banded spectrum given by myoglobin-nicotinate (————).

from combining with the myoglobin (Fig. 3). Of the picolines,
β-picoline gave the twin hemochromogen spectra but α-picoline
did not. (No pure γ-picoline was available for testing).

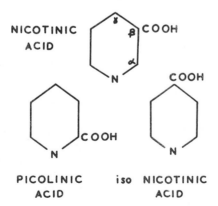

Figure 3. Formulae of nicotinic, picolinic, and isonicotinic
acids.

Other substances substituted in the $\alpha$ position such as pyrido-xine or coniine also failed to react.

Even when substitution is in the $\beta$ position, the size of the side chain affects the reaction.

Nicotinamide gives a modified form of the two hemo-chromogens in which the two $\alpha$-bands are less clearly defined and in which $\alpha$B is slightly higher than $\alpha$A. Nicotine, which gives a splendid hemochromogen with free heme, does not react with myoglobin under these conditions (Fig. 4).

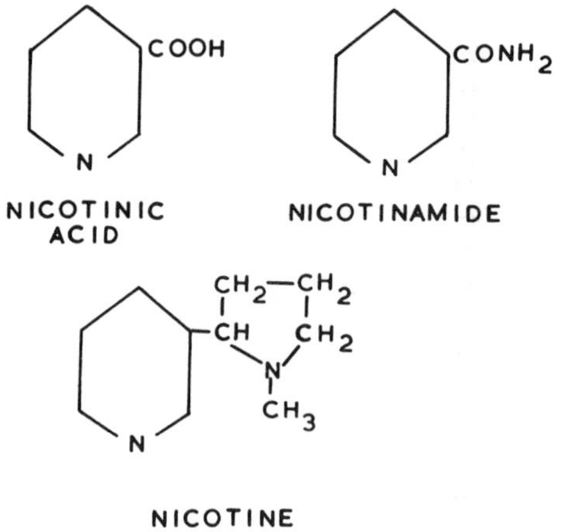

NICOTINIC
ACID

NICOTINAMIDE

NICOTINE

Figure 4. Formulae of nicotinic acid, nicotinamide, and nico-tine.

Imidazole, which also reacts very readily with free heme and with metmyoglobin, has to be added in very much higher con-centrations before it will combine with reduced myoglobin and then it only gives a modified twin hemochromogen spectrum like that given by nicotinamide. 4,5 methyl-imidazole reacts similarly. Neither histidine nor pilocarpine have any effect (Fig. 5). The fact that pilocarpine which readily gives a hemochromogen with free heme, fails to give a hemochromogen spectrum with myoglobin, provides good evidence that there is no free heme loosely bound to the myoglobin as had been postu-lated by Gonella and Vanotti to be responsible for the second hemochromogen with the 554 m$\mu$ $\alpha$-band.

Among other nitrogenous substances examined pyrroli-
dine gave a modified form of the twin hemochromogens (at pH
8.0 or higher) but so far this reaction has not been obtained
with pyrrol, piperidine, piperazine, or hydroxylamine, nor with
lysine or asparagine.

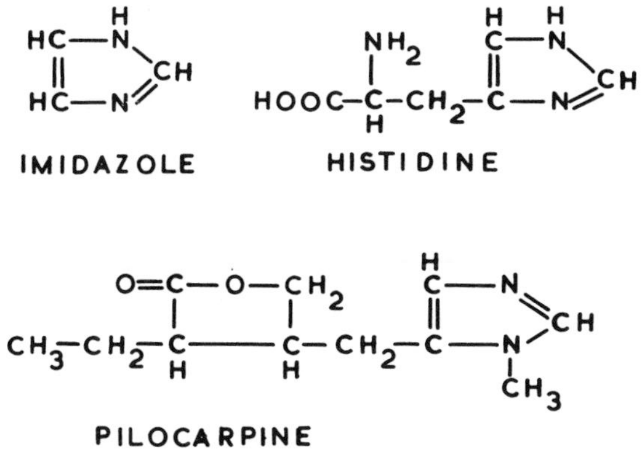

IMIDAZOLE  HISTIDINE

PILOCARPINE

Figure 5. Formulae of imidazole, histidine, and pilocarpine.

The steric limitations to which the ligand must conform
if it is to react with the iron atom of native myoglobin, may
be clearly visualized by examining the heme region of the contour map of the Fourier synthesis of myoglobin at 1.4 Å resolution (11) or by trying to insert a scale model of α-picoline or of isonicotinic acid into the sperm whale myoglobin
model. On one side of the plane of the heme lies the heme-
linked histidine while on the other there is very little room
for a ligand to enter so as to react with the heme iron. To
enable a molecule of nicotinic acid to do this, the distal
histidine would have to swing up out of the way to make room,
and it is easy to see that a substituent in the α-position
would hit the heme while one in the γ-position would tend to
get entangled in the peptide chain bearing the distal histidine.

To see what part the heme side chains played in the
formation of the twin hemochromogens, artificial myoglobins
were prepared from horse globin with protoheme, deuteroheme,
and aetioheme, and treated with nicotinate at pH 6.6 (Fig. 6).

The reconstituted proto-myoglobin behaved in every way
exactly like the original horse myoglobin. Deutero-myoglobin
also gave twin hemochromogens with nicotinate, the whole spectrum
being shifted to shorter wavelengths due to the absence of vinyl

groups. The main features of the deuteromyoglobin nicotinate are that the two α-bands are very close to each other, αB being equal to or slightly higher than αA (as in the case of proto-myoglobin with imidazole or nicotinamide) and that the β -bands are about the same height as the α-bands.

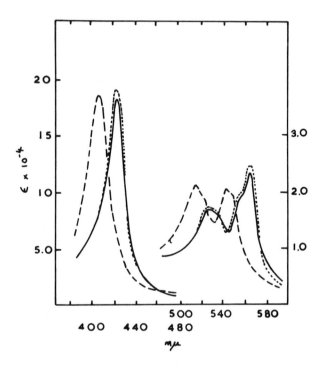

Figure 6. Absorption curves of nicotinate compounds of horse myoglobin (natural) · · · · ; reconstituted protoheme-myoglobin ———————; and deuteroheme myoglobin — — —.

In the case of aetiomyoglobin treated with nicotinate, the solution was very opalescent; αA was slightly higher than αB and the β-bands were lower than the α-bands. The positions of these absorption bands are shown in Table I. These results show that neither the vinyl groups nor the carboxyl groups which form the secondary attachments of the heme to the protein play any part in the formation of the twin hemochromogen spectra.

It was shown previously (2,8) that myoglobin giving the twin hemochromogens with dilute pyridine partly reverts to oxymyoglobin on shaking with air. It was therefore of interest to see the effect of CO on the twin hemochromogen spectra. Would we obtain a mixture of CO-myoglobin from twin A and CO-hemochromogen from twin B? On passing CO through a solution of myoglobin-nicotinate under the optimal conditions for the formation of the twin hemochromogens only CO-myoglobin was formed and there was no detectable CO-hemochromogen. These results were later confirmed at low temperatures. So whatever ' may be the nature of the reaction between myoglobin and nicotinate, the myoglobin can revert to its normal behavior in the presence of CO, suggesting that only one molecule of nicotinate is combined to the iron, that it is readily replaced by CO and that no irreversible denaturation has taken place.

TABLE I

Positions of the Absorption Bands of the Nicotinate

Compounds of Horse Myoglobin and Artificial

Proto-, Deutero- and Aetio-Myoglobins

| Myoglobin | Positions of absorption bands (m$\mu$) | | | |
| | $\alpha$A | $\alpha$B | $\beta$ | Soret |
| --- | --- | --- | --- | --- |
| Proto (natural) | 566 | 554 | 535 | 528 | 424 |
| Proto- (reconstituted) | 566 | 554 | 535 | 528 | 424 |
| Deutero- (reconstituted) | 548 | 542 | 523 | 516 | 407 |
| Aetio- (reconstituted) (opalescent) | 552 | 545 | 525 | 518 | 410 |

The optimum pH for the formation of the twin hemo-chromogens depends on the ligand. Pyridine, hydrazine, and the imidazoles require pH > 8, while nicotinate reacts best at pH 6-7 and gives the most stable compound. Nicotinate was therefore used in the investigation of the nature of the twin hemochromogen spectra as it seemed the least likely to have an adverse effect on the protein.

Titration of myoglobin with nicotinate to obtain optimum formation of the twin hemochromogens gave a good series of spectrophotometric curves with isosbestic points at 572 and 430 m$\mu$. From these results it was calculated that one molecule of nicotinate combined per atom of Fe. The dissociation constant measured for donkey myoglobin nicotinate, using the method described by George, Lyster, and Beetlestone (12) for phenol-ferrimyoglobin, gave a value of 0.43.

179

In general, high concentrations of ligand are required
to give the optimum twin hemochromogen spectra. By raising
the nicotinate concentration from 0.08 M to 2.8 M, a series
of spectra were obtained showing the development of the twin
hemochromogens and then a transition from this four-banded
spectrum to that of an ordinary two-banded hemochromogen. On
diluting this solution the spectrum reverted to the four-banded
form. Deutero-myoglobin behaved similarly but over a much
lower range of concentration of nicotinate (Table II).

TABLE II

Nicotinate/Myoglobin Ratio Required for Formation of

the Twin Hemochromogen Spectrum and Ordinary

Hemochromogen ($\alpha_{557}$ $m\mu$) at Room Temperature

| Myoglobin | Twin hemochromogens $\dfrac{[\text{nicotinate}]}{[\text{myoglobin}]} \times 10^{-5}$ | Hemochromogen $\alpha_{577}$ $\dfrac{[\text{nicotinate}]}{[\text{myoglobin}]} \times 10^{-5}$ |
|---|---|---|
| Donkey | 0.65 | 1.04 |
| Horse | 0.48 | 1.26 |
| Whale | 0.36 | 1.06 (not complete) |
| Deutero- (horse) globin | 0.005 | 1.32 |

The effect of low temperatures on the spectrum of the
myoglobin and ligand solution containing 50 percent glycerol
was examined with the microspectroscope. This proved of great
value in screening compounds giving spectra where it was
difficult to distinguish between atypical twin hemochromogens
or partially formed ordinary hemochromogen analogous to denatured globin hemochromogen. Whereas the spectrum of an
ordinary hemochromogen remained as two bands at low temperatures
the twin hemochromogen spectrum whether typical or atypical,
always showed four well separated bands under these conditions.
In nicotinate-myoglobin(Fig. 7) $\alpha$A is dominant while $\alpha$B and the
two $\beta$-bands are of roughly the same intensity. In the case of
imidazole-myoglobin (containing 50 percent v/v glycerol) in
which $\alpha$B is a little higher than $\alpha$A and the $\beta$-bands are represented only by a shoulder at room temperatures, freezing in
liquid $N_2$ caused the four bands to become clearly resolved

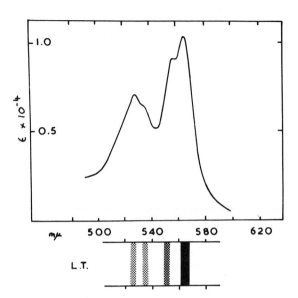

Figure 7. Absorption curve of donkey myoglobin-nicotinate at room temperature and the effect of low temperature on the spectrum.

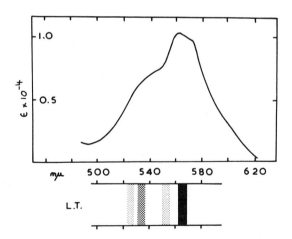

Figure 8. Absorption curve of donkey myoglobin-imidazole at room temperature and the effect of low temperature on the spectrum.

(Fig. 8). What is more, of the two $\alpha$-bands $\alpha A$ is now stronger than $\alpha B$, and of the $\beta$-bands the 535-band is stronger than the 528-band.

If the glycerol is omitted, then on freezing in liquid $N_2$ in the presence of the same concentration of imidazole, a two-banded hemochromogen spectrum is obtained just as if a great excess of ligand were present. Very low temperatures are not required to produce this effect which is readily obtained in a $CO_2$-alcohol mixture. It is, however, possible to obtain a four-banded spectrum at low temperatures if the imidazole concentration is very considerably reduced. The effect of nicotinate on a number of hemoproteins was investigated at both + 20° and at -190°. No 4-banded spectrum was observed with mammalian hemoglobins (from adult and newborn cow, pig, and man), bird hemoglobins (chicken, turkey, and pheasant), with the high molecular weight <u>Tubifex</u> hemoglobin or with the hemoglobins of <u>Gasterophilus</u> or <u>Chironomid</u> larvae, which have a molecular weight of 32,000 and contain two hemes per molecule.

However, the hemoglobin of the river lamprey (<u>Lampetra fluviatilis</u>) which resembles the myoglobins in its molecular weight and some other properties (13), did react with nicotinate. The spectrophotometric curve looked like that of an ordinary hemochromogen, the bands being just a shade broader than usual; with the microspectroscope the twin $\alpha$-bands were just discernable and the presence of the twin hemochromogens was confirmed at low temperature (Fig. 9). The same results were obtained with the hemoglobin of the sea lamprey. As in the case of myoglobin-nicotinate, lamprey Hb-nicotinate reacted normally with CO to give CO-hemoglobin.

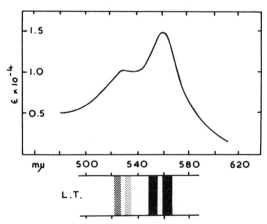

Figure 9. Absorption curve of river lamprey hemoglobin at room temperature and the effect of low temperature on the spectrum.

As at room temperature the twin hemochromogen spectra given by myoglobin always showed a single Soret band, it was of interest to see whether it would resolve into two components at low temperatures. Using the foam box method of Doebbler and Elliott (14) in a Carey 14 spectrophotometer (in Prof. E. C. Slater's department in Amsterdam) we found that in every case examined the Soret band was considerably sharpened and intensified but always remained single. This suggests that either the Soret bands of the twin hemochromogens must coincide or that we must regard the four bands in the visible region as belonging to a single compound. This point will be discussed more fully later.

Low temperatures were found to have a particularly interesting and curious effect on the myoglobin-hydrazine twin hemochromogen spectra. (Fig. 10). When such solutions were

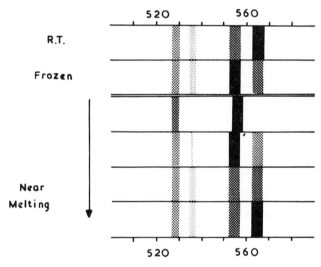

Figure 10. Effect of low temperatures and thawing on the myoglobin hydrazine spectrum as seen with the microspectroscope.

frozen in liquid $N_2$ in the absence of glycerol, the twin hemochromogen spectra were intensified but the αB band was now stronger than the αA band. As the opaque frozen sample gradually warmed up, αA became progressively weaker as αB became stronger. Then, for a brief moment, αA and the 535-band disappeared completely leaving αB at 556 mμ as the very strong α -band of a typical hemochromogen, with its β-band at 528 mμ.

Then the changes began to reverse: αA slowly reappeared and became dominant, the β-band at 535 also reappeared and the original picture was restored at just below melting point. A fine satellite band was sometimes seen between the two α-bands. These observations, taken together with the effect of low temperatures on the myoglobin-imidazole spectrum I described earlier, enable us to allocate the β-band at 535 mμ to hemochromogen A (α-band at 565 mμ) and the stronger β-band at 528 mμ to hemochromogen B (α -band at 554 mμ). The effect of progressive warming on the low temperature spectrum of myoglobin-hydrazine was studied in more detail with the double beam recording spectrophotometer at the Johnson Foundation. Recordings made in collaboration with Dr. D. F. Wilson showed that at -190° the twin hemochromogens were clearly defined, the two α -bands being nearly equal. In the high β -complex the 535-band formed a shoulder on the side of the 528-band. As the temperature slowly rose (-115°), αB at 554 mμ became slightly higher than αB and then suddenly, between -100° and -80°, the spectrum changed to a two-banded form like that of an ordinary hemochromogen, the α-band lying at 556 mμ. On further thawing the four bands returned but were much less intense, and the spectrum gradually reverted to that seen at room temperature (Fig. 11).

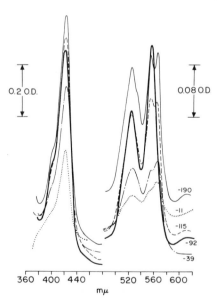

Figure 11. Absorption spectra of myoglobin-hydrazine at various temperatures. (Double beam spectrophotometer recordings.)

In one experiment refreezing after thawing gave rise to the two-banded spectrum which persisted down to -190°. On thawing the four-banded spectrum form returned when the temperature rose to above -80°C. The effects of slow and rapid freezing on these spectra of myoglobin-hydrazine still have to be investigated and are of particular interest in view of the fact that nicotinate-myoglobin does not give such great changes in pattern on thawing (Fig. 12).

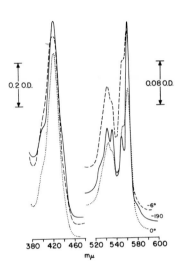

Figure 12. Absorption spectra of myoglobin-nicotinate at various temperatures. (Double beam spectrophotometer recordings).

What of the nature of these twin hemochromogens? In hemochromogen A in which the Fe is linked to two dissimilar nitrogenous groups (globin histidine F8 and the nitrogen of nicotinate) the position of the α-band at about 565 mμ is the same as that of the α-band of cyanide- or isocyanide-myoglobin where the Fe is attached to a nitrogenous ligand on one side of the heme and to the carbon of the cyanide or isocyanide on the other.

We may accept hemochromogen A as a hybrid hemochromogen demanding certain steric criteria of the ligand, the position of its α-bands at 565 mμ being due to the effect of the native globin. The ligand is easily displaced by CO giving CO myoglobin.

185

The formation of hemochromogen B also depends on the steric properties of the ligand. Its $\alpha$-band which appears to be at about 554 m$\mu$, is probably really at about 552 m$\mu$ (after making allowances for the additive effect of the absorption of the 565-band) that is, about 5 m$\mu$ from the position of the $\alpha$-band at 557 m$\mu$ of an ordinary hemochromogen such as denatured globin hemochromogen. It also appears that its $\beta$-band at 528 m$\mu$ is much higher relatively to the $\alpha$-band than is usual in a hemochromogen. Here again, the ligand is readily displaced by CO.

The problem, therefore, is to consider what is responsible for the presence of the absorption bands of hemochromogen B in the visible region only of the spectrum? Let us examine various possibilities.
1) The theory that these bands are due to the presence of free heme in the preparation (9) may readily be dismissed by the fact that pilocarpine fails to give any hemochromogen with myoglobin.
2) That hemochromogen B may be due to a small amount of denatured myoglobin is most unlikely in view of the position of its absorption bands, the normal CO-myoglobin given, the requirement of certain steric properties of the ligand and the relative constancy of the $\alpha$A/$\alpha$B density ratios at room temperature for a particular ligand obtained with different myoglobins under the conditions for optimal formation of the twin spectra.
3) Myoglobins may be fractionated electrophoretically or chromatographically (15-17) into a number of fractions and it was therefore possible that some fractions might react with a ligand to give either the twin A or twin B spectrum. This was investigated using 5 fractions of seal myoglobin kindly provided by Dr. N. Rumen: all the fractions reacted with nicotinate to give the four-banded spectrum. These findings do not exclude the existence of two populations of myoglobin molecules reacting differently with nicotinate but not lending themselves to separation by the procedures used to obtain these fractions. However, the necessity to postulate the existence of such differently réacting molecules is largely removed by considering the apparent interconversion of the twin spectra at low temperatures.

The most likely explanation of the four-banded spectrum which can be tentatively put forward at this stage of the work, is that the ligand reacts with the heme in a 1:1 ratio and that the 4 bands in the visible region coexisting with the single Soret band are due to asymmetry of the heme Fe-ligand bond caused by the restricted space available for the ligand. While it is easy to visualise this in the case of pyridine or nicotinate, the reaction with hydrazine, which is a comparatively small molecule, might require a slightly different explanation. The marked effects of low temperatures on the visible spectrum coexisting with little change in the single Soret band, support the theory of the four bands being produced by a condition of strain in the molecule. Obviously much experimental work remains to be done to substantiate this theory.

Other problems emerging from this work are a) the relationship of the twin spectra to "ordinary" hemochromogen formation and the early stages of protein denaturation and b) why is the four-banded spectrum given only by myoglobins and lamprey hemoglobin and not by other hemoglobins? This is of special interest when one considers that in lamprey hemoglobin and myoglobins there are greater differences in the environment of the heme than in the case of myoglobins and hemoglobins of larger molecular weight.

## References

1. Schumm, O. Hoppe-Seyler's Z. Physiol. Chem., 149, 111 (1925).

2. Bechtold, E. Der Muskelfarbstoff. Stuttgart (1935).

3. Bechtold, E., and K. Pfeilsticker. Biochem. Z., 307, 194 (1941).

4. Pfeilsticker, K. Biochem. Z., 316, 84 (1943).

5. Keilin, D. Proc. Roy. Soc. B., 98, 312 (1925).

6. Roche, J. C. R. Seanc. Soc. Biol., 121, 1026 (1936).

7. Fischer, H., and H. Gibian. Biochem. Z., 308, 129 (1941).

8. Kiese, M., and M. Kaeske. Biochem. Z., 312, 121 (1942).

9. Gonella, A., and A. Vanotti. Z. Ges. Exp. Med., 112, 405 (1943).

10. Theorell, H., and C. de Duve. Archs Biochem., 12, 113 (1947).

11. Kendrew, J. C. New Perspective in Biology, BBA Library, Vol. 4, 1964, p. 18.

12. George, P., R. L. Lyster, and J. Beetlestone. J. Biol. Chem., 236, 3246 (1961).

13. Rudloff, V., and C. Braunitzer. Unpublished results. Quoted by Braunitzer, C., K. Hilse, V. Rudloff, and N. Hilschmann, Adv. Protein Chem., 19, 1 (1964).

14. Doebbler, G. F., and W. B. Elliott. Biochim. Biophys. Acta, $\underline{94}$, 317 (1965).

15. Lewis, U. J., and B. S. Schweigert. J. Biol. Chem., $\underline{214}$ 647 (1955).

16. Rumen, N. Acta Chem. Scand., $\underline{13}$, 1542 (1959).

17. Åkeson, Å., and H. Theorell. Arch. Biochem. Biophys., $\underline{91}$, 319 (1960).

## DISCUSSION

Elliott:  In looking at a fairly large series of reduced cytochrome c's that Dr. Margoliash has provided us with, we have
not seen any splittings of any Soret peak even where the $\alpha$
peak splits up to 3.7 m$\mu$.  The most variations we have seen in
the Soret peaks from one to another is in the area on the blue
side, where a filled-in area occurs at the base of the peak
with some species.  In the Soret band, the maximum shift of the
reduced peak between species is about 2 m$\mu$.  So we can say that
we have not seen any splitting of the Soret band, or much movement of the Soret band with the changes in the $\alpha_1$-$\alpha_2$ peaks.  I
believe this is in agreement with what you have observed.  It
should be noted that any aggregation of pyridine hemochromogen,
such as occurs during the conversion of M. Smith's compound III
to compound II, is accompanied by a marked shift in the Soret
band, but only a slight shift in the $\alpha$ band towards the red (1).
Thus, your spectra would appear not to be due to a reaction of
this type.

Keilin:  In the twin spectra I was expecting to see splitting
of the Soret band due to having a mixture of the two compounds,
each with its own Soret band.  I was not assuming that there
was only one compound, and I was not looking for a split in its
Soret band.  We also observed some changes on the blue side of
the Soret band in certain myoglobin derivatives.

Lemberg:  I wonder whether these new findings are incompatible
with the old idea of "mixed hemochrome" formation explored in
my 1949 book (2).  It was then assumed that a uniform myoglobin
molecule could give a mixed hemochrome by the nitrogenous ligand replacing only the distal imidazole, with comparatively
little alteration of the protein conformation, whereas with
hemoglobin you had only denaturation.  It appears possible that
the new observation may be explained on the basis of the two
processes occurring simultaneously in myoglobin.

CO is not a very distinctive reagent since CO-heme, CO-
hemochrome, and CO-hemoglobins have quite similar spectra.  The
careful study of oxygen binding may be more revealing.

Keilin:  I understand that Bechtold (3) and also Kiese and
Kaeske (4) did show that the twin spectrum could revert to that

of oxygenated myoglobin, but the latter authors described the reaction in pyridine as showing only partial recovery to the oxygenated form.

Watson: Since the results of the high resolution structural studies of hemoglobin are not yet available, we cannot compare, in great detail, the heme environments in hemoglobin and myoglobin. It is possible, therefore, that the differences in hemochromogen splitting properties could be explained by detailed structural differences in the heme environments of these two proteins.

Nobbs: Kon and Davidson have some NMR evidence suggesting that indeed there is a difference in accessibility to the heme binding site in myoglobin (the more accessible) and hemoglobin (5). However, it is difficult to see on Perutz's 5.5 Å hemoglobin model why such a difference should exist.

Gouterman: How can you distinguish between two different species vs. two different sites and one species with a slightly split band due to asymmetry in the site? The lack of splitting of the Soret band in the presence of splitting of the $\alpha$ band suggests that it is one species being split by an asymmetry, rather than two distinct species; but this is not a strong statement.

Williams: I think it is time that we should be very clear how many species we are dealing with. We cannot discuss spectra on the level that Dr. Gouterman would like to discuss them unless we have it absolutely clear that the equilibrium studies show that there is only one molecule of base binding at a time. If there is more than one molecule binding, then there will be a series of equilibria, and these equilibria need not involve the iron itself. It is already known in many enzyme systems that organic molecules, such as these bases, will bind on the periphery of the molecule and alter the geometry, quite a long way away from the binding site. Thus, I think it would be a great mistake to get involved in a straight theoretical argument, unless Dr. Keilin can clear up the stoichiometry of the molecules which we are discussing.

George: Is the character of the twin peak hemochromogen at all affected by the pH of the medium?

Keilin: The character is not affected, but the optimum conditions for formation definitely are. It is very difficult to obtain the twin spectra if it is at the wrong pH for that particular ligand. The pattern of the spectrum is dependent upon the nature of the ligand.

Drabkin: This is a very fine paper by Dr. Joan Keilin. I wonder whether the simple possibility has been considered of two possible binding sites, one for the apo-protein and one for the ligand, which might produce a twin in this case, or must we settle at this stage for two structurally separate myoglobins?

Kamen: It appears the total transition moment in the nicotinate complex Soret absorption has changed greatly even though there is no splitting. I believe that is significant of something, and that it is important to look at the total integrated area of the curve and not just at the particular maxima. I do not understand why there is such a discrepancy between the changes in total area in the visible region compared to the Soret.

Williams: The Soret band is rising, is it not, as is usual with such spectra?

Kamen: There should be some correlation between the areas, and some conservation in transition moments.

Williams: No, I do not think so. I believe Dr. Gouterman could speak of electron configuration in situations like this. Intensities may shift from one band region to another.

King: Since the spectra are different in 5 percent and 20 percent pyridine, what are the spectra, or spectral changes, when very low concentrations of pyridine, say 1 mg/ml, are used?

Keilin: At concentrations lower than 5 percent you get the gradual transition from ordinary myoglobin to the twin spectrum, which is less well developed than at 5 percent pyridine. We selected 5 percent as the optimum concentration; you can go up to 8 percent, but then opalescence trouble occurs.

## References

1. Smith, M. H. Biochem. J., 73, 90 (1959).

2. Lemberg, R., and J. W. Legge. Hematin Compounds and Bile Pigments, Interscience Publishers, New York and London, 1949.

3. Bechtold, E. Der Muskelfarbstoff, Stuttgart, 1935.

4. Kiese, M., and M. Kaeske. Biochem. Z., 308, 129 (1941).

5. Kon, H., and N. Davidson. J. Mol. Biol., 1, 190 (1959).

# IV.

## Intermolecular Interactions of Crystalline and Soluble Myoglobin and Hemoglobin
### P. George, Chairman

# KINETIC STUDIES OF THE AZIDE FERRIMYOGLOBIN REACTION[*]

George H. Czerlinski

Johnson Research Foundation, University of Pennsylvania
Philadelphia, Pennsylvania

Recently, Alberty and his associates worked on the kinetics of the binding of ligands to sperm whale ferrimyoglobin. In their first paper (1) they investigated the binding of imidazole to ferrimyoglobin. In order to interpret their data they assumed two interlocking cyclic systems. One reaction cycle is principally active below pH 8, where the main species of myoglobin is that which has $H_2O$ next to the ferric iron, while the ligand is present in two forms: protonated and unprotonated. The protonic dissociation constant for imidazole is given by $pK_H \bullet 7.0$. Both forms of the imidazole react with myoglobin but the protonated form reacts about ten times slower than the unprotonated form (they found 33 and 300 $M^{-1}sec^{-1}$). The proton transfer reactions of free and bound imidazolium are assumed as very fast.

Above pH 8, the water molecule of the ferric iron dissociates a proton with a $pK_H = 8.9$. Both forms of myoglobin react with the unprotonated imidazole in a cyclic system, with proton transfer processes being quite fast. Binding of imidazole to hydroxy-myoglobin is still faster than the other two associations (435 $M^{-1}sec^{-1}$). The three monomolecular rate constants are almost identical (near 4 $sec^{-1}$ over the whole pH range from 6.0 to 8.6).

Alberty et al. studied also Benz-imidazole at pH 7, where the overall binding rate constant is three times faster than that for imidazole; the overall monomolecular rate constant for the binding of Benz-imidazole is two times faster than that for the binding of imidazole. This indicates that Benz-imidazole easily fits into the large protein configuration near the heme moiety of the enzyme.

[*]This work was supported by NSF Grant GB 4297.

In a later publication (2), the group of Alberty investigated the binding of azide and cyanate to myoglobin in the pH range of 5 to 7.5. Thereby they were able to omit consideration of the ionization of myoglobin with $pK_H = 8.9$. Their apparent bimolecular rate constant for azide at pH 5.1 was over 100 times larger than at pH 7.5 ($2.8 \times 10^5$ compared to $2.5 \times 10^3$ $M^{-1}sec^{-1}$). The apparent bimolecular rate constant for cyanate showed a similarly large change, but the specific values were smaller by a factor of 10 throughout. In their derivations the authors assumed from the onset that there is at least one kinetically important protonic ionizing group on myoglobin. They then derived their reaction systems with one and with two ionizing groups on the myoglobin. This leads to large multicyclic systems with four in the former, or even six in the latter case, bimolecular recombination constants. They cannot resolve all the rate constants, but they can isolate some of the individual bimolecular rate constants by successive approximation. They were unable to resolve any of the individual monomolecular rate constants. Their overall monomolecular rate constant for cyanate shows about the same pH dependence as that of the overall bimolecular rate constant (from 63 $sec^{-1}$ at pH 5.1 to 1.1 $sec^{-1}$ at 7.0). Their overall monomolecular rate constant for azide shows about a 20-fold change over their experimental range (from 4 $sec^{-1}$ at pH 5.1 to 0.2 $sec^{-1}$ at pH 7.5).

Although Alberty et al. (1,2) do not discuss a mechanism without protonic dissociation of metmyoglobin, Duffey and collaborators (3) did consider this simplest mechanism (4) and reached the conclusion that the data could satisfactorily be explained by a mechanismwhich does not include protonic dissociation of the myoglobin. Any steps of protonic dissociation of the myoglobin, however, would lead to a better fit of the theoretical curve to the experimental data (5). The main interpretation of the result was that the protonated forms of both ligands ($HN_3$, as well as HOCN, both thus uncharged) react very much faster than their unprotonated forms. This is the case at least for the bimolecular rate constants, which differ for charged and uncharged ligand at least by a factor of 100 (should be more below pH 5.1; $pK_H = 4.7$ for azide and $pK_H = 3.7$ for cyanate). Alberty's individual rate constants for the simpler system in which myoglobin dissociates one proton actually show a difference by a factor of over 400.

Duffey subsequently extended his experiments over a wider pH range (5). The experimental data at constant ionic strength alone did not permit him to differentiate between whether hydrazoic acid or a protonated form of the enzyme is the important species for the faster recombination step. But taking into account also that the rate constants are practically independent of ionic strength, one is strongly led to believe that at least one reactant is uncharged. It is much more likely that the species in the spatial surrounding of the reactive encounter in this reaction is $HN_3$ rather than myoglobin.

In summarizing the data of previous experiments on the binding of azide (and of cyanate as well), it is the feeling of this author that there should be one reaction cycle which is largely responsible for the experimental results. The error in the experimental data was large enough to justify the use of just one reaction cycle. We have recently found that a solution of myoglobin and azide easily oxidizes in air, leading to a considerable error in some data (6). The absorption at 422 mµ actually reduces soon below the absorption of myoglobin without any azide, while azide initially produces increased absorption at this wavelength. This is shown in detail in Fig. 1, which shows an early series with myoglobin from Seravac. Similar results were repeatedly obtained, although with variations in the shape of the curve (6). Fresh myoglobin from

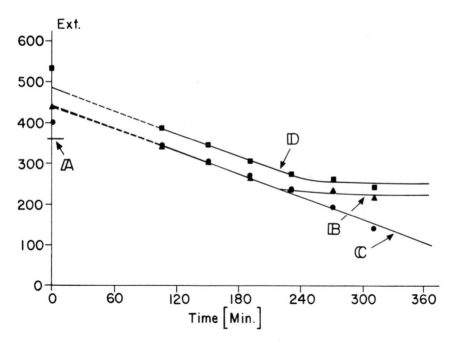

Figure 1. Time measurements on aerated reaction mixtures, all with 7 µM metmyoglobin, 0.03 M citrate, pH 5.0, 25° C, 422 mµ. A=reference without addition of azide; B and C with presence of 14 µM azide, B also with 1 mM EDTA; D = with 80 µM azide and with 1 mM EDTA.

197

Calbiochem showed this oxidation to a smaller extent. The oxidation products were not determined. This oxidation is substantial only at pH 5. Experiments at pH 6 showed only a small decrease in extinction with time.

Taking proper precautions, we have recently done some temperature jump experiments on this system at various temperatures. A summary of the results is given in Fig. 2. The strong temperature dependence of the intercept is quite evident from the experiments; the monomolecular rate constant is severely temperature–dependent, the bimolecular rate constant is less so, but is under further investigation (6).

Recently we conducted some rapid-flow experiments as well to establish the kinetics of the reaction at very low pH. Previous data did not show clearly whether the kinetics become pH–independent below pH 5. Flow experiments (7) showed that the overall bimolecular rate constant is pH–independent below pH 5, within the limits of the experimental error. This confirmed our former idea (3) that a protonic dissociation with a $pK_H$ of 4.7 is important for the master combination step. This

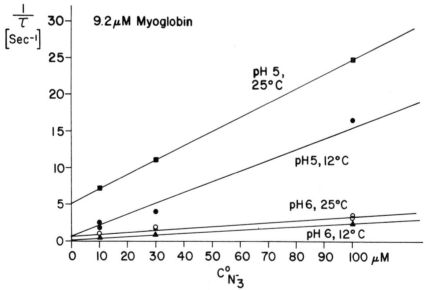

Figure 2. Kinetic results from temperature jump experiments on 9.2 μM myoglobin in 0.03 M nitrate, pH 5 and pH 6 (422 mμ), as indicated, and at two different temperatures. The analytical concentration of sodium azide is the independent variable.

$pK_H$ of 4.7 is equal to $pK_H$ of hydrazoic acid, but myoglobin also starts to show protonic dissociation below pH 4.7. Thus one cannot actually distinguish between the two possibilities, a protonic form of the enzyme, or hydrazoic acid, being the important species in the fast combination step. Eqn. (1) shows a scheme without specifying which one of the particular components is in a protonation equilibrium:

$$pK_H' \quad H^+ \begin{array}{c} AHB \xrightarrow[k_7]{} \xrightarrow{k_8} AH \\ B \\ AB \xrightarrow[k_1]{k_2} A \end{array} H^+ \quad pK_H' \quad (1)$$

The rate constants $k_1$ and $k_7$ are the slow bimolecular ones. Equality between $pK_H'$ and $pK_H'$ was assumed, demanding a very high degree of similarity between the pH-dependence of the overall association rate constant and that of the overall dissociation rate constant, as was found experimentally. Actually, the overall equilibrium constant should, under such circumstances, be pH-independent, as was found experimentally, although with some deviation from ideal independence at the pH extremes. Also, Chance (8) reported recently that the addition of azide to myoglobin is not connected with a change in hydronium-ion concentration.

One may now consider more closely the two alternatives of protonated species. It is difficult to visualize protonation quite near the active site of ferrimyoglobin. The proton might be located at the imidazole-residue of the (distal) histidine near the iron. But such a proton would make the area near the iron atom even more positive than it already is; in addition, one would expect that in contrast to experimental facts, the azide anion would react much better than hydrazoic acid.

We know from X-ray investigations on crystalline sperm whale metmyoglobin (9) that a sulfate anion is near the imidazole-residue, which is linked to the heme-iron via the $H_2O$ molecule. If such a highly negative charge near this distal imidazole is also present in solution, it could exert its electrostatic effects on the active site of the metmyoglobin. The azide anion would then have equal charge and would be repelled, while the hydrazoic acid would not be affected.

The ratio of the two diffusion-limited rate constants for hydrazoic acid and for azide in this reaction is given (compare ref. 10, section 12-4), by:

$$\frac{k_1}{k_1^o} = \frac{(\exp \frac{z_1 z_2 e_o^2}{4\pi \epsilon \epsilon_o a_D kT} - 1) \, a_D 4\pi \epsilon \epsilon_o kT}{z_1 z_2 e_o^2} = \frac{1}{\Phi_D} \tag{2}$$

In this equation, $k_1$ represents the bimolecular rate constant between two neutral molecules or between a neutral and a charged molecule; $k_1^o$ is the bimolecular rate constant between charged molecules; $z_1$ and $z_2$ are the valencies of the two charged reactants; $e_o$ is the charge of the electron ; $\epsilon$ is the dielectric constant (of water); $\epsilon_o$ is dielectric permittivity; $a_D$ is the "reaction distance" of the two molecules; k is the Boltzman constant; T, the absolute temperature. Although it is rather difficult to evaluate this ratio, it could certainly be as large as 100, as is known from electrostatic effects on the recombination rate constant of small molecules. The experimental difference of the bimolecular rate constants at pH 5 and at pH 7.5 could therefore be explained on the grounds of Eqn. (2).

If one writes the diffusion-limited expression for the bimolecular rate constants of the combination with hydrazoic acid, one obtains:

$$k_1 = 4\pi \, N_A D_{HN_3} a_D \tag{3}$$

In this equation, $N_A$ is the number of molecules per mole and $D_{HN_3}$ is the diffusion constant of $HN_3$ (in water); $k_1$ is generally approximately $10^{10} M^{-1} sec^{-1}$, although expected to be smaller for macromolecules (but $a_D$ is very difficult to define in this case). Experimentally, the rate constant is near $10^6$ $M^{-1} sec^{-1}$, which is unusually small for a diffusion-limited step. Extreme spatial restriction on the approach of hydrazoic acid to ferrimyoglobin would be required, resulting in a quite small correction factor $\delta$ for the surface-area-contribution $4\pi$ $(0 < \delta \ll 1)$. Although such spatial restriction seems still possible for the size of this macromolecule, it is not exceedingly likely.

However, the full reaction may require at least two additional steps. One monomolecular step would be located between the diffusion complex and the exchange positions just next to the water molecules at the iron atom. The other step involves the exchange of this water molecule with azide. If the imidazole residue should have negative charge characteristics due to a neighboring sulfate anion, the migration of the neutral hydrazoic acid to its exchange position next to the water molecule should certainly proceed much more easily than the equivalent migration of the negatively charged azide anion. An azide anion, on the other hand, could probably be bound more easily to the positively charged iron atom than hydrazoic acid, but the ejection of the water molecule from its site near the iron may finally be rate limiting. However, if this would be the case, one would not necessarily expect any difference between hydrazoic acid and the azide anion in the kinetics of the water-exchange step.

Summarizing thus far, it is felt that the hydrazoic acid is important for the fast combination reaction with ferrimyoglobin, and that the principal difference in the acidic and basic recombination and dissociation rate constants is given by the influence of the electrostatically negative area near the path of the small molecule into the exchange position with the water molecule. This charge effect of the intermediate reaction step would also lead to the extreme symmetry in the rate constant in the cyclic system, as found experimentally. Going back to Eqn. (1), A is then the azide and B the ferrimyoglobin molecule.

Looking now more closely at the above suggestion of a total of three steps in the overall reaction at either high or low pH, the full bimolecular combination with azide would be represented by:

$$Y_1 \underset{k_2}{\overset{k_1}{\rightleftharpoons}} Y_2 \underset{k_4}{\overset{k_3}{\rightleftharpoons}} Y_3 \underset{k_6}{\overset{k_5}{\rightleftharpoons}} Y_4 + Y_5 \qquad (4)$$

The indexing of these rate constants is indpendent of the indexing in scheme (1). The component $Y_4$ may then be free myoglobin and $Y_5$ free azide (as anion or as acid). Expressions for relaxation times are most easily derived for the condition $c_5^0 \gg c_4^0$ with $c_i^0$ = analytical concentration of the i-th component. Such a derivation seems advisable in order to find acceptable (and non-acceptable!) mechanisms for this simple step (and similar ones with "small" biomolecular rate constants quite in general).

Initially, it is assumed that one step is much slower than the other two. One obtains then three possible expressions for the slowest relaxation time. These possibilities are given by the conditions of Eqns. (5), (7), and (9), resulting in the three expressions (6), (8), and (10) for the slowest chemical relaxation time:

$$k_1, \; k_2 \ll k_3, \; k_4, \; k_5, \; k_6 c_5^{\,o} \tag{5}$$

$$\tau_3^{-1} = k_1 + k_2 \left[ 1 + K_{3,4} (1 + K_{5,6}/c_5^{\,o}) \right]^{-1} \tag{6}$$

$$k_3, \; k_4 \ll k_1, \; k_2, \; k_5, \; k_6 c_5^{\,o} \tag{7}$$

$$\tau_3^{-1} = k_3 \, (1 + K_{2,1})^{-1} + k_4 \, \frac{c_5^{\,o}}{K_{5,6} + c_5^{\,o}} \tag{8}$$

$$k_5, \; k_6 c_5^{\,o} \ll k_1, \; k_2, \; k_3, \; k_4 \tag{9}$$

$$\tau_3^{-1} = k_5 \left[ 1 + K_{4,3} \, (1 + K_{2,1}) \right]^{-1} + k_6 c_5^{\,o} \tag{10}$$

In these equations, it is $K_{m,n} = k_m/k_n$. Eqn. (6) is identical with Eqn. (5-112) and Eqn. (8) with Eqn. (5-110) of ref. 10. The relaxation time $\tau_3^{-1}$ becomes concentration-independent for $c_5^{\,o} \ll K_{5,6}$ for both equations (6) and (8). This was not found experimentally thus far for $c_5^{\,o} \leq 2$ mM. No such independence arises in Eqn. (10) [identical with Eqn. (5-121) of ref. 10]. The second term of all three equations (6), (8), and (10), however, vanishes for very small $c_5^{\,o}$. Only $\tau_3^{-1}$ in Eqn. (10) can be truly considered as diffusion limited. $\tau_3^{-1}$ in Eqn. (6) is limited by the $H_2O$-exchange and $\tau_3^{-1}$ in Eqn. (8) by the azide migration between two intermediary complexes.

An initial assumption will now be abolished, which is done stepwise out of Eqn. (10). The following conditions among rate constants may prevail:

$$k_3, \; k_6 c_5^{\,o} \ll k_1, \; k_2, \; k_4, \; k_5 \tag{11}$$

One immediately recognizes in conjunction with Eqn. (4) that the equilibrium concentration of $Y_3$ becomes relatively small:

$$\bar{c}_3 << \bar{c}_1, \bar{c}_2, \bar{c}_4 \tag{12}$$

The inverse relaxation time becomes now:

$$\tau_3^{-1} = k_3{'} (1 + K_{2,1})^{-1} + k_6{'} c_5^{o} \tag{13}$$

Another (similar) condition among rate constants is given by

$$k_1, k_6 c_5^{o} << k_2, k_3, k_4, k_5 \tag{14}$$

One obtains herewith a relation, which is quite similar to relation (12), namely:

$$\bar{c}_2, \bar{c}_3 << \bar{c}_1, \bar{c}_4 \tag{15}$$

The inverse relaxation time becomes;

$$\tau_3^{-1} = k_1{''} + k_6{''} c_5^{o} \tag{16}$$

The rate constants in Eqns. (13) and (16) are no longer rate constants of individual steps, but contain other much larger rate constants[*], although the dimension remains unaltered ($sec^{-1}$ and $M^{-1}sec^{-1}$, respectively). These new rate constants can now be much smaller than before, and the concept of limitation of the rate by diffusion may no longer be considered relevant for either Eqn. (13) or Eqn. (16).

There are other conditions among the rate constants which have not been considered. But they do not basically affect the magnitude of $k_6$, which was considered to belong to the two slowest rate-terms. As $c_5^{o}$ can actually have any size, $k_6 c_5^{o}$ could at least theoretically always be made quite large, but the signal change in the relaxation process would become immeasurably small. Practically, $c_5^{o}$ has to be kept near $K_{5,6}$ (for further details on this "proximity" condition, consult ref. 10; see also ref. 6).

[*]One easily derives, for instance:

$$k_3{'} = k_3 \frac{k_5}{k_4 + k_5} \quad \text{and} \quad k_6{'} = k_6 \frac{k_4}{k_4 + k_5} \tag{17}$$

With reference to the mechanism of the myoglobin reaction, relation (12) means that the concentration of the intermediate diffusion complex is negligibly small for practical purposes. Relation (15), on the other hand, means that both intermediate complexes are in negligibly small concentration, making their measurement practically impossible. Actually, conditions(11) and (14) may be rather frequent among enzyme reactions. One may have to anticipate the presence of such conditions whenever the bimolecular rate constant is below $10^8$ $M^{-1}sec^{-1}$. One should also remember that any spectral change is associated only with $Y_1$. The absorption spectra of $Y_2$ and $Y_3$ are those of

$Y_4$ = metmyoglobin.

## References

1. Diven, W. F., D. E. Goldsack, and R. A. Alberty. J. Biol. Chem., 240, 2437 (1965).

2. Goldsack, D. E., W. S. Eberlein, and R. A. Alberty. J. Biol. Chem., 240, 4312 (1965).

3. Duffey, D., B. Chance, and G. Czerlinski. Biochem. Biophys. Res. Comm., 19, 425 (1965).

4. Czerlinski, G. Abstract, American Chem. Soc. Symp. on Relaxation Techniques in Chemical Kinetics in Solution, Buffalo, New York, 1965, p. 11.

5. Duffey, D., B. Chance, and G. Czerlinski. In preparation.

6. Czerlinski, G., and N. Frable. In preparation.

7. Czerlinski, G., and R. Danish. In preparation.

8. Chance, B. This volume, p. 213.

9. Stryer, L., J. C. Kendrew, and H. C. Watson. J. Mol. Biol., 8, 96 (1964). See also Nobbs, C., this volume, p.

10. Czerlinski, G. Chemical Relaxation, An Introduction to the Theory and Application of Stepwise Perturbation, Marcel Dekker, Inc., New York, 1966.

DISCUSSION

<u>Nicholls</u>:  Two papers were published in 1965 dealing with the
reaction of azide with metmyoglobin, one from Dr. Alberty's
laboratory (1), the other by Duffey, Chance and Czerlinski(2).
The data from both groups indicate that there are no detectable

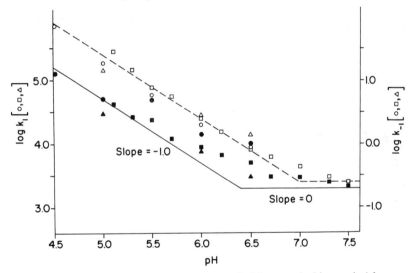

Figure 1.  Dixon plots of the association and dissociation
velocity constants of azide-metmyoglobin.  The logarithms of
the rate constants for formation $(k_1, M^{-1}sec^{-1})$ and dissociation $(k_{-1}, sec^{-1})$ of sperm whale metmyoglobin-azide are plotted against pH, using the following data:
$\Delta k_1, \blacktriangle k_{-1}$: stopped flow and equilibrium data of Duffey <u>et al</u>.(2)
$o k_1, \bullet k_{-1}$: temperature jump data of Duffey <u>et al</u>. (2)
$\square k_1, \blacksquare k_{-1}$:  temperature jump data of Goldsack <u>et al</u>. (1).
The continuous line is drawn with a pK of 6.4, and approxi-
mates the observations on $k_{-1}$ (closed symbols); the dashed
line is drawn with a pK of 7.0 and approximates the observations on $k_1$ (open symbols).  The kinetic constants obtained
from this plot are given in Equations 1-3.  25° C, approximately 0.1 M salt concentration in all experiments (1,2).  $k_1$
and $k_{-1}$ are given in terms of total azide and methemoglobin
concentrations in all cases.

intermediate stages in the reactions, which, in fact, follow very closely the kind of mechanism proposed several years ago by Dr. Chance for the fluoride and cyanide reactions (3). Fig. 1 shows a Dixon plot of the results, that is, the logarithm of the velocity constant involved plotted against the pH. We have six sets of determinations, three for the "on" velocity constand ($k_1$) and three for the "off" constant ($k_{-1}$) obtained in two ways: (a) by the rapid flow method, whereby Duffey, Chance and Czerlinski (2) were able to obtain $k_1$ for the azide reaction and consequently $k_{-1}$ by multiplying $k_1$ by the equilibrium constant obtained spectrophotometrically; (b) by the temperature jump method (used by both groups) giving both $k_1$ and $k_{-1}$ directly. The results in Fig. 1 show a fairly large scatter, but all the $k_1$ determinations agree within approximately 0.3 logarithmic units, which is about what you would expect. For $k_{-1}$, the flow equilibrium results (2) agree with the temperature jump results of Alberty (1), although the Duffey et al. temperature jump data (2) are slightly at variance with the others (Fig. 1).

The values of $k_{-1}$ show a pK of about 6.5 and the values of $k_1$ a pK towards the limit of the experimental pH conditions, around pH 5. These results can be explained by three simple equilibria (Equations 1-3).

$$MbH^+Fe^{+++}H_2O + HN_3 \underset{6.3 \times 10^5 M^{-1}sec^{-1}}{\overset{6.5 \times 10^5 M^{-1}sec^{-1}}{\rightleftharpoons}} MbH^+Fe^{+++}N_3^- + H_3O^+ \quad (1)$$

$$MbFe^{+++}H_2O + HN_3 \underset{0.25\ sec^{-1}}{\overset{6.3 \times 10^5 M^{-1}sec^{-1}}{\rightleftharpoons}} MbH^+Fe^{+++}N_3^- + H_2O \quad (2)$$

$$MbFe^{+++}H_2O + N_3^- \underset{0.25\ sec^{-1}}{\overset{1.6 \times 10^3 M^{-1}sec^{-1}}{\rightleftharpoons}} MbFe^{+++}N_3^- + H_2O \quad (3)$$

In the region below pH 6.5 (Equation 1) there is a dependence of $k_{-1}$ upon the hydrogen ion concentration and a similar dependence of $k_1$ because the free acid ($HN_3$) is, of course, in equilibrium with the anion. Then at pH values between 6.5 and 7 (Equation 2) there is a reaction where the equilibrium constant is dependent upon the hydrogen concentration because one has the heme-linked group changing from the basic to the acidic form and therefore, effective binding of the undissociated form of the azide. As the pH rises above 7, we reach a region where the experimental data at present available are a little ambiguous. But they are not inconsistent with an attack by the azide ion itself with release of a water molecule (Equation 3). So all the available data are explicable by three simple equilibria and a heme-linked ionization which shifts from a pK of 6.5 to one of ~7.0 on the binding of azide to metmyoglobin. This conclusion is similar to that reached previously by George (4).

Czerlinski: Dr. Nicholls derives from his Fig. 1 that two pro- tonic dissociations at pH 6.4 and at pH 7.0 might be involved in the kinetic data. It should be pointed out that Dr. Nicholls does not present the explicit forms for $k_1$ and for $k_{-1}$, the two overall rate constants. He interprets the data by three slow equilibration reactions, evidently neglecting any rapid equili- bration steps. His equation (1) implies a strong pH-dependence for the backward rate (and at any pH), but none for the forward rate. The experiments, however, show a pH-dependence (below pH 6.4) for both rate constants; the forward rate becomes pH- dependent by the dissociation equilibrium for $HN_3$, which Dr. Nicholls omitted. He also omitted the protonic dissociations of $MbH^+Fe^{+++}H_2O$ and of $MbH^+Fe^{+++}N_3^-$. These fast protonic dis- sociations cannot be allowed to be neglected.

Thus, the results are not explainable by the three equa- tions, given by Nicholls. He also requires three slow equili- brations, while Czerlinski (above) got along with two slow equilibrations, coupled to a cyclic system by two fast protonic reactions. Aside from the question of calling Fig. 1 a "Dixon plot", one may ask why Nicholls omitted the fourth possible slow equilibration reaction ($MbH^+Fe^{+++}H_2O$ reacts with $N_3^-$). Because of all the given deficiencies I would like to suggest to Dr. Nicholls that he elaborate further.

Nicholls: I should like to answer each of Dr. Czerlinski's points. First, concerning the explicit forms of $k_1$ and $k_{-1}$, if $k_f$ is the forward constant for $HN_3$ (given as $6.5 \times 10^5$ $M^{-1}$ $sec^{-1}$ in Equations 1 and 2), $k_f'$ that for $N_3^{--}$ ($1.6 \times 10^3$ $M^{-1}$ $sec^{-1}$ in Equation 3), $K_d$ the dissociation constant for reaction with $H_3O^+$ ($6.3 \times 10^5$ $M^{-1}$ $sec^{-1}$ in Equation 1), and $k_d'$ that for $H_2O$ ($0.25$ $sec^{-1}$ in Equations 2 and 3), then

$$k_1 \text{ (apparent)} = k_f' K_L / (K_L + [H^+]) + k_f[H^+] / (K_L + [H^+]) \quad (4)$$

or, when $K_L \gg [H^+]$, $k_1 \text{ (apparent)} = k_f' + k_f[H^+] / K_L \quad (5)$

and $k_{-1} \text{ (apparent)} = k_d' + k_d [H^+] \quad (6)$

At equilibrium, it is then thermodynamically necessary that the ratio $k_f' K_L / k_f = K_{H+MbN_3}$ and that $k_d' / k_d = K_{H+Mb^+}$. Here $K_L$ indicates the dissociation constant for $HN_3$ ($\sim 2.5 \times 10^{-5}$ M at $\mu = 0.1$ and $22^\circ$ C), $K_{H+Mb^+}$ the dissociation constant of the heme-linked group in acid metmyoglobin and $K_{H+MbN_3}$ that of the corresponding group in the azide metmyoglobin complex.

As for Dr. Czerlinski's second question, the rapid steps are neglected because Equations 1-3, together with Equation 7, automatically give the right proportions of ionized and unionized forms in any transition from one side to the other:

$$H^+ \text{ MetMb Fe}^{+++} H_2O + N_3^- \underset{6.3 \times 10^5 M^{-1} sec^{-1}}{\overset{1.6 \times 10^3 M^{-1} sec^{-1}}{\rightleftharpoons}} \text{MetMb Fe}^{+++} N_3^- + H_3O^+ \tag{7}$$

Czerlinski correctly points out that Equation 7 must be added to equations 1-3 to complete the system; it was omitted because it represents the transformation of protonated MetMb to unprotonated azide MetMb, a small contribution owing to the unfavorable pK values. It may be noted that in this mechanism, both metmyoglobin species react with both species of azide, and both species of azide complex react with $H_2O$ and $H_3O^+$; a reaction with $HN_3$ produces a protonated form, while a reaction with $N_3^-$ gives a nonprotonated form. It is not necessary to postulate any intermediates, for the attack by azide may be simultaneous with the departure of $H_2O$ or $H_3O^+$.

This leaves the question of the simplest mechanism for the azide reaction. Czerlinski's mechanism contains two pK's ("fast protonic reactions") and three independent velocity constants. That of Equations 1, 2, 3 and 7 contains three pK's but only two independent velocity constants. If the apparent values of $k_1$ and $k_{-1}$ show the same pK, that is, if $K_{eq}$ for the azide reaction is pH independent between pH 6 and 8, then there is no need to invoke two forms of metmyoglobin or the additional pK value. But when the pK's differ, as in Fig. 1, and $K_{eq}$ increases with increasing pH (1), then there must be two forms of the protein with different affinities for azide. In fact, as $H^+$ promotes the binding of azide, azide promotes the binding of $H^+$, and increases the pK from about 6.4 to about 7.0.

It is not claimed that the proposed mechanism must be the correct one. Subsequent calculations indeed show that more complicated assumptions must be made to explain the reactions involving $H_2S$ and $HCN$. But this caveat, of course, applies a fortiori to the mechanism of Czerlinski.

Czerlinski: Dr. Nicholls' Equations 5 and 6 now become rather similar to the two terms in brackets of my equation for the overall relaxation time for reaction scheme (1) of my contribution:

$$\tau_3^{-1} = [k_2 + k_8 \frac{\bar{\bar{c}}_H}{K_H' + \bar{\bar{c}}_H}] + [k_1 + k_7 \frac{\bar{\bar{c}}_H}{K_H + \bar{\bar{c}}_H}] c_A^o \tag{8}$$

This equation may easily be derived from Equations 7-38 of Ref. 5 for $c_A^o \gg c_B^o$, $k_8 \gg k_2$, $k_7 \gg k_1$ and $K_H$, $K_H' \gg 10^{-6}$ M. Here $c_A^o$ = analytical concentration of azide; $c_B^o$ = analytical concentration of metmyoglobin; $K_H$ = protonic dissociation constant of $HN_3$; $K_H'$ = protonic dissociation constant of $MbHN_3$. The four rate constants of Equation 8 are defined as shown by the reaction scheme of Equation 1 before and with A = azide and B = myoglobin. Three of the rate constants are independent, the fourth one is given by:

$$K_H \times \frac{k_8}{k_7} = K_H' \times \frac{k_2}{k_1} \tag{9}$$

This last equation derives from the cyclic nature of the reaction scheme (1).

Although Dr. Nicholls employs only four numerically different rate constants (as does Equation 8 above), he nevertheless employs a total of four slow steps. He also "buries" a number of protonic dissociations by incorporating them into rate constants. He may therefore not recognize that he has four cyclic systems, resulting in four (of a total of eight) independent rate constants. By pairwise equalization of rate constant he arrives at "two independent" rate constants. Thus I still feel that scheme (1) gives the simplest mechanism, which is also in agreement with the experimental results (assuming moderate precision).

It was formerly assumed that $pK_H = pK_H'$. But one may derive from the discussion of Nicholls that $pK_H - pK_H' = 0.6$. If this difference is assumed and $pK_H = 4.7$, $k_7 = 10^6$ M$^{-1}$sec$^{-1}$, $k_8 = 100$ sec$^{-1}$ and $k_1 = 3000$ M$^{-1}$sec$^{-1}$, one obtains with Equation 9 the remaining rate constant $k_2 = 0.075$ sec$^{-1}$. One may then plot intercept (first term in brackets) and slope (second term in brackets) of Equation 8 over a wide pH range. This is done in Fig. 2, demonstrating clearly the horizontal shift of the two curves within the experimental pH range 4.5 to 7; the two ordinates are lined up as in Fig. 1 by Nicholls

209

to "show" the same shift. The ratio between slope and intercept gives the overall equilibrium constant $K_{eq}$. The agreement of $K_{eq}$ with actual measurements is quite good within the
experimental range (compare Ref. 2).

Although the agreement so far is encouraging, the considerable excursion of the intercept-curve toward low values
for pH > 7 is rather disappointing for me, but probably not so
for Dr. Nicholls. However, intercepts cannot be derived from
"ordinary" temperature-jump experiments for any $\tau$ > 5 sec.
Above this limit, disturbances by convection ordinarily make
measurements impossible. While the curve for the slope becomes not affected by the formation of MbFeOH until pH > 8,
the curve for the intercept may be affected much earlier.
Recent experiments seem to indicate that hydroxide formation
extends its effects upon the intercept curve possibly down to
pH 7. This would result in an increase of the intercept curve
above the dotted line for pH > 7. Hopefully, the increase is
large enough to allow its measurement by the temperature-jump
method, which requires $k_2$ > 0.2 sec$^{-1}$.

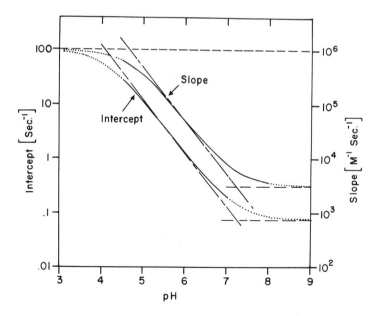

Figure 2. Theoretical plot of slope and intercept of Equation
(8). The dashed lines indicate idealized "slopes". The
dotted curves indicate extrapolations to non-experimental ranges, while the experimental range is denoted by the full sections of the curves.

# References

1. Goldsack, D. E., W. S. Eberlein, and R. A. Alberty. J. Biol. Chem., 240, 4312 (1965).

2. Duffey, D., B. Chance, and G. Czerlinski. Biochem. Biophys. Res. Comm., 19, 423 (1965).

3. Chance, B. J. Biol. Chem., 194, No. 2, 483 (1952).

4. George, P., and G. H. I. Hanania. Disc. Faraday Soc., 20, 216 (1955).

5. Czerlinski, G. Chemical Relaxation, An Introduction to the Theory and Application of Stepwise Perturbation, Marcel Dekker, Inc., New York, 1966.

# ON THE MEASUREMENT OF REACTIVITY OF HEMOPROTEINS IN THE CRYSTALLINE STATE[*]

Britton Chance[‡]

Johnson Research Foundation, University of Pennsylvania
Philadelphia, Pennsylvania

While much information has been presented today on the nature and properties of hemoprotein compounds, very little data have been brought forward to clarify the factors which may control the reactivity of hemoproteins, such as ferrihemoglobin and ferrimyoglobin, towards various ligands. Crystallization has afforded a means of altering the reactivity without change of gross chemical structure, not only for ferrimyoglobin (1), but also for horse liver alcohol dehydrogenase (2). These results are supported and extended by the recent work of Richards, who has shown that the reactivity of carboxypeptidase is considerably altered in the crystal structure (F. M. Richards, personal communication) and by Gurd, whose report appears in this volume (3). We may, therefore, employ crystallization as a method for studying the control of enzymatic activity in general (see Table I). This communication surveys critically the conditions for meaningful experimentation with hemoproteins.

## TABLE I

### Relative Activities of Some Soluble and Crystalline
### Proteins and Enzymes

| Material | Reactant | Reaction rate ratio Soluble/Crystalline |
|---|---|---|
| Horse ferrimyoglobin | Azide | 1/21 |
| Horse ferrihemoglobin | Azide | 1/17 |
| Horse liver ADH | DPN | $>1/1,000$ |
| Carboxypeptidase[**] | Carbobenzoxy-glycyl-phenylalanine | 1/300 |

[**]F. M. Richards, personal communication.

[*]This work was supported by NSF GB 2482 and PHS GM 12202.

[‡]Some of the experimental study was done at the Laboratory for Molecular Biology while an Overseas Fellow of Churchill College, Cambridge.

213

A description of the experimental method is available elsewhere (1), but here we may consider the chemical and physical parameters that have influenced our experimental design.

Choice of reaction. The reaction to be studied should be second-order so that the rate can be adjusted to suit the limitations of the recording instrument. It should be relatively rapid so that a first-order step involved in ligand binding in the crystalline state or in solution may be identified. The reaction should also have a readily measurable pH and temperature dependence, in order to allow the comparison of the reaction mechanism in solution with that in the crystalline material The reaction of hydrazoic acid with ferrimyoglobin is one of the fastest exhibited by this hemoprotein; it has a clearcut pH sensitivity and a large temperature coefficient (4). A number of other reactions are less suitable; that with cyanide is rather slow, and that with peroxide is of unknown mechanism and shows an anomalously small value for the second-order velocity constant, as compared with other hemoproteins.

One suitable alternative to the azide reaction would be those with hydroxide or hydrogen ions, although at first sight they seemed so fast that diffusion might well become a limiting factor.

Choice of experimental methods. Since the second-order velocity constants to be studied are large, rapid reaction techniques are highly desirable, particularly to determine whether a first-order step limits the rate of the reaction. However, since the reaction medium contains between 2 and 4 M ammonium sulfate, problems in the use of the flow apparatus should be considered. Difficulties have already been encountered in the application of a 4-jet mixer to the reaction of a concentrated solution of ammonium sulfate containing xanthine oxidase with an aqueous solution of its substrate (B. Chance and D. E. Green, unpublished observations, 1939). Now, however, the two-stage multi-jet mixer deals adequately with the mixing of concentrated salt solutions with water (5). It is also useful to mix the ammonium sulfate solution containing the crystals with an ammonium sulfate solution of the same concentration containing the ligand. Under these conditions, one must only consider the problem presented by the high viscosity of the concentrated ammonium sulfate solutions which, insofar as we can determine, does not cause any measurable decrease of mixing efficiency. Thus the various forms of the flow apparatus--stopped, accelerated, and continuous flow--may be applied to the problem (5).

Perturbation methods provide a less direct approach to chemical kinetics than do mixing techniques. The temperature-jump method is not presently applicable, as is readily evidenced by calculation and experiment; the conductivity of concentrated ammonium sulfate solutions is so great that a redesign of the power supply would be required. The fact that erythrocytes can readily be destroyed by laser heating at 694 mμ or 1,060 mμ suggests, however, that laser-induced temperature jumps in the crystals themselves would be very effective, in spite of the rather small absorption of light at these wavelengths in small crystals. For high-spin compounds, 1,060 mμ is rather favorable; the extinction coefficient for ferrimyoglobin, for example, is approximately $1.0 \text{ cm}^{-1} \text{ mM}^{-1}$, permitting the use of relatively small crystals and avoiding problems with either optical measurements or diffusion. The application of both ruby and neodymium lasers to this problem is under consideration.

Optical measurements. Suspensions of crystals are turbid because of their light-scattering properties, and so the dual-wavelength spectrophotometric technique is well suited to the measurement of the small absorbance changes caused by ligand binding. In addition, rod-like material orients in flow streams to cause "flow birefringence", as has already been observed in suspensions of rod-like bacteria, where the absorbance changes to be measured are small (6). This same phenomenon is also seen in suspensions of crystals where, however, the absorption changes are larger than in the bacteria, and no significant artifacts have been observed so long as the dual wavelength technique is used.

Choice of wavelengths. Concentrations of hemoproteins in some crystals are equivalent to 30 mM. Thus, absorbance measurements can only be made effectively at crystal dimensions and extinction coefficients that are suitably small. We have chosen the long wave band of ferrimyoglobin at 630 mμ for most measurements, where crystals several μ in diameter give suitable absorbance changes (on the order of 0.01 O.D./μ). Under these conditions, average concentrations of the hemoprotein, equivalent to a 40 μM solution, give satisfactory registrations. The reference wavelength for the dual wavelength technique is usually set at a convenient longer value, such as 700 mμ.

In some cases is is desirable, in fact, necessary, to measure not only the disappearance of the characteristic absorption band of ferrimyoglobin, but also the appearance of the absorption band due to the formation of its compound with the ligand. Thus, the reference wavelength may be set at 580 mμ for studies of the formation of the azide, cyanide, and hydroxide compounds. The absorption of the fluoride compound at 610 mμ provides a convenient marker to demonstrate its formation in the presence of these other compounds. Measurement of absorbance changes in the infra-red region of the spectrum is also feasible, but requires more concentrated suspensions of crystals; also, the performance of photo-surfaces in this wavelength region is inferior to that obtainable at shorter wavelengths.

Evaluation of crystal sizes. Crystal sizes are observed in a microscope equipped with a calibrated reticle. Generally, averages of the shortest dimension of a number of crystals are taken. This dimension is relevant to the chemical reaction which will, of course, occur most rapidly along the shortest dimension; it is also relevant to the optical assay, which will be most sensitive to the shortest dimension of the crystals, since distortions due to self absorption occur along the longer optical path.

Diffusion. A consideration of diffusion of the ligand to the active site in a water phase is necessary for a suitable experimental design. The equation below indicates the parameters of a system in which diffusion and chemical reaction are occurring simultaneously (7):

$$\frac{[Az] \text{ mean inside}}{[Az] \text{at surface of cylinder}} = \frac{2}{R}\left(\frac{D}{k_1[Mb]_o}\right)^{\frac{1}{2}} \frac{I_1\left(R\left(\frac{k_1[Mb]_o}{D}\right)^{\frac{1}{2}}\right)}{I_o\left(R\left(\frac{k_1[Mb]_o}{D}\right)^{\frac{1}{2}}\right)}$$

The parameters here are R, the radius of the crystal; $k_1$, the second-order velocity constant for the reaction of the ligand with the protein in the crystal; and $[Mb]_o$, the concentration of the protein. The latter value is not readily controllable in the crystals; however, the change from ferrimyoglobin to ferrihemoglobin gives a decrease in the concentration of the hemoprotein in the crystal of a factor of 3.8. The diffusion constant, D, may be decreased somewhat by using glycerol as solvent, but it is difficult to increase D; the value for D ($10^{-6}$ to $10^{-5}$ cm$^2$/sec) employed in these calculations is typical of that for small molecules in an aqueous phase (see Appendix I, ref. 1). Thus the calculations below indicate the extent by which slow diffusion of the ligand into the aqueous phase would reduce the pseudo first-order reaction velocity constant from the solution value of ($k_1[Az]$ outside) to the value ($k_1[Az]$ inside).

The two accessible parameters are R, the crystal radius, and $k_1$, the second-order reaction velocity constant. Given one, it is possible to choose the other in such a way that diffusion will not exert a significant influence on the reactivity of the crystals.  Calculations based on a crystal radius of 2 μ show that the reaction velocity constant must not exceed $10^5$ $M^{-1}$ $sec^{-1}$ for the crystals to react at no less than half the speed of the reaction in solution.  Many other combinations are possible; for example, the slower reactions with cyanide or fluoride allow a larger crystal radius, but their smaller second-order reaction velocity constants might not afford as sensitive an indication of crystal reactivity changes.

We may use the diffusion equation to compare the kinetics of the reactions of crystalline ferrihemoglobin and ferrimyoglobin with azide.  Table II, which summarizes the available kinetic constants (1) for the four conditions of the reaction of azide with the two hemoproteins, gives the hemoprotein concentrations in the crystals and the measured reaction velocity constants in the dissolved and crystalline states.[*]

TABLE II

Reaction Velocity Constants for Crystalline Hemoproteins

| Hemoprotein | Concentration in crystals (M) | Velocity constant for azide reaction at pH 6.0 | |
|---|---|---|---|
| | | Crystals | Solution |
| Ferrimyoglobin | 0.030 | $3.5 \times 10^3$ | $8.5 \times 10^4$ |
| Ferrihemoglobin | 0.0075 | $1.7 \times 10^2$ | $3.5 \times 10^3$ |

If we assume that the diffusion constant for azide in crystalline hemoglobin is no less than it is in crystals of myoglobin, we may use the data of Table I to make an objective test of Eqn. 1.  First, the concentration of hemoprotein in the hemoglobin crystal is 3.8-fold smaller than in myoglobin crystals.  Second, the reaction velocity constant for the reaction with azide in solution is 24-fold smaller for hemoglobin than for myoglobin.  Substituting these values into Eqn. 1, we

[*]One qualification is necessary in the case of the hemoglobin data:  for reasons possibly having to do with differences in the nature of intermolecular contacts in crystalline ferrimyoglobin and ferrihemoglobin, the reaction velocity constant for the initial portion of the reaction of ferrihemoglobin with azide is 9 times faster than that for the final portion (1). Whatever the cause of this may be, it cannot be explained on the basis of the equation for combined diffusion and reaction in the same crystal.

find that $\left(\dfrac{D}{k_1[Hb]_o}\right)^{1/2} = 10\left(\dfrac{D}{k_1[Mb]_o}\right)^{1/2}$ and thus, for a dif-

fusion-limited reaction, the azide concentration inside the hemoglobin crystal should be ten times larger than that within the myoglobin crystal. Therefore, the fact that the hemoglobin crystals actually show a reaction that is just as slow relative to that of the soluble material would seem to eliminate conclusively the possibility that diffusion in a water phase is a factor of significance in the reduced reactivity of the crystals under our experimental conditions.

As additional documentation of these conclusions, we may calculate the first term of Eqn. 1 above for the case of hemoglobin. This first term is identical with the equation for combined reaction and diffusion in a thin plate of thickness, T, and applies satisfactorily to the case where diffusion predominates as a rate-limiting factor (7):

$$\dfrac{[Az]\ \text{inside}}{[Az]\ \text{outside}} = \dfrac{1}{\dfrac{T}{2}\left(\dfrac{k_1[Hb]_o}{D}\right)1/2} \tag{2}$$

For $k_1 = 3.5 \times 10^3$ $M^{-1}$ $sec^{-1}$, $T = 4 \times 10^{-4}$ cm, and $[Hb]_o = 7 \times 10^{-3}$ M, the ratio of the rates in the crystal and in solution is equal to 1/20 (Chance and Ravilly, in preparation). D would then have to be as small as $5 \times 10^{-9}$ $cm^2$/sec to explain the experimental data. This value is at least 1,000 times smaller than that for small molecules such as azide.

It is, then, possible to substitute into Eqn. 1 the approximately 20-fold smaller value for the reaction velocity constant, $k_1$, for the reactions of azide with the crystalline material. This causes the ratio of the mean azide concentration inside the cylindrical crystal to that at its surface to approach unity even more closely (by a factor of $\sim\sqrt{20}$, or 4.6). Under these conditions, the azide concentration gradient due to diffusion would be undetectable in both ferrimyoglobin and ferrihemoglobin. Alternatively, crystals of 4.6-fold greater radius could be used with no increase of diffusion effect.

## SUMMARY

The foregoing data set forth experimental conditions for the observation of the kinetics of ligand binding in hemoproteins when structural changes caused by crystallization control the reactivity (control of transitional conformation).

It is not clear that all ligands can be studied in this manner. It is probable that the oxygen reaction is sufficiently rapid that a diffusion limitation is involved. Other reactions may be so slow that transitional conformation is not effective in controlling the reactivity. Nevertheless, the experimental results are very useful in demonstrating directly one means of activity control in hemoproteins and, as described elsewhere, in a dehydrogenase as well (2).

## References

1. Chance, B., A. Ravilly, and N. Rumen. J. Mol. Biol., 17, 525 (1966).

2. Theorell, H., B. Chance, and T. Yonetani. J. Mol. Biol., 17, 513 (1966).

3. Gurd, F. R. N., L. J. Banaszak, A. J. Veros, and J. F. Clark. This volume, p. 221.

4. Czerlinski, G. This volume, p. 195.

5. Chance, B. In Rapid Mixing and Sampling Techniques in Biochemistry (B. Chance, Q. H. Gibson, R. Eisenhart, and K. K. Lonberg-Holm, eds.), Academic Press, Inc., New York, 1964, pp. 39, 125.

6. Chance, B., T. Horio, M. D. Kamen, and S. Tanaguchi. Biochim. Biophys. Acta, 112, 1 (1966).

7. Roughton, F. J. W. Proc. Roy. Soc. (London) B, 111, 1 (1932).

## DISCUSSION

Watson:  We were not surprised to hear that the rate of reaction of azide with myoglobin was significantly slower in the crystal than in solution.  Kendrew and I realized soon after the myoglobin structure came out that there was not room to get a ligand to or from the binding site without disturbing the molecular structure in some way.  It so happens that the molecular packing within the crystal lattice is such than any transitional conformational change must be more restricted in the crystal than in solution.

Chance:  I completely agree; this feature was pointed out to me by Kendrew early in the model construction because it fitted in so well with kinetic studies of catalase (1) and with equilibrium studies of hemoglobin (2).  But it is always nice to have direct experimental evidence that the steric restrictions are sufficiently great to be a factor in the overall reactivity in ligand binding in the crystalline state.  Also broad generalizations on reactions with all ligands are not substantiated; azide, a rapidly reacting ligand, shows a much more marked decrease of reactivity towards the crystals than do other ligands.

### References

1.  Chance, B.  J. Biol. Chem., $\underline{179}$, No. 3, 1341 (1949).

2.  St. George, R. C. C., and L. Pauling.  Science, $\underline{114}$, 629 (1951).

CHEMICAL MODIFICATION OF SPERM WHALE MYOGLOBIN IN
THE CRYSTALLINE STATE*

Frank R. N. Gurd, Leonard J. Banaszak[+]
Angelo J. Veros, and Julia F. Clark[‡]

Department of Biochemistry
Indiana University School of Medicine
Indianapolis, Indiana

## Introduction

The determination of the crystalline structure of sperm whale myoglobin (1;2) has opened the way for a detailed correlation of structure with reactivity (3-7). The crystalline structure shows a remarkable variety in the surface topography. The environment of every side chain exposed to the solvent is special, unlike that of any other side chain. Taken at face value, the crystalline structure offers a great opportunity to examine the effects of environment on the reactivity of the side chain groups in the surface. The same may be said of the internal side chains that are not exposed to solvent, although the methods of probing the reactivity of such groups are less obvious.

Choice of a chemical reagent. The reactivity of individual groups exposed to solvent in the surface of the protein can be studied by following their reaction with a reagent that fulfills the following criteria. 1) The reagent should react under some conditions as nearly as possible with a single class of side chains of special interest. 2) The products of the reaction should be readily identifiable and subject to quantitative estimation. 3) The reagent should have solubility characteristics that will restrict it to the aqueous environment and prevent its penetration within the protein, a process that may cause disruption of the structure of the protein. 4) Neither the reagent nor its reaction products should show any tendency to disrupt the structure after the manner, for example, of the

*This work was supported by USPHS Grants HE-05556, HE-06308.
+Present address: Department of Physiology, Washington University School of Medicine, St. Louis, Missouri.
‡Present address: Biological Laboratory, Harvard University, Cambridge, Massachusetts.

classical denaturing agents.  5) The reagent should preferably represent a member of a class of compounds whose chemical reactivity and stereochemistry are subject to fine gradations, so that the series of studies can be expanded without drastic adjustments of technology.  6) If the reagent is to be used with the crystalline state of the protein, it should be of a size that is known to be able to pass through the channels between protein molecules in the crystal.

For sperm whale myoglobin an alkyl halide such as bromoacetate is a suitable reagent.  1) Near pH 7 its reaction is limited nearly completely to imidazole groups of histidine residues.  The potential reaction with methionine residues occurs only if the protein structure is disrupted by other means.  The potential reaction with amino groups is almost eliminated by choice of pH (5).  The histidine residues are of particular interest, since their environments in the crystalline form show a great variety (8), and furthermore, they are known to be devided almost equally, on the basis of studies in  solution, into two broad categories of "exposed" and "masked" (3).  2) The products of the reaction are well known (9-11).  Both nitrogen atoms in the imidazole ring are reactive.  Two monocarboxymethyl histidine derivatives are formed, one at nitrogen 1, the other at nitrogen 3.  The 1,3-dicarboxymethyl derivative is also formed.  3) The reaction proceeds with the elimination of bromide ion from bromoacetate.  Neither charged species would be expected to forsake the aqueous external environment for the non-polar interior.  4) Bromoacetate and bromide ion in certain pH ranges are relatively innocuous for  several proteins (11).  5) Both the alkyl moiety and halide atom can be varied.  The alkyl group can be extended with or without branching, and with optical isomerism.  The optical isomers may behave differently under the crowded conditions offered by the histidine residues in a protein (12,13).  Iodine is a practical alternative to bromine for the halide atoms, although some more stringent precautions are needed (11).  6) Bromoacetate is smaller than some molecules known to penetrate the channels in myoglobin crystals (14).

Reactivity in the crystalline state.  There are strong reasons for wishing to probe the reactivity of myoglobin in the crystalline state.  First, the implications of the crystalline structure should indicate which imidazole nitrogen atoms, for example, are sufficiently exposed for reaction.  The predictions can be tested by two independent means.  The first is by analysis of segments of the polypeptide chain to establish which histidine residues are modified and to which products.  The second is by X-ray diffraction analysis itself of the reacted crystals.

Combining chemical with crystallographic determination of the points of reaction on the protein will achieve a second objective. It will provide unequivocal evidence of the ability of the crystallographic technique to give support to a chemical technique that leads to the introduction of covalently bonded adducts. For the reason given in the next paragraph, this will be a major type of exploitation of the crystallographers' initial achievement, perhaps comparable to the remarkable difference studies recently reported on coordination complexes of myoglobin (15-17). The parallel studies with chemical determinations should do much for planning and interpreting the crucial crystallographic studies of enzyme-substrate or enzyme-inhibitor interactions (18,19).

A third main reason for studying the reactivity of myoglobin in the crystalline state is that the results should form a basis for interpreting the same study made with the protein in solution. In so far as the degree of selective reactivity observed in the crystal reaction is matched in the solution reaction there will be strong evidence for similarity of structure between crystal and solution. The results of the reaction in solution already point strongly to similarities with the crystal structure (5,6). Independently, Fasold has carried out elegant studies with bifunctional reagents leading to a similar conclusion (20).

Comparison of reactivity in solution and in the crystalline state. In the crystalline state the elements of the protein molecule undergo thermal motion which is taken into account in the crystallographic analysis. Presumably the crystal lattice energy limits to some extent the amplitude of such motions and causes some restriction of the variety of conformations that the protein will assume relative to its behavior in solution, or at least limits the fraction of time spent in opened-up or partially disrupted conformations.

In a molecule of the size of myoglobin it is quite conceivable that a limited region may undergo conformational change without extensive disruption elsewhere in the molecule. If the regional disruption is relatively hindered in the crystalline form, it is possible that some groups that are masked from reaction in the crystal will be more likely to undergo reaction in solution. As will be shown later in this report, myoglobin does indeed appear to react with bromoacetate at more histidine residues in solution than in the crystalline form.

This report describes experiments begun in 1962. The earliest peptide-mapping experiments on preparations reacted in the crystalline state showed similarities with the preparations obtained by reaction in solution (5,6). These results indicated

that the structure in solution was very similar to that in the
crystalline state. Recent measurements of low angle X-ray
scattering (21,22) point to the same conclusion. The results
of optical rotatory dispersion studies support the idea that
much or all of the helical content is retained after the
crystalline protein is dissolved (23-29).

The present series of experiments were designed to establish a reliable procedure for preparing reacted crystals suitable to compare many properties with those of the unmodified
protein and with the product of carboxymethylation in solution.

## Experimental Methods

Reaction of myoglobin crystals with bromoacetate. Type A
crystals of myoglobin (30) prepared by low temperature fractionation with ethanol and metallic ions (31) were grown from
ammonium sulfate solutions, usually in the presence of phosphate buffers. The pH range for crystallization was usually
chosen as 6.8-7.1 to correspond to the pH of the alkylation
reaction. In at least one case, however, the original crystallization was made at pH 6.1 which has some advantages for the
quality of crystals obtained. Since this latter case (preparation G) yielded good results, there seems to be some advantage
in making a practice of crystallizing at pH 6.1-6.4. Crystallization was generally obtained from 70-75 percent saturation
with ammonium sulfate. The initial concentration of protein
was usually 1.5 to 2.0 g per 100 ml.

The reaction was initiated by replacing the mother liquor
with a solution containing sodium bromoacetate, phosphate buffer and ammonium sulfate. The bromoacetate was prepared from
recrystallized bromoacetic acid. The usual concentrations were
0.2 M sodium bromoacetate, 3.8 M ammonium sulfate and 0.2 M
phosphate buffer to adjust the pH to 6.9-7.1. Sodium is the
alkali ion of choice because of the risk of crystallizing out
potassium sulfate from the reaction mixture. The reaction was
carried out at 22-24°.

To avoid the loss of an effective concentration of bromoacetate and to minimize any fall in pH by release of acid, the
reaction medium was renewed from time to time. The simplest
technique was to siphon off mother liquor or reaction medium
from the crystals contained in a small vial and to replace with
a fresh charge of reaction medium. For most purposes this procedure is the most satisfactory. The pH of the withdrawn
reaction medium should read 6.8-7.0. The reaction medium was
usually changed within the first day and again at intervals of
about 3 to 7 days. The volume of each charge of reaction medium

is conveniently kept close to that from which the original crystallization was made. In this way 1 to 1.5 μ moles of protein are bathed by 1 ml of the reaction medium.

A similar arrangement that has been used effectively is to contain the crystals in a sintered glass thimble so that the reaction medium can be conveniently removed.

In the early experiments a flow technique was used. The crystal bed was supported on a filter in a tube and reaction mixture pumped through. This technique has some advantages for large batches. An upward flow through the crystal bed has some advantages in avoiding mechanical damage from packing. The continuous flow method was used to counter the possible objection that reacted molecules might dissolve, complete their reaction in solution, and recrystallize, a process that might go unnoticed in the batch method. Provided the ammonium sulfate concentration was maintained high enough, however, practically no protein was carried away. The method has the disadvantage of rather more manipulation of the crystals than is desirable, although one batch so treated (preparation D) was successfully tested for crystal integrity by X-ray analysis.

At the completion of the desired reaction period the reaction medium was replaced with a washing solution of identical composition except for the omission of the sodium bromoacetate. The pH of the washing solution may be adjusted down to pH 5.9 or 6.0 if desired in preparation for X-ray analysis. Washing was usually effected with several changes of medium over a 48-hour period, or by continuous flow.

Those crystals not used for X-ray examination were dissolved in water or 0.2 M phosphate and dialyzed exhaustively against water. The crystals were not as readily soluble in water as the crystals of the unmodified protein. In some cases it was convenient to redissolve the crystals to make solutions of the order of 2 g per 100 ml by raising the pH to 8-8.5 with an alkaline phosphate or dilute sodium hydroxide solution.

Other techniques followed previous reports of amino acid analysis (5) and other characterization procedures (3,4,28,31). The X-ray diffraction observations were made by one of us (L.J. Banaszak) in collaboration with Drs. P. Bretscher, J. C. Kendrew and H. C. Watson, and by Dr. L. K. Steinrauf. Complete three-dimensional analyses of representative crystals are being made in Cambridge and are referred to by H. C. Watson elsewhere in this volume (32).

## Results

Course of the reaction. The course of the reaction is illustrated in Fig. 1. The number of histidine residues remaining per molecule as a function of reaction time in days is shown for a crystal preparation (closed circle). The results of reaction in solution (open circles) and in 8 M urea (half-closed circles) are taken from a previous paper (5), and apply to the same pH, $7.0 \pm 0.1$.

The relative rates in solution and in the crystalline state are not distinguishable in this study. Considering the time scale of the reaction and the fact that most crystals were of the order of magnitude of 0.1 mm or less, it is scarcely surprising that the rates appear comparable. The higher rates and degrees of reaction in the presence of strong urea have been described (5).

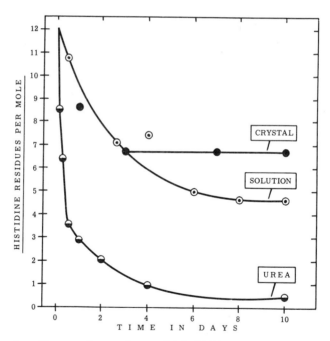

Figure 1. Change in number of histidine residues in metmyoglobin with time in days for reaction in the crystalline state (—●——●——●—) compared, from a previous publication (5), with reaction in solution (—○——○——○—) and in the presence of 8 M urea (—◉——◉——◉—).

The ultimate minimum value at which the histidine content leveled off is clearly higher in the crystalline state than in solution. With one exception to be discussed later, no reactions in the crystalline state have proved to yield less than 6 unaltered histidine residues per molecule. On the other hand, levels of 5 or even 4 unaltered histidine residues are reached frequently in solution (5).

Composition of reacted preparations. Table I shows the composition with respect to histidine and its derivatives of 8 preparations obtained by reaction in the crystalline state. The analyses were performed on the whole protein after removal of heme and number of residues per molecule computed as before (5). Previous observations were confirmed as to the nearly complete restriction of reaction to histidine residues (5).

The results in Table I show values for histidine between 6.0 and 7.9. The values for dicarboxymethylhistidine fall between 2.1 and 4.0, for 3-monocarboxymethylhistidine between 1.4 and 2.2, and for 1-monocarboxymethylhistidine between 0.6 and 0.8 residues per molecule, except for one preparation (M) in which the latter value was enough lower that an accurate estimate was not made.

TABLE I

Content of Histidine and Derivatives in Myoglobin Treated
in the Crystalline State with Bromoacetate
Reaction conditions are described in the text.

| Prepara-tion | Reaction Time, Days | Histidine | Carboxymethyl Histidines 1,3-di | 3-mono | 1-mono | Total |
|---|---|---|---|---|---|---|
| A | 10 | 7.3 | 2.1 | 1.5 | 0.7 | 11.6 |
| B | 20 | 6.9 | 2.3 | 1.6 | 0.7 | 11.5 |
| C | 10 | 6.8 | 2.6 | 2.2 | 0.6 | 12.2 |
| D | 10 | 6.0 | 2.5 | 1.8 | 0.8 | 11.1 |
| E | 14 | 6.0 | 3.1 | 1.5 | 0.6 | 11.2 |
| K | 30 | 6.1 | 3.5 | 1.6 | 0.6 | 11.8 |
| M | 10 | 7.9 | 3.0 | 1.4 | --- | 12.3 |
| N | 13 | 6.8 | 4.0 | 1.4 | 0.6 | 12.8 |

Ultimate values for each form of carboxymethylhistidine
cannot be predicted with certainty. The reaction cannot pro-
fitably be run indefinitely because some reaction does occur
with lysine residues. For example, preparation K contained
17.8 residues per molecule of lysine instead of the theoretical
19. It is possible that one particularly reactive lysine residue is present. The maximum value for dicarboxymethylhistidine
probably is not less than 4. Both of the monocarboxymethyl
isomers can undergo a second step of alkylation to form the
dicarboxymethyl derivative. Dr. D. K. Ray has shown with solution reactions that the 3-isomer passes through a clear maximum
during the course of the reaction (D. K. Ray and F. R. N. Gurd,
in preparation). This is to be expected, since the 1-position
is probably usually the more hindered. One is tempted to try
to assign an ultimate value to the 3-isomer of 1 or 2 and to
the 1-isomer of 1 or 0. There remains the real possibility
that one or more residues in the protein will be reactive at
either nitrogen atom initially but will have a tendency to
assume an orientation after the first reaction step such that
neither monocarboxymethyl isomer will react further.

Table II shows comparable analytical values for myoglobin
in solution reacted with bromoacetate. The most striking difference is in the higher content of the dicarboxymethyl form,
which clearly can reach values of 5 or 6 residues per molecule.
Values for monocarboxymethyl isomers are generally comparable
or lower.

TABLE II

Content of Histidine and Derivatives in Myoglobin Treated
in Solution with Bromoacetate

┌─Residues per Myoglobin Molecule ─┐

| Histidine | Carboxymethyl Histidines | | | Total |
|:---:|:---:|:---:|:---:|:---:|
| | 1,3-di | 3-mono | 1-mono | |
| 5.1 | 5.2 | 1.2 | 0.4 | 11.9* |
| 4.7 | 5.9 | 1.0 | 0.3 | 11.9* |
| 5.6 | 4.8 | 1.1 | 0.6 | 12.1* |
| 6.0 | 4.4 | 0.9 | 0.4 | 11.7* |
| 5.2 | 4.8 | 1.2 | 0.7 | 11.9 |
| 5.8 | 4.3 | 1.8 | 0.4 | 12.3 |
| 5.5 | 3.8 | 1.1 | 0.9 | 11.3 |
| 5.3 | 4.4 | 1.6 | --- | 11.3 |

*These results were made available through the kindness of
Dr. D. K. Ray.

Reactions proceeding to denaturation. A previous report
has been made of the course of the carboxymethylation reaction
under frankly denaturing conditions such as the presence of
8 M urea (c.f. Fig. 1), high temperature or low pH (5). In
solution it has been possible in one case with long exposure
to bromoacetate, under otherwise standard conditions, to obtain
a preparation apparently containing some quite altered material
(5,6). This material contained the following numbers of residues per molecule of lysine, histidine, dicarboxymethylhistidine, and the 3- and 1-monocarboxymethylhistidines, respectively:
18.4, 3.7, 7.4, 0.6, and a mere trace. These results suggest
that the carboxymethylation reaction can be forced in solution
to the point of conversion of monocarboxymethyl derivatives
almost completely to dicarboxymethylhistidine. These results
were obtained at the expense of some degree of drastic denaturation: it was possible to separate by ammonium sulfate
precipitation a fraction much richer in reacted histidine,
leaving in solution a fraction of higher content in unreacted
histidine. The observations suggest an all-or-none process in
which a fraction of the material was altered enough to be considered denatured. Such results were difficult to repeat. It
appears that a limit of 4 unreacted histidine residues is not
readily passed in solution.

However, in one case we have been surprised to obtain a
highly altered preparation from a reaction in the solid state.
The conditions were close to those used in preparation K
(Table I) and the crystal batch was the same. The crystals
were treated in a column supported by a sintered glass disk
with a reaction mixture composed of 0.2M sodium bromoacetate
and 0.1 M sodium phosphate in saturated ammonium sulfate with
final adjustment to pH 7 with NaOH.The reaction mixture was
pumped through the crystal bed at approximately 1 to 2 ml per
hour. Fresh reaction mixture was prepared at intervals of
about 4 days. After 29 days at $23^0$ the reaction mixture was
replaced with 3.8 M ammonium sulfate solution. After 4 days
of washing, the reacted myoglobin was dissolved in water and
dialyzed against water. A portion of the reacted myoglobin
was separated and examined microscopically without being dissolved. It was found to have lost its original crystalline
structure.

This preparation was found to contain 11.1 residues per
molecule of dicarboxymethylhistidine and only traces of histidine and the two monocarobxymethyl derivatives. Values for
lysine and methionine fell within normal limits. Absorption
spectra and ORD behavior indicated as fully denatured a preparation as we have obtained by any means (28). Unless some
unsuspected accident occurred, the only suggestion for a basis

for the trouble is that the ammonium sulfate concentration was kept as nearly saturated as possible, somewhat above the 3.8 M that we should now prefer. Myoglobin appears to be somewhat sensitive to surface denaturation in the presence of ammonium sulfate. It is significant that in the present case no protein was carried away in solution during the continuous flow procedure.

Evidence for penetration of crystals by bromoacetate. Before proceeding to discuss the properties of the reacted protein preparations and to elaborate on the differences between the reaction in the crystal and in solution, it is useful to give evidence to establish that the bromoacetate did have access throughout the crystals. The most direct evidence is offered by zone electrophoresis which shows that the crystal-reacted preparations contained no protein with the electrophoretic properties of the original myoglobin. Carboxymethylation contributes to the negative charge on the protein, so that all preparations have proved to be strongly anionic in the pH range of 7.0 to 7.5. Unreacted myoglobin will bear little charge under such conditions and will show migration either in the opposite direction or respond to the effects of anion binding or endosmosis by migrating very slightly as an anion.

Most preparations obtained by reaction in the crystalline state have been tested for the presence of unreacted protein by gel electrophoresis in a buffer of pH 7.0-7.5, 0.01 M with respect to phosphate and 0.002 M with respect to EDTA (31). In no case has unreacted protein been demonstrated. Unreacted control protein characteristically shows little migration under these conditions, although it is not itself electrophoretically homogeneous (31). Reacted samples show the many-banded appearance noted with the unreacted material at a suitable pH (31). The clear separation from the unreacted protein has also been seen with preparations mixed with unreacted protein before electrophoresis.

Properties of the reacted preparations. Some of the properties of myoglobin preparations treated in the crystalline state with bromoacetate are given in Table III. The reaction time, molarity of bromoacetate, number of charges of bromoacetate used, and number of histidine residues per molecule all fill in or expand information already given. The sixth column shows which preparations were demonstrated by X-ray analysis to be crystalline at the completion of the bromoacetate treatment. All other preparations listed retained their characteristic microscopic appearance but were not subjected to X-ray study. The seventh column similarly lists those preparations on which electrophoretic observations were made, again showing in all cases tested the absence of unreacted protein. The eighth column shows $S_{20 \cdot w}$ values where available, measured at a protein concentration of about 0.6 g per 100 ml. These values fall close to those previously reported for the unreacted protein (4,23,34). Single symmetrical peaks were observed. The known tendency of myoglobin to aggregate to some extent (21) does not seem to be exaggerated in these preparations. However, one should bear in mind that most of these preparations dissolve more slowly than the unmodified protein.

The ninth and tenth columns in Table III show some molar extinction ratios observed with these preparations. These fall in the range of normal for the unreacted protein (31). A more detailed consideration of the effect of carboxymethylation of the heme spectrum of the protein will be published separately (D. K. Ray and F. R. N. Gurd, in preparation). It is enough to point out that a preparation such as N has been found to be remarkably similar to the unreacted protein, and, further, that abnormal spectra were not usually detected except in the case of preparations reacted in solution and carried to a stage in which less than five unreacted histidine residues remained.

The last column in Table III shows some values of mean residue rotation at 233 m$\mu$, $[m']_{233}$. This parameter gives some measure of apparent helix content (24,28). The values for preparations G and N correspond to that of the native protein measured with the same equipment (28). Those for preparations A and H represent rather low values. The latter measurements were made after the preparations had stood at 4$^\circ$ for some months, and should probably not be taken as a basis for pessimism. Preparations obtained by reaction in solution have generally given values comparable to that of preparation G.

Titration behavior. The titration curve of preparation N, shown in Fig. 2, is very similar to that of the unmodified protein (3). The arrows show the direction of titration around the hysteresis loop, and the points show that the hysteresis loop is reproducible. This latter observation makes a point of difference from the unmodified protein. The possible bases of this effect are discussed elsewhere (J. F. Clark, C. R. Hartzell and F. R. N. Gurd, in preparation), along with a detailed analysis of the curve in Fig. 2. It is noteworthy that the maximum span of the difference curve, resulting from the release of histidine residues masked in the basic unprotonated form, which is near 5 proton units per mole, is close to the characteristic value of 6 found with the unmodified protein. A series of preparations alkylated in solution have shown the same behavior.

TABLE III

Properties of Myoglobin Preparations Treated in the Crystalline State with Bromoacetate

| Preparation | Reaction Time, Days | Bromoacetate M | No. of Charges | Histidine Residues per Molecule | Crystalline by X-ray | Absence of Unreacted Protein | $S_{20/w}$ | $\epsilon_{409}/\epsilon_{280}$ | $\epsilon_{503}/\epsilon_{630}$ | $[m']_{233}$ |
|---|---|---|---|---|---|---|---|---|---|---|
| A | 10 | 0.2 | 1 | 7.3 | | + | 2.00 | | 2.6 | -8100 |
| B | 20 | 0.2 | 1 | 6.9 | | | | | 2.6 | |
| C | 10 | 0.2 | *f | 6.8 | | + | 2.24 | | | |
| D | 10 | 0.2 | f* | 6.0 | + | + | 2.09 | | 2.4 | |
| E | 14 | 0.2 | f* | 6.0 | + | + | 2.21 | | | |
| F | 27 | 0.2 | 4 | 6.8 | + | | | | 2.5 | |
| G | 20 | 0.1 | 7 | 6.3 | + | + | 2.08 | | 2.5 | -8750 |
| H | 17 | 0.2 | | 7.8 | | + | 2.29 | | 2.6 | -8000 |
| J | 9 | 0.2 | 4 | 7.1 | | + | | 5.1 | | |
| K | 30 | 0.2 | 9 | 6.1 | | | | 5.4 | | |
| L | 10 | 0.2 | 4 | 6.7 | | + | | | 2.5 | |
| M | 10 | 0.2 | 5 | 7.9 | + | + | | 5.4 | | |
| N | 13 | 0.2 | 9 | 6.8 | | | | | 5.3 | -9000 |

* f = Continuous flow

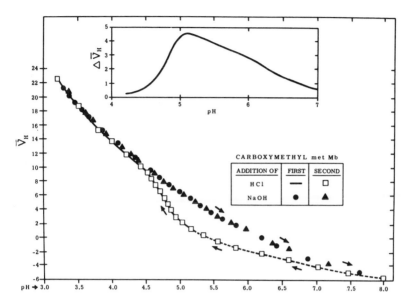

**Figure 2.** Titration of carboxymethyl metmyoglobin prepared by reaction in the crystalline state (preparation N). The ordinate is $\bar{\nu}_H$, the average number of hydrogen ions bound per molecule, starting from pH 5.4, the pH at which the dialyzed solution was obtained. The temperature was $25°$, ionic strength 0.16 provided by KCl. The course of titration is indicated by arrows and the symbols in the figure. The difference curve between forward and back titrations is inset.

Preparation N also shows a point of quantitative similarity with several preparations obtained by reaction in solution. The titration curve of the native form shows a span in the average number of hydrogen ions taken up between pH 8.0 and 5.3 corresponding to a number arrived at by allowing for the fact that dicarboxymethylhistidine groups are lost from titration in this range (J. F. Clark, C. R. Hartzell, and F. R. N. Gurd, in preparation). This fact fits with the assumption that none of the normally masked histidine residues has been released to an exposed form by any conformational change induced by the alkylation process (5). In other words, the results support the idea that in such a preparation only exposed histidine residues are alkylated by bromoacetate, and that this process does not cause any of the masked histidine residues to be everted.

Reactive histidine residues. For reasons discussed
below, no recent evidence has been added to the previous chemical identification of reactive and unreactive histidine residues (5,6). Peptide maps of crystal-reacted carboxymethyl
myoglobin are so similar to those derived from the solution
reacted protein that the general evidence for similarity is
well supported.

The fact that the reaction proceeds farther in solution
than in the crystalline state implies that redissolved crystal-
reacted protein would react further with bromoacetate. Such
is found to be the case. If the protein is first reacted in
the crystalline state and then redissolved and exposed again
to bromoacetate, the number of unreacted histidine residues
per molecule falls to values between 4 and 5.

## Discussion

The evidence presented above shows that myoglobin in the
crystalline state reacts with bromoacetate to form a product
that retains many of the properties of the native, unmodified
molecule. Irreversible aggregation was not detected. The
spectral properties ascribable to the heme were not modified.
Preparations were obtained in which the apparent helix content,
judged from values for $[m']_{233}$ (28), was not changed. The titration behavior indicated that the reacted histidine residues
belonged to the exposed class of imidazole groups that are
capable of entering into equilibrium with hydrogen ions.
Furthermore, the reaction left intact virtually the whole class
of masked imidazole groups that do not equilibrate in the native protein with hydrogen ions but are confined to the basic,
uncharged form within the structure (3).

The full value of the modification will be realized with
the completion of X-ray diffraction and chemical analyses. The
X-ray diffraction analysis should show the occupancy of poten-
tially reactive histidine sites and perhaps give indications
of the attitude taken up by the added carboxymethyl groups.
The chemical analyses will confirm these results and be capable
of extension by similar techniques to other reaction products.
The latter type of extension has already been done in part for
the case of the product obtained from reaction in solution (5,
6).

Up to the present we have biased our plans a little in
the direction of service to the crystallographic studies. For
purposes of the crystallography it has seemed best for the sake

of consistency to use the whole myoglobin preparation. This
contains several components probably having unitary differences
in amide content (31,35,36). The whole myoglobin has been used
in the past for the crystallographic analysis since the amide
and carboxyl groups are indistinguishable except for potential
differences in hydrogen bonding patterns. It was used in our
earliest work to conserve material (3).

We have recently turned to a necesssary step in simplify-
ing the chemical identification of the reactive histidine residues. This will require the preparation of appreciable
quantities of the major component by adaptation of known methods
(31,34,35). With an initial preparation that is electrophoretically homogeneous, it should be possible to develop a
simpler scheme of digestion and separation of peptide fragments.
Furthermore, any electrophoretic heterogeneity in the reacted
protein will be more directly interpretable.

The results in Fig. 1 and Tables I and II show that the
reaction in the crystalline state involves the modification of
6 histidine residues on the average, whereas in the dissolved
state 7 residues are usually affected. The difference appears
as an increase in dicarboxymethylhistidine. These results may
mean that the protein is held in a more rigid form in the crystalline state than in solution. At face value the implication
is that some opening up of the molecule can occur in solution
leading to the exposure of at least one more reactive histidine
residue. This interpretation is reasonable in that prolonged
reaction in solution to the point of reaction at 8 or more histidine residues does seem to bring on noticeable changes in
conformation (28). One has only to postulate that the seventh
histidine residue to react requires some opening up of the molecule but that, once reacted, it does not affect the conformation of the protein to a detectable degree. A clear interpretation on this basis is hampered by the fact that the reacted
proteins must be somewhat heterogeneous and we do not know the
distributions around the mean compositions.

The most direct form of evidence to settle the question
will come from complete chemical determination (5,6,35,41) of
the points of reaction in a preparation continuing 7 reacted
histidine residues. If one of the reacted residues proves to
be one not exposed in the crystalline structure, as judged by
steric factors apparent in the molecular model, then good evidence for opening up at that region of the molecule will have
been obtained. If such an apparent opening up is observed, it
will still be necessary to judge whether or not the process is
promoted by the existance of carboxymethyl groups on other histidine residues in the molecule, as a result of a consecutive
reaction (5).

Apart from possible differences in conformational lability, two other types of factors must be considered in comparing the results of reaction in the crystalline and dissolved states. The first is geometrical and the second has to do with solvent effects.

First, the dimensions of the channels between protein molecules in the crystal must be considered. In some cases adequate access to an otherwise exposed histidine residue may be denied by the crystal packing itself. This question can be tested to some extent by calculations based on the known atomic coordinates and relations between molecules. Thermal motion in the crystal may affect the effective channel dimensions. The effect of channel dimensions near a given histidine residue on the rate of reaction at that residue will be difficult to predict if room for the bromoacetate to maneuver becomes restricted.

Second, differences in solvent environment likewise may so change the rate of reaction that the extent of reaction in the crystal appears to be less than that in solution. Variation of ammonium sulfate concentration between 0.0 and 0.8 M in the presence of 0.2 M phosphate buffer has been found to have no detectable effect on the extent and pattern of reaction in solution after 10 days. However, in the crystalline state the occupation of certain sites by sulfate ions may well influence reactivity, for example at histidine E7 (15). One must bear in mind the interesting effects of sulfate and phosphate in restricting carboxymethylation in ribonuclease (42).

An attempt to compare the reaction in the crystalline and amorphous precipitated states in 3.8 M ammonium sulfate was hampered by the tendency of the protein to pass into the crystalline state from the amorphous. Experiments are being planned to test the effect of solvent variation by the use of cross-linked protein preparations (19).

## Acknowledgments

The advice and encouragement of Drs. J. C. Kendrew, H. C. Watson, F. M. Richards, E. Breslow, L. K. Steinrauf, D. K. Ray, E. H. Eylar, and H. L. Mermall are gratefully acknowledged. Mrs. R. Morrow provided essential help.

This is the 23rd paper in a series dealing with coordination complexes and catalytic properties of protein and related substances. Some of the material is taken from the thesis of J. F. Clark submitted to Indiana University in partial fulfullment of the requirements for the Ph.D. degree, 1966.

## References

1. Kendrew, J. C., R. E. Dickerson, B. E. Strandberg, R. G. Hart, D. R. Davies, D. C. Phillips, and V. C. Shore. Nature, 185, 422 (1960).

2. Kendrew, J. C., H. C. Watson, B. E. Strandberg, R. E. Dickerson, D. C. Phillips, and V. C. Shore. Nature, 190, 666 (1961).

3. Breslow, E., and F. R. N. Gurd. J. Biol. Chem., 237, 371 (1962).

4. Banaszak, L. J., E. H. Eylar and F. R. N. Gurd. J. Biol. Chem., 238, 1989 (1963).

5. Banaszak, L. J., P. A. Andrews, J. W. Burgner, E. H. Eylar and F. R. N. Gurd. J. Biol. Chem., 238, 3307 (1963).

6. Banaszak, L. J., and F. R. N. Gurd. J. Biol. Chem., 239, 1836 (1964).

7. Richards, F. M. Ann. Rev. Biochem., 32, 269 (1963).

8. Kendrew, J. C. Brookhaven Symp. Biol., 15, 216 (1962).

9. Crestfield, A. M., W. H. Stein, and S. Moore. J. Biol. Chem., 238, 2413 (1963).

10. Hapner, K. D., and R. W. Roeske. Abstracts of American Chemical Society Meeting, Denver, Colo., January, 1964, p. 38A.

11. Gurd, F. R. N. In Enzyme Structure, Section in Vol. 6, Carboxymethylation (C. H. W. Hirs, ed.). In Methods in Enzymology, Carboxymethylation (S. P. Colowick and N. O. Kaplan, eds.), Academic Press, Inc., in press.

12. Heinrikson, R. L., W. H. Stein, A. M. Crestfield, and S. Moore. J. Biol. Chem., 240, 2921 (1965).

13. Gurd, F. R. N. Biochem. J., 95, 60P (1965).

14. Bodo, G., H. M. Dintzis, J. C. Kendrew, and H. W. Wycoff. Proc. Roy. Soc. (London), A253, p. 70 (1959).

15. Stryer, L., J. C. Kendrew, and H. C. Watson. J. Mol. Biol., 8, 96 (1964).

16. Banaszak, L. J., H. C. Watson, and J. C. Kendrew. J. Mol. Biol., 12, 130 (1965).

17. Nobbs, C. L., H. C. Watson, and J. C. Kendrew. Nature, 209, 339 (1966).

18. Blake, C. C. F., D. F. Koenig, G. A. Mair, A. North, D. C. Phillips, and V. R. Sarma. Nature, 206, 757 (1965).

19. Richards, F. M., V. Kenkare, F. Quicho, H. Wycoff, and T. Inagami. Abstracts of National Meeting, American Chemical Society, Atlantic City, N. J., September, 1965, p. 32C.

20. Fasold, H. Biochem. Z., 342, 295 (1965).

21. Sztankay, Z. G., J. W. Anderegg, and W. W. Beeman. Abstracts of Biophysical Society Meeting, San Francisco, Calif., February, 1965, p. 145.

22. Krigbaum, W. R., and R. T. Brierre. Nature, 206, 396 (1965).

23. Urnes, P. J., K. Imahori, and P. M. Doty. Proc. Nat. Acad. Sci. U. S., 47, 1675 (1961).

24. Beychok, S., and E. R. Blout. J. Mol. Biol., 3, 769 (1961).

25. Beychok, S., C. de Loze, and E. R. Blout. J. Mol. Biol., 4, 421 (1962).

26. Samejima, T., and J. T. Yang. J. Mol. Biol., 8, 863 (1964).

27. Harrison, S. C., and E. R. Blout. J. Mol. Biol., 240, 299 (1965).

28. Breslow, E., S. Beychok, K. D. Hardman, and F. R. N. Gurd. J. Biol. Chem., 240, 704 (1965).

29. Urnes, P. J. Gen. Physiol., 49, 75 (1965).

30. Kendrew, J. C., and R. G. Parrish. Proc. Roy. Soc. (London), A238, 305 (1957).

31. Hardman, K. D., E. H. Eylar, D. K. Ray, L. J. Banaszak, and F. R. N. Gurd. J. Biol. Chem., 241, 432 (1966).

32. Watson, H. C. This volume, p. 63.

33. Breslow, E. J. Biol. Chem., 239, 486 (1964).

34. Crumpton, J. J., and A. Polson. J. Mol. Biol., 11, 722 (1965).

35. Edmundson, A. B., and C. H. W. Hirs. Nature, 190, 663 (1961)

36. Edmundson, A. B., and C. H. W. Hirs. J. Mol. Biol., 5, 663 (1962).

37. Edmundson, A. B., and C. H. W. Hirs. J. Mol. Biol., 5, 683 (1962).

38. Edmundson, A. B., and C. H. W. Hirs. J. Mol. Biol., 5, 706 (1962).

39. Edmundson, A. B. Nature, 198, 754 (1963).

40. Edmundson, A. B. Nature, 205, 883 (1965).

41. Harris, C. M. Thesis, Duke University, 1965.

42. Crestfield, A. M., W. H. Stein, and S. Moore. J. Biol. Chem., 238, 2421 (1963).

DISCUSSION

Urnes: I would like to ask Dr. Gurd two questions. The first is whether he has studied the reaction of bromoacetate with metmyoglobin crystals formed in phosphate buffer. Since these crystals have a different morphology from those obtained with ammonium sulfate, the pattern of reactivity of the histidine may also differ, and thereby indicate the effect of steric restraint imposed on the reaction by the crystalline lattice.

The second question is whether the distal histidine reacts with bromoacetate.* If it does, the binding of the sulfate ion might be prevented. One would thus have a preparation for studying the roles played by this ion and the distal histidine in the reduction and deoxygenation of myoglobin.

Gurd: Our normal reaction conditions have had about 0.2 M phosphate buffer in with the ammonium sulfate. As stated in my paper, in the absence of ammonium sulfate the reaction in solution in the presence of 0.8 M phosphate did not appear to change the pattern. We have not worked with the classical Kendrew and Parrish phosphate crystals, as we could have, because the X-ray work has been done mainly on ammonium sulfate crystals and the location of bound sulfate is established. We believe that the distal histidine probably reacts in solution, but we are not certain. Now that we have a homogenous starting material from the point of view of charge, we intend to go into that type of work. We have tried to get at the question of a relation between the state of the iron, with respect to valence or ligand occupancy, and the state of the distal histidine with respect to reactivity or modification. One way, attempted with Dr. D. K. Ray, is to compare the reaction of bromoacetate with metmyoglobin with that with the CO derivative of myoglobin. There is a small and reproducible tendency for the reaction with the CO derivative to lead to a fractionally higher quantity of the 1-monocarboxymethyl-histidine derivative. The point must be checked by isolating an appropriate peptide segment from the reacted protein.

*Editors' note: Perutz and Mathews (1) have recently found that the sulfate is not present on the E7 histidine in crystals of horse ferrihemoglobin.

Watson: The complete three-dimensional X-ray data for the carboxy methylated derivative of metmyoglobin has been collected and processed. We are now in a position to inspect each histidine in the Fourier synthesis to see if its $\delta$ or $\epsilon$ imidazole nitrogens have reacted with bromoacetate.

## References

1. Perutz, M. F., and N. Mathews    J. Mol. Biol., in press.

METHEMOGLOBIN M$_{\text{BOSTON}}$; A SUBUNIT INTERACTION OBSERVED

BY NMR RELAXATION

T. L. Fabry and S. H. Koenig

IBM Watson Laboratory, Columbia University
New York City, New York

Hemoglobin $M_B$ is an abnormal hemoglobin characterized by the replacement of the histidine residue at position 58 by a tyrosine in each of the two $\alpha$ chains. The major effect of this mutation is that the Fe atom of each $\alpha$ chain is rapidly oxidized to the ferric or "met" state at physiologic oxygen partial pressures (1).

By studying the nuclear magnetic relaxation time of protons in water in which the hemoglobin is dissolved, one can study the accessibility of the paramagnetic ions to the solvent molecules (2). The main result that we wish to report here is the discovery that when the four iron atoms per molecule are oxidized, those of the $\beta$ chains (the "normal" chains) are more accessible to the solvent water molecules than those of the $\alpha$ chain; their contribution per iron to the proton relaxation rate is about five times that of the $\alpha$ $Fe^{+++}$ ions, which in turn roughly equals the rate per iron of fully oxidized normal adult hemoglobin. We have as yet no way of determining, however, whether the $\beta$ heme irons are permanently in this accessible position, or only become so upon oxidation of either the $\alpha$ or $\beta$ heme irons.

## Experimental Procedures

Blood of a patient suffering from methemoglobinemia containing hemoglobin $M_B$ was kindly provided by Dr. Joan Harris. He also sent us a sample of normal blood drawn at the same time. Hemoglobin was prepared by the Drabkin procedure (3), but the final step was dialysis against EDTA to eliminate any free paramagnetic ion impurity. The hemoglobin A concentration was determined by the absorption at 576 and 540 m$\mu$. All chemicals were reagent grade from the usual supply houses.

The proton spin relaxation times were measured by a slight variation of standard pulse-echo techniques (4). A $180^\circ$ pulse of 25 mc rf magnetic field is first applied to the sample, inverting the nuclear magnetization. At a variable time $\tau$ later a $90^\circ - 180^\circ$ pair of pulses is applied to sample the remaining magnetization, which decays exponentially to its equilibrium value with a time constant $T_1$. The echo that follows the $90^\circ - 180^\circ$ pair, proportional to the magnetization at time $\tau$, is fed to a gated integrator, the output is manually plotted vs $\tau$, which is accurately measured with an electronic interval timer. This procedure allows the determination of $T_1$ with a scatter of $\sim 2$ percent from run to run (5).

The spectra were recorded on a Cary 14 spectrophotometer.

### Experimental Results

Unbuffered samples ($\sim 1$ cm$^3$) of hemoglobin A and hemoglobin M of equal concentration were run at first. A small amount of reducing agent, sodium dithionite, was added to the M, which was then run several times over a span of 6 hours. It took several hours for the M solution to reach its final value of $T_1$. (It was independently ascertained that the sodium dithionite has negligible effect on $T_1$). These data, corrected for dissolved $O_2$ and normalized to a concentration of $1.17 \times 10^{-3}$ M which was the concentration of the buffered solutions used subsequently, are in Table I.

TABLE I

Proton nuclear magnetic relaxation rates, normalized to a molar concentration of $1.17 \times 10^{-3}$, for a sample of hemoglobin A and of hemoglobin M$_B$ under varying conditions.

| Sample | $T_1^{-1}$ | | $T_1^{-1}$ |
|---|---|---|---|
| Type A, oxygenated | 0.58(a) | Type A, oxidized | 2.06(b) |
| | 0.63(b) | | |
| | 0.60(B) | | |
| Type M, oxygenated | 0.88(c) | Type M, oxidized | 2.75(c) |
| Type M, deoxy | 0.89(d) | | 2.75(B) |
| Type M, reduced | 0.62(d) | | 2.68(B) |

(a) Result from earlier measurements on hemoglobin A from another source.
(b),(c),(d) Indicate a particular aliquot.
(B) Solution in pH 6.85, 0.1N phosphate buffer.

From previous work, we know that the rates for oxyhemo-globin A and deoxyhemoglobin A are essentially equal (6). The results in the left hand part of Table I show that the reduced M (no met heme groups) and the normal A produce the same $T_1$. Additionally, from this data one can in principle compute the effect on the relaxation rate per $Fe^{+++}$ ion in the $\alpha$ chain of hemoglobin M. Unfortunately, the exact amount of hemoglobin M in the "M" sample is unknown, but is of the order of 30 percent (P. S. Gerald, personal communication).

The results show that the reduction obeys first order kinetics with a half-life of 35 minutes. This compares with the results of Gerald (7) who quotes 20 min at pH 10 and "somewhat longer at lower pH."

The following day different aliquots of the same samples were run as a function of $K_3Fe(CN)_6$ added as an oxidizing agent. These samples were buffered in pH 6.85, 0.1 N phosphate buffer to minimize pH changes upon oxidation. Controls run before and after buffering showed that no effect other than those expected from dilution occurred. All pertinent data are in Table I.

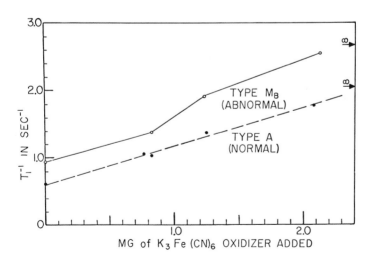

Figure 1. Relaxation rate of water protons in solutions of similar concentrations of hemoglobin $M_B$ and hemoglobin A as a function of oxidizer added. The type $M_B$, were it fully reduced initially, would have the same ordinate as the type A.

The relative relaxation rate induced per $Fe^{+++}$ for the various heme sites are shown in Table II for the expected limits of the fraction of M molecules in the type M sample. These are obtained in a fairly obvious manner from Table I. The main result of the experiment is readily seen in the figure. From Table II, it is seen that the met heme in the chain of type M relaxes protons at about the same rate as a typical met heme in type A. Therefore, the difference between the two curves in the figure at full oxidation can only be due to the larger relaxation rate induced by the $Fe^{+++}$ heme groups on the $\beta$ chain of the ~30 percent of the molecules that are hemoglobin M's.

TABLE II

Paramagnetic relaxation rates due to different heme groups, for different heme groups, for different hemoglobin $M_B$ content.

| Percent HbM | A | M | M |
|---|---|---|---|
| 20 | 1.45 | 2.6 | 6.9 |
| 30 | 1.45 | 1.7 | 5.5 |
| 50 | 1.45 | 1.0 | 4.5 |

Discussion

The main result reported here, despite the wide limits of uncertainty of some parameters characterizing the experiment, is unequivocal: the "normal" or $\beta$ hemes of hemoglobin $M_B$ **have** several hemoglobins. To discuss the nature of the change in the $\beta$ hemes and conjecture as to the mechanism of the subunit interaction requires recourse to the equation of interaction of the hemes with the solvent protons (8):

$$\frac{1}{NT_1} = \text{const.} \langle r^{-6} \rangle \tau_c \left[ 1 + \frac{7/3}{1 + \omega_s^2 \tau_c^2} \right] \quad (1)$$

which for our situation simplifies to

$$\frac{1}{NT_1} = \text{const.} \tau_s \langle r^{-6} \rangle \quad (2)$$

Here N is the concentration of paramagnetic centers and $<r^{-6}>$ is an appropriate ensemble average of the paramagnetic spin-proton separation, which reduces to some power to the distance of closest approach. $\tau_c$ is the time that the spin of an inter-acting proton remains correlated in spatial position and orientation with the spin of the paramagnetic center. For a spin bound to a large, slowly tumbling protein, $\tau_c \sim \tau_s$ , the spin lattice relaxation time of the paramagnetic spin, assuming that the hydration time is greater than $\sim 10^{-9}$ sec. For any reasonable value of $\tau_s$, obtained for example by extrapolating to room temperature the results of Hayashi et al.(9), $(\omega_s \tau_c)^2 \gg 1.$

Hayashi et al. (9) have reported the ESR spectrum of hemoglobin $M_B$ as well as methemoglobin A and methemoglobin $M_B$. The resonance amplitude of the $\alpha$ hemes of hemoglobin $M_B$ is ~50 times that of the type A, which would make the $\beta$ heme contribution of the met $M_B$ unobservable, in agreement with their findings. If the amplitude is so much greater, the intrinsic line width (determined in the main by $\tau_s$) is narrower; one concludes $\tau_{s_{\alpha,M}} \gg \tau_{s_{\beta,M}}$ and $\tau_{s_{\alpha,M}} \gg \tau_{s_A}$ .
From a close look at the data, one may also conclude $\tau_{s_{\beta,M}} \lesssim \tau_{s_A}$ .
Combining the Hayashi results with Eq. 2 and the data from Table II, one concludes that $<r^{-6}>_{\alpha,M} < <r^{-6}>_A$

or that water cannot get too close to the abnormal hemes in hemoglobin $M_B$. This would result from the conjecture of Gerald and Scott (1) that the phenol group of the tyrosine as a ligand produces a conformational distortion of the $\alpha$ chain which is mechanically transmitted to the $\beta$ chain, which in turn distorts so as to expose the $\beta$ hemes more to the solvent. The distortion is of a magnitude which makes these heme groups as accessible to the water as those in myoglobin (10). [ Note added in proof: It has been pointed out to us by Aisen that a somewhat different interpretation is possible; the oxidation of the $\beta$ hemes might cause an allosteric interaction and change the conformation at the site of the $\alpha$ hemes.]

A more quantitative discussion must await a programmatic study of the relaxation rate as a function of frequency, preferably on 100 percent hemoglobin $M_B$.

## Acknowledgements

We thank Dr. P. S. Gerald for furnishing the blood specimens from which the hemoglobin was obtained, Cathy Volin for preparing the hemoglobin, W. S. Schillinger and Al Goldbaum for their aid in collecting and reducing the data, and Miss M. E. Riepe for helpful discussions.

## References

1.  c.f., Gerald, P. S., and E. M. Scott. The Metabolic Basis of Inherited Disease (J. B. Stanbury, J. B. Wyngaarden, and D. S. Fredrickson, eds.), 2nd Edition, McGraw-Hill, New York, 1966, p. 1090.

2.  A discussion and a complete list of earlier references is to be found in the review by A. Kowalsky and M. Cohn. Ann. Rev. Biochemistry, 1964, p. 481.

3.  Drabkin, D. L.  J. Biol. Chem., 158, 703 (1946).

4.  Carr, H. Y., and E. M. Purcell.  Phys. Rev., 94, 630 (1954).

5.  This apparatus is very similar to that described by H. A. Reich and R. L. Garwin.  Phys. Rev., 115, 1478 (1959).

6.  Fabry, T. L., and H. A. Reich.  Biochem. Biophys. Res. Comm., 22, 700 (1966), and extensive unpublished measurements of the authors.

7.  Gerald, P. S., and P. George.  Science, 129, 393 (1959).

8.  Solomon, I.  Phys. Rev., 99, 559 (1955).

9.  Hayashi, A., A. Shimizu, Y. Yumamura, and H. Watari. Science, 152, 207 (1966); Biochim. Biophys. Acta, 102, 626 (1965).

10. Kon, H., and N. Davidson.  J. Mol. Biol., 1, 190 (1959).

THE ROLE OF INTERMOLECULAR INTERACTIONS, AS DISTINCT FROM
INTRAMOLECULAR INTERACTIONS, IN HEMOGLOBIN-OXYGEN EQUILIBRIA*

Abel Schejter

Department of Biochemistry, Tel-Aviv University
Tel-Aviv, Israel

Hemes and hematins are polydisperse in aqueous solutions
(1). The first important modification in the properties of
heme caused by its binding to a protein consists in the stabilization of its monomeric state. A short peptide chain is not
enough for this purpose; heme peptides derived from cytochrome
c are still complicated polydisperse systems (2,3). In order
to maximize the capabilities of the heme group for small ligand
binding, its sixth coordination position must be strongly protected from binding by polyvalent ligands, such as protein
chains. This protection is afforded by the specific conformation of heme proteins; a certain measure of crevice closedness
(4) is a useful structural feature for hemoproteins endowed
with oxygen storage and transport functions such as myoglobin
and hemoglobin.

On the other hand, multicellular animals thrive on a deli-
cately adjusted system of oxygen transport, physico-chemically
expressed in sigmoid curves for oxygen concentration as a
function of the fraction of reaction completed. A necessary
condition for this type of behavior is the presence of more
than one heme group per molecule.

The evolutionary process apparently reached a functional
compromise in the structure of the hemoglobins because these
molecules exist in physiological conditions as aggregates of
monomeric hemoprotein chains. On the basis of this structure,
several thermodynamic situations can cause the sigmoid shape
of the titration curves of the hemoglobin-oxygen equilibria.
Of these, the most widely discussed are those defined as intramolecular and intermolecular interactions.

*This work was supported by United States Public Health Service
Grant No. AM-03187-10.

The hypothesis of intramolecular interactions, which considers tetramic hemoglobin as the only molecular species participating in the equilibrium, was first formulated by Adair (5). This hypothesis implies that the hemes of a single molecule are not independent of each other in their affinity for oxygen. The mathematical consequences of such a situation have been exhaustively analyzed by Wyman (6), and its physical meaning is contained in the definition of a free energy of intramolecular interaction. If the hemes of tetrameric hemoglobin bind oxygen independently and with identical affinity, the successive macroscopic association constants will be related to each other by ratios predicted from statistical considerations; in this case, the titration curve will be hyperbolic. If, however, the free hemes of some partially oxygenated species have a different affinity than that expected on statistical grounds, intramolecular interaction occurs, and sigmoid titration curves are obtained.

Many years ago, Douglas, Haldane and Haldane (7) advanced a different explanation. They assumed that the intermolecular affinity of aggregated hemoglobin molecules was decreased by oxygenation, and derived on this basis equations that describe sigmoid titration curves. We shall refer to this interpretation as the intermolecular interaction hypothesis.

Very accurate measurements, especially at low and high percentages of saturation, permitted the estimation of the macroscopic association constants (8) defined by Adair. However, some old and some new facts cannot be justified on the basis of Adair's equation:

$$x = \frac{K_1 p + 2K_1 K_2 p^2 + 3K_1 K_2 K_3 p^3 + 4K_1 K_2 K_3 K_4 p^4}{4(1 + K_1 p + K_1 K_2 p^2 + K_1 K_2 K_3 p^3 + K_1 K2 K_3 K_4 p^4)} \qquad (1)$$

where x is the fraction of "total" reaction; p, the partial pressure of oxygen at equilibrium; and $K_1$, $K_2$, $K_3$, $K_4$, the successive macroscopic association constants.

It should be noticed that the total concentration of the titrated species, hemoglobin, does not appear in Equation 1. One would expect from this that at a constant set of thermodynamic constraints, hemoglobin concentration would not affect the shape or the position of the titration curves. That this is not so has been known for a long time. Barcroft was the first to point out that dilution of hemoglobin solutions caused the oxygenation curves to move to the left (9). An extensive investigation on the part of Hill showed concentration effects of varying degrees in the hemoglobins of nine different

species (10). More recent work shows the strong concentration
effects present in tadpole hemoglobin (11). A detailed study
on sheep hemoglobin, performed by Roughton and coworkers (8),
permitted the evaluation of the four macroscopic association
constants at two different concentrations. The first three
constants were found to be concentration dependent; thus, although providing a proper empirical description of the shape
of the titration curves at a single concentration, they lack
physiochemical meaning in stoichiometric terms.

The concentration effect has been interpreted by Roughton
(12) as due to van der Waals' interactions between adjacent
tetrameric hemoglobin molecules. The fundamental issue here
is not, however, the nature of the forces involved in these
interactions. The problem to be faced is whether it is correct
to disregard the concentration effects in writing the equations
that describe the hemoglobin-oxygen equilibrium. Actually, the
existence of concentration effects can be taken as evidence
that the intermolecular interaction hypothesis is, at least to
a certain extent, correct; concentration effects on the position of the equilibrium occur only in reactions where there
is a change in the number of molecules.

There are cases for which the generalized stoichiometric
equation (13):

$$p \; Hb_a + n \; L \rightleftharpoons q \; Hb_b L_{n/q} \tag{2}$$

applies almost quantitatively. The best example is the oxygenation of lamprey hemoglobin, studied by Briehl (14). In the
oxygenated state, this hemoglobin is a monomer, namely, it contains one heme per protein chain, up to appreciable concentrations; when deoxygenated, it is largely monomeric at low concentrations, and its·sedimentation constant increases as the
concentration is raised, reaching a value appropriate for a
trimer. Hence, in first approximation one can write the reaction as follows:

$$Hb_3 + 3 \; O_2 \rightleftharpoons 3 \; HbO_2 \tag{3}$$

If x designates the fraction of total reaction, it will be
related to the concentration of free ligand, and thus to p, by
the function:

$$-\log p = -\frac{1}{3}(\log K'_{obs}) + \frac{1}{3}(\log \frac{1}{3}) - \frac{2}{3}(\log C_{Hb}) + \frac{1}{3}(\log \frac{1-x}{x^3})$$

where $C_{Hb}$ is the total hemoglobin concentration (13).

Using Briehl's results (14), the predicted linear dependence was found, as shown in Fig. 1. The slope of the linear function is 0.36, very close to the predicted value of 0.33.

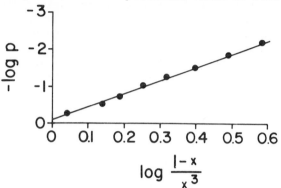

Figure 1. A plot of -log p vs. log $(1-x/x^3)$, using the titration of lamprey hemoglobin with oxygen at a hemoglobin concentration giving an absorbancy reading of E=535 at 275 mμ (data from (3)).

Equation 4, furthermore, permits us to estimate quite successfully the shape of the titration curve at a different concentration, as shown in Fig. 2.

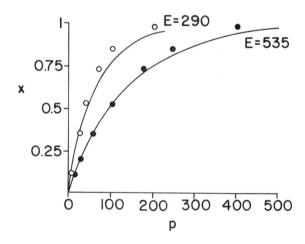

Figure 2. Oxygenation equilibria of lamprey hemoglobin at two different concentrations, expressed in absorbancies at 275 mμ (data from (3)). The points are calculated on the basis of Equation 4; the full lines represent the experimental results.

In the case of lamprey hemoglobin, treated with the intermolecular interactions assumption, there is no contradiction
between molecular weight determinations and titration data.
On the other hand, although most hemoglobins present concentration effects of varying degrees, the fully oxygenated forms
fail to show the differences in molecular weight expected from
a reaction described by Equation 2, with $p \neq q$. An alternative formulation of the equilibrium for a tetrameric hemoglobin in equilibrium with its dimers, is the following (13):

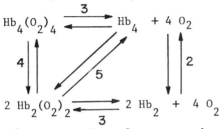

In this scheme, the aggregation of oxygenated and deoxygenated
hemoglobin is represented by reactions 2 and 4. If reaction 4
favors strongly the dimeric state, and reaction 2 favors
strongly the tetrameric state, we fall into the particular case
of lamprey hemoglobin, although with different stoichiometric
coefficients. This case is indicated by the diagonal reaction 5.

This system will give rise to sigmoid oxygenation curves
if the aggregation constants are different. The magnitude of
their difference determines the extent to which the titration
curve will deviate from the case where intermolecular interactions between oxygenated and deoxygenated hemoglobin dimers
are the same. It is by no means necessary that the difference
be of such a degree as in the case of lamprey hemoglobin.
However, it is reasonable to expect that oxygenation of mammalian tetrameric hemoglobins should cause a perceptible change
in their average molecular weight. Differences of this nature
have already been reported, although at concentrations substantially lower than those found in physiological conditions
(Gilbert, quoted by Roughton [12]).

The fact that the sedimentation constants of hemoglobin
and oxyhemoglobin at physiological concentrations approach the
values expected for a tetramer, seemingly militates against
the existence of different intermolecular interactions, or affinities, in the two states. Nevertheless, a number of observations indicates that dimers do exist even at large concentrations. Thus, measurements of escape time through membranes
indicate appreciable deaggregation of carboxyhemoglobin at
concentrations of 4 gm/100 ml (15). Moreover, the different
extent of hybridization observed under nitrogen and under oxygen

(16) can be explained if the proportion of dimers is larger in the oxygenated than in the deoxygenated state.

Another fact that is in keeping with the intermolecular interaction hypothesis, while in open contradiction with the intramolecular interaction hypothesis, is the effect of salt concentration on the oxygenation curves (9,17). In this case the direct relationship between the shape of the titration curves and the extent of deaggregation is clear: the molecular weight decreases, while the interactions increase, at high salt concentrations (17,18). Antonini (19) has pointed out that this result is paradoxical in terms of the intramolecular interaction hypothesis.

It is possible to envisage a compromise between both theories and the experimental facts, by assuming that the partially oxygenated intermediates are in equilibrium with their deaggregation products. This would lead to a system of consecutive boxes:

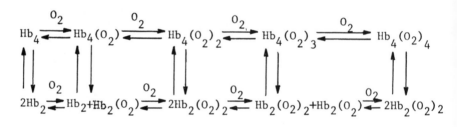

This already complicated scheme does not include all the possible intermediates; distinguishable dimeric species may occur, due to the different structure of the $\alpha$ and $\beta$ chains. The hypothesis of consecutive boxes does not require appreciable values for the deaggregation constants of all the tetrameric intermediates; in fact, if only one of these intermediates splits into dimers, the oxygenation curve will have sigmoid shape. In this system, free energies of deaggregation play the role reserved for the free energies of intramolecular interaction in Adair's hypothesis. If, in addition, the latter have significant values, there will be a cooperative effect between both types of interactions. The important fact is that where deaggregation constants have favorable magnitudes, they can be incorporated in the function that describes x, and with them the overall concentration of hemoglobin is also introduced, thus providing an explanation for the concentration effects. It also appears that the effect of high salt concentration is larger on the aggregation constants than on the intramolecular interactions. Undoubtedly the incorporation of aggregation constants complicates the estimation of thermody-namic parameters; at the same time, it takes into account con-centration effects in agreement with the observed facts. The equations that will finally describe such a system will also permit quantitative prediction of the concentration effects and will allow estimation of the true magnitude of the intra-molecular interactions.

The system of consecutive boxes also suggests an explana-tion for the striking dependence of viscosity and dielectric increment of hemoglobin solutions on the degree of oxygenation. These properties do not vary steadily, but instead they in-crease and decrease twice, showing maxima at about 25% and 75% saturation (20,21). It is possible that only some of the partially oxygenated intermediates deaggregate to a certain extent, thus causing observable changes in hydrodynamic and electrostatic properties of the whole system. In other words, tetrameric hemoglobins may have deaggregation constants of appreciable value only for some of the oxygenated intermediates.

In conclusion, it can be said that the effect of hemo-globin concentration on the hemoglobin-oxygen equilibria indi-cates that aggregation changes occur in the course of the reac-tion. Their extent must be determined experimentally, and this will show whether cooperative intramolecular interactions are also of measurable magnitude. The fact that in many cases hy-drodynamic properties do not show the changes expected from ligand binding studies is paradoxical. This problem is yet to be solved, but its relevance to the physiological situation is unclear, since recent work shows that the degree of aggrega-tion of the hemoglobin subunits may change drastically upon hemolysis (22). Evolution may have chosen both intra- and intermolecular interactions to fulfill the requirements of a useful oxygen transport system; most contemporary species seem to reflect this fact in their intermediate behavior.

## ACKNOWLEDGEMENTS

I wish to thank Dr. A. D. Adler for his advice and Dr. Nehamah Frowirt for many helpful discussions.

## References

1. Adler, A. Thesis, University of Pennsylvania, 1960.

2. Ehrenberg, A., and H. Theorell. Acta Chem. Scand., 9, 1193 (1955).

3. Margoliash, E., N. Frohwirt, and E. Weiner. Biochem. J., 71, 559 (1959).

4.  George, P., and R. L. J. Lyster. Proc. Natl. Acad. Sci., 44, 1088 (1958).

5.  Adair, G. S. J. Biol. Chem., 63, 529 (1925).

6.  Wyman, J. In Advances in Protein Chemistry (C. B. Anfinsen Jr., M. L. Anson, J. T. Edsall and F. M. Richards, eds.), Vol. 19, Academic Press, Inc., New York, 1964, p. 223.

7.  Douglass, C. G., J. S. Haldane, and J. B. S. Haldane. J. Physiol. (London), 44, 275 (1925).

8.  Roughton, F. J. W., A. B. Otis, and R. L. J. Lyster. Proc. Roy. Soc. London, 144B, 29 (1955).

9.  Barcroft, J. The Respiratory Function of the Blood, Part II, Hemoglobin, Cambridge University Press, Cambridge, 1928.

10. Hill, R., and H. P. Wolvekamp. Proc. Roy. Soc. London, 120B, 484 (1936).

11. Riggs, A. Can. J. Biochem., 42, 763 (1964).

12. Roughton, F. J. W. J. Gen. Physiol., 49, 105 (1965).

13. Schejter, A., A. Adler, and S. C. Glauser. Science, 141, 784 (1963).

14. Briehl, R. W. J. Biol. Chem., 238, 2361 (1963).

15. Guidotti, G., and L. C. Craig. Proc. Nat. Acad. Sci., 50, 46 (1963).

16. Ranney, H. M., R. E. Benesch, R. Benesch, and A. Jacobs. Biochim. Biophys. Acta, 74, 544 (1963).

17. Rossi-Fanelli, A., E. Antonini, and A. Caputo. J. Biol. Chem., 236, 397 (1961).

18. Rossi-Fanelli, A., E. Antonini, and A. Caputo. J. Biol. Chem., 236, 391 (1961).

19. Antonini, E. Physiol. Rev., 45, 123 (1965).

20. Matsumiya, H., and R. Lumry. Abstracts Am. Chem. Soc. 134th Meeting, Chicago, 1958, 24 c.

21. Takashima, S., and R. Lumry. J. Am. Chem. Soc., 80, 4238 (1958).

22. Riggs, A., B. Sullivan, and J. R. Agee. Proc. Natl. Acad. Sci., 51, 1127 (1964).

REDOX POTENTIAL STUDIES ON PYRIDINE PROTOHEMIN*

Alan D. Adler

Department of Biology, University of Pennsylvania
Philadelphia, Pennsylvania

Almost all of our present knowledge of the potentiometric behavior of metalloporphyrin systems comes from the extensive investigations of Clark and his co-workers (1). In particular, this work includes an intensive study of pyridine protohemin (2). However, all of this research was carried out at only one temperature, 30°C. Therefore, any knowledge of the enthalpy and entropy changes involved in these redox processes remains unknown. The importance of a knowledge of the values of such thermodynamic quantities in understanding hemoprotein redox processes has been stressed (3). Therefore, a reinvestigation of the pyridine protohemin system was undertaken with the object of determining such thermodynamic parameters for the oxidation-reduction reaction (4).

## Methods and Materials

These studies were performed upon recrystallized and crude horse blood hemin, prepared according to Fischer (5) and, also, on three commercial samples (one each from Eastman Kodak, L. Light and Co., and California Biochemical Corp.). The purity of these particular samples has been previously reported (6,7), wherein it was established that the only major impurity (with the exception of the "crude" sample) was adsorbed acetic acid. The inorganic chemicals used were all reagent grade and were used without further purification. All organic dyes employed were recrystallized before use. The pyridine employed was reagent grade and was usually used without further purification, although some titrations were performed with redistilled material (8).

All measurements were made with a Beckman Model GS pH meter and potentiometer in a closed titration system designed for the purpose (4). The temperature was held to within 0.1°C

*Supported by PHS Grant AM-03187 and U. S. Army Research Office Grant Da-31-124-ARO(D)-101.

by use of a 75 cc jacketed vessel and a circulating temperature bath. Magnetic stirring was employed. Gases were passed
through a gas train consisting of water, alkaline pyrogallol,
acidic vanadous chloride, and a final water "scrub". Titrants
delivered under nitrogen from 10 cc microburet readable to
0.001 cc were reduced in a special vessel by hydrogen over
palladized asbestos and transferred to the buret under nitrogen. Beckman fiber junction saturated calomel electrodes were
used as the reference electrodes. Beckman platinum thimble
electrodes were used in the majority of the titrations as the
"inert" electrode.

Grounding arrangements were proven adequate by the use of
nearby RF equipment. The level of residual oxygen was established as being acceptable by the tests given by Michaelis (9).
The stability of the electrodes was occasionally checked by
titration of a standard ferricyanide solution. Titration of
this standard gave an overall accuracy and precision of ± 1 mV
for the system by comparison with the reported literature
values (10).

Solutions were prepared as follows: a weighed hemin
sample was transferred to a volumetric flask, sufficient pyridine added to bring the solution to the desired final concentration in pyridine, solid NaCl added to bring the pyridine
volume to the proper ionic strength, and then dilution to the
mark with the desired buffer at the desired ionic strength.
The nominal pH value of the final solution was then taken with
an amber glass electrode after equilibration at the experimental temperature. All solutions were flushed for 15 minutes
with the purified $N_2$ prior to titration after transferance of
a 30-40 cc aliquot to the titration vessel. Reductants were
made up in the buffer at 10 to 50 times the concentration of
the hemin solutions to minimize dilution of the titration
volume.

## Results

Several preliminary titrations were carried out at 30°C,
pH 7.2, ionic strength 0.1 in phosphate buffer at a pyridine
concentration of 2.5 M and a hemin concentration of 1.0 x 10$^{-4}$
M using reduced anthraquinone-β-sulfonate as the titrant. No
agreement could be obtained between different samples nor with
the literature values (2). The data for a given sample were
difficult to reproduce until it was discovered that the titration characteristics of each given sample changed with time. A
typical titration curve is shown in Fig. 1. Note that it is
asymmetric to inversion through the midpoint, as are all metalloporphyrin titrations (1,4).

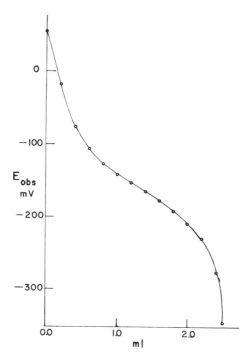

Figure 1. Typical experimental titration curve; T = 30° C, pH = 7.2, ionic strength 0.1, 2.5 M pyridine, and 1 x 10⁻⁴ protohemin. Potentials are versus the calomel electrode and the reductant is anthraquinone-β-sulfonate.

A number of important conclusions could be drawn from these titrations, however. First, end points can be determined experimentally, and the points for an oxidative back titration with ferricyanide fell on those for the forward reductive titration showing that the system is reversible. In addition, the ratio of equivalents of ferricyanide to hemin is found to be 1 : 1 in agreement with the data of Conant (11). Secondly, electrode equilibrium could be reached under these conditions in a few minutes, and the potential was found to be stable to within ± 1 mV for 45 minutes to 1 hour. A 10 to 20 point titration can therefore be carried out in this time interval with a drift not exceeding the expected experimental error. It should also be noted that the more concentrated the solution or the higher the ionic strength, the faster was the equilibration time. Thirdly, if the titration procedure was standardized with respect to time after preparation of the solution, then reproducible results could be obtained for each separate sample (but still no agreement between samples) taken at standardized times up to 24 hours after preparation. After 24 hours reproducible results could no longer be obtained for a given sample, the variation of the midpoint potentials often being of the order of ± 8 mV as compared to the acceptable ± 1 mV variation.

Duplicate sets of titrations were now run at standardized times after preparation for each sample. Some typical data for the average midpoint potentials at initial time (immediate titration after preparation), 6 hours, 24 hours, and 6 days are shown in Table I. Note that each sample has its own characteristic time behavior. The shape of each sample's titration curves about its midpoint changes with time as well as the midpoint translating along the potential axis with time. At 6 days the curves show several pronounced inflection points.

TABLE I

Midpoint Potential (vs. S.H.E.) at Various Times after Preparation in mV

| Sample | Initial | 6 hrs | 24 hrs | 6 days |
|--------|---------|-------|--------|--------|
| Recrystallized | 92 | 92 | 94 | 122 |
| Kodak | 105 | 108 | 116 | 124 |
| Light | 92 | 100 | 100 | 127 |
| Calbiochem | 106 | 90 | 91 | 121 |
| Crude | 102 | 104 | 106 | 125 |

The effect of concentration was next studied. A single set of titrations was carried out on the recrystallized sample at three different initial concentrations. The other conditions were as above: 30°C, 2.5 M pyridine, pH 7.2, ionic strength 0.1, and 1 hour after preparation. Again the shape of the curve about the midpoint was found to change as well as the midpoint itself moving its potential. This change in asymmetric shape can readily be seen by comparing the relative values of the differences between the index potential as defined by Michaelis (12), i.e. $| E_{1/2} - E_{1/4} |$ and $| E_{3/4} - E_{1/2} |$ For an ideal one-electron titration under these conditions, these index potentials should both equal 28.7 mV. The results are shown in Table II.

## TABLE II

Index and Midpoint Potential Variation
with Concentration in mV

| Concentration | $E_{1/2}$ | $\left\| E_{1/2} - E_{1/4} \right\|$ | $\left\| E_{3/4} - E_{1/2} \right\|$ |
|---|---|---|---|
| $1 \times 10^{-3}$ M | 178 | 16 | 10 |
| $5 \times 10^{-4}$ M | 155 | 17 | 14 |
| $1 \times 10^{-4}$ M | 92 | 38 | 39 |

In order to be sure that this potentiometric behavior
arises from the chemistry of the metalloporphyrin system
itself, a number of controls were next tried. To within an
accepted variation of ± 3 mV the titration characteristics of
a $1 \times 10^{-4}$ M recrystallized hemin sample was found to be invariant from the "standard" titration to: a ± 1°C variation in
temperature, a ± 0.2 variation in pH, a ± 0.05 variation in
ionic strength, a ± 0.5 M variation in pyridine, the conditions
of illumination, the area of the electrode or the electrode
surface (gold gave same results as bright platinum or platinum
black), the titrant (rosindone and methyl viologen gave same
results as anthraquinone-β-sulfonate), the pyridine purification
(technical and redistilled pyridine gave same results as
reagent grade), the gas purification (no gas train after the
tank $N_2$ and another stage of methyl viologen in the gas train
gave same results as the original train), addition of small
amounts of detergent ($1 \times 10^{-5}$ M in lauryl sulfate), the potentiometer, and finally the investigator. It was concluded
therefore that the time, concentration, and sample variations
in these titrations reflect the chemistry of pyridine hemin and
not the minor variation of some extraneous constraint on the
system. Finally, similar behavior was found for some explora-
tory titrations on cyanide protohemin and more recently for
pyridine deuterohemin, indicating that this behavior is not
restricted only to pyridine or protohemin, but might be typically expected for all metalloporphyrin solutions.

### Discussion

An extensive mathematical theory based on the work of
Michaelis (12) has been developed for the analysis of redox
titration data and its dependence on the stoichiometry of the
system (4). This will be presented elsewhere. The application
of these methods to the data, however, enables several useful
conclusions to be drawn about the chemical behavior of hemin
in an aqueous pyridine solution.

For a constant set of thermodynamic constraints (T, pH,
ligand concentration, ionic strength, etc.) during titration,
asymmetric curves result from one of two causes:  1) the system changes its state of aggregation as a result of the redox
process, or 2) the system contains more than one chemically
defined species capable of undergoing an independently distinguishable redox change, e.g., an impurity, an intermediate in a
several step process, or an "irreversibly" converted form of
the original species generated by any chemical event during
the course of titration.  Note acid-base or ligand equilibria
will not affect the shape of the curve but only its overall
position along the potential axis, provided the pH or ligand
concentration is held fixed during the titration.  These two
cases may be distinguished by the fact that, except for very
special cases, the first type of behavior is dependent on the
total concentration of the titrated species, translating the
curve along the potential axis with change in concentration,
while the second case is independent of such a change for an
otherwise fixed set of thermodynamic constraints.  It should
be further noted, however, that a positive concentration effect
does not preclude the possibility of both types of behavior
being present at the same time.

On this basis, it can be unequivocally asserted that aggregative phenomena play a very important role in characterizing
the chemistry of this system.  While the presence of such aggregative phenomena in porphyrin solutions has been long recognized
(1,4,13,14), the pronounced extent to which they actually determine and control the observed physical and chemical behavior
of these systems has not always received the careful attention
it deserves.  The fact that the titration curves change shape
as well as translate along the potential axis upon change in
total concentration and time means that something more complicated than a simple aggregation change, e.g., oxidized dimer $\rightleftharpoons$
2 reduced monomer (12,), must be taking place.

The analytical chemistry of these samples and the controls rule out introduced impurities as the sources of these
additional complications.  Similarly, the 1 : 1 stoichiometry
with ferricyanide rules out complications arising from higher
or lower oxidation states of these materials under these particular conditions.  The pronounced degeneration of the potentiometric behavior after 24 hours after preparation suggests
instability of the material in solution.  In fact, bile pigment formation can be readily detected in these systems after
24 hours by the methods previously described (7).  Such changes
have also been previously noted (13,14).  While this accounts
for the behavior of the system after 24 hours, however, it cannot account for the initial behavior, since then the samples

are free of bile pigments (7) and the conversion to bile pigment takes place slowly, only accounting for some 5 to 10 percent of the system at 24 hours.

Hence, the initial data can only be accounted for in terms of more complicated aggregative phenomena, such as a series of equilibria between various aggregated forms and the presence of partially reduced aggregates at equilibrium (e.g., $Fe_2^{+++} + e^- \leftrightarrow Fe^{++} - Fe^{+++}$ and $Fe^{++} - Fe^{+++} + e^- \leftrightarrow 2\ Fe^{++}$). In addition, the variation between different samples of comparable purity suggests that these systems are colloidally metastable, each particular sample dissolving to give a different polydisperse system that changes slowly with time to some stable form. This is supported by the spectral behavior of such solutions (2,7,15).

In view of the above considerations, the inconsistencies found between the results of various authors and in the thermodynamic data from different studies of metalloporphyrin solutions (14) become understandable. Therefore, while it can be concluded that the observed reduction potential for pyridine protohemin under these conditions is in the vicinity of 90 mV in agreement with the previously reported value (2,1), it must also be concluded that any further meaningful interpretation of such potentiometric data in thermodynamic and chemical terms must await a better characterization of the aggregative equilibria present in porphyrin solutions in thermodynamic and chemical terms.

## Acknowledgements

The author would like to express his indebtedness to Dr. Philip George for encouraging him to pursue this line of investigation.

## References

1. Clark, W. M. Oxidation-Reduction Potentials of Organic Systems, The Williams and Wilkins Co., Baltimore, 1960, Chap. 8.

2. Shack, J., and W. M. Clark. J. Biol. Chem., 171, 143 (1947).

3. George, P. In Currents in Biochemical Research (D. E. Green, ed.), Interscience Publishers, Inc., New York, 1957, pp. 338-375.

4. Adler, A. D. Thesis, University of Pennsylvania, 1960.

5. Fischer, H., and H. Orth. Die Chemie des Pyrrols, Bd. II, 1 Hälfte, Akademische Verlagsgesellschaft, Leipzig, 1937, p. 377.

6. Adler, A. D., and P. George. Anal. Biochem., 11, 159 (1965).

7. Adler, A. D., and J. L. Harris. Anal. Biochem., 14, 472 (1966).

8. Weissberger, A., E. S. Proskauer, J. A. Riddick, and E. E. Toops. Organic Solvents, 2nd Edition, Interscience Publishers, Inc., New York, 1955, pp. 445-447.

9. Michaelis, L. In Physical Methods of Organic Chemistry (A. Weissberger, ed.), Part II, 2nd Edition, Chap. XXVII, Interscience Publishers, Inc., New York, 1949, p. 1766.

10. Kolthoff, I. M., and W. J. Tomsicek. J. Phys. Chem., 39, 945 (1935).

11. Conant, J. B., G. A. Alles, and C. O. Tongberg. J. Biol. Chem., 79, 89 (1928).

12. Michaelis, L., and M. P. Schubert. Chem. Rev., 22, 437 (1938).

13. Falk, J. E. Porphyrins and Metalloporphyrins, Chap. 1, 2, 3, 5, Elsevier Publishing Co., New York, 1964.

14. Lemberg, R., and J. W. Legge. Hematin Compounds and Bile Pigments, Interscience Publishers, Inc., New York, 1949.

15. Gallagher, W. A., and W. B. Elliott. Biochem. J., 97, 187 (1965).

# ANION INTERACTION WITH SPERM WHALE FERRIMYOGLOBIN*
## IN SOLUTION

B. F. Cameron

New England Institute for Medical Research, Ridgefield, Conn.

and

G. I. H. Hanania and H. Tayim

Department of Chemistry, American University, Beirut, Lebanon

In connection with the comparison of ligand binding to ferrimyoglobin in the crystalline state and in solution, it is relevant to note that very little attention has been given to the study of non-specific anion binding to hemoproteins, despite the interest in the thermodynamics of myoglobin and hemoglobin reactions in aqueous solution.

We have recently investigated this problem by a potentiometric technique. A vibrating capacitor electrometer and sensitive null point detector, constructed at the American University of Beirut, were used to obtain emf measurements using the cell:

$$\text{Ag, AgCl(s) } / \text{KCl}(c_1) \, / \, \text{KCl}(c_1), \text{ Mb } / \text{ AgCl(s), Ag}$$

where $c_1$ is the total molar concentration of potassium chloride. The electromotive force was measured under varying conditions of pH, ferrimyoglobin concentration, and chloride concentration.

The emf of this cell may be due to a real difference in activity of $Cl^-$ in the two half-cells, or to a liquid-junction potential, or to a combination of both effects. Our measurements showed that the emf drops to a plateau at high pH (see Fig. 1 for $1.0 \times 10^{-3}$ M Mb in $1.0 \times 10^{-2}$ M KCl). Here it may be assumed that the binding of anion is minimal, and therefore that the limiting emf gives a measure of the liquid-junction potential. This allows one to calculate a net emf which is due solely to binding of $Cl^-$ to the protein.

*This work supported by U. S. PHS Grants HF-11508 and HE-04994.

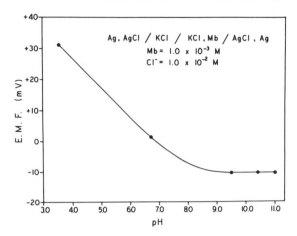

Figure 1. Variation of measured emf with pH (T = 25.0° C).

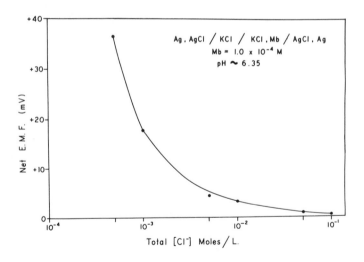

Figure 2. Chloride titration curve of sperm whale ferrimyoglobin (T = 25.0° C).

Fig. 2 shows a plot of the net emf as a function of total added KCl concentration (1.0 x $10^{-4}$ M Mb, at pH 6.35). This graph represents a $Cl^-$ titration curve for ferrimyoglobin. Analysis of the data by the method of Scatchard (1) requires the further assumption that the effect of protein on the $Cl^-$ activity coefficient is negligible in dilute solutions.

On this basis, the results obtained lead to the conclusion that sperm whale ferrimyoglobin in dilute aqueous solution has three classes of chloride-binding sites with differing relative affinities for the anion, as shown in Table I.

TABLE I

Chloride Binding Sites and their Constants

$Mb = 1.0 \times 10^{-4} M$; pH 6.4, $T = 25^\circ$ C.

|           | Number of Sites | Binding Constant |
|-----------|:---------------:|:----------------:|
| Group I   | 1               | 50,000           |
| Group II  | 6               | 5,000            |
| Group III | 13              | 20               |

It should be noted that the correction for the liquid-junction potential is empirical. We are at present investigating the validity of this correction by measurement of emf using "Cl$^-$ equilibrated" ferrimyoglobin. If confirmed, these results would indicate that the effect of protein on liquid-junction potential is substantially greater than has been previously recognized. However, irrespective of the validity of the above correction, it is apparent that Cl$^-$ ions interact reversibly with the protein. Such an equilibrium should be considered in any thermodynamic study of the reactions of myoglobin, since measurements are frequently made in solutions where the concentration of neutral salt is high relative to that of the hemoprotein.

The analysis of the data requires the three classes of sites indicated. It is tempting to associate those sites of the Class II with the six accessible histidines of sperm whale ferrimyoglobin as demonstrated by Breslow and Gurd (2), and the sites of Class III with lysine –NH$_3^+$ groups. The single Class I site could possibly be the special sulfate-binding site observed by Kendrew and co-workers in their X-ray studies of the sperm whale ferrimyoglobin-azide complex (3).

## References

1. Scatchard, G.  Ann. N. Y. Acad. Sci., 51, 660 (1949).

2. Breslow, E., and F. R. N. Gurd.  J. Biol. Chem., 237, 371 (1962).

3. Stryer, L., J. C. Kendrew, and H. C. Watson.  J. Mol. Biol., 8, 96 (1964).

# EFFECT OF ELECTROSTATIC ENVIRONMENT OF REDOX POTENTIALS*

P. George, G. I. H. Hanania,[‡] and W. A. Eaton**

Department of Chemistry, University of Pennsylvania
Philadelphia, Pennsylvania

In considering the factors which determine the relative stabilities of oxidation states of iron in hemoproteins, it is relevant to ask to what extent redox potentials are influenced by the electrostatic environment of the metal. It is not possible to make a direct assessment of the effect, since the hemoproteins have somewhat different structures, electronic states and bond types. We have examined this question using complex ion systems and with particular reference to (a) intramolecular electrostatic charge effects, and (b) medium and salt effects.

For intramolecular effects, let us consider the series of complex ions shown in Table I. These complexes are nitrogen-coordinated octahedral low-spin rigid structures, differing principally in their net charge. It is seen that the tris-phenanthroline and tris-dipyridyl-iron(III)/(II) couples have redox potentials about 1.1 volt, whereas the analogous tris-(4,7-dihydroxyphenanthroline)-iron(III)/(II) couple has a redox potential of -0.1 volt at $pH \geq 10$ where all its six hydroxyl groups are ionized. Thus, the redox potential is seen to drop as the electrostatic charge in the neighborhood of the iron atom becomes more negative, spanning the very wide range of nearly 30 kcal/mole. The data also show that the effect is reflected mainly in the decreased exothermocity of the cell reaction and to a lesser but still significant extent, in the unfavorable entropy change.

In the case of the hemoproteins, the low redox potentials are obviously due in part to the effect of the pyrrole nitrogens to which the iron atom is directly attached and which reduce the formal charge of iron from 3+ to 1+. Thermodynamic parameters for hemoprotein cell reactions are available for cytochrome c, hemoglobin and myoglobin only (see Table I). The

*This work supported by U.S. PHS Grant AM 03187.

‡Permanent address: Department of Chemistry, American University, Beirut, Lebanon.

**Pennsylvania Plan Scholar.

267

electrostatic environment of iron is known to be similar in both hemoglobin and myoglobin, and it is interesting to note how close the thermodynamic data for their cell reactions are. But in the case of cytochrome $\underline{c}$ the protein is known to be much more positively charged and, on that basis alone, one might expect a considerably higher redox potential. It is noteworthy that the higher redox potential of cytochrome $\underline{c}$ is indeed reflected in a somewhat more negative $\Delta H$. In view of the current idea that a marked conformation change accompanies the reduction of ferricytochrome $\underline{c}$, it may appear surprising that the entropy change for the cell reaction is similar to the corresponding values for hemoglobin and myoglobin. However, since the iron-protein bonds in cytochrome $\underline{c}$ are different from those in hemoglobin and myoglobin, no strict comparison can be made at this stage.

In addition to the above charge effects, redox potentials of complex ions are also affected, though to a lesser extent, by electrostatic effects from the solvent medium. These effects include ion-association, ionic strength, as well as the specific structure-promoting or breaking effect of ions on the water molecules. We have examined these effects for the hexacyanoferrate (III)/(II) couple, a system which is important because of its high charge and also because of its prevalent use in the study of hemoprotein reactions. The accompanying Fig. 1 shows how the redox potential of the couple depends markedly on the nature of the supporting electrolyte. Thus, all ordinary neutral salts appear to increase the redox potential, whereas the electrostatically weaker quaternary ammonium salts cause a sharp salting-out and progressive decrease in redox potential. Although all these are 1:1 salts, it is seen that their effects can differ by 150 millivolts at ionic strength around 0.5M; the differences are large in the presence of divalent ions and also presumably larger at higher ionic strengths. Clearly, such effects cannot be ignored in solutions of finite concentration.

We have shown that the above effects can be account for mainly in terms of the unequal binding of cations to oxidant and reductant anions (1). In sufficiently dilute solutions, all salt effects are seen to approach the limiting behavior predicted by the Debye-Huckel theory, thus enabling one to determine rigorous thermodynamic values.

In the case of hemoproteins, a sharp reversal of ionic strength effect has been shown to occur in the ionization equilibrium of the iron-bound water molecule in ferrimyoglobin (2), and there is no reason to suppose that a variety of medium effects do not play a significant role in all hemoprotein reactions at finite concentrations in aqueous solutions.

TABLE I

Thermodynamic Data for Iron(III)/(II) Couples

| | Charge O/R | $E^o(25^o)$ volt | $\Delta H^o$ kcal/mole | $\Delta S^o(25^o)$ e.u. | $\bar{S}^o_R - \bar{S}^o_0$ e.u. | Ref. |
|---|---|---|---|---|---|---|
| $Fe_{aq}$ | 3+/2+ | 0.771 | -9.95 | 26.4 | 42.0 | (3) |
| $Fe(phen)_3$ | 3+/2+ | 1.141 | -32.5 | -21 | -5 | (4) |
| $Fe(dipy)_3$ | 3+/2+ | 1.120 | -32.7 | -23 | -7 | (4) |
| $Fe(dipy\ Me_2)_3$ | 3+/2+ | 0.941 | -26.8 | -17 | -1 | (5) |
| $Fe(pyr-2-aldoxime)_3$ | 0/1- | 0.347 | -21.0 | -43 | -27 | (6) |
| $Fe(pyr-2,6-dialdoxime)_2$ | 1-/2- | 0.204 | -24.7 | -67 | -41 | (6) |
| $Fe(4,7-dihydroxyphen)_3$ | 3-/4- | -0.13 | -9 | -40 | -24 | (unpublished results) |
| Cytochrome-c(horse heart, pH 6.5, I = 0.05) | ---- | 0.27 | -18* | -41 | -25 | (unpublished results) |
| Hemoglobin (horse blood, pH 5.9, I = 0.25) | ---- | 0.16 | -15 | -38 | -22 | (7) |
| Myoglobin (horse heart, pH 5.9, I = 0.25) | ---- | 0.12 | -14 | -38 | -22 | (7) |

*calorimetric determination at pH 6.5, I = 0.14

269

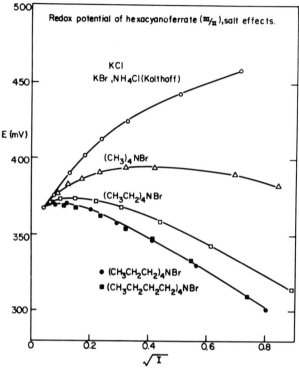

Figure 1. Redox potential of hexacyanoferrate (III/II), salt effects (T = 25.0° C).

## References

1. Hanania, G. I. H., P. George, and W. A. Eaton. Amer. Chem. Soc., Abstract N45, 151st Mtg., Pittsburgh, March, 1966.

2. George, P., and G. I. H. Hanania. Biochem. J., $\underline{52}$, 517 (1952).

3. Connick, R. E., and W. H. McVey. J. Am. Chem. Soc., $\underline{73}$, 1798 (1951).

4. George, P., G. I. H. Hanania, and D. H. Irvine. J. Chem. Soc., 2548 (1959).

5. Irvine, D. H. J. Chem. Soc., 2977 (1959).

6. Hanania, G. I. H., D. H. Irvine, M. Michaelides, and F. Shurayh. 9th Intl. Conf. Coord. Chem., Switzerland, September, 1966, in press.

7. Hanania, G. H. I. Ph.D. thesis, Cambridge, England, 1953.

DISCUSSION

Czerlinski: Dr. Hanania, where, on your last slide, are the data for sodium salts?

Hanania: Kolthoff had done this in the 1930's (1). Practically all cations--sodium, potassium, ammonium, caesium, lithium, calcium--do more or less the same thing as potassium. Only the electrostatically weak quaternary ammonium salts cause this salting out. The effect has not been reported before.

References

1. Kolthoff, I. M. J. Phys. Chem., <u>39</u>, 945 (1935).

GENERAL DISCUSSION

I. Dissolved vs. Crystalline Conformation

Watson: My colleague, Dr. Nobbs, tried to provoke discussion after his talk this morning by asking the question, "Is the water molecule in the sixth coordination position present in myoglobin in solution?" I should like to continue the discussion on this topic by asking, "Why should the reduced myoglobin structure in solution be any different from that in the crystal?"

Urnes With regard to the issue of whether water occupies the sixth coordination position in reduced myoglobin in solution, I would like to cite the measurements of Perutz which indicate that the visible absorption spectra of crystalline myoglobin and hemoglobin do not change upon dissolving (1). Since the characteristic spectra of single crystals of reduced, oxy-, and methemoglobin, reduced and metmyoglobin, and the azide and imidazole derivatives of methemoglobin persist in solution, one may infer that the identity of the ligand in each case does not change when the crystals dissolve.* It would, therefore, be reasonable to conclude that if nothing occupies the sixth position in crystalline reduced myoglobin, a void is likewise present in solution.

Heme spectra are also dependent upon the structure and composition of the globin, for large changes occur with denaturation while small but distinct variations reflect species differences among native hemoglobins and myoglobins. The identity of heme spectra in crystal and solution thus provides evidence that the immediate contacts of side chains with the prosthetic group are preserved as the protein dissolves. When taken with other evidence on the folding of the polypeptide chain in myoglobin, as given by its high helical content in solution, these spectroscopic findings can serve to rule out a great many alternative structures of the molecule in the dissolved state (2).

Wang: In trying to explain why the sixth ligand position of ferrous ion in myoglobin is not occupied by a water molecule, I think it would be an oversimplification to consider the structure of heme only, and disregard the environment. It is

*Editors' note: Subsequent to this meeting significant spectroscopic differences between dissolved and crystalline yeast cytochrome c peroxidase have been discovered (Yonetani, Thorell, Williams, unpublished data).

almost certain that in an aqueous solution of free heme molecules, there are two water molecules coordinated to each heme,
one on each side of the heme plane. But in myoglobin or hemoglobin, because of the hydrophobic environment of the binding
site, one must break a larger number of water-water hydrogen
bonds to bring a water molecule from the outside solution to
the binding site. If the free energy required to break the
hydrogen bonds is larger than the lowering of free energy due
to the formation of a weak coordination bond between water and
the ferrous ion of myoglobin, the system is better off, with
respect to free energy, to leave the sixth coordination position vacant.

Gouterman: An important question is whether the absorption
spectra are expected to be diagnostic of the presence or absence of water as a sixth ligand. Recent calculations, which
we will report on later, indicate that if iron is out of plane
pointing toward a fifth ligand, water as a sixth ligand 2.1 Å
from the porphyrin plane has very little influence on the molecular orbital energy levels.

Williams: I wish to speak directly on the subject of changes
in the structure of a molecule on going from a crystal to a
solution.* Physical methods must be used to detect this change.
One method is to measure the spectrum of the molecule in the
crystal, and then to measure the spectrum of the same molecule
in solution. There is no doubt that in certain cases changes
are well-established. One of the best cases I can give you is
not that of the particular molecules with which we are here
concerned, but rather the case of the vitamin $B_{12}$ coenzyme.
There is no doubt at all that a considerable alteration of
spectrum occurs on changing from a crystalline to an aqueous
environment or on changing solvent, or that a change of conformation can be shown by circular dichroism on changing temperature. Now, the groups which are responsible for these
changes may well be the amide side chains, which are fairly
near to the metal; therefore, they can only be compared with
groups fairly close to the heme of hemoglobin or myoglobin.

Watson: Vitamin $B_{12}$ is really a small molecule and does not,
therefore, possess the unique properties of a protein, for example, for $B_{12}$ no hydrophobic interior. For this reason, I feel
that it is somewhat dangerous to extend structural arguments
from $B_{12}$ to a protein.

Williams: But the point to be stressed is the technique to be
used rather than the possible differences. The technique I
suggested is dependent upon the examination of such parameters

*See footnote, page 273

as the positions and intensities of the vibration-dependent spectrum. From this you might see, in the major low frequency absorption band, fairly clear indications of differences in geometry as you go down to low temperatures. It may not be easy to interpret these results in detail, of course. If one saw no difference at all between crystal and solution spectra, one would feel very happy. When one starts seeing differences that are considerable, one starts to worry.

Hochstrasser: Dr. Eaton and I have recently examined the electronic spectra of single crystals of horse heart ferricytochrome c and acidic ferrimyoglobin in polarized light. The spectral band positions in the visible region as well as in the environment-sensitive 6950 Å region of cytochrome c, are unchanged by crystallization of the protein. Furthermore, the intensities and relative intensities of these bands are about the same in crystal and in solution. We conclude that there are no significant crystallization-induced impositions on the $\pi$-electron orbitals of the heme, or on the coordination sphere of the metal.

Yonetani: In connection with our interest in the electronic structure of a hemoprotein in dissolved and crystalline states, we have examined light- and electron paramagnetic resonance absorption spectra of cytochrome c peroxidase and complex ES in dissolved and crystalline states, as shown in Figs. 3-6 of our paper (3). As can be seen from these figures, absorption spectra of the hematin compounds in crystalline states are essentially identical to those in dissolved states. We, therefore, assume that the electronic structure of the hematin prosthetic group of these compounds is essentially independent of their physical state.*

Chance: We are apparently in agreement that the absorption bands of the heme do not change measurably on crystallization. But is the spectrum of the heme going to tell us everything about small changes in the structure of the hemoprotein? Elsewhere (4) we present kinetic evidence which shows that crystals react with azide more slowly than does the soluble material. It is apparent that the reactivity, at least, is affected by crystallization.

Watson: Before we move on to another topic, I should like to make the point that the crystals with which we work do go reversibly through the process of oxygenation. So that although our material may differ from that in solution, the molecules in the crystal do possess the same basic physiological properties as those in solution.

*See footnote, page 273

Chance: On the other hand, we have attempted to photodisso-
ciate carboxymyoglobin and -hemoglobin crystals and have failed
to do so. Have you tried this, Dr. Gibson?

Gibson: No, but I have tried a paste of Am2SO4 precipitate and
saw nothing, perhaps because of the high concentration. In
the erythrocyte, you can just barely see something by conventional methods; I think you might succeed with a laser.

Chance: This should be further examined to determine whether
CO is not trapped by the histidine to a greater extent in the
crystal structure than in the solution.

I may also comment on the xenon binding to the proximal
side of the heme of ferrimyoglobin. In preliminary experiments Benno Schoenborn and I have formed the xenon compound
under conditions identical to those used in his crystallographic
studies, namely, sperm whale myoglobin crystals saturated with
xenon (5) at 2 atmospheres for 15 minutes. Then we quickly
reacted the crystals with 1 mM azide and measured the half-time
of the reaction. We found no significant change in the half-
time. In other words, the presence of the xenon on the proximal side of the heme did not measurably decrease the reactivity
of the distal side towards the azide. I think the result is
interesting, since it bears on the idea of anesthesia by the
noble gasses and also eliminates the idea of the entry of any
ligand on the proximal side of the heme; this route would be
blocked by the xenon.

II. Porphyrin Structure and the Nature of the Ligand

(H$_2$O or OH$^-$)

Watson: The X-ray structure of (reduced) myoglobin suggests
that the iron is five-coordinated. This is of considerable
importance when considering the details of ligand binding and
we should perhaps discuss this point more extensively.

Caughey: I question the designation of "water" as a ligand in
acid metmyoglobin or acid methemoglobin. The requirement of
charge neutralization in the Fe(III) oxidation state suggests
the presence of a hydroxide ion rather than water. The
figure below illustrates the structural situations of the acid
and alkaline metmyoglobin types, in which the iron-bound oxygen
atom is represented as hydroxide ion linked by a hydrogen bond
to the nitrogen of the E7 histidine.

276

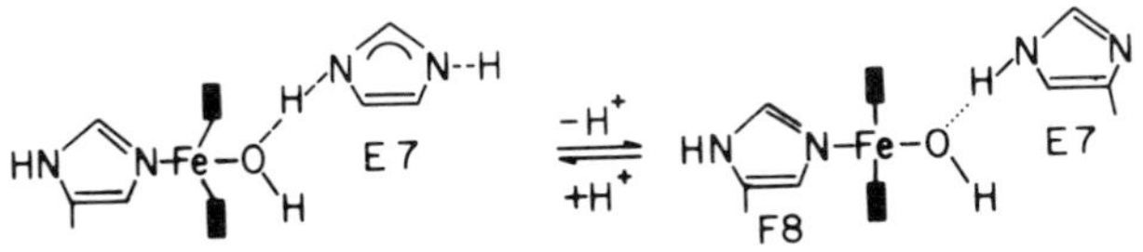

**Figure 1.** Proposed mechanism of the acid-alkaline transition of ferric hemoproteins.

The strength of this hydrogen bond can be influenced by the environment of the nitrogen (N$\delta$) of E7 more remote from the iron. This nitrogen is exposed to the external medium. Changes in the environment at N$\delta$ (e.g., changes in pH, hydration, metal ions) can be reflected in the strength of the hydrogen bond to iron-bound oxygen (1). For example, at low pH, where strong hydrogen bonding to the iron-bound oxygen is possible, this may result in a weak and long Fe-O bond, an iron position out-of-plane towards histidine F8 and a high-spin state. On the other hand, at high pH, where only weak hydrogen bonding to N$\delta$ can occur, the hydrogen bonding from nitrogen to iron-bound oxygen must be weak and, therefore, a shorter, stronger Fe-O bond, in-plane iron, and a low spin state result. In this manner, spin state and absorption spectrum changes can occur with very little change in protein structure, although a change in the location of the iron with respect to the plane of the porphyrin can be expected.

Certainly the ligand cannot be considered to be an "ordinary" aquo-ligand. However, as illustrated in the following figure, only the locations of hydrogens need be changed between the Stryer, Kendrew, and Watson representation for acid metmyoglobin and the alternative description I prefer (see Fig. 2).

Watson: We do not locate hydrogen atoms in X-ray analyses of proteins, so I cannot answer the question on the basis of crystallographic data alone. There is, however, a definite spectral change when the pH is raised from 7.0 to 9.5 which we have always considered to be indicative of the formation of the hydroxide compound.

Caughey: If, as a consequence of this change of pH there is a change in spin-state, then is it unreasonable to expect a change in spectrum as well?

Watson: I suppose not.

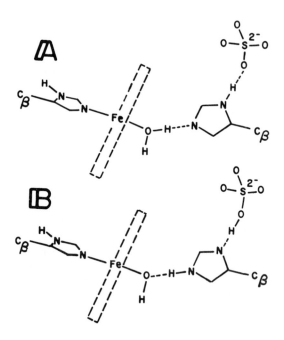

Figure 2. Alternative structures for water or hydroxide bonded to heme in ferrimyoglobin. (A) illustrates Stryer, Kendrew and Watson (1964) representation for acid metmyoglobin; (B) illustrates alternative representation preferred by Caughey (see text).

Caughey: Then there is a further question: are you sure there could be no change in the position of the iron with respect to the porphyrin plane?

Chance: Perhaps this is the key question; it seems unlikely that the small change of O bonding in Figs. 1 and 2 would result in such a large change of spin state or spectrum as is observed in the conversion of acid to alkaline ferrimyoglobin. I think Caughey's mechanism requires a movement of the Fe relative to porphyrin. Results on this point obtained with Watson are taken up later (6).

What is the exact nature of the spin state of ferrimyoglobin hydroxide?

Williams: I believe it is agreed that the hydroxide is a mixture of spin states.

Ehrenberg: The high-spin form of the hydroxide is rather different from other high-spin forms of myoglobin. It is asymmetric in the plane of the heme group, as inferred from the
structure of the $g = 6$ ESR absorption. This asymmetry would
fit well with a change of the orientation of the heme relative
to the surroundings, which would cause the low-spin form to be
stable at low temperatures.

Williams: Distortion of porphyrin rings can be produced by a
steric effect or by an electronic effect. In the latter, the
electron density which is coming off the z-axis ligand atom
alters the ring geometry. This is best shown by the structure
of various $B_{12}$ derivatives as shown by Hodgkin et al. (7).

Mildvan: I believe Dr. Caughey's structure, which is similar
to one previously suggested by Nicholls and Schonbaum (8) is
quite attractive and is compatible with the observed effect of
raising the pH. In effect, instead of having water and an uncharged imidazole, one has a hydroxyl on the iron accepting a
hydrogen bond from a cationic imidazolium and, therefore, as
one raises the pH, one would convert the cationic imidazolium
to an uncharged imidazole. The hydroxide ion, then being less
strongly hydrogen-bonded, could move into the iron, giving a
low-spin complex. In fact, the spectral shifts are of about
the right order of magnitude for the loss of a strong hydrogen
bond.

Caughey: I wonder if five-coordination is not a result to be
expected in the light of present knowledge of heme coordination
chemistry. Deoxymyoglobin and deoxyhemoglobin are high-spin
Fe(II). As Dr. Hoard mentioned earlier (9), the Fe-N distance
is too large for the Fe atom to be accomodated in the plane of
the porphyrin ring. With the Fe atom necessarily displaced
appreciably towards the F8 histidine, the bond to any trans-
water ligand would be too long and weak to retain a water
molecule at all firmly. High-spin iron will stay far out-of-
plane and be bound to histidine on the back side; if, then,
you wish to place a water ligand trans to the histidine, the
resulting bond will necessarily be very weak, if it forms at
all.

Watson:  The iron-water distance found in metmyoglobin is 2.1 Å.
This is the accepted distance for an iron-oxygen covalent linkage and, as such, cannot be considered to be a weak bond.

Caughey:  Then my explanation, of course, is that in the Fe(III)
case, a hydroxide is there, as it is needed to neutralize the
charge.

Hoard:  I am essentially in agreement with Dr. Caughey as to
the difference between ferrous and ferric ion when this is
displaced out-of-plane away from the sixth ligand.  The strength
of the field reaching the sixth ligand must be much smaller
from ferrous than from ferric ion; one expects little or no
complexing of a neutral species such as $H_2O$ in the case of ferrous ion.

Williams:  I am sure that no inorganic chemist could make a
prediction about five-coordination from any of the evidence
that is available about the bonding in such a molecule.  Moreover and quite obviously, when you go over the Fe(III) enzyme,
something does bind in the sixth position, and you have the
same problem.

Gouterman:  Dr. Caughey's suggestion that the pH dependence
found for the spin is correlated with a motion of the iron
atom towards the plane of the molecule fits very nicely with
our calculational results.  I should in this context point out
that an early mystery of iron porphyrins was the existence of
high-spin complexes.  By standard valence bond theory we suppose either $dsp^2$ hybridization for square planar complexes or
$d^2sp^3$ for octahedral.  These two cases yield, respectively,
intermediate or low spin.  Recent molecular orbital calculations (10,11) have given the same results.  With iron in-plane,
only intermediate-spin or low-spin states were obtained.  With
iron out-of-plane, high spin could be obtained.  These calculations imply that the "ionic" complex, a term introduced by
Pauling for this high spin situation (12), is inherently related to a non-planar iron.  A motion of iron from a non-planar
to a planar geometry, as proposed by Dr. Caughey, could well
explain the observed spin changes with pH.

Hoard:  Does this theory apply to four- and six-coordinate
species as well as to five-, and are you confining this treatment to the porphyrin situation?  There are, of course, many
known cases of high-spin iron in essentially regular octahedral
coordination for systems other than porphyrins.

Gouterman: Our calculations were done on iron porphyrins, and the statements about spin state and geometry apply to that particular case. With iron in-plane, the weakest fifth ligand produces low spin, although the intermediate spin state is low lying. With iron out-of-plane, weak ligands give high spin and strong ligands give low spin. In this context, $H_2O$ or CO were weak and strong ligands for ferrous and $OH^-$ and $CN^-$ were weak and strong ligands for ferric. We did not use $H_2O$ as a ligand for ferric because, for various theoretical reasons, we wanted to calculate only electrically neutral systems.

Lemberg: Perhaps the physical chemists consider the porphyrin structure a little too rigid. I should like them to explain how porphyrin complexes with beryllium.

Gouterman: We have recently given some attention to this rather surprising beryllium complex. Becker reported excess Be salts in his Be-porphyrin crystals (13). Based on this, and on the small covalent Be radius, we calculated the electronic structure with two Be atoms located in the two bridge positions between opposite pairs of nitrogens. For electric neutrality, two chlorine atoms were placed above and below this plane. Our calculations showed this to be a quite reasonable structure (10).

Adler: I hate to add to the complications, but there exist a lot of earlier data on porphyrins which are best explained in terms of hepto-coordination (14).

Hoard: A seven-coordination group in the heme of either oxymyoglobin or oxyhemoglobin is required if, in fact, the two atoms of the oxygen molecule are to be symmetrically attached to the iron atom. Both of the distinctive configurations that are consistent with effective $C_{2v}$ symmetry exemplify the entirely general rule that a seven-coordination group must involve large steric repulsions between pairs of contiguous ligands, as compared with the standard octahedral case. If, moreover, the iron atom be displaced out-of-plane away from the oxygen molecule, the importance of such steric repulsions is highly accentuated; the associated repulsive energy may be of the order of 20 kcal/mole. These matters along with bonding considerations are to be discussed in some detail in our paper dealing with the stereochemistry of the aquohydroxyiron (III)tetraphenylporphine molecule (M. D. Glick, G. H. Cohen and J. L. Hoard, unpublished results).

III.  The Oxygen Bonding

Watson:  It seems, from what Dr. Hoard and Dr. Caughey have said, that the absence of the heme-linked water molecule in reduced myoglobin could have been predicted.  Would anyone like to predict the details of the binding of oxygen to myoglobin before the experimental results become available?

Lang:  The one comment I would like to make concerns the temperature dependence of the Mössbauer spectra of oxyhemoglobin. The quadrupole splitting varies from 2.2 mm/sec at $4^{\circ}$ K to 1.9 at $195^{\circ}$ K.  Now, temperature dependence in the quadrupole splitting is often associated with electronic excitations which reduce electron charge asymmetry.  However, it is hard to imagine how this would occur without simultaneous occurrence of paramagnetism.  There is, in oxyhemoglobin, some kind of excitation which does not allow unpairing of spin.  This could correspond to some motion of the structure, possibly a rotation of the oxygen molecule.

Moss:  I want to point out that the temperature dependence of the oxyhemoglobin Mössbauer spectrum, instead of presenting an unanswered question, may fit in very well with Lang's model of the horizontal oxygen molecule.  That model requires extensive delocalization of iron electrons to molecular orbitals of oxygen character.  With such delocalization, any effect which changes the $O_2$ molecular orbitals will be transmitted to the iron nucleus and affect the Mössbauer spectrum.  In this case, we do not need to consider excitations of ionic electronic states to account for the temperature dependence.  Once the iron d-orbitals are coupled to the $O_2$ orbitals, there are many other possibilities for temperature variation.  Work with bispyridine hemes, in which similar electron delocalization is observed, shows that effects far from the iron ion can alter the Mössbauer spectrum.  Mesoheme and diacetyl deuteroheme, with ethyl and vinyl side chains on the periphery of the porphyrin ring, show very different quadrupole splittings.  In analogy, temperature effects far from the iron, transmitted to it through the delocalized bond proposed by Lang, may cause the temperature dependence of the oxyhemoglobin Mössbauer spectrum.

Maricic:  I believe that one of the most important problems in the study of hemoproteins is still the explanation of reversible oxygenation.  A first step towards solving it would be a direct knowledge of the bond type between oxygen and the hemoprotein. Although this is being gradually solved by X-ray crystallographic methods, we have also approached it through $^{17}O$ - NMR spectroscopy. Our sample was prepared almost a year ago in Zagreb in collaboration with Dr. Sunko, and thanks to Dr. Samuel of the Weizmann Institute who kindly sent us oxygen gas enriched in $^{17}O$ to some 65 atom percent. The recording of the NMR spectra was done here in Dr. Cohn's laboratory by Mr. Leigh and myself. After a lengthy and unsuccessful search for the line up- and down-field within 2000 ppm of what we believed was the $^{17}O$-resonance from ordinary water (solvent), we examined the possibility that the hemoglobin-$^{17}O$ resonance may be superimposed on the $H_2^{17}O$. This was indicated by consideration of the intensity ratio between the hemoglobin and a blank-sample line. The final proof for the hemoglobin-$^{17}O$-resonance came from an experiment during which $^{17}O$ absorbed by hemoglobin gradually exchanged with oxygen from the atmosphere, as observed by a gradual decrease in signal intensities. Before this final experiment, we had added $MnCl_2$ to our sample in an amount which was found on a blank-sample to be sufficient to broaden the $H_2^{17}O$ line beyond detectability. The initial spectra recorded at two different sweep conditions are shown on the graph below (lines 2 and 4). Line 3 covers the same sweep range, but was recorded some 16 hours after the former two, indicating a complete loss of measurable $^{17}O$ NMR signal. The $H_2^{17}O$ signal is also absent, as expected. Immediately after the negative recording, line 1, from an 11 percent $^{17}O$-enriched water was recorded, and shows the difference between a normal $H_2^{17}O$ line and the one due to $^{17}O$ absorbed on hemoglobin (line 2).

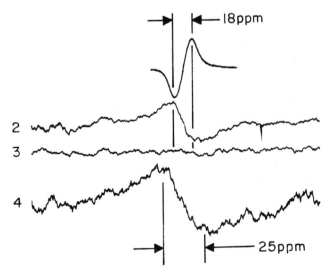

So far, all our preliminary analysis of this data seems to prove that the observed $^{17}O$ resonance line is due to the total $^{17}O$ bound to hemoglobin. Also, we could not find any asymmetry of the spectrum which could not be accounted for within the rather poor signal-to-noise ratio. Thus, to put it in a safe understatement, we are presently inclined to interpret our result as if the two oxygen atoms were not strikingly dissimilar. This, of course, is consistent with the parallel-to-heme orientation put forward in 1956 by Griffith (15).

Traylor: On what time scale?

Maricic: This would not really matter. In the case of parallel orientation, any rotation around the axis of cylindrical symmetry would not change anything in the magnetic equivalence of the two oxygens. If we suppose Pauling's inclined end-on orientation (16), a similar reoreintation would not equalize magnetically the two sites, so that with or without such rotations the two cases ought to be distinguishable.

Traylor: I have in mind the flip-flop exchange of oxygen atoms between the two sites.

Maricic: You are right, and we really must check this possibility by a temperature study of the spectra; however, this mechanism does not seem to me to be very probable for Pauling's configuration.

Watson: If you look at the heme environment in the myoglobin structure, you will find that several groups are in close contact with the heme and the ligand binding site. Unless these groups are moved on oxygenation, they will severely limit the possible orientation of the in-plane oxygen molecule.

Williams: At the risk of repeating myself, I should like to make very clear the facts about the hemoglobin-$O_2$ Mössbauer spectrum. We have taken the Mössbauer spectra of a series of model compounds of iron (II) in a square, or nearly enough square, environment, varying the fifth and sixth ligands on top and bottom (17). You can then see how the isomer shift and the quadrupole splittings change along the series of compounds, e.g., you can take phthalocyanine and put two cyanides, two imidazoles, or any other two bases top and bottom. You then get a linear relationship between isomer shift and quadrupole splitting, not only in this series of compounds, but in three others. The relationship, as indicated by the slope of the line (cf. 16) is roughly the same in all series. However, when you go from the CO-compound of hemoglobin to the oxy compound of hemoglobin, the relationship fails. This suggests straight away that there is something very different, possibly about the symmetry, of the oxygen complex. The way in which most monodentate ligands go on to a complex is just as a symmetrical top. The model I have in mind for the $O_2$ complex has the oxygen at an angle so as to split strongly the xz and yz orbitals. This could be different in different hemoglobins. It is very noticeable that $H_2O$, which is not binding symmetrically to high-spin iron (III), also gives rise to a very large quadrupole splitting where only a small one would have been expected. The exact geometry of oxygen complexes of other heme proteins may be different also. This difference in geometry, enforced by the steric requirements of the protein, could generate oxidase, rather than oxygen-carrying, ability.

Watson: The movement of the iron atom in and out of the heme plane could form the basis for heme-heme interaction in hemoglobin. The movement of only a few tenths of an Ångstrom unit of the iron atom would cause the heme-linked helix F to move. Once a very small movement has occurred, the rearrangement of the subunits would be necessary for the molecule as a whole to drop to its new potential minima. Thus, a small shift of the iron atom could produce the 7 Å subunit shift actually observed in going from reduced to oxyhemoglobin.

Williams: This mechanism is one I used when I knew nothing about the position of the iron in this system (18). All I said then was that if you took a system in which you have a high-spin Fe bond to a nitrogen and then change to a low spin by adding oxygen, the Fe-N z-axis bond will be shortened; the change to low spin gives a shortening of about 0.1 Å. But of course, going to low spin will also strengthen $\pi$-binding and tend to keep the heme undistorted (flatter); you can get very considerable further movement by this type of mechanism in the protein. In the above reference I did mention a forced movement of the imidazole geometry relative to that of the porphyrin.

Caughey: A further refinement on the Griffith type of oxygen binding was included in a structure we proposed in 1964 at the ISOX meeting (19). We suggested as a reasonable structure one in which molecular oxygen was not only bound to the iron atom but also to a residue on the protein. The bonding to the protein would be between the bonding $\pi$-orbital of oxygen and a positive center on protein, most reasonably a hydrogen bond from E7 histidine in the case of myoglobin. Such bonding would be analogous to the protonation of an ethylenic double bond. I wonder if anyone would comment on the structure of Figure 3.

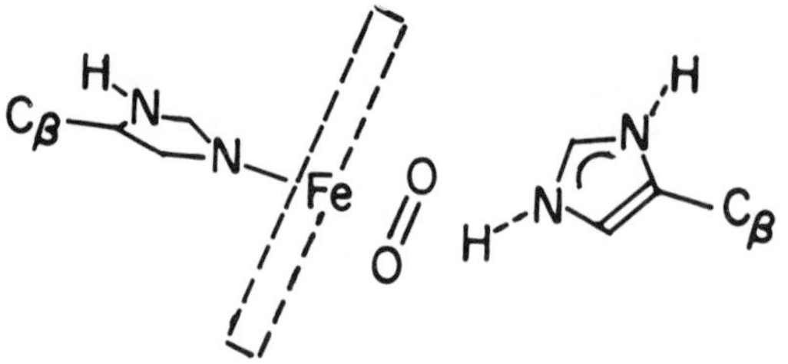

<u>Figure 3</u>.   Spatial relationship of oxygen in myoglobin.

Also, would the crystallographers care to comment on the following question:   If the carbonyl were perpendicular and the oxygen parallel, to the porphyrin plane, would carboxy and oxy compounds give isomorphous crystals?

<u>Lemberg</u>:   I wonder whether distal imidazole is absolutely required.   We can learn from abnormal hemoglobins; those which have at the position of the distal imidazole an oxygen-carrying amino-acid residue are definitely pathological (hemoglobins M) and non-functional.   Yet hemoglobin Zürich which has replaced this with argenine is functional.

<u>Watson</u>:   When the distal histidine is replaced by tyrosine, we find that the hydroxyl group bonds directly on to the iron atom, thus markedly affecting the properties of the molecule.   Hemoglobin Zürich has an arginine residue in the position of the distal histidine.   As far as I am aware, however, this hemoglobin has abnormal properties, and I do not believe that its existence diminishes the argument for the necessity of the distal histidine in normal hemoglobins.

<u>Zerner</u>:   A result of the recent calculations performed by Dr. Gouterman and myself strongly suggests that the histidine is present to prevent the oxygen molecule from becoming perpendicular to the heme plane.   Oxygen is paramagnetic because its top orbitals, a degenerate pair $1\pi_g$, each contain one electron with the two spins parallel.   When oxygen approaches the heme with its axis along the heme symmetry axis, these orbitals strongly couple with the iron $3d\pi$ orbitals.   The oxygen $1\pi_g$ is depressed in energy far below the iron $3d\pi$, whose energy is raised.   (A diagram is supplied in the formal presentation of our results later in this meeting(20).)   The orbital energy diagram suggests an immediate flow of electrons from the filled iron $\underline{d}$ orbitals to the half filled oxygen orbitals.   Indeed, oxidation is the fate of unprotected ferrous porphyrins when exposed to $O_2$.   On the other hand, when we calculate an oxygen

complex with $O_2$ in the symmetric position parallel to the heme plane, the degeneracy of the $1\pi g$ is lifted with the orbital pointing into the plane going to higher energy. The energies of the two $1\pi g$ orbitals are now sufficiently different that both electrons go into the lower orbital. In this case their spins are antiparallel so paramagnetism is removed. Both oxygen orbitals are calculated to have higher energy than the filled d orbitals, so that no oxidation is expected.

Wang: Actually, this question on the stability of the Fe(II) state of hemoglobin or myoglobin was answered at the last Hematin Enzyme Symposium at Canberra eight years ago (21). The coordination of the ferrous ion in hemoglobin or myoglobin by imidazole nitrogen does stabilize the ferrous state, but this coordination alone is not sufficient to prevent oxidation. This is shown by the simple fact that dipyridine and di-imidazole hemochromes in aqueous solution are immediately oxidized on exposure to air.

## References

1. Perutz, M. F.  Acta Cryst., 6, 859 (1953).

2. Urnes, P.  J. Gen. Physiol., 49 (2), 75 (1965).

3. Yonetani, T., H. Schleyer, B. Chance, and A. Ehrenberg. This volume, p. 293.

4. Chance, B.  This volume, p. 213.

5. Schoenborn, B. P., H. C. Watson, and J. C. Kendrew. Nature, 207, 28 (1965).

6. Watson, H. C., and B. Chance. This volume, p. 149.

7. Hodgkin, D. C., J. Lindsey, M. MacKay, and K. N. Trueblood.  Proc. Roy. Soc. (London), A, 266, 475 (1962).

8. Nicholls, P.  This volume, p.307  and Schonbaum, G. R., and F. Jajeczey.  This volume, p. 327.

9. Hoard, J. L.  This volume, p. 9.

10. Zerner, M., and M. Gouterman.  Theoret. Chim. Acta, 4, 44 (1966).

11. Zerner, M.  Ph.D. Thesis, Department of Chemistry, Harvard University, 1966.

12. Pauling, L., and C. D. Coryell.  Proc. Nat. Acad. Sci., 22, 159, 210 (1936).

13. Becker, R. S., and J. B. Allison.  J. Phys. Chem., 67, 2669 (1963).

14. Lemberg, R., and J. W. Legge. In Hematin Compounds and Bile Pigments, Interscience Publishers, New York, 1949, p. 180.

15. Griffith, J. S. Proc. Roy. Soc. (London) A, 235, 23 (1956).

16. Pauling, L. Nature, 203, 182 (1964).

17. Williams, R. J. P. This volume, p. 577.

18. Williams, R. J. P. Federation Proc., 20, 5 (1961).

19. Caughey, W. S., J. O. Alben, and C. A. Beaudreau. In Oxidases and Related Redox Systems (T. E. King, H. S. Mason, and M. Morrison, eds.), John Wiley and Sons, New York, 1965, p. 97.

20. Zerner, M., and M. Gouterman. This volume, p. 589.

21. Wang, J. H., A. Nakahara, and E. B. Fleischer. J. Am. Chem. Soc., 80, 1109 (1958), and Wang, J. H. Hematin Enzymes, IUB Symposium Series, Vol. 19, 1959, p. 98.

# STRUCTURE AND REACTIVITY OF
# HEMATIN ENZYMES: CATALASES, PEROXIDASES,
# CYTOCHROMES, AND OXIDASES

# V.
## Structure and Reactivity of Hydro-Peroxidases
### B. Chance, Chairman

# THE CHEMICAL NATURE OF COMPLEX ES OF CYTOCHROME c PEROXIDASE*

Takashi Yonetani, Heinz Schleyer, Britton Chance

Johnson Research Foundation, University of Pennsylvania
Philadelphia, Pennsylvania

and

Anders Ehrenberg

The Nobel Medical Institute, Department of Biochemistry
Karolinska Institutet, Stockholm, Sweden

Cytochrome c peroxidase (CCP) catalyzes the rapid oxidation of ferrocytochrome c in the presence of hydroperoxide.
This enzyme was discovered by Altschul et al. (1) and has been
recently crystallized (2). It is found exclusively in mitochondrial fractions of aerobically grown yeasts (3). The prosthetic group of this peroxidase is shown to be protohematin
(4). No transition metal other than hematin iron is found in
the crystalline preparation of this enzyme.

One of the most interesting properties of this enzyme is
its ability to form an enzymically active yet highly stable
red compound, which we call Complex ES (ES), with hydroperoxide. The formation of ES is compared with that of Complexes
I and II of horse-radish peroxidase (HRP) in Fig. 1. As Chance
(5) demonstrated some 20 years ago, HRP is rapidly converted
to Complex I, then gradually converted to Complex II of red
color (7), which spontaneously decomposes on standing. On the
addition of peroxide, CCP is rapidly converted to ES of red
color (4). No green intermediate can be detected in this time
scale. The ES so formed is very stable. The rate of the combination of CCP and $H_2O_2$ is examined by a rapid flow technique
(cf. Fig. 2). No green intermediate (Complex I) can be detected at 1.7 msec after mixing under the given conditions, as
shown in trace (a) in which the measuring wavelength is set at
414 mμ, near the isosbestic point of the CCP-ES pair. We can only
detect slight disturbances from Complex II due to the inexact
setting of the wavelength to the isosbestic points. Assuming
the green Complex I to have the same spectrum as that of the

*This work was supported by research grants from the U.S. PHS
(GM 12202 and AM 5895), and from NSF (G 10813).

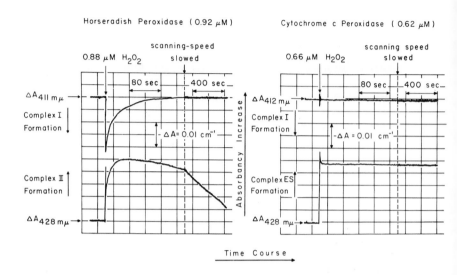

**Figure 1.** Kinetics of formation and decomposition of peroxide-complexes of horseradish and cytochrome c peroxidases (4).

the horse-radish enzyme, an upward deflection of the 414 mµ trace of 2.5 scale divisions could be expected. Trace (B) shows that the formation of ES, which is observed at 426 mµ, is approximately 90 percent complete at 1.7 msec after mixing, indicating a very rapid rate of their combination. The second order rate constant of their combination is estimated to be of the order of $10^8$ $M^{-1}$ $sec^{-1}$.

We have recently found that crystals of CCP can be readily converted to those of ES by the addition of peroxide (2). The conversion is easily detected by the color change of crystals from brown to red. No apparent modification in the crystalline form is observed during the conversion. Crystals of CCP and ES, therefore, appear to be isomorphous. Since they are large and stable, these crystals appear to be suitable for X-ray crystallography and electron-paramagnetic-resonance (EPR) spectroscopy of single crystals of a hematin enzyme and its enzymically active reaction intermediate. Although the molecular weight of CCP of about 50,000 may make crystallographer hestant to tackle these crystals, it should be mentioned that the intra-molecular structure near the hematin prosthetic group of this enzyme appears to be quite similar to that of ferrimyoglobin. Thus, complementary information on the structure of the active center of CCP may be found in X-ray data of ferrimyoglobin which are already available (8).

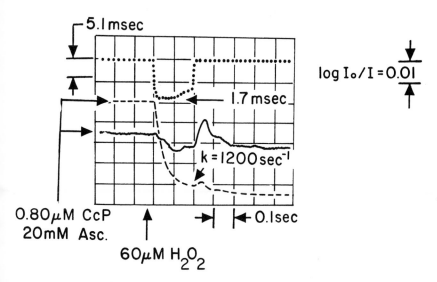

Figure 2. The rapid-flow kinetics of the combination of cyto-chrome $c$ peroxidase and $H_2O_2$. ———, Complex I, measured at 414-455 mµ; - - -, Complex II, measured at 426 - 455 mµ; • • •, flow velocity. A downward deflection of the trace corresponds to increased absorption at 426 and 414 mµ.

As shown in Fig. 3, the conversion of the enzyme crystals to those of ES has been more quantitatively confirmed by the measurement of absorption spectra of a single crystal of CCP before and after the addition of peroxide (2) with a micro-spectrophotometer (9).

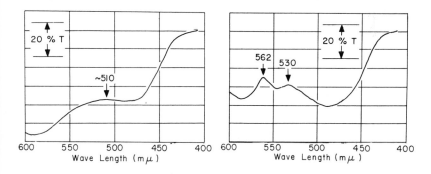

Figure 3. Light absorption spectra of a single crystal of cytochrome $c$ peroxidase before and after the addition of per-oxide at $23°$ (measured by Dr. C. Ritter).

295

The corresponding spectra of CCP and ES in dissolved preparations are shown in Fig. 4. An indication of the presence of high and low-spin hematin compounds can be found in the spectrum of CCP. The peaks at 505 and 645 mμ are often associated with ferrihemoproteins of a high-spin type, while the shoulder around 550 mμ can be ascribed to a contribution of a low-spin compound.

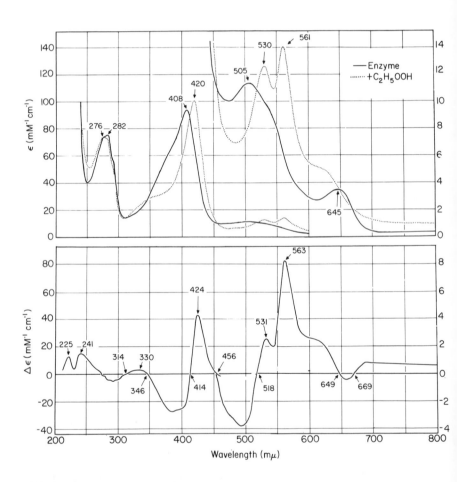

Figure 4. Light absorption spectra of cytochrome c peroxidase and Complex ES in dissolved forms at 23° (pH 6.0). The expanded spectra from 450 to 800 mμ should be referred to the right-hand ordinates. The top figure illustrates absolute spectra, while the bottom figure shows difference spectra between Complex ES and the free enzyme.

Such an indication is more clearly seen in Fig. 5, in which are shown the spectra of CCP and ES measured at 77° K with a split-beam spectrophotometer combined with a low temperature accessory (10). In the spectra of the free enzyme, the absorption maxima at 500 and 635 mµ and those at 535 and 575 mµ are typical contributions of high and low-spin ferric compounds, respectively.

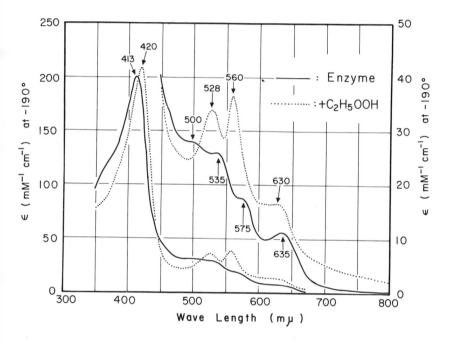

Figure 5. Light absorption spectra of cytochrome c peroxidase and Complex ES in dissolved forms at 77° K (pH 6.0). Measured by Dr. D. Wilson.

The conversion of CCP crystals to those of ES is further confirmed by the measurement of EPR spectra of crystals of CCP and ES as shown in Fig. 6 (11). EPR spectra of the enzyme exhibit well defined signals at g-values of 6.0, 4.3, 2.7, 2.2, 2.0, and 1.8. EPR spectra of this type of complexity have been often interpreted to be due to the presence of a thermal equilibrium mixture of high and low-spin forms in a hematin compound, for example, in the cases of ferrimyoglobin and ferrihemoglobin derivatives. The EPR signals of the free enzyme disappear almost completely by the addition of an equimolar amount of peroxide and are replaced by an intense narrow signal of a free radical type at g = 2.00 (cf. the discussion comment by H. Schleyer on this EPR signal). On the basis of the first-moment calculation, the spin concentration of this free radical type signal is estimated to be of the order of 1 equivalent of the enzyme hematin (11).

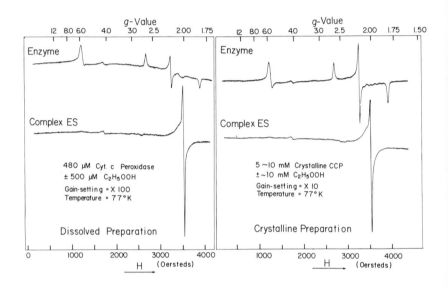

Figure 6. EPR-absorption spectra of cytochrome c peroxidase and Complex ES in dissolved and crystalline frozen samples at 77° K (pH 6.0) (11). Since reproducible packing of crystalline samples in tubes is difficult, EPR spectra of crystalline samples should be treated qualitatively.

We have recently reported spectrophotometric titration of ES with ferrocytochrome c and ferrocyanide (12,13). ES is shown to retain two oxidizing equivalents per hematin unit. Fig. 7 illustrates a similar titration of ES with ferrocytochrome c as measured by EPR spectroscopy (11). CCP at 450 μM is first converted to ES by the addition of 450 μM $C_2H_5OOH$ (cf. absorption spectra A and B). Absorption spectra C, D, and E are made after additions of 0.7, 1.4, and 2.0 equivalents of

ferrocytochrome c, respectively. ES is almost completely converted to the free enzyme by the addition of two equivalents
of ferrocytochrome c. The amplitude of the free radical signal
appears to decrease to 50 percent on the addition of 0.7 equivalent of ferrocytochrome c (cf. spectrum c). However, it is
not yet possible to determine whether or not the free radical
is preferentially reduced by ferrocytochrome c, until the spin
concentrations of these samples are accurately measured by double integration of these spectra.

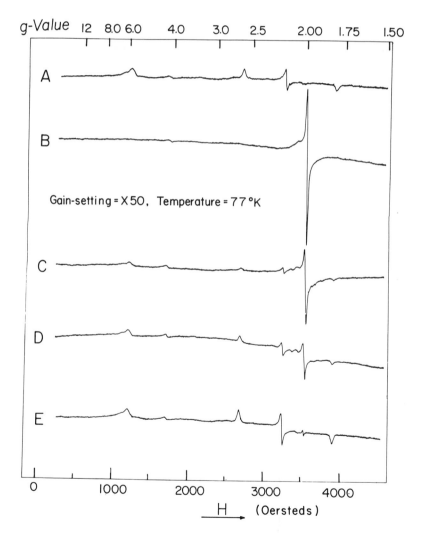

Figure 7. The EPR titration of Complex ES with ferrocytochrome
c (11).

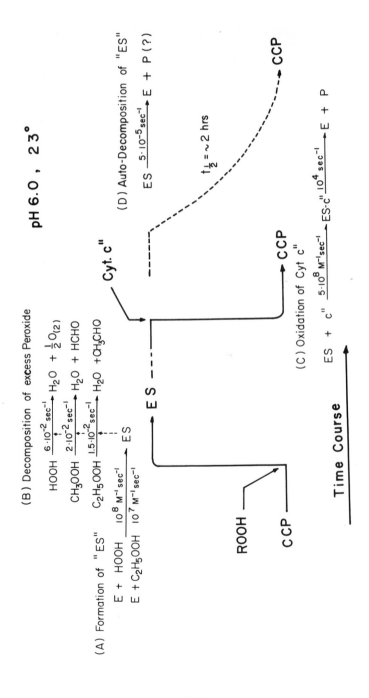

Figure 8. The schematic presentation of kinetics of formation and decomposition of Complex ES.

Fig. 8 schematically illustrates kinetics of formation and decomposition of ES. Rate constants of these reactions have been determined as indicated in Fig. 8. Reaction A, the formation of ES, is very rapid. The second order rate constant of their combination is of the order of $10^7$ to $10^8$ $M^{-1}$ $sec^{-1}$. These values are approximately 10 times larger than the corresponding values obtained with HRP by Chance (5). Reaction C, the oxidation of ferrocytochrome $\underline{c}$ by ES, is also extremely rapid. The second order rate constant of their combination has been estimated to be 5 x $10^8$ $M^{-1}$ $sec^{-1}$ (14). Since both CCP and ferrocytochrome $\underline{c}$ are large proteins, the rate constant of this order of magnitude indicates that the rate of their combination is nearly diffusion-limited. When an excess peroxide is added to CCP, a part of the peroxide is consumed in the formation of ES in Reaction A and the rest is slowly decomposed by the catalatic activity of ES in Reaction B. These rate constants indicate that the catalatic activity of ES is very weak. After the excess peroxide has been consumed, ES decomposes spontaneously in Reaction D. The rate of its decomposition is highly dependent on the purity of the enzyme preparation. In a recrystallized preparation of CCP, the first order rate constant is found to be of the order of $10^{-5}$ $sec^{-1}$ at pH 6 and 23°. With a preparation of 90 percent purity, the same constant was found to be $10^{-4}$ $sec^{-1}$ under the identical conditions. The half-time of the decomposition of ES is about two hours at 23° in the dissolved form of ES, while it is more than four hours in the crystalline form of ES. The rate of Reactions A and B are dependent on the type of the peroxide used, while those of Reactions C and D are independent of the type of the peroxide used.

We shall discuss now the similarity and dissimilarity between Complex II of HRP and ES of CCP. Both complexes are formed by the addition of similar oxidizing agents. Absorption spectra of these two complexes are almost identical (4,15). Therefore, ES was previously called Complex II of CCP. However, there are distinctive differences between these two complexes. George (16) showed that Complex II of HRP retains only one oxidizing equivalent per hematin unit. His finding is recently confirmed by us (13). We find, however, that ES retains two oxidizing equivalents per hematin unit (11-13). Theorell and Ehrenberg (17) reported that Complex II of HRP has a magnetic moment of spin one per hematin, while we find that ES has a magnetic moment of spin 3/2 per hematin (11). The formation of ES is accompanied by the large change in the ultraviolet absorption, while no appreciable change has been observed in the formation of Complex II from HRP. Since the formation of a stable but enzymically reactive free radical and the large change in the ultraviolet absorption are observed on the formation of ES from CCP, it is tempting to

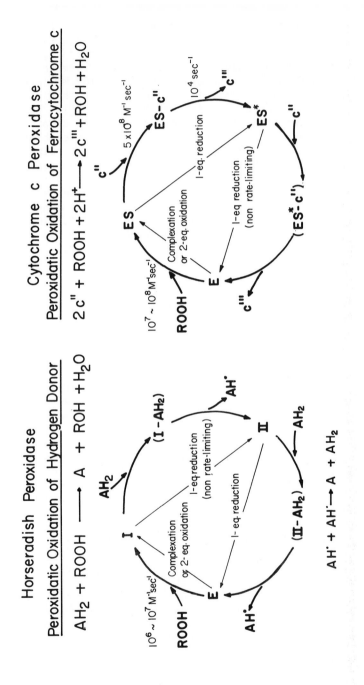

Figure 9. The comparison of the overall reactions catalyzed by horseradish and cytochrome c peroxidases.

speculate that one of the two oxidizing equivalents of ES may be retained in the form of a stable and reversible radical of an aromatic amino acid residue of the enzyme protein. Such a possibility is currently investigated by chemical and biophysical means in our laboratories. The elucidation of the mechanism by which two presumably unstable species, namely, a free radical and ferryl iron, co-exist in a stable state in Complex ES is of importance in order to understand the detailed mechanism of the peroxidase-catalyzed reaction.

Fig. 9 illustrates the comparison of the overall reactions catalyzed by HRP and CCP. HRP reacts with peroxide to form the green Complex I of Theorell (6). Complex I is then converted to the red Complex II of Keilin and Mann (7) by one equivalent reduction with a hydrogen donor. Complex II is in turn converted to the free enzyme by one equivalent reduction with the second molecule of hydrogen donors. The dismutation of two free radical products from the donor shown in Fig. 9 was proposed by Chance (18) and experimentally demonstrated by Yamazaki (19). Chance showed that Complex II is a rate-limiting intermediate of the overall reaction. In other words, the second 1-equivalent reduction is slower than the first one. The corresponding cycle of CCP is shown on the right in Fig. 9. ES is converted to the free enzyme by two consecutive steps of 1-equivalent reduction (15). It should be noted that the oxidation state of ES is equal to that of Complex I of green color, but light absorption spectrum of ES is similar to that of Complex II of red color. The intermediate ES* has not been experimentally detected. We, therefore, assume that the 1-equivalent reduction of ES to the free enzyme is extremely rapid. The first 1-equivalent reduction step of ES appears to be the rate-limiting step of the overall reaction in the CCP system (15). The second ternary complex, ES*-ferrocytochrome c, may not be formed. In other words, the second 1-equivalent reduction of ES* by ferrocytochrome c may be diffusion-limited.

Fig. 10 schematically illustrates the inter-relationship among enzymically active complexes of hydroperoxidases. By following George's concept of higher oxidation states of iron (20), speculative structure of these complexes, or compounds if you prefer to call them, are also shown here. On the addition of peroxide, a brown hydroperoxidase is converted to Complex I of green color. This step will be either complexation or 2-equivalent oxidation depending on the chemical nature of Complex I. Complex I is then converted to Complex ES of red color by either 2-equivalent oxidation or dismutation. Complex ES is then converted to Complex II of the same color by 1-equivalent reduction. The free enzyme of brown color is regenerated by 1-equivalent reduction of Complex II. Complex ES has not been detected in HRP systems, while Complexes I and II have not been observed in CCP systems.

303

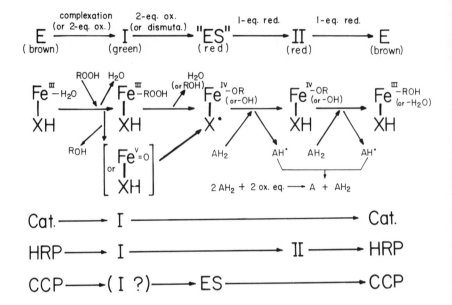

Figure 10. The inter-relationship among enzymatically active complexes of hydroperoxidases.

I would like to conclude by asking the following questions:

1. Is the hematin group of CCP in a crevice within the molecule as we see in ferrimyoglobin? If so, is the crevice large enough to accommodate relatively large substrates such as 2,5-dimethylhexane-2,5-dihydroperoxide?

2. Is the hematin group the initial site of the interaction with peroxide and other oxidizing agents?

3. If the hematin group is in the crevice of the CCP molecule, obviously large molecules such as ferrocytochrome c can not interact directly with the prosthetic group of the enzyme. How can the oxidizing equivalents of ES at the free radical and the ferryl iron be transmitted to the initial site of ferrocytochrome-interaction?

4. What kind of EPR spectra can we expect for Fe(IV) and Fe(V)?

# References

1. Altschul, A. M., R. Abrams, and T. R. Hogness. J. Biol. Chem., 136, 777 (1940).

2. Yonetani, T., B. Chance, and S. Kajiwara. J. Biol. Chem., 241, 2981 (1966).

3. Yonetani, T., and T. Ohnishi. J. Biol Chem., 241, 2983 (1966).

4. Yonetani, T., and G. S. Ray. J. Biol. Chem., 240, 4503 (1965).

5. Chance, B. Arch. Biochem. Biophys., 22, 224 (1949).

6. Theorell, H. Enzymologia, 10, 250 (1941).

7. Keilin, D., and T. Mann. Proc. Roy. Soc. (London), 122B, 119 (1937).

8. Kendrew, J. C., H. C. Watson, B. E. Strandberg, and R. E. Dickerson. Nature, 190, 660 (1961).

9. Chance, B., R. Perry, L. Akerman, and B. Theorell. Rev. Sci. Instr., 30, 735 (1959).

10. Estabrook, R. W. J. Biol. Chem., 223, 781 (1956).

11. Yonetani, T., H. Schleyer, and A. Ehrenberg. J. Biol. Chem., 241, 3240 (1966).

12. Yonetani, T. J. Biol. Chem., 240, 4509 (1965).

13. Yonetani, T. J. Biol. Chem., 240, 2562 (1966).

14. Yonetani, T., and G. S. Ray. J. Biol. Chem., 241, 700 (1966).

15. Chance, B. Arch. Biochem. Biophys., 41, 404 (1952).

16. George, P. Biochem. J., 54, 267 (1953).

17. Theorell, H., and A. Ehrenberg. Arch. Biochem. Biophys. 41, 442 (1952).

18. Chance, B. Arch. Biochem. Biophys., 41, 416 (1952).

19. Yamazaki, I., and L. H. Piette. Biochim. Biophys. Acta, 50, 62 (1961).

20. George, P. Advances in Catalysis, 4, 367 (1952).

# HORSE-RADISH PEROXIDASE:  THE ROLE OF THE ENDOGENOUS DONOR*

Peter Nicholls

Department of Biochemistry, State University of
New York at Buffalo, Buffalo, New York

One of the most striking characteristics of the peroxide compounds of the hydroperoxidases is their instability in the absence of added hydrogen donors (1,2).  Peroxidase and catalase primary peroxide compounds decay to the corresponding secondary compounds, and the latter to the free enzyme, the acceptor of the oxidizing equivalents involved being unknown. However, there must be a number of accessible equivalents of this endogenous hydrogen donor available, for it is possible to carry the peroxide compounds through ten or more cycles of formation and decomposition at very similar rates.  On the other hand, various ill-defined conditions inducing minor modifications of the protein also cause marked changes in the endogenous donor activity--sometimes decreasing, sometimes increasing the pseudo first order rate constants concerned (1,4). Anionic ligands binding the heme iron also promote the activity of the endogenous donor (i.e., decrease peroxide compound stability)(3).

Table I summarizes the data on the rates of the endogenous donor reactions for horse radish peroxidase, catalase and cytochrome $\underline{c}$ peroxidase.  The most rapid rate of compound II formation is shown by cytochrome $\underline{c}$ peroxidase, for which the intermediate formation of compound I remains unproven.  The decomposition of compound II ($k'_4$) is accelerated by anions in all three cases, and, in the case of catalases, its formation ($k'_7$) is also accelerated.  The endogenous donor dependent oxidation of cytochrome $\underline{c}$ by horse-radish peroxidase (see below) also gives a comparatively high value of $k_4$.

Recent studies of the available oxidizing equivalents in compound II of cytochrome $\underline{c}$ peroxidase have suggested an even more central role for the endogenous donor in this enzyme (8). Eqn. 1 indicates the two pathways of compound II reduction postulated for horse-radish peroxidase (5), and Eqns. 2 and 3, two alternative mechanisms for cytochrome $\underline{c}$ peroxidase activity.

*This work was supported by U. S. PHS Grant No. GM 11691.

307

$$HRP_{BH} \xrightarrow{H_2O_2} I_{BH} \xrightarrow{AH} II_{BH} \begin{array}{c} \nearrow^{AH} HRP_{BH} \\ \downarrow AH \\ \searrow_{k'_4} HRP_B \cdot \end{array} \qquad (1)$$

$$CCP_{BH} \xrightarrow{H_2O_2} CCP \left[ H_2O_2 \right] \text{ complex} \xrightarrow{2\underline{c}^{++}} CCP \qquad (2)$$

$$CCP_{BH} \xrightarrow{H_2O_2} CCP_{BH} \left[ H_2O_2 \right] \xrightarrow{k'_7} II_B \cdot \xrightarrow{2\underline{c}^{++}} CCP_{BH} \qquad (3)$$

$$\text{compound I} \qquad \text{compound II}$$

Reaction 2 has been proposed by Yonetani (9)(but see preceding paper for modified view); reaction 3 is proposed by analogy with reaction 1 and predicts that:

(a) a differential reactivity should be detectable between the two oxidizing equivalents in CCP compound II;

(b) CCP compound II should show a free radical signal equal in intensity to the concentration of the peroxide compound (cf. metmyoglobin peroxide);*

(c) the magnetic susceptibility of CCP compound II should approximate the sum of the susceptibilities of HRP compound II and a single unpaired electron, i.e. (5040 + 1270) x $10^6$ or 6310 x $10^6$.*

The experiments described below were carried out to define a role for the endogenous donor in horse-radish peroxidase (i.e., to prove the mechanism of Eqn. 1 and to delineate the conditions under which one or another path predominates), and thereby to obtain a basis for comparative studies of all the hemoproteins. Some suggestions may be made concerning the nature of the endogenous donor and its relationship to the peroxide compound, although a precise identification still eludes us.

---

*This has now been shown (see preceding paper by T. Yonetani).

TABLE I

Endogenous donor activity of three hydroperoxidases.
pH 5-7; 25° C; $k_1(M^{-1}sec^{-1})$ rate constant for compound I formation, $k_7(sec^{-1})$ rate constant for transition from compound I
to compound II, $k_4(sec^{-1})$ rate constant for spontaneous decomposition of compound II.

| Enzyme | Conditions | $k_1$ | $k_7$ | $k_4$ |
|---|---|---|---|---|
| Horse-radish peroxidase[1,5] (pH 4.6) | a. Direct measurement | $9 \times 10^6$ | 4.0 | 0.02 |
| | b. Direct measurement in presence of ex-cess acetate. | $9 \times 10^6$ | 4.0 | 4.0 |
| | c. Indirect measure-ment from cyto-chrome c oxidation (see text). | $8 \times 10^6$ | 5.0 | 4.0 |
| Catalase[2,4] (pH 6.5) | a. Direct measurement | $6 \times 10^6$ | $2 \times 10^{-3}$ | $5 \times 10^{-4}$ |
| | b. Direct measurement in presence of an excess of anions. | $6 \times 10^6$ | 0.15 | 0.05 |
| Cytochrome c peroxidase[6,7] (pH 6.0) | a. Direct measurement (George) | -- | -- | $2 \times 10^{-3}$ |
| | b. Direct measurement in presence of an excess of anions. | -- | -- | 0.02 |
| | c. Direct measurement (Yonetani) | $1.5 \times 10^8$ | $10^4$ | $5 \times 10^{-5}$ |

## Methods and Materials

The horse-radish peroxidase preparation was that described
previously (5). Cytochrome c peroxidase was made by a modification of the method of Altschul et al. (10). Cytochrome c
from horse heart was prepared in the laboratory or obtained
from Sigma (Type III).

Spectrophotometric assays of cytochrome c oxidation were
carried out at 550 and 418 mμ, and of ferrocyanide oxidation
at 420 mμ (appearance of ferricyanide, $E_{mM}$ 1.0). Phosphate
buffers used were usually pH 7.4, 0.01 M; the addition of saturated KCl to such a buffer to a final KCl concentration of
2.0 M lowers the pH to ~6.8. All experiments were carried out
at room temperature (20-25°C).

## Results

As reported previously (5), at low ionic strengths horse-radish peroxidase oxidizes ferrocyanide rapidly in a reaction first order in both enzyme and ferrocyanide. The overall velocity constant, $8 \times 10^4$ $M^{-1}sec^{-1}$, implies a reaction with compound II of at least $4 \times 10^4$ $M^{-1}sec^{-1}$, or a decomposition of compound II (40 µM) by stoichiometric ferrocyanide concentrations with a half-time of ~0.5 seconds. An almost instantaneous reduction ($t_{1/2} < 2$ seconds) was in fact observed.

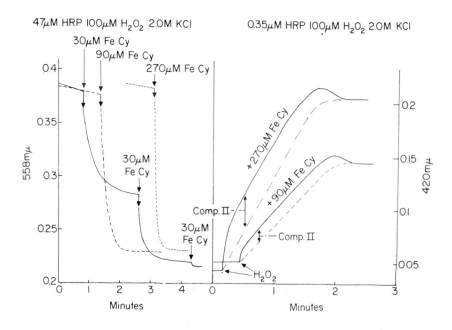

Figure 1. Reduction of compound II by ferrocyanide, and oxidation of ferrocyanide by peroxidase at high ionic strengths. 47 µM HRP in 0.01 M phosphate pH 6.8 plus 2.0 M KCl, compound II formed with 100 µM $H_2O_2$ at 558 mµ and decomposition by ferrocyanide (30, 90, 270 µM) followed as indicated. 0.35 µM HRP in 0.01 M phosphate pH 6.8 plus 2.0 M KCl, ferricyanide formed with 100 µM $H_2O_2$, followed at 420 mµ, from 270 and 90 µM ferrocyanide. Initial rapid rise and subsequent fall at 420 mµ due to compound II formation and decomposition. 2.5 ml final volume, 1 cm cuvette, 20-25° C for all experiments.

Fig. 1 shows that at high ionic strengths, however, the rate of reduction of compound II by ferrocyanide is measurable ($k = 8 \times 10^2$ $M^{-1}sec^{-1}$) although the stoichiometry of compound II reduced; ferrocyanide remains ~1 as reported previously (11).

Under these conditions, the oxidation of ferrocyanide, dependent on a high steady state concentration of compound II, is independent of ferrocyanide concentration and considerably faster than 2 times the rate of the reaction between compound II and ferrocyanide.

Similarly, the oxidation of cytochrome c (Fig. 2) which shows mixed kinetics at low ionic strenths becomes zero order at high ionic strength or low pH. In this case, 2.0 M KCl actually increases the overall rate of the reaction.

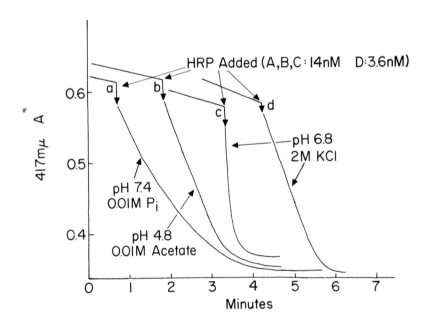

Figure 2. Oxidation of cytochrome c by HRP and $H_2O_2$. 1.2 μM cytochrome c in pH 7.4, 0.01 M phosphate (A), pH 4.8, 0.01 M acetate (B), pH 6.8, 2.0 M KCl (C and D), with 192 μM $H_2O_2$ present in all cases. 14 nM HRP added to A, B, and C; 3.6 nM HRP to D. 10 ml final volume, 4 cm cuvette, 20-25° C.

Such changes in the reactivity of peroxidase do not reflect changes in the nature of the peroxide compounds themselves. Fig. 3 shows that under conditions where the reactivity of compound II has diminished by a factor of ~100, the
visible absorption spectra of free peroxidase and of compound
II are almost unchanged. The relationships between the peroxide compounds are affected, however.

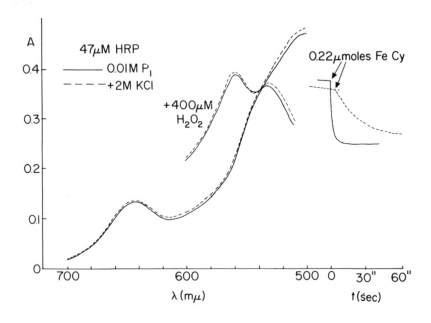

Figure 3. Spectra of peroxidase and its secondary peroxide
compound in 2.0 M KCl, and reactivity with ferrocyanide. 47
μM HRP in 0.01 M phosphate pH 7.4 (————) or 2.0 M KCl, pH
6.8 (- - - - -)plus H₂O₂ (400 μM) as indicated. Reduction
of the peroxide compounds so formed followed at 558 mμ after
addition of 0.22 μmoles ferrocyanide (right hand traces). 2.5
ml final volume, 1 cm cuvette, 20-25° C.


Fig. 4 shows that while compound II is formed in 2.0 M
KCl, its steady state concentration is markedly diminished
(50 percent II + 50 percent I compared with 75 percent II and
25 percent I in 0.01 M phosphate). In the presence of ferrocyanide, its steady state is the same as in 0.01 M phosphate,
but the duration of this steady state is dependent on the
presence of the ferrocyanide (right hand curves, Fig. 4).

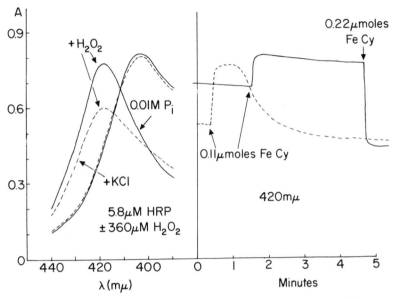

Figure 4. Soret spectra of peroxidase and its secondary peroxide compound in 2.0 M KCl and reactivity with ferrocyanide.
5.8 μM HRP in 0.01 M phosphate pH 7.4 (—————) or 2.0 M KCl
pH 6.8 (- - - - -) plus H₂O₂ as indicated. Reduction of steady
state compound I to II by ferrocyanide and subsequent decomposition of compound II followed at 420 mμ. 2.5 ml final volume,
1 cm cuvette, 20-25° C.


Evidently the bimolecular reactions with exogenous one-
electron donors are markedly inhibited by high ionic strength
(∼ 60-fold decrease in going from 0.01 M to 2.0 M salt for
both ferrocyanide and cytochrome c) whereas the zero order
reaction is slightly promoted under the same conditions. The
rate of the latter reaction, its order, and its independence
of the nature of the hydrogen donor, indicate that it is associated with the endogenous donor. Yet how are we to account
for the high turnover number? Table I shows that a rate at
least equal to that achieved by the addition of excess anion
is observed in the oxidation of cytochrome c. Yet the stability of HRP compound II is not markedly decreased by 2.0 M Cl⁻.
Moreover, the effect of ferrocyanide on the steady state of
compound II (Figs. 1 and 4), which is present as ∼ 90 percent
of the total enzyme, indicates that compound I must decay to
compound II some five to ten times faster than the rate of
compound II reduction itself.

Either the endogenous donor must exist in more than one activity state, or there must be more than one type of endogenous donor. This restriction on the precision of the endogenous donor concept is at once its weakness (the concept can be stretched to fit variegated phenomena) and its strength (it accounts for otherwise baffling properties of the enzymes). Chance (12) showed a variability in the activity of both horseradish and yeast peroxidases, a diminution due to incubation with peroxide restorable by a phenolic donor. Table II gives the results of a similar experiment on the oxidation of ferrocyanide.

## TABLE II

Experiment demonstrating that only the indirect reaction is affected by incubation with peroxide, and that both direct and indirect reactions occur at low ionic strength. pH 7.4 (0.01 M phosphate), pH 6.8 (2.0 M KCl), approximately 0.5 $\mu$M HRP, 48 $\mu$M $H_2O_2$, 11 $\mu$M additions of ferrocyanide.
$k_a$ = observed peroxidase turnover in 2.0 M KCl (4 sec$^{-1}$)
$k_b$ = observed peroxidase turnover in 2.0 M KCl (2nd ferrocyanide addition)
$k_c$ = observed peroxidase turnover in 0.01 M phosphate
$k_d$ = observed peroxidase turnover in 0.01 M phosphate (2nd ferrocyanide addition)

| Reactions Inhibited by $H_2O_2$ Incubation | Reactions Occurring at Low Ionic Strength | $k_a$ | $k_b$ | $k_c$ | $k_d$ |
|---|---|---|---|---|---|
| 1. Zero order reaction only | First order reaction only | 4 | 0.08 | 0.8 | 0.8 |
| 2. Both reactions | First order reaction only | 4 | 0.08 | 0.8 | 0.018 |
| 3. Zero order reaction only | Both reactions | 4 | 0.08 | 4.7 | 0.75 |
| 4. Both reactions | Both reactions | 4 | 0.08 | 4.7 | 0.093 |
| Experimental observations | | 4 | 0.11 | 2.0 | 0.67 |

From the rates of the zero order reaction at high ionic strength and the rates of the reaction with compound II at both high and low ionic strengths, one may calculate the overall reaction rate for the oxidation under both conditions before and after the enzyme has stood in presence of peroxide. The experimental observations (line 5, Table II) lie between the predicted values of "theories" 1 and 3. That is, only the zero order (endogenous donor) reaction is inhibited by incubation with peroxide, and both reactions occur at low ionic strength, the zero order reaction being slower than that at high ionic strength (as in the case of cytochrome $\underline{c}$, Fig. 2).

Consider the cycle of Eqn. 4 (compare Eqns. 1 and 3):

$$EBH_2 \xrightarrow{H_2O_2} IBH_2 \longrightarrow IIBH\cdot \xrightarrow{AH} IIBH_2 \qquad (4a)$$

$$IIBH_2 \longrightarrow EBH\cdot \xrightarrow{AH} EBH_2 \qquad (4b)$$

If the exogenous donor is not present to react with BH$\cdot$, the latter may disappear by one of several pathways (Eqn. 5);

By dismutation:
$$\left.\begin{array}{c} 2 \ II\,BH\cdot \\ 2 \ E\ BH\cdot \end{array}\right\} \longleftrightarrow \left\{\begin{array}{l} IIB + BH_2 \\ EB\ + EBH_2 \end{array}\right. \qquad (5a)$$

By further
oxidation:
$$II\ BH\cdot \longrightarrow EB \qquad (5b)$$

By reduction or oxidation by a secondary endogenous donor:
$$(YH_2)\ IIB \longrightarrow (YH)\ II\ BH\cdot \longrightarrow (Y)\ II\ BH_2 \quad (5c)$$

Despite the high and continued endogenous donor activity of catalase and peroxidase proteins, in neither mammalian catalase nor horse-radish peroxidase is a free radical (ESR) signal, attributable to the proposed 'BH$\cdot$', found in samples of compound II prepared from compound I in the absence of added donors (13,14). Processes such as those of Eqn. 5 must occur rapidly. In the reactions of metmyoglobin (13) and possibly of yeast peroxidase (8)*, this may not be the case. A free radical ESR signal is then observable; and the apparent oxidizing equivalents per heme group may rise above George's value of one (11).

Table III summarizes the results of a series of titrations of three peroxide compounds carried out with nitrite (a two-electron donor) and ferrocyanide (a one-electron donor) under acid conditions. Horse-radish peroxidase has no reactive groups except the compound II heme. Catalase (which cannot be titrated with ferrocyanide) contains a few groups reacting with the initial product of $HNO_2$ oxidation ($NO_2^+$), but these may be unrelated to the endogenous donor proper (15).

*See preceding paper by T. Yonetani.

## TABLE III

Titrations of myoglobin, peroxidase and catalase.  pH 5.6, 0.02 M phosphate, nitrite and ferrocyanide as donors.

| Peroxide compound | Hemes reduced/molecule donor | | Equivalents/heme | |
|---|---|---|---|---|
| | $HNO_2$ | $K_4Fe(CN)_6$ | $HNO_2$ | $K_4Fe(CN)_6$ |
| Catalase compound II | 1.50 (1.2-1.8) | --- | 1.3 (1.7-1.1) | --- |
| HRP compound II | 1.97 | 1.12 | 1.01 | 0.90 |
| Metmyoglobin peroxide | 1.19 (0.91-1.64) | 0.70 (0.56-0.83) | 1.68 (2.2-1.2) | 1.43 (1.8-1.2) |

Metmyoglobin peroxide shows a variable excess of oxidizing equivalents at pH 5.6 with both nitrite and ferrocyanide; acid conditions are also optimal for the appearance of the donor-sensitive ESR signal (13).

Such intermediate types of behavior reinforce the likelihood of the mechanism of Eqn. 3 being a correct description of the cytochrome c peroxidase reaction.  A search for reactions of the type given in Eqn. 5 may then be necessary to reconcile the differences between the findings of Yonetani (8) and of George (11) with this enzyme.

## Discussion

How is the endogenous donor oxidized, what is its chemical nature, and where is it located on the peroxidase protein?

The available evidence indicates that oxidizing equivalents reach the endogenous donor in an intramolecular reaction (3) closely dependent upon the precise configuration of the protein (1,4).  The stimulation by anions bound to the heme iron (3) suggests that a bridge may be formed between the iron and an oxidizable group lying above the heme.  The number of oxidizing equivalents that can be accommodated favors an additional mechanism of secondary transfer from this oxidizable group such as that suggested by Winfield (16).  His further suggestion of aromatic residues as the primary electron donor for such a system is supported by the ESR signal given by the metmyoglobin peroxide compound.  The absence of fine structure and closeness of 'g' to the free spin value in the case of metmyoglobin indicate an electron in a conjugated system.

316

This would seem to eliminate the other oxidizable side chains, such as those of serine, threonine, cysteine, and methionine, from candidacy. The sulfhydryl group is also eliminated by the absence of effects of SH reagents on the activity of the endogenous donor. The location of the most reactive donor group may be near the heme, but the subsidiary groups will be some distance away. The existence of such a spectrum of donor moieties may explain some of the observed variation in activity

Fig. 5 illustrates some of the present concepts for HRP activity involving one endogenous donor group. The initial endogenous transformations are written as reversible; such reversibility of the initial reaction could account for the otherwise puzzling fact that the rate of compound II formation by peroxidase does not always give rise to the steady state concentration calculable from its rate of decomposition (see, e.g., Fig. 4). Cytochrome c peroxidase may be simpler than horse-radish peroxidase in that compound I does not appear (Eqn. 3); it is, however, more complex in that its reactions are not purely bimolecular collision processes but involve either the formation of reversible enzyme-donor complexes (17) or monomolecular rate constants dependent on the nature of the donor (9). Two pathways have therefore been indicated, both yielding an enzyme-ferric cytochrome c complex, one directly and one via an intermediate enzyme-ferrous cytochrome c complex. Whether both pathways can be found in a single enzyme preparation, whether the one or other pathway is an artifact, and whether one mechanism derives from the other, are all controversial points at the present time.

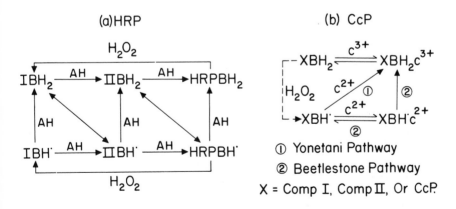

Figure 5. Steady state patterns proposed for horse-radish and cytochrome c peroxidases and their peroxide compounds.

According to the present hypothesis, therefore, all the hemoproteins can form the reactive 'oxidized donor' intermediate BH˙. In the case of HRP its formation is reasonably fast, its stability is very low, and its reactivity is moderate; for catalase, formation is slow and stability and reactivity are both low; for metmyoglobin, the formation is fast but incomplete, the stability is good, but the reactivity is poor; while in CCP alone, the formation is fast and complete and both stability and reactivity are high. This summary, of course, disguises the fact that under the heading of 'endogenous donor' designated '$BH_2$', we have probably hidden a galaxy of very different chemical reactions.

## References

1.  Chance, B.  Arch. Biochem. Biophys., 22, 224 (1949).

2.  Chance, B.  Biochem. J., 46, 387 (1950).

3.  Nicholls, P.  Biochem. J., 81, 365 (1961).

4.  Nicholls, P.  Biochim. Biophys. Acta, 60, 217 (1962).

5.  Nicholls, P.  Arch. Biochem. Biophys., 106, 25 (1964).

6.  George, P.  Biochem. J., 55, 220 (1953).

7.  Yonetani, T., and G. S. Ray.  J. Biol Chem., 240, 4503 (1965).

8.  Yonetani, T.  J. Biol. Chem., 240, 4509 (1965).

9.  Yonetani, T., and G. S. Ray.  J. Biol Chem., 241, 700 (1966).

10. Altschul, A. M., R. Abrams, and T. R. Hogness.  J. Biol. Chem., 136, 777 (1940).

11. George, P.  Biochem. J., 54, 267 (1953).

12. Chance, B.  Fed. Proc., 9, 160 (1950).

13. Gibson, J. F., D. J. E. Ingram, and P. Nicholls.  Nature, 181, 1398 (1958).

14. Chance, B., and R. R. Fergusson.  In Mechanism of Enzyme Action (W. D. McElroy and B. Glass, eds.), Johns Hopkins University Press, 1954, p. 389.

15. Nicholls, P.  Biochim. Biophys. Acta, 81, 479 (1964).

16. Winfield, M. E.  J. Mol. Biol., 12, 600 (1965).

17. Beetlestone, J.  Arch. Biochem. Biophys., 89, 35 (1960).

# HORSE-RADISH PEROXIDASE COMPOUND III*

I. Yamazaki, K. Yokota and M. Tamura

Biophysics Division, Research Institute of Applied Electricity
Hokkaido University, Sapporo, Japan

Peroxidase Compound III was found by Keilin and Mann (1) in the presence of excess $H_2O_2$. This compound was also observed by Swedin and Theorell (2) during the aerobic oxidation of dihydroxyfumarate catalyzed by this enzyme. An oxyferroperoxidase structure has been suggested for peroxidase Compound III (3,4). This idea, however, has not been generally accepted (5), since ferroperoxidase is thought to be oxidized directly to ferriperoxidase without the formation of an oxyferrous compound (6,7,8). Recently, experimental evidence has been accumulated in our laboratory which suggests that ferroperoxidase reacts with molecular oxygen to form Compound III. The stability of this compound greatly depends upon the experimental conditions, and these conditions have given diverse results, causing confusion as to the concept of Compound III.

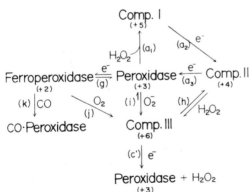

Figure 1. Tentative scheme for the relationship between peroxidase derivatives which appear during the peroxidase-oxidase reaction. Numbers in parentheses show the effective oxidation level of the iron of peroxidase derivatives. Yokota and Yamazaki, Biochim. Biophys. Acta, 105, 301 (1965).

*This work supported by US PHS Grant AM-06518.

Formation of Compound III. Fig. 1 shows five "effective" oxidation states of peroxidase which may participate in the peroxidase-oxidase reaction (9). Reactions $a_1$, $a_2$ and $a_3$ show a cycle of ordinary peroxidase reaction. Here, three possible paths of Compound III formation are discussed.

Mechanism h. Mechanism h shows a path of Compound III formation when excess $H_2O_2$ is present, as suggested by Chance (10) and George (11):

$$\text{Compound II} + H_2O_2 \rightleftharpoons \text{Compound III}$$

Mechanism i. Now I would like to mention two more possible paths of formation which might be present in the peroxidase-oxidase reaction, the reactions between ferriperoxidase and $O_2^-$ and between ferroperoxidase and $O_2$. Reaction i is thought to be a main path of Compound III formation during the aerobic oxidation of dihydroxyfumatate and NADH (9). This mechanism is supported mainly by stoichiometry of the following overall reaction: (Equation 1)

$$2 \text{ DHF} + 2 \text{ Peroxidase} + 2O_2 + H_2O_2 \longrightarrow 2 \text{ DKS} + 2 \text{ Compound III} + 2H_2O$$

where DHF and DKS are dihydroxyfumarate and diketosuccinate, respectively. In the absence of $H_2O_2$, Compound III formation is very slow in the aerobic solution of peroxidase and dihydroxyfumarate. An addition of 4 μM $H_2O_2$ causes the rapid formation of 6.3 μM Compound III at the expense of 7.8 μM dihydroxyfumarate. The molar ratio of $H_2O_2$ : DHF : Compound III is approximately 1 : 2.5 : 1.6 and close to the overall Equation 1 above. This stoichiometry may be explained by assuming that peroxidase catalyzes the formation of one-equivalent oxidized dihydroxyfumarate, which reduces $O_2$ to $O_2^-$. This $O_2^-$ is assumed to react effectively with ferriperoxidase to form Compound III. So, Equation 1 is probably composed of the three following reactions in which the ES compounds of steps $a_1$, $a_2$ and $a_3$ are omitted (see ref. 3 of Editors' note on p. 326):

$$2 \text{ DHF} + H_2O_2 \xrightarrow{\text{peroxidase}} 2 \text{ DHF}^{\bullet} + 2H_2O \quad (2)$$

$$\text{DHF}^{\bullet} + O_2 \longrightarrow \text{DKS} + O_2^- \quad (3)$$

$$O_2^- + \text{Peroxidase} \longrightarrow \text{Compound III} \quad (4)$$

where $\text{DHF}^{\bullet}$ is one-equivalent oxidized dihydroxyfumarate. Equations 2 and 3 have been confirmed using an electron spin resonance spectroscopy (12). The slight deviation of the experimental results from the stoichiometry of Equation 1 may be due to the dismutation of $\text{DHF}^{\bullet}$ and $O_2^-$.

Mechanism j. One more path of Compound III formation is a direct reaction between ferroperoxidase and $O_2$ (see Fig. 2). In this experiment dithionite is used as a reductant for peroxidase. This kind of experiment seems to be very simple, but

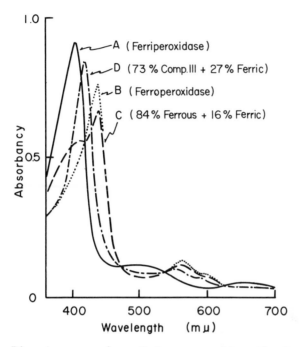

**Figure 2.** Direct conversion of ferroperoxidase to Compound III by the introduction of molecular oxygen. A: 8.3 μM ferriperoxidase in 0.1 M phosphate, pH 8. B: Ferroperoxidase. Dithionite solution (20 mM) added little by little to the partially anaerobic (A) until absorbance at 437 mμ reached a maximum. C: Solution of 84 percent ferroperoxidase and 16 percent ferriperoxidase resulting from bubbling commercial $N_2$ gas (~1 percent $O_2$) through (B) until 16 percent peroxidase was reoxidized. D: 73 percent Compound III and 27 percent ferriperoxidase resulting from addition of 0.1 ml $O_2$-saturated solution to 3 ml (C). Compound III decomposed to ferriperoxidase during measurement.

it has given ambiguous results which occasionally lead to an erroneous conclusion, for instance, a negative conclusion for the existence of oxyferroperoxidase. In the experiment of Fig. 2, peroxidase is initially reduced by slightly excess dithionite and then commercial $N_2$ gas (may be about 1 percent $O_2$) is carefully bubbled through the solution until 16 percent peroxidase is reoxidized (Spectrum C). At this step, both dithionite and oxygen must be completely absent from the solution. A sufficient amount of $O_2$ solution is added to the solution (C) at once. 73 percent ferroperoxidase (see fig. legend) converts to Compound III. The half decay time of the Compound III is about 2 minutes between pH 5 and 8, as shown in Fig. 3.

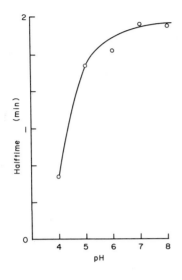

Figure 3. pH dependence of Compound III stability. Experimental procedure the same as that of the experiment of Fig. 2. Tris-HCl for pH 7 and 6, acetate for pH 5 and 4. Buffer concentration 0.1 M.

A similar result has been observed when peroxidase is reduced by NADH (13).

Compound III is now clearly observed as a rather stable intermediate in the reaction between ferroperoxidase and $O_2$. Why has it been missed by many workers? The reason is probably due to the delicate dependence of the stability of Compound III upon the existence of oxidants or reductants. The possible contribution of $O_2^-$ structure in Compound III may suggest the following three tentative mechanisms for the decomposition of Compound III.

I. Reductive decomposition:

$$Fe_p^{+++} \cdot O_2^- \text{ (Comp. III)} \xrightarrow{+e^-} Fe_p^{+++} + O_2^{--} \text{ } (H_2O_2) \quad (5)$$

Compound III has been found to react with quite a number of hydrogen donors (14,15). It should be mentioned here that ferroperoxidase also seems to be a nice electron donor in Equation 5. As an introduction of insufficient amount of $O_2$ into ferroperoxidase solution makes a mixture of Compound III and ferroperoxidase, the rapid decomposition of Compound III will occur according to Equation 5.

As can be seen in Fig. 4, a 17 percent decrease in the conversion and an over ten-fold decrease in the half decay time of Compound II are observed when insufficient $O_2$ is admitted to the ferroperoxidase solution. Compound III might not be observed in the presence of excess dithionite.

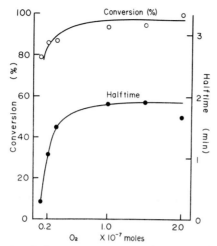

Figure 4. Effect of $O_2$ amount upon the efficiency of conversion from ferroperoxidase to Compound III and its half decay time. Experimental procedure was the same as that of Fig. 2, except in the amount of $O_2$ added. 0.1 M phosphate, pH 7.0. $O_2$ saturated solution was added to get above 0.1 μmoles $O_2$ and an air equilibrated solution below 0.03 μmoles $O_2$. Ferroperoxidase was 0.023 μmoles. Unexpected high conversion percentage obtained at the lowest $O_2$ addition may be due to the spontaneous introduction of $O_2$ from the air which is inevitable in this procedure.

## II. Oxidative decomposition:

$$Fe_p^{+++} \cdot O_2^- \text{ (Comp. III)} \xrightarrow{-e^-} Fe_p^{+++} + O_2 \qquad (6)$$

An addition of a small amount of $H_2O_2$ causes the rapid decomposition of Compound III. The direct demonstration of the reaction of Compound I with Compound III is experimentally difficult. Compound II, on the other hand, is found to react very rapidly with Compound III. When Compound II and Compound III are combined at about pH 5, the resulting mixture cannot be observed by the ordinary recording technique. It may reasonably be concluded that Compound II acts as an electron-acceptor in Equation 6.

## III. Autodecomposition:

$$Fe_p^{+++} \cdot O_2^- \text{ (Comp. III)} \xrightarrow{H_2O} Fe_p^{+++}OH \text{ (Comp.II)} + HO_2^- \quad (7)$$

$$Fe_p^{+++} \cdot O_2^- \text{ (Comp. III)} \longrightarrow Fe_p^{+++} + O_2^- \text{ } (O_2 + H_2O_2) \quad (8)$$

These reactions may be described as either autodecomposition of
Compound III or autoxidation of ferroperoxidase.  Both reactions
produce $H_2O_2$.  So, Compounds I and II must be involved as intermediates in the reaction of Compound III decomposition.  There is
no result to suggest that Compound I reacts with Compound III,
but Compound I is known to be very unstable and converts spontaneously into Compound II.  Compound II then reacts very rapidly wit
Compound III.  So, it is reasonable to assume that the rate-limiting step in the autodecomposition of Compound III is Reaction 7
or 8.  Our results on the Compound III decomposition are consister
with this assumption and one of the results is shown in Fig. 5.
In this case, half decay time is about 2 minutes and clear isosbestic points of Compound III and ferriperoxidase indicate that
no observable intermediates are present in the reaction.

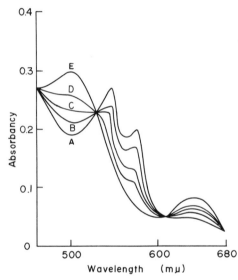

Figure 5.  Autodecomposition
of Compound III.  26 µM peroxidase, 0.05 M acetate, pH
5.  Experimental procedure
was almost the same as that
of Fig. 2.  Spectrum A was
taken just after 0.2 ml $O_2$
saturated solution was added
to the 85 percent ferrous
and 15 percent ferric peroxidase mixture.  Spectra B,
C, D and E were taken about
1, 2, 3 and 4 min after A,
respectively.

Function of Peroxidase Compound III.  Two physiological
functions of Compound III will be emphasized here.  First, it
has a relatively high affinity toward indoleacetate (15).  Rate
constants of the reactions of indoleacetate with peroxidase
Compound III and Compound II are $2.2 \times 10^3$ and $1.8 \times 10^4$, respectively, at pH 5.  The ratio is about 0.12.  This ratio is
much higher than those of the other peroxidase hydrogen donors
which are around 0.001.  A special oxidation product of indoleacetate might be expected when it reacts with Compound III, and
this is now under investigation.

Second, the role of Compound III is quite unusual in the
NADH oxidation and is thought to be a kind of regulator,
which causes oscillatory oxidation of NADH when oxygen is introduced continuously into the solution of NADH and peroxidase (16).

## Conclusion and Summary

Peroxidase Compound III is clearly identified as an intermediate in reaction between ferroperoxidase and $O_2$, and its half decay time is about 2 minutes between pH 5 and 8. The absorption spectrum of Compound III is very similar to that of oxymyoglobin, except for the lower intensity of $\alpha$-band for Compound III. Like oxymyoglobin, Compound III has no absorption band at 670 m$\mu$. This absorption appeared in Compound III formed in the presence of excess $H_2O_2$ and was considered to be given by a peroxidase with a modified prosthetic group (17). The delicate stability of Compound III is influenced in the presence of specific oxidants and reductants. Peroxidase Compound III seems to represent a model of $O_2$ activation by hemoprotein and in this respect Compound III will differ from oxymyoglobin.

## References

1. Keilin, D. and T. Mann. Proc. Roy. Soc., 122B, 119 (1937).

2. Swedin, B. and H. Theorell. Nature, 145, 71 (1940).

3. George, P. Advances in Catalysis, 4, 367 (1952).

4. Mason, H.S. Advances in Enzymology, 19, 79 (1957).

5. Nicholls, P. In Oxygenases (O. Hayaishi, ed.) Academic Press, New York, 1962, p. 273.

6. Theorell, H. Advances in Enzymology, 7, 265 (1947).

7. Harbury, H.A. J. Biol. Chem., 225, 1009 (1957).

8. Chance, B. In Oxidases and Related Redox Systems (T.E. King, H.S. Mason and M. Morrison, eds.) Wiley, New York, 1965 p. 504.

9. Yokota, K. and I. Yamazaki. Biochim. Biophys. Acta, 105, 301 (1965).

10. Chance, B. Arch. Biochem. Biophys., 41, 404 (1952).

11. George, P. J. Biol. Chem., 201, 427 (1953).

12. Yamazaki, I. and L.H. Piette. Biochem. Biophys. Acta, 77, 47, (1963).

13. Yamazaki, I. and K. Yokota. Biochem. Biophys. Res. Comm., 19, 249 (1965).

14. Chance, B. Advances in Enzymology, 12, 153 (1951).

15. Yokota, K. and I. Yamazaki. Biochem. Biophys. Res. Comm. 18, 48 (1965).

16. Yamazaki, I., K. Yokota, and R. Nakajima. Biochem. Biophys. Res. Comm., 21, 582 (1965).

17. Keilin, D. and E. F. Hartree. Biochem. J., 49, 88 (1951).

Editors' note: Other data are of significance in elucidating the nature of Compound III. One of them is well known, namely, that Compound III can be formed from Compound II by the addition of peroxide, particularly if Compound II is formed with methyl hydrogen peroxide. (Addition of 1.3 mM peroxide results in the formation of Compound III in about 2 min (see 1,2).) This property of Compound II should be taken into account in considering the oxidative decomposition reactions, particularly Equation 6 of the paper above.

The rate of reaction of ferroperoxidase with oxygen is of importance in interpreting experiments and it is apparent that ferroperoxidase can disappear rapidly under appropriate experimental conditions. We were unable to demonstrate ferroperoxidase even a few msec after mixing with oxygen. The reaction product formed in 5 msec was not Compound III, but remains incompletely identified (3).

Experiments with Yamazaki prior to this symposium and subsequently confirmed by him in Japan (personal communication) indicate that the formation of Compound III from the reaction of oxygen with the enzyme plus dithionite is a slow reaction; the half-times under experimental conditions in this laboratory were about 1 sec at a 16 $\mu$M oxygen concentration ($k_1$ ~5 x $10^4$ $M^{-1}$ $sec^{-1}$. In addition, J. Wittenberg (personal communication) reports measurements of the kinetics of formation of Compound III, or, as he terms it, "oxyperoxidase", in the reaction of oxygen with horse-radish peroxidase reduced by one-equivalent of dithionite. A second-order velocity constant of approximately 5 x $10^4$ $M^{-1}$ $sec^{-1}$ is observed.

These values are approximately 1/1000 the value for cytochrome oxidase. If indeed the reaction of ferroperoxidase with oxygen is involved in enzymatic activity, the slowness of the oxygen reaction would require a very high oxygen concentration for maximal activity. Lastly, it should be emphasized that proof of the existence of an oxyferroperoxidase requires demonstration of the removal of molecular oxygen from such a compound; such a demonstration has not yet been made. Until then, Compound III can be any one of the series $Fe^{+2}O_2$, $Fe^{+3}O_2^-$, $Fe^{+4}O_2^{--}$, etc.

## References

1. Chance, B. Arch. Biochem. Biophys., 41, No. 2, 404 (1952).

2. Keilin, D., and E. F. Hartree. Biochem. J., 49, 88 (1951).

3. Chance, B. In Oxidases and Related Redox Systems (T. E. King, H. S. Mason, and M. Morrison, eds.), John Wiley and Sons, Inc., New York, 1965, p. 504.

# SELECTIVE MODIFICATION OF CATALASES*

G. R. Schonbaum and F. Jajczay

Department of Biochemistry, University of Alberta
Edmonton, Alberta, Canada

The characterization of enzymic active sites is one of
the most vigorously pursued objectives in contemporary biochemistry. The traditional approach in such investigations --
apart from kinetic studies -- involves attempts at selective
modifications of specific groups, a procedure fraught with
many difficulties, and which, even when successful, may not
allow an unequivocal interpretation of the observed effects.
Nonetheless the lack of alternative, more incisive, simpler
methods of inquiry even in this day of X-ray crystallography
confronts one with little choice and renders the chemical modification of enzymes a useful undertaking.

This approach seemed of particular interest in the case
of catalase, an enzyme in which the role of protein is unknown (1), and whose activity is therefore discussed only in
terms of the chemistry of its prosthetic group (ferriprotoporphyrin IX), the active site. To effect the modification
of catalase a variety of reagents was considered. However,
since the primary steps in the catalase-mediated reactions
might involve a nucleophilic attack by the enzyme on its substrate, hydrogen peroxide, it was decided to inquire  whether
any interaction occurs between hydroperoxidases and various
electrophilic regents. Of the compounds chosen several showed
promise, but the most intriguing proved to be the pseudohalo-
gen, cyanogen bromide.

In the following account we shall describe only the horse
blood catalase-BrCN  system, although the generalizations which
will be outlined apply but for minor changes to the reactions
of bovine liver catalase and hog blood catalase.

Studies of the horse blood catalase-cyanogen bromide
system. The reaction between cyanogen bromide and the enzyme
occurs in at least two stages. In the first or fast phase of

*This work was supported by Research Grants MT 1270 and G-64-36
from the Medical Research Council of Canada and Life Insurance
Medical Research Fund.

the reaction, approximately 14 ± 2 sulfhydryl groups are oxidized, with the simultaneous liberation of cyanide ion from cyanogen bromide. The detailed investigation of the mechanism and products of oxidation of sulfhydryl groups have not been carried out because the physical and catalytic properties of the enzyme are barely affected by such modifications. However, the elimination of sulfhydryl groups, which can be also effected with p-hydroxymercuribenzoate, permits more incisive investigation of the second, or slower, phase of catalase-BrCN reaction. This process leads to the formation of a stable, inactive form of enzyme and involves consumption of four moles of cyanogen bromide per mole of catalase. The result is particularly noteworthy in view of wide reactivity of cyanogen bromide (2-4).

As to the locus of reaction — a study not yet completed — the following evidence suggests that the modification does not directly involve the prosthetic group but alters four amino acids out of approximately 2300 residues. Thus: (a) the spectroscopic features of the ferriprotoporphyrin extracted from the native and inhibited catalases were nearly identical; (b) treatment of catalase (in which free sulfhydryl groups were eliminated) with $C^{14}$ cyanogen bromide indicated retention of radioactivity in the protein moiety; (c) there are numerous similarities between cyanogen bromide modified catalase and the derivative obtained on treating catalase compound I with 3-aminotriazole, a derivative in which the properties of an amino acid group have been altered (5,6).

These results do not rigorously preclude the possibility of protohemin modification but demand that on extracting the prosthetic group from the inhibited enzyme the "protohemin" reverts to the native form with the simultaneous transfer of the modifying group to the protein. Such a course of events is not very likely.

Regarding the effect of cyanogen bromide on the integrity of the protein, we have examined sedimentation properties and optical rotatory dispersion between 220 and 320 m$\mu$ and have shown that these parameters were not altered by "cyanobromination". Furthermore, the absorption difference between the native and modified catalases in the protein absorption region were barely noticeable, suggesting that no major alteration occurs in the environment of tyrosine, tryptophan or phenylalanine. On the other hand, significant differences were observed in the position and extinction coefficients of charge transfer, $\alpha$-, $\beta$- and Soret bands, implying a change in the ferriprotoporphyrin-apoenzyme interaction.

328

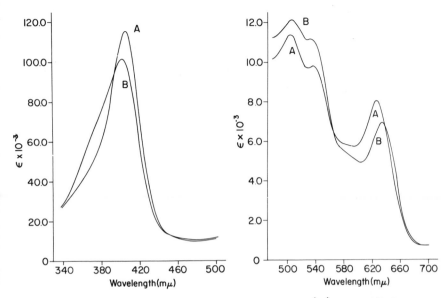

Figure 1. Spectra of horse blood catalase (A) and catalase-"BrCN" derivative (B). 0.01 M phosphate buffer, pH 7.15; 25° C. Extinction coefficients expressed in terms of hematin-Fe.

The kinetic investigations also revealed some interesting features. Thus, the second-order rate constant for the inactivation reaction ($90 \pm 10$ $M^{-1}sec^{-1}$) is nearly pH invariant from pH 4 to 8.5 and therefore prototropic equilibria do not appear to be involved in the rate determining step. These observations are consistent with the concept of reaction at a non-ionizing group but do not exclude the possibility that the ionization state of the group participating in the reaction does not change in the investigated pH region. Studies over a wider pH range will be necessary to resolve these questions.

The inactivation of catalase is inhibited by peroxides, hydrocyanic and formic acid; thus in this respect as well as in its pH dependence the reaction between catalase and BrCN parallels the behavior of the enzyme-peroxide system. Furthermore, judging by spectrophotometric assays, the modified catalase does not react with hydrocyanic and formic acids, even when the concentration of the ligands is increased 10-fold above the level necessary to give the derivatives with the native enzyme.

329

The problem to be resolved is whether the apparent similarities in the peroxide and cyanogen bromide reactions with catalase are due to the modification of a common locus or whether they arise in some adventitious manner, for instance, due to steric effects. Studies of BrCN reaction with other hemoproteins, particularly metmyoglobin, promise to provide answers bearing on the steric aspect of the problem (7). But whatever the answers prove to be, the presence of a uniquely reactive nucleophilic group in catalase, situated in the proximity of the prosthetic group, has been strongly implied.

The specific role of such a group in the formation of compound I and its redox reactions would constitute one of the differentiating features among various hemoproteins containing the same coenzyme.

## References

1. Nicholls, P., and G. R. Schonbaum. In Catalases in the Enzymes (P. D. Boyer, H. Lardy, and K. Myrbäck, eds.), Vol. VIII, Academic Press, New York, 196⁷, p. 147.

2. Witkop, E., and B. Gross. J. Biol. Chem., 2³7, 1856 (1962).

3. Schreiber, J., and B. Witkop. J. Am. Chem. Soc., 86, 2441 (1965).

4. Elderfield, R. C., and M. Green. J. Org. Chem., 17, 4³1 (1952).

5. Margoliash, E., and A. Novogrodsky. Biochem. J., 68, 468 (1958).

6. Margoliash, E., A. Novogrodsky, and A. Schejter. Biochem. J., 74, 3³9(1960).

7. Gurd, F. This volume, p. 221.

# MAGNETIC MEASUREMENTS OF PEROXIDE COMPOUNDS*

## A. Ehrenberg

Biokemiska Institutionen, Medicinska Nobelinstitutet
Karolinska Institutet, Stockholm, Sweden

The observation of the formation of a compound between a hemoprotein and peroxide dates back to 1900, when the color change upon addition of $H_2O_2$ to ferrihemoglobin was noticed by Kobert (1). In the years 1935 to 1950 a number of these compounds were detected by Keilin, Theorell and Chance, and characterized by observations with the spectroscope or by recording the light absorption spectrum. With high speed spectrophotometry Chance was further able to determine the rate constants of the enzymatic reactions.

We know that these hemoprotein peroxide compounds contain two or one more oxidizing equivalents than the ferrihemoprotein itself. This renders it quite impossible to draw safe conclusions concerning the state of the heme iron complex solely from the light absorption. This was realized at an early stage and a first attempt to determine the paramagnetic susceptibility was made in 1942 by Theorell (2). This measurement was made on an unknown mixture of hydrogen peroxide compounds I and II of horse-radish peroxidase. It nevertheless gave a value of about the right magnitude since the difference between the susceptibilities of these compounds is not very large, as our later measurements have shown (Table I).

With an improved instrument for the magnetic determinations and by simultaneous analysis of the reaction mixture by spectrophotometric measurements at suitable wavelengths we succeeded in determining the susceptibility of the two compounds separately as well as of a few other hemoprotein peroxide compounds (3,4). Even though these measurements were made nearly 15 years ago, we would use the same procedure today if we wanted to make the measurements again. Thus it might still be worthwhile to describe very briefly how the results were obtained.

*This work was in part supported by grant US PHS AM-05895.

We measured horse-radish compounds of methyl hydrogen peroxide (MeOOH), which are fairly stable in the absence of added donor substrate. The isosbestic points of the Soret-region of enzyme and compound I, of enzyme and compound II, and of compounds I and II were accurately determined under the experimental conditions to be employed. Since these light absorptions at the high peroxidase concentrations necessary for measurement of the magnetic susceptibility are very strong, we had to use light paths of only 0.015 cm.

A suitably buffered peroxidase solution was mixed with a small volume of concentrated MeOOH, and the sample tube of the magnetic balance immediately filled with one portion of the mixture and the optical cuvette with the other. The readings were immediately started. Examples of the results are shown in Figs. 1 and 2. It should be noted that at pH 8.85, Compound I rapidly disappears, whereas Compound II decays more slowly. A reliable value for $\chi_{II}$ is thus easily obtained at pH 8.85, merely by correcting for the contribution of the free enzyme. At pH 3.43,

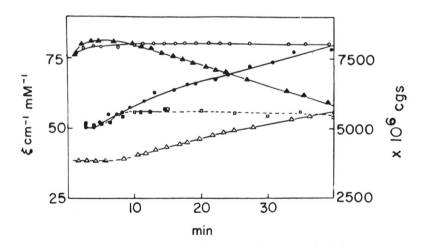

Figure 1.   Experiments 12 and 15 on horse-radish peroxidase MeOOH at pH 8.85.
Experiment 12:   Extinction at △-△-△ 390 mμ; o-o-o 411 mμ;
▲-▲-▲ 427 mμ.  ●-●-● observed magnetic susceptibility values; ☐-☐-☐ susceptibility of Compound II, obtained by correction for the amount of free enzyme present.
Experiment 15:   ■—■—■ Susceptibility values corrected as in Expt. 12.  From Theorell and Ehrenberg (4).

332

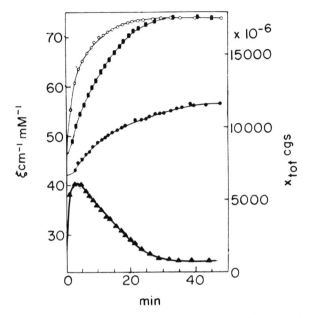

Figure 2.  Experiment with horse-radish peroxidase + MeOOH at pH 3.43.  Extinction at 390 mμ,▲—▲—▲▲— ; at 411 mμ o-o-o; at 427 mμ, —■—■—■—.  Observed magnetic susceptibility,●—●—●. From  Theorell and Ehrenberg (4).

Compound I predominates during the first short period of the experiment.  When compound I decays, compound II is formed, reaches a maximum concentration and later decays.  From the light absorption curves the molar fractions of the three components could be calculated at suitable time intervals.  The susceptibilities of compounds I and II were finally calculated by means of the least square method.  Determinations were also made on compound II of horse erythrocyte catalase with MeOOH and on  compound III of myoglobin with MeOOH and $H_2O_2$. In the latter case paramagnetic oxygen was evolved and excess oxygen was removed by equilibration with air prior to the magnetic measurement.

Compound I of catalase was too short-lived to be measured in the way.  Brill, den Hartog and Legallais (5), however, constructed a Rankine balance combined with a flow system with a time resolution better than 1 sec.  With this instrument it was possible to measure the susceptibility of the transient compound I of catalase (6,7).  The susceptibility of compound III of myoglobin and MeOOH was redetermined (8) and the new value agreed very closely with our earlier determination (4).

Very recently Yonetani obtained preparations of cytochrome c peroxidase of high purity (9). We have measured the susceptibility of this enzyme and of some of its derivatives. The compound with EtOOH, which from spectrophotometry could be characterized as being of type II, attracted special attention, since it had been shown (9) that it contained the same number of oxidizing equivalents as is normal for compounds of type I. No compound of the latter type could, however, be detected for this enzyme. The result of one experiment in the magnetic balance is shown in Fig. 3.

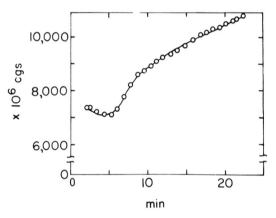

Figure 3. Observed magnetic susceptibilities after addition of EtOOH to cytochrome c peroxidase. Unpublished work by Ehrenberg and Yonetani.

The effective magnetic moment, $\mu_{eff}$, of the peroxide compounds and the corresponding ferrihemoproteins are collected in Table I. It must be kept in mind that these values are based on total susceptibilities, including contributions from the heme iron as well as from free radicals. It has been shown that small amounts of free radicals are formed in the reactions with peroxide of myoglobin (8,10), catalase (6), and horse radish peroxidase (11). The radical concentrations reported are, however, so small that a correction for their paramagnetism will not change the $\mu_{eff}$-values to any appreciable extent.

In the case of cytochrome c peroxidase compound II, the situation is different and a correction must be made. The ESR recordings (Fig. 4) indicate that one full equivalent of free radicals is present in the system. The total width of the radical absorption, several hundred gauss, suggests further that this radical is situated not too far away from the

334

paramagnetic heme. When correction is made for one equivalent of free radicals, assuming normal susceptibility of the radicals, the effective magnetic moment of the heme of compound II of cytochrome c peroxidase decreases from 4.1 to 3.7 Bohr magnetons (B.m.).

## TABLE I

Effective magnetic moments, $_{eff}$, in Bohr magnetons of various hemoproteins and their peroxide compounds.

| Compound according to light absorption | Enzyme Catalase (horse erythrocyte or bacteria | Horse-radish peroxidase | Cytochrome c peroxidase | Myoglobin (horse muscle) |
|---|---|---|---|---|
| E | 5.66 | 5.27 | 5.50 | 5.73 |
| I | 3.90 | 3.99 | ——— | ——— |
| II | 2.93 | 3.53 | (4.1) 3.7 | ——— |
| III | ——— | ——— | ——— | 2.85 |

A certain systematic trend can be seen in the values of Table I (12). First we compare the magnetic moments of catalase and horse radish peroxidase and of their peroxide compounds. We note that catalase has more high spin, weak ligand field, character than the peroxidase. The two compounds I both have magnetic moments close to the value 3.87 B.m. expected for the spin-only contribution of three unpaired electrons. This shows that compound I contains iron of formal valence 5, but it does not distinguish between the strong and weak field alternatives. It is, however, reasonable to assume that there is an extra $\pi$-bond between the peroxide (or the peroxide residue)and the iron. If this holds true, one of the non-binding orbitals will be used and we are led to assume that the compounds I are of the weak field type. This means that the normal catalase reaction

$$\text{Cat} + \text{XOOH} \longrightarrow \text{Cat I} \cdot \text{XOOH} \xrightarrow{+S} \text{Cat} + \text{P}$$

can proceed without any large changes of the ligand field, i.e. without large changes of molecular orbitals or of the molecular charge distribution. Such large changes are, however, needed both for formation and substrate reaction of catalase compound II, which is of the strong field type. This should be compared with the comparative sluggishness by which catalase compound II is formed or acts as a peroxidase.

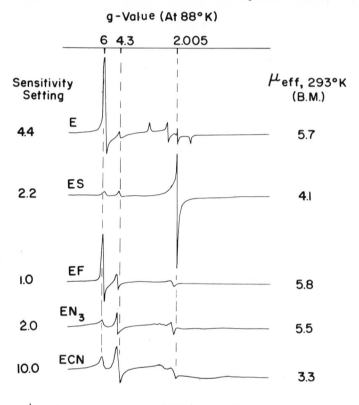

Figure 4. Low temperature ESR recordings and room temperature magnetic moments of cytochrome c peroxidase and some of its derivatives. Unpublished work by Yonetani, Ehrenberg, and Schleyer.

In the case of horse-radish peroxidase both enzyme and compound II are of the mixed spin, intermediate field type. This would indicate that the enzymatic cycle also in this case could proceed without large changes of the ligand field. It might also be suggested that compound I has more of the intermediate than of the weak field character. This would be possible if the proposed ∏-bonding is not too strong. The same arguments (except for that concerning compound I) apply as well for cytochrome c peroxidase.

For myoglobin, which is essentially a weak field compound, and its compound III, which is of the strong field type, the situation is analogous to that of catalase, and its compound III is practically inactive as oxidizing agent of donors.

The discussion presented here is admittedly speculative, based as it is on a still only fragmentary knowledge about the structure of the hemoprotein peroxide compounds. Further detailed physico-chemical studies of these compounds is badly needed.

## References

1. Kobert, R. Arch. Ges. Physiol. (Pflügers), 82, 603 (1900).

2. Theorell, H. Arkiv Kemi Mineral. Geol., 16A, No. 3 (1942).

3. Theorell, H., A. Ehrenberg, and B. Chance. Arch. Biochem. Biophys., 37, 327 (1952).

4. Theorell, H., and A. Ehrenberg. Arch. Biochem. Biophys., 41, 442 (1952).

5. Brill, A., H. den Hartog, and V. Legallais. Rev. Sci. Instr., 29, 383 (1958).

6. Brill, A. In Free Radicals in Biological Systems Blois, et al., eds.), Academic Press, Inc., New York, 1961, p. 53.

7. Brill, A., and R. J. P. Williams. Biochem. J., 78, 253 (1961).

8. Brill, A., A. Ehrenberg, and H. den Hartog. Biochim. Biophys. Acta, 40, 313 (1960).

9. Yonetani, T. This volume, p. 293.

10. Gibson, J. F., D. J. E. Ingram, and P. Nicholls. Nature, 181, 1398 (1958).

11. Morita, Y., and H. S. Mason. J. Biol Chem., 240, 2654 (1965).

12. Ehrenberg, A. Adv. Chem. Phys., 7, 602 (1964).

# ON THE NATURE OF HEME LINKAGES

## Britton Chance

Johnson Research Foundation, University of Pennsylvania
Philadelphia, Pennsylvania

The renewed interest in Theorell's "heme-linked hydroxyl group" (1) occasioned by the paper of Nicholls and Schonbaum (2) and brought forward in today's discussions of the heme linkage in myoglobin (3,4,5) suggests the desirability of reassessing the criteria on which titration data may be judged to be consistent or inconsistent with the proposed formulation.

Two general approaches to the investigation of heme linkages are possible. The first is a titration with ligands of various pK's over a sufficiently wide range of pH values to determine the pH sensitivity of binding constants for the anion and for the acid. While this approach has been applied in detail to a number of hemoproteins, it is apparent that a high stability of the hemoprotein is essential for a meaningful investigation. The instability of ferrimyoglobin at room temperature does not allow measurements of dissociation constants at pH values equal to the pK's of a number of important ligands. Peroxidase is little better in this respect, but catalase is much more resistant, and permits a titration of this hemoprotein into the region of the pK's of acetic, formic, and hydrazoic acids, and very nearly to the pK of hydrofluoric acid at pH 3.1 (6).

We had previously considered six equations for the reaction of hemoproteins with anions or acids (7).

$$FeH_2O + HA \rightleftharpoons FeA^- + H_2O^+ \qquad (1)$$

$$FeH_2O + A^- \rightleftharpoons FeA^- + H_2O \qquad (2)$$

$$FeH_2O + HA \rightleftharpoons FeHA + H_2O \qquad (3)$$

$$FeOH + HA \rightleftharpoons FeA + H_2O \qquad (4)$$

$$FeOH + A^- \rightleftharpoons FeA + OH^- \qquad (5)$$

$$FeOH + HA \rightleftharpoons FeHA + OH^- \qquad (6)$$

Certain of these observations place important boundary conditions on the generality of structures that have been proposed for myoglobin.

Perhaps the most important observations come from the study of the partial reactions where, in the case of catalase and formate, the dissociation velocity was found to be independent of pH (7). This would seem to eliminate those reactions involving a hydrogen or a hydroxyl ion on the right-hand side (Eqns. 1,5,6) and to favor Eqns. 2,3, and 4.

The fact that the reaction velocity for the combination of catalase with formate increased with decreasing pH was itself consistent with the idea of a reaction of the undissociated form of the acid. However, the pK of 3.7 for formic acid made experiments on the acid side of this value somewhat difficult, even for catalase. In the case of azide, the reaction rate was somewhat out of the range of the methods available at the time, but titrations were carried out down to pH 3.2 (7), 1.5 units on the acid side of its pK. In this case, strong evidence for the reaction of the undissociated hydrazoic acid with catalase was obtained. As might be expected, no inconsistencies were observed in titrations with formic, hydrofluoric, and hydrocyanic acids. These data appeared to be inconsistent with the anion reaction of Eqn. 2, however, and leave as possibilities reactions with the aquo form of Eqn. 3 or the hydroxy form of Eqn. 4. The experimental data with azide allow us to set limits on the pK for the hydroxy form of its iron; in catalase, such a pK is on the acid side of pH 3.2 and in ferrimyoglobin it is on the acid side of pH 5.0, limited in both cases by the stability of the hemoproteins. In other words, the hydroxy form of the iron gives no evidence of its existence in the range in which the hemoproteins are stable.

Similar arguments apply to the postulate that a proton acceptor other than the iron itself is involved; its pK, again, must be too far in the acid region to be detected prior to splitting of the hemoprotein. Thus, for simplicity and for consistency with the available experimental evidence, the overall reaction mechanism of Eqn. 3 appears preferable.

## References

1. Agner, K., and H. Theorell. Arch. Biochem., 10, 321 (1946).

2. Nicholls, P., and G. Schonbaum. In The Enzymes (P. D. Boyer, H. Lardy, K. Myrbäck, eds.), Vol. 8, Academic Press, Inc., New York, 1963, p. 147.

3. Mildvan, A. This volume, p. 279.

4. Caughey, W. S. This volume, p. 276.

5. George, P. This volume, p. 357.

6. Chance, B. J. Biol. Chem., 194, 471 (1952).

7. Chance, B. J. Biol. Chem., 194, 483 (1952).

# EVIDENCE FOR THE PRESENCE OF A SHORT-LIVED PEROXIDE DERIVATIVE CATALYZING THE INACTIVATION OF MyPO-$H_2O_2$ (COMPOUND II) BY FERRIC ION*

J. Schultz and N. Felberg

Department of Biological Chemistry, Hahnemann Medical College
Philadelphia, Pennsylvania

Ferric ion and hydrogen peroxide were recently proposed as the intermediates in the inactivation of myeloperoxidase by ferrous ion-oxygen and phosphate (1). While ferrous ion requires both oxygen and phosphate, the ferric ion requires neither. For more complete rapid inactivation by ferric ion hydrogen peroxide is necessary, and is effective only when added in the presence of iron (2,3). The effect of ferric ion, however, added after hydrogen peroxide causes a degree of inactivation which depends on the time of addition. It is the purpose of this report to propose that following the addition of hydrogen peroxide to myeloperoxidase, there exists a short-lived derivative of $H_2O_2$ which can catalyze the inactivation by ferric ion more completely than when the ferric ion is added two minutes after compound II is formed.

## Results and Discussion

The formation of compound II of MyPO following the addition of hydrogen peroxide as indicated by the development of the absorption of light at 453 mμ is rapid and stable for the time interval used in these experiments (Fig. 1). Enzyme inactivation (Table I) at the level of peroxidase used in these experiments due to $H_2O_2$ when added before $Fe^{+++}$ is from 6-20 percent over a 20-fold range of concentration of peroxide. The amount of inactivation due to $Fe^{+++}$ when added before or after peroxide, is rather consistent (Experiments 1-6) when the metal is added 2 minutes after the peroxide, even over a 20-fold range of concentration of the latter. The inactivation due to peroxide, however, is more than twice as great at each concentration when the peroxide is added in the presence of ferric ion. Of significance, however, is the rapid inactivation by $Fe^{+++}$ (Exp. 7), when it is added 45 secs after the addition of peroxide.

*This work was supported in part by USPHS Grant CA-03715.

These above data can be examined in at least two possible ways: the effect of hydrogen peroxide and ferric ion are independent, additive and involve two difference sites, or the ferric ion attacks the enzyme at a point other than that occupied by the hydrogen peroxide of Complex II, causes a change in conformation of the protein and thus exposes an allosteric site to the attack of hydrogen peroxide; which events explain the increased inactivation by the peroxide when added in the presence of the trivalent metal (Experiments 1-3 vs. 4-6). While the above alternatives are discussed in detail in a recent communication (2,3), in the present report, we are concerned with the fact that the addition of ferric ion within 45 secs results in 75 percent inactivation, while only 50 percent is obtained when added after 2 minutes. It must be pointed out that the time elapsed after the addition of hydrogen peroxide in Experiment 7, and the loss of 75 percent of the activity is less than 3 minutes, while in all other experiments, the total time is at least 4 minutes. As a general rule, the

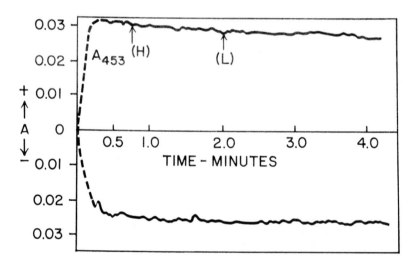

Figure 1. Change in absorption of MyPO at 453 mμ upon the addition of $H_2O_2$, showing formation of MPO - $H_2O_2$ Compound II and indicating interval of high (H) and low (L) sensitivity. 200 μg of MyPO in 3.0 ml of 10 percent ammonium sulfate, at pH 6.5. At time zero, 0.54 μmoles $H_2O_2$ were added in a volume of 1 μl. Upper curve, 453 mμ, lower curve 426 mμ.

inactivation when iron is added before or after the peroxide is not greater than 50 percent even after 5-10 minutes. Therefore, it is quite possible that in Experiment 7, at 45 seconds, there is present some peroxide derivative which catalyzes the inactivation process. The mechanism of the reaction, based on spectrophotometric data (2,3), the demonstration of two chemically different peptides with Soret absorption and the report by Baker

TABLE I

Inactivation of Myeloperoxidase by Ferric Ion When Added
Before and After Formation of MPO.H$_2$O$_2$, Compound II (6)

To about 75 μg of peroxidase in 0.5 ml of 10 percent ammonium sulfate at pH 6.2, 1 μl of 1 M ferric ammonium sulfate was added at 0 time, and 2 min later, an amount of H$_2$O$_2$ to yield the indicated concentration were added (Experiments 1-3). In Experiments 4-6, the order of addition was reversed. The ferric ion in Experiment 7 was added 45 seconds after the addition of H$_2$O$_2$. The figures in parenthesis represent results obtained at an enzyme concentration of 50 μg per test solution (0.5 ml).

H$_2$O$_2$ ADDED AFTER IRON

| Experiment No. | H$_2$O$_2$ mM | Loss after H$_2$O$_2$ percent | Loss after Fe$^{+++}$ percent |
|---|---|---|---|
| 1 | 0.180 | +30 (42) | 42 (35) |
| 2 | 0.018 | +14 (25) | 37 (37) |
| 3 | 0.009 | 0 (11) | 40 (31) |

H$_2$O$_2$ ADDED BEFORE IRON

| | | | |
|---|---|---|---|
| 4 | 0.180 | 4 (20) | +40 (38) |
| 5 | 0.018 | 3 (12) | +39 (33) |
| 6 | 0.009 | 5 (6) | +45 (39) |
| 7* | 0.180 | (2)** | (+75)* |
| 8 | 0.180 | (18) | (+50) |

**Enzyme activity measured after 25 sec.

and Schultz of the formation of an iron peptide containing phosphate and serine (4) suggests an initial reaction of iron with a susceptible serine. This is supported by the findings of Taborsky and Grant (5) who recently reported the phosphorylation of phosphoprotein by autoxidation of ferrous iron. Such an attack could then expose to hydrogen peroxide or its derivatives a previously unavailable site. Two minutes after the addition of peroxide, all of the hydrogen peroxide is either bound to the site, forming compound II, or has been decomposed. It is upon these premises which the concept of an "active" peroxide derivative is proposed whose existence is evident at 45 seconds, but not after 120 seconds (Schultz and Rosenthal, unpublished results).

## References

1. Schultz, J. and S. Rosenthal. J. Biol. Chem., __234__, 2486 (1959).

2. Rosenthal, S. and J. Schultz. IEG No. 1, Scientific Memo No. 375 (1966).

3. Rosenthal, S. and J. Schultz. 150th Meeting, Amer. Chem. Soc., Atlantic City, 1965, p. 18 C.

4. Baker, A. and J. Schultz. Federation Proc., 2_3_, 224 (1964).

5. Taborsky, G. and C. T. Grant. Biochem., _5_, 544 (1966).

# LACTOPEROXIDASE[*]

M. Morrison, W. A. Rombauts and W. A. Schroeder

City of Hope Medical Center, Medical Research Institute
Duarte, California

The mammalian lactoperoxidase has a number of properties which make it of unusual interest form both the chemical and biological point of view.

Table 1 presents some of the physical-chemical properties of this enzyme. One of the unusual things about the enzyme is its high protein/heme ratio, which is the highest ratio among the highly purified peroxidases. Despite the large amount of protein per unit heme, the enzyme is very stable. It withstands heat denaturation up to 60° and the enzyme activity is not readily destroyed even by proteolytic activity. In Table II is presented some data on the amino acid composition of lactoperoxidase which is not unusual for a protein. The high carbohydrate content which appears to be present in lactoperoxidase may be a unique characteristic of peroxidases. The

### TABLE I

Physical-Chemical Properties of Lactoperoxidase

| | |
|---|---|
| Molecular weight | 78,000 |
| Partial specific volume** | 0.74 |
| Diffusion coefficient (1) | $5.2 \times 10^{-7}$ cm sec$^{-1}$ |
| Heme/mole | 1 |

** Rombauts, Schroeder and Morrison, unpublished data.

[*]This work was supported in part by U.S. Public Health Service Research Grant GM-08964.

TABLE II

Chemical Analysis of Lactoperoxidase*

|  | Residues/Mole |
|---|---|
| **Amino Acid** |  |
| Lysine | 33 |
| Histidine | 14 |
| Arginine | 39 |
| Cystine/2 | 16 |
| Aspartic acid | 71 |
| Threonine | 30 |
| Serine | 31 |
| Glutamic | 60 |
| Proline | 42 |
| Glycine | 41 |
| Alanine | 40 |
| Valine | 29 |
| Methionine | 12 |
| Isoleucine | 28 |
| Leucine | 67 |
| Tyrosine | 15 |
| Phenylalanine | 32 |
| Tryptophane | 16 |
| **Carbohydrate** |  |
| Glucosamine | 20 |
| Galactosamine | 10 |
| Neutral carbohydrate | 8 |
| **Acyl Groups** | $10 \pm 2$ |
| **Iron** | 1 |
| **End Groups** |  |
| N-terminal: |  |
| Leucine | 1 |
| (Serine also a possible end group) |  |
| C-terminal: |  |
| Asparagine (?) | 1 |

*Unpublished data of Rombauts, Schroeder and Morrison.

346

well-characterized peroxidases, horseradish and turnip, both have significant amounts of carbohydrate and this is, I believe, the first report of similar carbohydrate content in animal peroxidases. The carbohydrate may play a unique role in the peroxidases, and, in fact, might well be the internal hydrogen donor noted as present in peroxidases.

In contrast to the plant peroxidases, lactoperoxidase has a rather unique prosthetic group. The prosthetic group of lactoperoxidase is bound by covalent bond to the protein and this bond appears to be an ester bond (2). It can be cleaved from the protein by reductive cleavage with HI and gives rise to mesoporphyrin 9, a type III porphyrin. Thus, it is directly related to protoporphyrin 9, the most common iron tetrapyrrole present in living tissues. A direct hemochromogen of the intact protein gives an alpha band at 565 mµ which has been construed by some workers as indicating an iron tetrapyrrole containing electron withdrawing groups on the side chains of the porphyrin. However, if a hemochromogen of a heme peptide prepared by the proteolytic digestion of lactoperoxidase is made, it gives a pyridine hemochromogen at 556 which is indistinguishable from protoheme. Thus, it would appear that one of the ligands of the heme is held rather rigidly in juxaposition to the heme and is not readily displaced by pyridine. When the protein structure is removed, however, the ligand is removed. This ligand certainly is more electropositive than histidine and may very well be a lysine or arginine group as illustrated in Fig. 1.

As an enzyme, lactoperoxidase has certain specificities for electron donors that also make it unique among peroxidases. Lactoperoxidase will not oxidize sulfhydryl compounds. It will, as a matter of fact, form a sulf-lactoperoxidase very similar to the derivatives formed in hemoglobin and catalase. Except for chloroperoxidase and perhaps some of the bacterial and yeast peroxidases which we have not investigated, lactoperoxidase is the most efficient peroxidase in the oxidation of halogens such as iodine (Hosoya and Morrison, in preparation). This may be very important for its biological role, for lactoperoxidase has been shown to occur in the ectodermal gland, the salivary gland, the lacrimal gland and the harderian gland, but in no other tissues of mammalian sources. Its presence uniquely in these tissues, which also are very efficient in the concentration of such halogens as iodine, is presumptive evidence that it may play a role in the halogenation reactions which occur in mammalian tissues.

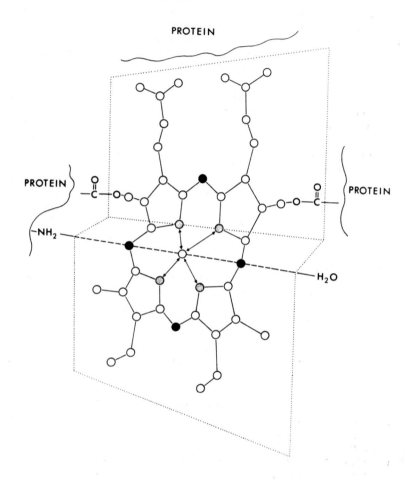

Figure 1. Proposed structure for prosthetic group of lacto-peroxidase.

## References

1. Allen, P. Z., and M. Morrison. Arch. Biochem. Biophys., 113, No. 3, 540 (1966).

2. Hultquist, D. E., and M. Morrison. J. Biol. Chem., 238, 2843 (1963).

# A POSSIBLE MODEL REACTION
# FOR PEROXIDASE AND CATALASE*

Gordon A. Hamilton

Frick Chemical Laboratory, Princeton University
Princeton, New Jersey

Some time ago we observed that anisole is hydroxylated by hydrogen peroxide if catalytic amounts of ferric ion and catechol are present (1). At that time we suggested that the oxidizing agent is formed by the loss of a molecule of water from a complex of ferric ion, catechol, and hydrogen peroxide. The proposed oxidizing agent (Fig. 1) has an oxygen atom attached directly to an iron atom and thus bears some resemblance to structures proposed by George (2) for the intermediates in catalase and peroxidase catalyzed reactions. We have now studied the model reaction more thoroughly (3,4) and the results substantiate the original suggestion for the structure of the oxidizing agent.

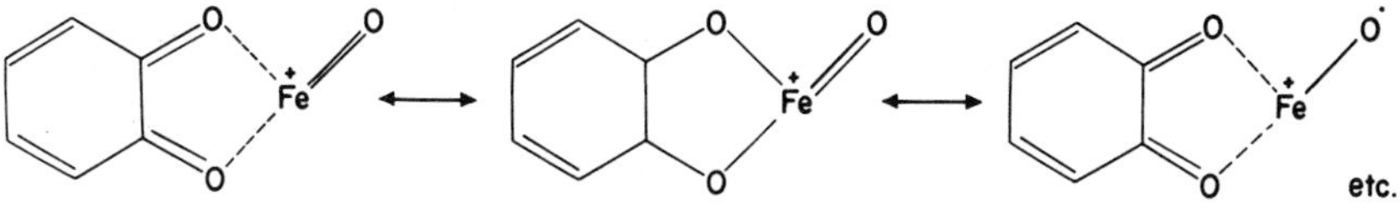

Figure 1. The proposed oxidizing agent formed from ferric ion, catechol and hydrogen peroxide.

Although most of our mechanism work on the model reaction has been done on the aromatic hydroxylation reaction (which is an overall two electron oxidation), some of the results indicate that the oxidizing agent can act as a one or two electron oxidant. For example, the intermediate apparently abstracts hydrogen atoms from aliphatic compounds because the hydroxylation is inhibited by low concentrations of ether or acetone. In

*This work was supported by U.S. Public Health Service (Division of General Medical Sciences) Research Grant GM-09585.

this respect the model reaction is like peroxidase-catalyzed oxidations, most of which apparently involve one-electron steps. The model system will also oxidize alcohols to aldehydes and ketones and this suggests that the reaction may be similar to catalase catalyzed reactions. However, the model system does not appreciably catalyze the disproportionation of hydrogen peroxide to oxygen and water, apparently because the catalyst, catechol, is oxidized under these conditions.

Most of the evidence for the structure of the oxidizing agent in the model system comes from a detailed study of the scope, kinetics, and products of the reaction. These studies eliminate a number of other possible oxidizing agents, for example, the reaction is not a chain mechanism, the hydroxyl and perhydroxyl radicals are not the oxidizing agents, etc. Since only compounds like catechol and hydroquinone (which are capable of reversible oxidation and reduction) can act as catalysts in the reaction (resorcinol is not a catalyst), we believe that an oxidized form of the catalyst complexed to ferric ion helps to stabilize the intermediate which has the oxygen atom attached to the metal ion (1). In such a complex (Fig. 1) the iron is formally in the plus five state if the complexed catachol is assumed to be in its normal reduced state, but if the catechol is assumed to be complexed as catecholquinone, the iron is formally in the plus three valence state. Since the orbitals on the iron overlap with those on the catechol, the true structure of the complex should be considered a resonance hybrid of all such structures. Thus, in such a complex one can only ascribe an oxidation level to the complex as a whole; the oxidation state of the iron and of the catechol has no meaning. In catalase and peroxidase reactions the heme group could perform the same function in stabilizing the intermediate as the catechol in the model reaction, because a number of resonance structures involving oxidized forms of the porphyrin ring system can be drawn. The work on the model system indicates that structures similar to those suggested by George (2) for the intermediates in the enzyme reactions can be observed in other reactions, and further, since the model and enzyme reactions are somewhat similar, the work suggests that the structures proposed by George are in fact the correct ones for the enzyme intermediates.

## References

1. Hamilton, G. A., and J. P. Friedman. J. Am. Chem. Soc., 85, 1008 (1963).

2. George, P. In Currents in Biochemical Research (D. E. Green, ed.), Interscience Publishers, New York, 1956, p.338.

3.  Hamilton, G. A., J. P. Friedman, and P. M. Campbell. J. Am. Chem. Soc., in press.

4.  Hamilton, G. A., J. W. Hanifin, Jr., and J. P. Friedman. J. Am. Chem. Soc., in press.

## DISCUSSION

Estabrook:  Although these models are very illuminating in terms of the mechanism of hydroxylation reactions, they certainly are non-specific as far as enzymatic hydroxylation reactions are concerned.

Schonbaum:  As an addendum to Dr. Estabrook's remarks, I might mention that oxidation of ethanol by catalase compound I occurs stereospecifically.  Dr. Ho and myself have reached this conclusion by analyzing the deuterium content in acetaldehyde, obtained by oxidation of S-1-deuteroethanol.  I should add that these results have no direct bearing on Dr. Hamilton's proposals, since the relevance of the mechanism based on the studies of a model system cannot be assessed in terms of the specificity.

GENERAL DISCUSSION

Chance: It is appropriate to open this discussion by stating that we could not have held the meeting itself without the pioneer contributions of D. Keilin (1) and H. Theorell (2) to the topic of enzyme-substrate compounds.

Dr. Ehrenberg has brought us to a suitable point for starting the discussion on the physical properties of these intermediates, and I believe that Dr. Schleyer has some comments on the radical signal in the complex ES of Yonetani. What is hiding under the shoulder of the g = 2 signal of ES?

Schleyer: The question has been raised, "Is this really a free radical signal?" I should stress the point that Drs. Yonetani, Ehrenberg, and I have been referring to the signal of complex ES as a "free radical-type signal"; it could equally well be described as a "narrow line signal at g = 2".

The statement has also been made that the signal in complex ES seems to be asymmetric. It is impossible here to predict, on theoretical grounds, what line shape one should expect in a frozen solution; the spectra that Dr. Yonetani showed were recorded at liquid nitrogen temperature. Indeed, the degree of asymmetry found is surprisingly small.

The fact which is most important, however, is the very unusual line shape. The center part of the signal in the first derivative presentation is like a "normal" narrow line signal, with a peak-to-peak line width of the order of about 20 Oersteds. But there are unusually broad "wings" on either side; obviously, something is hiding underneath.

Our studies of the properties of complex ES are not yet complete; therefore, I do not wish to discuss our findings in great detail. So far, we have studied both enzyme and complex ES in frozen solution as well as in crystalline form over a wide range of temperatures. We have begun to take samples up to temperatures above the freezing point to examine possible hyperfine structural details. At about -10° it has been possible to achieve a partial resolution of the spectrum of complex ES into a narrow signal at g = 2.0 and a broader signal

353

centered at somewhat lower field. Under these conditions the characteristic hemoprotein absorption would be completely broadened out and therefore undetectable.

The spectrum of the enzyme in the frozen solution can be analyzed and interpreted in terms of two species, a high-spin component with axial symmetry and absorption stretching out from $g \sim 6$ to $g \sim 2$, and a low-spin component with principal g-values at $g \sim 2.7$, $2.2$, and $1.8$ approximately, having less than axial symmetry.

As Dr. Yonetani remarked, the purpose of our studies with the crystalline material was to compare those parameters obtained from dissolved samples with those from crystalline material to see if there were any differences in principal g-values or in signal intensity ratios. Crystals which are small enough can indeed be frozen in a quasi-random orientation, thus allowing us to determine the symmetries involved without the need for complex and as yet uncertain assumptions. This unusual, and, so far as we know, new approach is quite useful as a diagnostic tool. We found that the principal g-values and symmetry characteristics for all the species of both enzyme and complex ES are identical within the limits of the instrumentation. More complete data will be obtained from single crystal work.

Palmer: I would like to bring to your attention the fact that Fe(V) is formally isoelectric with Cr(III) and certain ethylene-diamine complexes of Cr(III) show EPR spectra which look exactly like Yonetani's complex ES, vis., a narrow signal at $g = 2$ with rather broad wings.

Chance: You are implying that the ESR signal may not be a radical of protein? This is a very important consideration; on the other hand, would you have an explanation for the two oxidizing equivalents?

Palmer: If the observed EPR signal really indicates Fe(V), then the source of the two oxidizing equivalents is understandable.*

---

*Editor's note: The absence of a $g = 2$ signal in green Complex I "Fe(V)" was previously noted (3); this complex retains the two oxidizing equivalents of peroxide. The red Complex II of horse-radish peroxidase retains only one oxidizing equivalent and has a very small ESR signal (3). The spectroscopically identical red "Complex ES" of yeast cytochrome c peroxidase retains two oxidizing equivalents (4).

Beinert: Did you look into the power dependence? It seems to me that the temperature studies showed that the broad under-lying signal represents quite a lot of material, more than just what you call the "free radical"; power dependence may help to differentiate these two signals more clearly. I wonder whether one should not look at this broad signal as well, rather than at the radical signal only.

Traylor: Why is the broad line so broad in Dr. Schleyer's EPR spectrum at high temperature? In an alkyl peroxy radical, it is only about 12-13 gauss wide.

Schleyer: We have not yet studied the system under these con-ditions in sufficient detail to answer your question. The modulation amplitudes employed were certainly not small com-pared with the line width of the narrow signal. We do not know at present if an alkyl peroxy radical of the line width you quote is involved.

Estabrook: Can you explain the difference in the proportions of high- and low-spin forms between the experiments done in Stockholm and those done here at the Johnson Foundation?

Ehrenberg: We do not know at present. We were operating at various pH's in the range 6.0 - 7.0 and also at different ionic strengths in the two series of experiments. Also, the measure-ments in Stockholm were made at $88^\circ$ K and those here at $77^\circ$ K; we do not know to what extent the high-spin to low-spin ratio changes with temperature.

Schleyer: I wonder if anyone would comment on the possible implications of the fact that we find axial symmetry for the high-spin form but less-than-axial symmetry for the low-spin form?

Palmer: A detailed discussion of axial vs. rhombic symmetry can be found in Griffith's book (5).

Schleyer: My question was not "Why is this so?", but rather, "Can one use this information to learn something about the arrangement around the iron?"

I agree that the difference in symmetries is a well-known phenomenon, although not often so clearly seen as here in Dr. Yonetani's preparation. At least eight years ago, its use as a possible diagnostic tool was suggested (6), and its exis-tence in the methemoglobin series has recently been well docu-mented (7). But does this difference in symmetry represent the orientation of a ligand, such as histidine, to the plane of the heme? This could certainly be one way, though not the only one, to interpret the experimental EPR data.

**Williams:** I think I can answer. If there are very small changes in the environment, the g-values can move a long way, as has been shown particularly with iridium and ruthenium ($d^5$, low-spin) in compounds such as $[IrCl_6]^{--}$ and $[Ru(NH_3)_6]^{+++}$. It would be a great mistake to try to interpret these signals in terms of movement of particular ligands. Thus, $(NH_4)_2IrCl_6$ and $Na_2IrCl_6$ give very different signals which are due to very small rhombic field changes.

**Chance:** Let us consider the combination of peroxide and hematin iron from the structural point of view. On the basis of what was said yesterday, it is unlikely to have a water molecule in a high-spin ferric compound (8); a hydroxide is favored. It seems reasonable that hydrogen peroxide would react similarly to water, particularly since the water molecule is replaced with an $H_2O_2$ to form one of the first intermediates. We may also consider a hydrogen bond to a histidine. All these bonds are broken before an oxidation-reduction reaction has taken place.

**Williams:** The reaction with $H_2O_2$ will probably give a fast intermediate which is more like the azide complex ($HN_3$) than the $H_2O$ complex. This will result from the shape of these small molecules. On combination they will tend to lie across the porphyrin and destroy its symmetry. From the respective spectra, this process goes further in the $H_2O_2$ complexes -I than in the azide. As a consequence, the $H_2O_2$ interaction looks to be so strong as to be considered to be compound formation as discussed by Brill and Williams. Alternatively, the $H_2O_2$ may split, and one half combine with the iron while the other half binds to a protein side chain. In turn, this could produce distortion of the heme. Several compounds may be in labile equilibrium.

**Chance:** Can you comment on the reason why, if this kind of intermediate is formed in ferrimyoglobin, it is so labile that it has never been observed?

**Williams:** There are two possibilities which we can think of immediately: 1) The porphyrin rings are not under equal strain. This is definitely indicated by the spectra of myoglobin and peroxidase simple proteins. 2) The protein groups in the neighborhood of the heme will be different, and different possible radicals can then be formed. Their stability will be very different both intrinsically and because of their very different environments. I think it is time that I, or someone else, attempts to predict the effect of porphyrin distortions on the physical properties of heme compounds.

Chance: Another question is whether there is motion of the porphyrin group in the formation of these intermediates. The ESR data suggest that $Mb^+ \cdot H_2O_2$ is a low-spin, strongly bonded compound, and one might expect motion of the porphyrin. Is $Mb^+ \cdot H_2O_2$ indeed a low-spin compound such as $Mb^+ \cdot$ cyanide?

Ehrenberg: In compound I, we cannot distinguish between high spin and low spin, since they both give the same magnetic moment. We should rather speak about the ligand field, which could, of course be strong (corresponding to low spin). Myoglobin compound III is apparently nearly completely low spin (i.e., strong ligand field).

Chance: Watson and I attempted to look for some movement of the porphyrin in the formation of ferrimyoglobin peroxide. The results may be summarized by saying that there seems to be very little change in the Fourier difference synthesis between $Mb^+$ and ferrimyoglobin peroxide. It seems that the change from Fe-O-H to Fe-O occurs as expected from the chemical data.
　　　H

George: I would like to introduce a general consideration right at the outset since much of the discussion yesterday was centered on structural features of the parent hemoproteins, myoglobin and hemoglobin, and the possible influence of groups in close vicinity to the heme upon the ligand combination reactions. There is the very striking difference in the way ferrimyoglobin and ferrihemoglobin react with peroxides and other oxidizing agents compared to ferriperoxidase and ferricatalase. There is also a very striking difference in the way these two classes of ferrihemoprotein react with ligands such as cyanide, azide, fluoride, etc. These differences may well arise because of a common difference in the structures of ferrimyoglobin and ferrihemoglobin on the one hand, and ferriperoxidase and ferricatalase on the other; and, if we understood the ligand combination reactions of ferriperoxidase and ferricatalase better, we would be in a better position to understand their more complicated oxidation-reduction reactions.

The difference between the ligand combination reactions is quite simple. When ferrimyoglobin and ferrihemoglobin form their cyanide, azide and fluoride complexes, the way the stability constants vary with pH corresponds very closely to that expected for the replacement of an iron bound water molecule by an anionic ligand. However, in the case of ferriperoxidase and ferricatalase, over the same pH range about neutrality, the pH variation indicates that a proton is also bound.

Theorell suggested that OH was bonded to the iron in ferriperoxidase and ferricatalase (instead of $H_2O$) so a proton would be consumed in forming $H_2O$ as the OH was replaced by the anionic ligand. But this explanation is difficult to reconcile with the known ionization of ferriperoxidase which closely resembles that of ferrimyoglobin and ferrihemoglobin attributed to an iron bound water molecule. Chance suggested that the ligands were bound as their conjugate acids, e.g., HF, HCN, etc. However, this seems rather unlikely since similar species form inorganic complexes, i.e. $HFe(CN)_6^{---}$, that are quite strong acids. Another, and very interesting, possibility is that when an anionic ligand reacts with ferriperoxidase and ferricatalase a protein residue is either released from the iron or made available through a change in conformation--and it is this residue which combines with the proton. The $-O^-$ group of tyrosine or serine could play such a role. X-ray studies on ferriperoxidase and catalase are therefore going to be very important in the light of this possibility; and the participation of a protein residue in the oxidation-reduction reactions might well be the very feature responsible for the specific reactivity of peroxidase and catalase towards peroxides and other strong oxidizing agents. To sum up--just as yesterday we were all wondering where the water went--there is this other problem of where the proton went. Furthermore, in the oxidation-reduction reactions of peroxidase and catalase there is yet another problem of where the oxidation equivalents went.

Some fifteen years ago I had the privilege of doing some of the early studies on cytochrome c peroxidase in the Johnson Foundation, and I note an important difference between the titrations as carried out then and those reported by Dr. Yonetani. He finds that the red compound formed in the reaction of CCP and peroxides has two oxidizing equivalents with respect to the ferric oxidation state. The earlier titrations gave one equivalent, and this result was consistent with the observation that 2 moles of the red compound could be formed from 1 mole of peroxide. Perhaps the state of purity of the enzyme had something to do with this, maybe via the participation of endogenous (rather than exogenous) donor as Dr. Nicholls has suggested. Perhaps with Dr. Yonetani's pure preparation one of the two oxidizing equivalents of the peroxide is retained as a relatively stable free radical, whereas in the earlier impure preparations further reaction of this free radical oxidizing equivalent led to the formation of a second equivalent of the red compound. The formation of radical species in the reaction of a ferrihemoprotein with peroxides was well established in the case of ferrimyoglobin some years ago (9). Whatever the final answer is to this particular question, it is clear that in interpreting the oxidation-reduction reactions of the ferrihemoproteins the site of oxidation may be the ferriheme group, yielding a higher oxidation state of the iron or a radical species, or a protein residue in close vicinity to the heme, yielding its own radical species. Such a reaction scheme can be varied in so many ways for multi-oxidation equivalent processes that high degrees of specificity could readily be accounted for.

Chance: Of course, we do want to know what the intermediates are in peroxidase and catalase, but we are making the assumption that they might be something like those in myoglobin. I think it worth considering the question of what are the protein groups with the electron donating capabilities.

Nicholls: Concerning the ESR data, and in support of Dr. George, I would like to point out that, although there is no catalytically very active endogenous donor in metmyoglobin, a free radical is nevertheless produced when you react $H_2O_2$ or ethyl-hydroperoxide with metmyoglobin. This radical has a signal very similar to the cytochrome c peroxidase signal, although the proportion of free radical which is produced is smaller. This signal is removed by the donors which reduce the peroxide compound itself, and therefore the metmyoglobin case may be of considerable interest as a model.

Morrison: All the peroxidases which have been well purified and analyzed appear to have carbohydrate groups covalently linked to the protein. These groups may very well provide the endogenous reactive groups in the peroxidases.

Watson: I showed a slide yesterday illustrating all the heme-group contacts in myoglobin (10). I might point out, in addition, that the phenylalanine $CD_1$ which is common to all the globin chains is in such a position as to touch many atoms of the heme group and also to touch ligands at the sixth coordination position.

Chance: There is one bit of evidence that should not be ignored on this point, namely, that Yonetani has a UV shift in the Complex ES spectrum. Dr. Yonetani, would you comment on the possible nature of this shift?

Yonetani: This shift is found in the light absorption difference spectra between Complex ES and free enzyme (11). The

359

difference extinction coefficient is +14 mM$^{-1}$ cm$^{-1}$ (at 241 m$\mu$). This is rather large for protein absorption. We do not know whether this is phenylalanine, tyrosine, or some other aromatic amino acids.

Chance: This is relevant to Dr. Palmer's statement; the UV shift would not be expected for a change of iron alone.

Nicholls: In the case of catalase the promotion of the endogenous donor reactions of compounds I and II by anions indicates that those ligands such as fluoride and acetate which bind the free enzyme to give high spin complexes, also bind compounds I and II with approximately the same dissociation constants and pH dependence. This is something which is very difficult to explain by any theory which involves higher oxidation states or any modifications of the iron, and it is one of the strongest pieces of evidence that the peroxide compounds involve modifications of the porphyrin ring.

Chance: Dr. Nicholls, have you measured binding and dissociation constants for the anion reaction? Are these the same as those for anions with heme?

Nicholls: If you measure the rate at which catalase compound I is reduced to compound II, or the rate at which compound II is reduced to free catalase by the endogenous donor in the presence of the anion, and plot the velocity against the anion concentration, the kinetics are of the Michaelis type. The concentration of anion giving half-maximal stimulation of the transition corresponds to the amount of anion required for half-maximal binding of the free enzyme. The $K_d$ values are equal within, shall we say, the usual 50 percent limits.

Margoliash: It may be in order to point out, in connection with Dr. Nicholls' paper, that it is possible to obtain peroxidase preparations which appear to be quite free of so-called "endogenous" donor, as evidenced by the stability of the hydrogen peroxide complex I for several hours, at least, in the absence of any added endogenous donor. With regard to Dr. Schonbaum's contribution, I do not know whether it was pointed out clearly enough that practically all the properties of cyanogen bromide-reacted catalase are identical to those of the aminotriazole inhibited enzyme. The only difference I can make out is that the aminotriazole specifically reacts with compound I, whereas the cyanogen bromide apparently reacts with the free enzyme. The product, however, is the same in its general characteristics.

Schonbaum: I agree with Dr. Margoliash. As I have mentioned this morning, the spectroscopic resemblance between the inhibited enzyme obtained via cyanogen bromide reaction and the derivative resulting from treatment of compound I with 3-aminotriazole is quite striking. There are, however, some differences, particularly in the position of isosbestic points. This may be due to the incomplete inhibition of catalase in aminotriazole compound I reactions.

Nicholls: In response to Dr. Schonbaum and Dr. Margoliash concerning the aminotriazole-inhibited and cyanogen bromide-inhibited catalase, it should be noted that reducible catalase which has been prepared simply by lyophilization has very similar spectral properties. One does not have to assume a modification of a specific residue in order to get these spectral characteristics.

Schonbaum: Indeed, there are some spectroscopic similarities between reducible catalase and the inhibited enzyme. However, whereas the reducible catalase combines with hydrogen peroxide and a variety of other ligands, the cyanogen bromide-inactivated enzyme is almost completely inert, not only in the catalatic reaction but also in the reactions with cyanide and formate. Moreover, the inhibited enzyme is not reducible with dithionite.

Williams: The spectra of the Complex I type substances have parallels in quite a number of systems. One of the best examples that you can find is that of cytochrome $\underline{o}$ which will be discussed later this afternoon. Its spectrum is very like that of Complex I. Cytochrome $\underline{o}$ is well known not to react with many ligands. This suggests general interaction between the protein and the heme, causing strain. In fact, I have a general idea of why the particular change in spectrum occurs and shall give a detailed summary later (12) which will explain the observations on $N_3^-$ complexes generally, Complex I, peroxidase, and inhibited complexes of peroxidase and catalase. It may well apply to some cytochrome $\underline{a}$ complexes as well.

## References

1. Keilin, D., and T. Mann. Proc. Roy. Soc. (London) B, 122, 119 (1937).

2. Theorell, H. Enzymologia, 10, No. 3, 250 (1942).

3. Chance, B., and R. R. Fergusson. In A Symposium on the Mechanism of Enzyme Action (W. D. McElvoy and B. Glass, eds.), Johns Hopkins Press, Baltimore, 1954, p. 389.

4. Yonetani, T., H. Schleyer, and B. Chance. This volume, p. 293.

5. Griffith, J. S. The Theory of Transition Metal Chemistry, Cambridge University Press, Cambridge, 1961, p. 350 et seq.

6. Ingram, D. J. E. In Paramagnetic Resonance (W. Low, ed.), Academic Press, Inc., New York, 1963, pp. 832-835.

7. Rein, H., and O. Ristan. Biochim. Biophys. Acta, 94, 516 (1965).

8. Discussion, This volume, p. 53.

9. Gibson, J. F., D. J. E. Ingram, and P. Nicholls. Nature, 181, 1398 (1958).

10. Watson, H. C. This volume, Frontispiece.

11. Yonetani, T., H. Schleyer, and B. Chance. This volume, p. 296, Figure 4.

12. Williams, R. J. P. This volume, p. 585.

# VI.
## Physical Properties of Cytochromes $c$ and $b_5$
### R. W. Estabrook, Chairman

# A CRYSTALLOGRAPHIC STUDY OF HORSE HEART CYTOCHROME $c$*

R. E. Dickerson, M. L. Kopka, Jon Weinzierl
J. Varnum, and C. L. Borders

Gates and Crellin Laboratories of Chemistry
California Institue of Technology
Pasadena, California

This is an interim progress report on an X-ray structure analysis of horse heart cytochrome $c$ being carried out in this laboratory with the cooperation and collaboration of Dr. E. Margoliash of the Abbott Laboratories in Chicago. Cytochrome $c$, extracted from frozen horse hearts by a method developed by Margoliash, is crystallized from 90-95 percent saturated ammonium sulfate with 1 M NaCl in a tetragonal crystal form, space group $P4_1$, with cell dimensions: a = b = 58.5 Å, c = 42.3 A. The measured density of 1.264 $gm/cm^3$ and the known molecular weight of 12,400 indicate that there are four molecules per unit cell, related by the fourfold screw axis along the $c$ direction (one molecule per asymmetric unit), and that the crystal is 44.9 percent protein by weight, the rest being liquid of crystallization. This is a very well-behaved protein crystallographically except for its great solubility, which requires a high ionic strength medium to keep the crystals out of solution.

Several other species have been examined using crystals supplied by Margoliash. Tuna crystallizes in the same form as horse but with much poorer quality crystals. Moth (Samia cynthia) crystallizes in an orthorhombic form with only 40 percent solvent, in which the crystallographically unique unit is a pair of molecules. Duck cytochrome crystallizes in a monoclinic form with only 32 percent solvent, again with a pair of molecules as the asymmetric unit and with severe twinning of crystals. Crystallographic dimerization of horse crystals in ammonium sulfate can be induced by adding a 1:1 or 2:1 molar excess of $TlCl_6^{3-}$ ions. The tetragonal cell, space group $P4_1$, is reduced to monoclinic $P2_1$ with two molecules per asymmetric unit, and the a and b axes shrink to 52.86 and 57.23 Å while the $c$ axis remains virtually unchanged.

*This work was supported by U. S. PHS Grant GM-12121.

With such an open structure -- with over half the crystal being liquid of crystallization -- it should be easier than usual to separate molecules in the final electron density map and relatively easy to diffuse in heavy atom groups. On the other hand, the high salt concentration required creates two difficulties of its own. The solubilities of many potential heavy atom reagents in such concentrated ammonium sulfate are small. Moreover, the electron density of 90 percent saturated ammonium sulfate solution is calculated to be almost exactly equal to that of the interior of myoglobin. This is reflected with cytochrome in the fact that the inner reflections in the X-ray pattern are almost completely missing. The electron density map obtained from sulfate crystal data will have relatively low contrast between molecules and background.

Extensive trials of potential heavy atom derivatives in ammonium sulfate crystal suspensions -- 99 photographic trials of 69 different reagents -- have produced appreciable X-ray diffraction pattern intensity changes in only two cases, $PtCl_4^=$ and mersalyl:$(HO-Hg-CH_2-CH(O-CH_3)-CH_2-NH-CO-(m-C_6H_4)-O-CH_2-COO^-)$ Each of these compounds, as will be mentioned later, has been shown to bind at a single site per molecule.

The search for heavy atom derivatives in ammonium sulfate preparations has focused on two classes of compounds: mercury-organic compounds and transition metal complex ions. Cations were ruled out because of the high cationic charge on the cytochrome molecule itself at the crystallizing pH range of 5-7. It was expected that the mercurials would react with a possibly exposed histidine and that the transition metal ions would complex with lone-pair donors on the protein in a ligand displacement reaction, or possibly an oxidation of a metal such as $Pt^{II}$ to a state with a higher coordination number. The difficulty in forming such complexes has been attributed partly to the extreme insolubility of most heavy atom compounds in such a concentrated salt solution and partly to competition by free ammonia in solution with potential ligand groups on the protein for the coordination sites on the heavy atoms added (1).

A search has been made for a suitable ammonia-free medium for cytochrome c. Magnesium sulfate, sodium sulfate, sodium acetate, and sodium citrate were all unsuitable because of their inability even at saturation to raise the ionic strength high enough to keep the crystals out of solution. Lanthanum nitrate, a hopeful combination of a trivalent cation with a solubilizing anion, produced an asymmetrical swelling which turned needle crystals into corkscrews which are probably related to the sense of the fourfold screw axis on the molecular level. The appearance of these crystals has prompted the remark that there are grounds for hope -- even if the protein itself is not helica

the crystals are! It was found that crystals grown in ammonium
sulfate can be transferred to a mixed phosphate buffer at a
total concentration of 3.7-4.7 molar in phosphate, and will
remain stable for months, although attempts to grow crystals
from such media have been unsuccessful.

Once the competition from ammonia is eliminated, and if
the protein is really binding to the transition metal by donating an electron pair and becoming part of its coordination shell,
it should matter relatively little what ligands are initially
attached to the transition metal. Of course these replaceable
ligands must be weaker complex-formers than the protein group,
which is probably a nitrogen lone pair. Since a typical series
of decreasingly strong complex forming ligands is (2):

$$CN^- > NO_2^- > En > NH_3 > H_2O > EtOH > F^- > Cl^- > Br^- > I$$

it is pointless to try any cyanide or nitro or thiocyanide com-
pexes. The obvious choices are halogen complexes of transition
metals, and it should make little difference, for example,
whether palladium was put in as $PdCl_4^=$ or as $PdCl_2$, as the
unused coordination sites would probably be filled with water
or with $Cl^-$ ions immediately upon addition.

Both $PdCl_2$ and $PdCl_4^=$ have been tried with phosphate
buffer crystals, and have been found to produce the same intensity changes, demonstrating equivalence of binding. Neither
reagent would work in ammonium sulfate. Both $PtCl_4^=$ and mersalyl
have been found to produce intensity changes in phosphate
identical to those found in sulfate, and quite different from
one another and from the palladium changes. Other different
and characteristic changes have been observed in phosphate with
dimethyl gold bromide and with 2-bromoacetamide-5-iodobenzoic
acid, a potential reagent for methionine and unionized histidine.

Difference Patterson vector maps have been prepared for
$PtCl_4$ in three dimensions at 4 Å with 1400 reflections used,
and for mersalyl in two-dimensional projection at 5 Å with 109
reflections. The Patterson map for platinum showing all
possible interatomic vectors between the four Pt sites in the
cell, is shown in Figure 1. The origin peak is in the upper
left corner at section 0/48, and the expected single peaks at
12/48 and at 24/48 are present. An identical peak to the 12/48
peak is present in the 36/48 section, not shown. As a measure
of the cleanness of background of the map, all other peaks of
height two contours or more are also shown. These peaks are
background noise and have no significance.

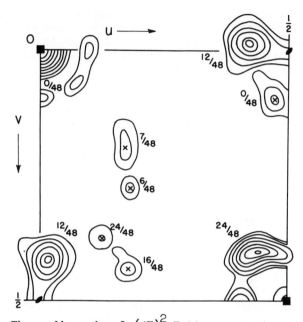

Figure 1. Three dimensional $(\Delta F)^2$ Patterson vector map for the $\overline{PtCl_4}^=$ derivative of horse heart cytochrome $\underline{c}$ at 4 Å resolution. (u, v, w) are the components of the interatomic vectors between Pt atoms (u = $x_2$ - $x_1$, etc.). Only the symmetry-independent one-eighth of the full map is shown, from 0 to 1/2 in each direction. Coordinate w is vertical out of the plane of the paper, calculated in 48 sections. Numbers beside peaks are section numbers. The remaining three-quarters of a given section are generated by action of the fourfold axes at the upper left and lower right corners. Sections 25/48 to 47/48, not shown, are related by a mirror plane in sections 0/48 and in 24/48 (i.e., sections 23 and 25 are identical, 22 and 26, etc.). For interpretations of the map, see text.

From the location of the Pt atom in Fig. 1, <u>tentative</u> signs for all hko-class reflections can be obtained which permit one to calculate a difference Fourier map which should show the heavy atom site itself. This, for Pt, is shown in Fig. 2. The map is abnormally clean because the signs themselves came from this assumed model. However, these tentative signs can be used with intensity changes produced by the mersalyl reagent, and the results with 180 terms at 4 Å are as in Fig. 3. This map shows a single (and different) site for attachment of the mercury atom, identical to that predicted by the Hg Patterson vector map. The background noise in Fig. 3 is attributable partly to the fact that the Pt signs are at this point probably

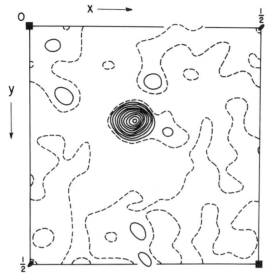

**Figure 2.** Two-dimensional ($\Delta F$) Difference Fourier map of the $PtCl_4^=$ derivative, showing the location of the Pt atom. This is a projection of the full map down the fourfold screw axis onto the _ab_ plane. Arbitrary but equal contours are shown, with the zero contour dashed.

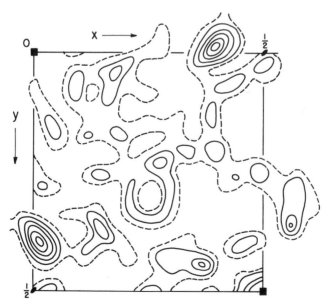

**Figure 3.** Two-dimensional ($\Delta F$) Difference Fourier projection of the mersalyl derivative, showing position of the Hg atom. For discussion, see text.

369

somewhat in error and partly to the fact that there is a large
organic group attached to the mercury which will scatter X-rays
as well.

The absent inner reflections of ammonium sulfate crystals
reappear in phosphate buffer, reflecting the fact that the
crystallizing medium is sufficiently more dense than the protein molecules to restore good contrast between molecules and
surroundings. These "salt effects" are being used to help
locate the outlines of the molecules and the molecular packing.

Thus there are at present two usable single-site derivatives of horse heart cytochrome c (although the mersalyl may
be usable only at low resolution), and the expectation of more.
The strong salt effect indicates that it may be relatively
easy to delineate the molecule once the electron density
synthesis has been performed.

## References

1. Sigler, P., and D. M. Blow. J. Mol. Biol., 14, 640 (1965).

2. Orgel, L. An Introduction to Transition-Metal Chemistry,
   Methuen, London, 1960, p. 46.

## DISCUSSION COMMENT

Watson: The data presented on Dr. Dickerson's behalf suggest
that the heavy-atom problem for cytochrome c is virtually
solved. This means that it is just a matter of time before
this group presents a Fourier map of the cytochrome structure.

STRUCTURE-FUNCTION RELATIONS IN CYTOCHROME $\underline{c}$

E. Margoliash

Department of Molecular Biology, Abbott Laboratories
North Chicago, Illinois

## I. Introduction

Classically, there have been two different approaches to
the study of structure-function relations in proteins. The
first has consisted in the measurement of a variety of physico-
chemical parameters, characteristic of proteins in general or
of the protein being investigated in particular, followed by
attempts to interpret these measurements in terms of similar
parameters determined on appropriate simple model compounds.
For example, it was the studies of Anson and Mirsky (1,2) on
the spectra of ferroheme and those of Keilin (3) on the spectra
of ferriheme, coordinated with a wide variety of nitrogenous
basic compounds, that led to the conclusion that the hemochrome-
forming groups in cytochrome $\underline{c}$ must be nitrogenous basic side
chains of amino acid residues, their coordination with the heme
iron leading to the characteristic spectrum of the protein.
In the same general way the classical identification by
Theorell and Åkesson (4,5) of these hemochrome-forming groups
as imidazole side chains of histidyl residues depended on comparisons of the acid-base titration behavior of the protein
and of the corresponding heats of ionization with the same
parameters for the imidazole group of free histidine. Similarly,
attempts have repeatedly been made to correlate the physico-
chemical behavior of heme peptides derived from cytochrome $\underline{c}$
with the possibly analogous situation in the native protein
(6-12). More recently, a parallel approach has been taken in
the identification of a histidyl imidazole as the group displaced by the entering ligand in the cyanide complex of cytochrome $\underline{c}$ (13). Here again the diagnosis depended on a comparison of some thermodynamic parameters for the displaced
function and for free imidazole.

However, in addition to a variety of difficulties associated with each particular type of experiment, this approach
suffers from the more or less implied assumption that in the
environment of the protein the structures under investigation

371

will exhibit physico-chemical properties which are sufficiently
similar to those of the same structures in aqueous solution to
make the identifications meaningful.

The second approach to structure-function relations is a
relatively more recent development. It consists of combining
the protein with a variety of chemical reagents that are supposed to be specific for particular residue side chains, and
comparing the physico-chemical and functional characteristics
of the resulting derivatives with those of the intact protein.
Thus, cytochrome c has been xanthylated (14), coupled with
diazo compounds (15), acetylated (16-18), succinylated (17),
trinitrophenylated (19), trifluoracetylated (20), guanidinated
(17,21-23), iodinated (15), photo-oxidized (24), carboxymethylated with bromoacetate (25) or with iodo-acetate (26-28), and
reacted with diazonium tetrazole (29). This type of experiment
is often even more difficult to interpret than are the direct
physico-chemical examination. Indeed, in order to be able to
conclude that the chemical substitution is itself responsible
for the observed effects, three requirements must be met. It
is necessary, first, to obtain a product which consists of a
single molecular species, second, to show what is the exact
covalent structure of the material, and finally to demonstrate
that the tertiary structure of the protein has not been de-
ranged. In most cases for cytochrome c even the first requirement has not been met, though in the more recent trinitropheny-
lations and carboxymethylations with iodo-acetate both the first
and second conditions can be considered to have been satisfied.
The third requirement is the most difficult to achieve and has
never yet been conformed to with cytochrome c, since it involves determining the tertiary structure of the derivative,
preferably by a relatively unambiguous method such as X-ray
crystallography. If this last proviso is not strictly adhered
to, it is always possible that the residue substitution trans-
mits its effect to an entirely different region of the molecule through a change in spatial conformation.

The recent determination of the complete amino acid sequences of some 25 cytochromes c from different species has
made it possible to explore a third approach to structure-
function relations (see review by Margoliash and Schejter, 30).
This involves comparisons of the available primary structures
in terms of constant and variable features, together with
attempts to unravel from such comparisons the minimal structural
requirements of a protein able to function as cytochrome c.
The reasoning involved in such an endeavor presupposes an
understanding of the forces guiding the evolution of the protein, and the evolutionary basis, in a number of cases which
will be illustrated below, indeed affords compelling arguments
for a variety of conclusions referring to structure-function
relations.

Pro ── ── ── ── ── ── Gly ── ── ── ── ── Gly ── ── ── Phe ── ── ── ──
-6                     1                                10

Cys ── ── Cys-His ── ── ── ── ── ── ── ── Lys ── Gly-Pro ──
└── HEME ──┘       20                                  30

Leu ── Gly ── ── ── Arg ── ── Gly ── ── ── Gly ── ── Tyr ──
                                 40

── Ala-Asn ── ── ── ── ── ── Trp ── ── ── ── ── ── ── Tyr-Leu
50                          60

── Asn-Pro-Lys-Lys-Tyr-Ile-Pro-Gly-Thr-Lys-Met ── Phe ── Gly
70                                  80

── ── Lys ── ── ── Arg ── ── ── ── ── ── ── ── ── ── ── ── ──
      90                            100

Figure 1. Invariant Residues in 25 Cytochromes c. The amino acid sequences of the cytochromes c from the following species have been used to compile this figure: horse (65-71); man (72); hog (73); chicken (42); bakers' yeast (iso-1-cytochrome c) (74); cow (75); sheep (76); tuna (38,39); Macacus mulatta (77); rabbit (78); a saturnid moth, Samia cynthia (45); dog (79); the kangaroo, Macropus canguru (40); rattlesnake (80); the snapping turtle, Chelydra serpentina (41); turkey, Peking duck, pigeon, King penguin, screw worm fly (43); Neurospora crassa (37); Candida krusei (81); donkey (82); chimpanzee (83); bakers' yeast (iso-2-cytochrome c) (36).

The fourth and perhaps definitive approach to structure-function relations will be possible when it becomes practicable to obtain cytochromes c having primary structures in which individual amino acid residues can be varied as may be necessary to study the functions of each residue alone and in conjunction with others with which it may interact. This would involve the complete chemical synthesis of the polypeptide chain, an undertaking which is quite feasible even within the limitations of present techniques. A more circumscribed, but possibly just as effective method, uses naturally biosynthesized cytochrome c mutants having single or more complex amino acid substitutions. A few preliminary results with mutant proteins of the iso-1-cytochrome c of bakers' yeast will be described.

## II. The Evolutionary Approach to Structure-Function Relations in Cytochrome c

The available set of known polypeptide chains of cytochrome c are homologous from at least two points of view. They are structurally homologous because of extensive similarities in amino acid sequence (30). They are also functionally homologous, since these proteins will substitute for one another in the manifold reactions in which cytochrome c activity can be measured, including the fairly complete biological system of more or less intact mitochondria (31; see Reference 30).

Conserved structures. Similarities in structure can be detected at three different levels of organization. In order of increasing complexity these are:

1. Identical residues in identical positions occupy about 33 percent of the entire polypeptide chain (see Fig. 1).

2. A substantial proportion of the variable positions contain residues the chemical structures of which are so alike that one may consider that all such variants are in fact able to play the same structural or functional roles (see Fig. 2). These are the so-called "conservative" substitutions (30,32,33), which are to be distinguished from "radical" substitutions in which more extensive differences in structure preclude any similarity in function. It should, however, be pointed out that the final diagnosis of whether a particular substitution is conservative or radical will depend on an accurate knowledge of the exact function of the residues in question, and will probably have to await, at the very least, the determination of the tertiary structure of the protein. Thus, any present classification can only be tentative.

3. The entire polypeptide chain, or segments of it, tend to conserve particular physico-chemical characters. There are thus eight segments of the protein which are highly hydrophobic containing the vast preponderance of residues carrying large aliphatic or aromatic side chains (Fig. 3). The quality which appears to be conserved in evolution is the hydrophobic nature of each segment as such, rather than the hydrophobic character of individual residues in these clusters. There is also a similar, though less rigid type of grouping of basic residues (30,32,33). It is less likely that the hydrophobic clusters are kept intact in the manifold variations imposed by evolutionary transitions simply because they afford the critical hydrophobic interactions which determine the specific spatial conformation of cytochrome c.

```
                Glu              Ser                          Lys
      Pro       Ser        Asn Ala Lys            Asn Thr    Thr Met
  Ala Gly Val Pro Gln      Ser Val Ala Lys    Ala Thr Leu    Val Thr
 — Thr-Glu-Phe-Lys-Ala —  Asp-Ile-Glu-Asn — Lys-Lys-Ile —  Ile-Glu
 -6                        1                                10


                                 Lys
                                 Gly
          Ala Leu        Glu     Ala        Thr Asn        Thr
  Arg     Ser Glu    Gly Ile Gly Glu Asn Leu Pro Gln       Ile
  Lys — Glu-Gln — — Thr-Val-Glu-Asn-Gly-Gly-Lys-His — Val — —
                          20                                   30


                                             Pro
                                             Ala
                                             Val
         Trp     Phe Ile                     Asp
 Ala     Asn     Leu Tyr Ser      His Ser  Ser Val Glu    Phe Ser
 Asn — His-Gly-Ile-Phe-Gly —    Lys-Thr — Gln-Ala-Gln — Tyr-Thr —
                                    40


                 Arg
                 Lys             Glu     Lys
                 Ala             Thr     Gly     Pro
 Ala Glu         Gln             Val   Ala Glu Glu
 Ser Asp     Lys Gln Ala Gly Val Leu   Asp Asp Asp Thr Leu Phe Asp
 Thr-Asn — — Ile-Asn-Lys-Asn-Ile-Ile — Asn-Asn-Asn-Asn-Met-Met-Glu
    50                                      60


                                         Val
                                 Ala     Thr
         Thr                     Val     Ala     Leu Ser
 — — Glu — — — — — — — — — — — — Ile — Gly — Ile-Lys —
       70                         80


    Lys         Val
    Thr         Thr                                      D
 Pro Ser        Ala                                     Lys
 Thr Ala        Gly                             Ser     Cys
 Ala Gly        Glu                             Gln     Ser D
 Asp Glu        Asp                         Glu Lys D  Thr Lys
 Glu Asp Glu    Gln Asn Ile Val Thr Phe Met Leu Asp Ser Ser Ala Ala
 Lys-Asn-Asp — Asn-Asp-Leu-Ile-Ala-Tyr-Leu-Lys-Lys-Ala-Thr-Asn-Glu
    90                                          100
```

Figure 2. Residue substitutions observed in 25 cytochromes c. See Fig. 1 for references to the primary structures of the different cytochromes c.

Similarly, the net charge of the polypeptide chain varies between the narrow limits of +8 to +10 cationic charge units (30), and the isoionic points are, within experimental error, the same for all the cytochromes c which have been examined,

```
                Lys                              Lys
     Val        Val                     Leu      Val       Arg
-- -- Phe-Lys -- -- -- Ile-Lys -- -- Lys-Lys-Ile-Phe-Ile-Met-Lys
-5               1                               10

-- -- Leu -- His -- Val -- Lys -- -- Lys-His-Lys-Val -- -- -- Leu
              20           30

         Phe Ile
His      Leu Tyr        His                 Tyr
Trp -- Ile-Phe -- Arg-Lys -- -- -- -- Val -- Phe -- Tyr -- -- --
                      40                              50

                   Leu
    Lys          Val Val                  Met Phe
-- Ile-Lys-Lys -- Ile-Ile-Trp-Lys -- -- -- Leu-Met -- Tyr-Leu --
                         60

                                    Val          Leu
-- -- Lys-Lys-Tyr-Ile -- -- -- Lys-Met-Ile-Phe-Val -- Ile-Lys-Lys
70                              80

                 Val
Lys-Lys -- Arg -- -- Leu-Ile -- Tyr-Leu-Lys-Lys-Lys -- Lys-Lys
       90                               100              104
```

Figure 3. Composite Distribution of Hydrophobic and Basic
Residues in Cytochrome c. The basic residues are underlined.
See Fig. 1 for references to the primary structures of the
different cytochromes.

being at pH 10.04 ± 0.04 (34,35) (see TABLE I). This remarkable
conservatism of net charge and isoionic point is maintained in
the face of quite large variations in the content of basic and
acidic residues, indicating the occurrence of interrelated
evolutionary variations. Indeed, it would appear that any mutation resulting in a change of charge must favor the subsequent fixation of mutations which tend to reestablish the most
favorable balance of charges (35). In terms of function, there
is little doubt that the net charge and isoionic point of
cytochrome c are of particular importance in regulating the
interactions of the protein with other members of the terminal
oxidation chain.

In general, it appears likely that residues and segments
that are stubbornly maintained invariant in evolution are
likely to represent areas, the function of which entail highly
specific structural requirements, while areas which change
extensively necessarily have functions compatible with a variety of structures.

376

TABLE I

Isoionic Points, Content of Charged Residues, and Net Charges of Cytochromes c from Various Species

| Species | Isoionic Point (20°) pH |
|---|---|
| Pig | 10.07 |
| Pigeon | 10.06 |
| Turkey | 9.98 |
| Peking duck | 10.02 |
| Man | 10.09 |
| Horse | 10.05 |
| Samia cynthia | 10.03 |
| Screw worm fly | 9.96 |
| Tuna | 10.04 |

| Species | Number of Charged Residues per Molecule | | | | | Net Cationic Charge at Neutral pH |
|---|---|---|---|---|---|---|
| | Lys | His | Arg | Asp | Glu | |
| Candida krusei | 12 | 4 | 4 | 4 | 6 | 8 |
| Snapping turtle | 18 | 2 | 2 | 3 | 9 | 8 |
| Kangaroo | 18 | 2 | 2 | 5 | 7 | 8 |
| Cow, Sheep, Pig, Dog | 18 | 3 | 2 | 3 | 9 | 8.5 |
| Pigeon | 18 | 3 | 2 | 4 | 8 | 8.5 |
| Rabbit, Chicken, Turkey, King penguin, Peking duck | 18 | 3 | 2 | 5 | 7 | 8.5 |
| Tuna | 16 | 2 | 2 | 4 | 5 | 9 |
| Man, Chimpanzee, M. mulatta | 18 | 3 | 2 | 3 | 8 | 9.5 |
| Horse, Donkey | 19 | 3 | 2 | 3 | 9 | 9.5 |
| Screw worm fly | 16 | 3 | 3 | 5 | 6 | 9.5 |
| Samia cynthia | 14 | 3 | 3 | 3 | 6 | 9.5 |
| Baker's yeast (iso-1) | 16 | 4 | 3 | 4 | 7 | 10 |

The isoionic points are taken from Barlow and Margoliash (35). The net charges are calculated from the amino acid compositions, disregarding the effect of the heme. In the case of the vertebrate proteins, because of the acetylated amino-terminal residue, the carboxy-terminal group provides an extra negative charge. See Fig. 1 for references to the amino acid sequence.

377

The most remarkable constant segment of the polypeptide is that extending from Residue 70 to Residue 80:

Asn-Pro-Lys-Lys-Tyr-Ile-Pro-Gly-Thr-Lys-Met
70                                          80

This sequence has been maintained strictly intact in cytochromes c from all species examined to date, covering the entire phylogenetic scale, from yeasts and molds to the most advanced vertebrates. Such a behavior can only reflect interaction with a structure, which on an evolutionary time scale, has remained invariant. There are in fact very few such structures, and these are essentially limited to the micromolecular prosthetic groups and cofactors. Other possible reasons for invariance, such as the requirements of a particular folding of the polypeptide chain, or of an area of interaction with another protein, or even those of a so-called "active site", are all compatible with some variation in amino acid sequence. Indeed a variety of polypeptide chains can form identical tertiary structures; two interacting proteins can both vary during the course of evolution and "active sites" may have relatively few absolute structural requirements, as will be discussed below for the heme peptide of cytochrome c. Together with the more recent chemical evidence, also considered below, on the role of the methionyl residue in position 80, which makes it probable that this amino acid in fact bears the second hemochrome-forming group of the protein, it is likely that the invariant sequence is in close approximation, intramolecularly, with the cytochrome c heme. This would explain both its invariance and the drastic results of chemical substitutions at some of the residues in it. The next largest invariant segments are no longer than two residues (see Fig. 1), emphasizing the outstanding situation with regard to Residues 70-80.

This type of reasoning can be extended to the many other invariant residues in the protein, such as the tryptophan in position 59 or the arginyl residues in positions 38 and 91 (see Fig. 1). However, it must be clearly stated that even though evolutionary considerations can point to the undoubted importance of conserved structures, they are incapable, by themselves, of determining what their functions are. In every case supplementary data of an entirely different nature are required. Nevertheless, with a considerable degree of confidence, it can be expected that when a sufficient variety of naturally occurring and artificially induced cytochrome c primary structures have been inspected, a fairly narrow definition of the minimal structural requirements of protein able to function as cytochrome c, will indeed be forthcoming. In this regard the mutant yeast proteins are likely to be particularly valuable (see Section IV).

Variable structures. If evolutionarily conserved regions
are functionally critical, then variable areas must have functions consistent with limited structural specificities. In
this regard it is particularly important to extend considerations of specificity to include the attributes which are in
fact conserved even in variable regions. These extend from
the lowest common denominator of protein chains, namely the
mere occurrence of a polypeptide of $\alpha$-amino acids, to partially
restricted specificities, such as those exhibited by the
hydrophobic clusters. From another point of view considerations of variability yield two distinct types of useful information. The first is to eliminate possibilities depending on
the invariant presence of specific residues in certain positions. The second and perhaps more important is to permit the
determination of which behavioral parameters change concomi-
tantly with variations in structure, thus leading to the establishment of clear-cut links between structure and function.

Thus, for example, considering the structures of the
regions adjacent to the heme attachment to cysteinyl residues
14 and 17, only five residues out of a total of 18 are in fact
invariant (see Fig. 5). These include the phenylalanine in
position 10, the two cysteines, the histidine in position 18
and the lysine in position 27. Of the three histidines often
present in cytochrome c only the residue at position 18 is
invariant. The histidyl residue commonly found in position 26
is replaced by an asparagine in the iso-2-cytochrome c of
Baker's yeast (36) and by a glutamine in the Neurospora crassa
protein (37); that often occurring in position 33 is replaced
by tryptophan or asparagine in the proteins from the tuna (38,
39), the kangaroo (40) and the snapping turtle (41). Therefore, if the conformations of these proteins are the same in
all essential details, and there is no reason to believe they
are not while there are numerous indications that they are in
fact similar, only a single histidine can possibly be involved
in hemochrome formation.

Another remarkable consequence of the above comparisons is
the unexpected paucity of specific amino acid requirements in
a region which must represent at least part of the area concerned with the electron transfer properties of cytochrome c.
In fact the minimal requirements exhibited by the heme peptide
appear not to be specific to cytochrome c as such, but rather
to cytochromes of the c group in general. This is evident from
the structures of the heme peptides from Rhodospirillum rubrum
cytochrome $c_2$, Chromatium cytochrome cc, and Pseudomonas
fluorescens cytochrome-551, listed in Fig. 6. Like cytochrome
c these proteins exhibit the basic residue preceding the heme
attachment, the two cysteines separated by two other residues,
and the histidine immediately following the second cysteine.

```
                 10                13 14          17 18   20                      26 27
      Ile-Phe-Val-Gln-Lys-Cys-Ala-Gln-Cys-His-Thr-Val-Glu-Lys-Gly-Gly-Lys-His-Lys
                                └─────────── HEME ───────────┘
```

| | 10 | 13 14 | 17 18 | | 20 | 26 27 |
|---|---|---|---|---|---|---|
| Horse   Cow   Rabbit }<br>Donkey   Pig   Kanagroo }<br>Dog   Sheep   Snapping turtle } | | | | | | |
| Chimpanzee   Man }<br>M. mulatta } | | Ile-Met | Ser | | | |
| Turkey   King penguin }<br>Chicken   Pigeon }<br>Pekin duck } | | | Ser | | | |
| Rattlesnake | | Thr-Met | Ser | | | |
| Tuna | Thr | | | | Asn | |
| Screw worm fly }<br>Samia cynthia } | | Arg | | | Ala | |
| Yeast Iso-1 | Leu | Lys-Thr-Arg | Glu-Leu | | | Pro |
| Yeast Iso-2 | Leu | Lys-Thr-Arg | Glu | Ile | Glu | Pro-Asn |
| Candida krusei | Leu | Lys-Thr-Arg | Glu | Ile | Ala | Pro |
| Neurospora crassa | Leu | Lys-Thr-Arg | Glu | | Glu | Gly-Glu-Gly-Gly-Asn-Leu-Thr-Gln |
| | 10 | 13 14 | 17 18 | | 20 | 26 27 |

Figure 5. Primary Structure of the Regions Adjacent to the Heme Attachments in Cytochrome c. Only those residues are indicated which differ from the first sequence given at the top of the figure. See Fig. 1 for references to the primary structures of the different cytochromes c.

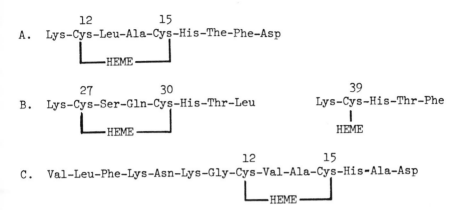

Figure 6. Structures of heme peptides of bacterial cytochromes of the c type. A. Rhodospirillum rubrum cytochrome c₂ (84,85); B. Chromatium cytochrome cc'(85-88); C. Pseudomonas fluorescens cytochrome-551 (89,90).

A simple example of the utilization of primary structure variations to understand certain aspects of the behavior of the protein comes from comparisons of the amino-terminal sequences of cytochrome c with its susceptibility to proteolytic digestion. All vertebrate cytochromes c, in the native form, are rather difficult to digest completely at near neutral pH with chymotrypsin or with trypsin. Repeated additions of enzyme and digestion periods up to about 10-30 hours are required. Among the most slowly hydrolyzed are the bird proteins which differ from the other vertebrate cytochromes c by carrying an isoleucine instead of a valine at position 3 (42,43). The non-vertebrate cytochromes c are generally hydrolyzed to completion much more readily, yeast iso-1-cytochrome c being entirely broken down to peptides, under the same conditions, in about three hours (44). These non-vertebrate cytochromes c are characterized by lacking the amino-terminal blocking acetyl group, carrying instead several extra amino acids (see (Fig. 7). It is nevertheless remarkable that the screw worm fly protein having a valine at position 3 (43) instead of the alanine occurring in the Samia cynthia cytochrome c (45), is digested about as slowly as the common vertebrate proteins, even though at other positions it is far more similar in structure to the moth than to the vertebrate cytochromes c. Clearly the hydrophobicity of the residue at position 3 is critical in determining the rate of hydrolysis of cytochrome c, presumably because it forms an intramolecular bond which is important in maintaining the native configuration.

```
                                    1                      6                      10                   14
                      Acetyl-Gly-Asp-Val-Glu-Lys-Gly-Lys-Lys-Ile-Phe-Val-Gln-Lys-Cys

Horse   Pig   Kangaroo  ⎫
Donkey  Cow   Rabbit    ⎬
Duck    Sheep Dog       ⎭
Snapping turtle

Man Chimpanzee M. mulatta                                                        Ile-Met

Chicken Turkey  ⎫
Pigeon Penguin  ⎭                                            Ile

Rattlesnake                                                                      Thr-Met

Tuna                                                    Ala               Thr

Screw worm fly        Gly-Val-Pro-Ala                   Asn                              Arg

Samia cynthia         Gly-Val-Pro-Ala                   Asn-Ala  Asn                     Arg

Bakers' yeast (Iso-1) Thr-Glu-Phe-Lys-Ala              Ser-Ala-Lys       Ala-Thr-Leu    Lys-Thr-Arg

Candida krusei        Pro-Ala-Pro-Phe-Glu-Gln          Ser-Ala-Lys       Ala-Thr-Leu    Lys-Thr-Arg

Neurospora crassa     Gly-Phe-Ser-Ala     Ser-Lys                        Ala-Asn-Leu    Lys-Thr-Arg
                      -4                   1            6                 10             14
```

Figure 7. Amino-terminal Sequences of Cytochrome c. Only those residues are indicated which differ from the first sequence given at the top of the figure. See Fig. 1 for references to the primary structures of the different cytochromes c.

Various cytochromes c, used as reagents having comparable structures which nevertheless differ in a graduated fashion, have been essential in locating the antigenic determinants of the protein (46,47), and in correlating structure with minor differences in spectrum (48). Such an approach will doubtlessly be utilized to great advantage in a variety of structure-function studies.

### III.  Some Recent Chemical Derivatives of Cytochrome c

In conjunction with the evolutionary approach to structure-function relations in cytochrome c it is important to consider some recent observations with derivatives of the protein. Okunuki et al. (19) obtained a monotrinitrophenyl substituted beef heart preparation, in which the entering group was bound to the $\epsilon$-amino group of one of the lysines in position 72 or 73, located near the amino-terminal end of the invariant sequence. This derivative showed about 50 percent of the activity of the native protein in the cytochrome oxidase system. Tsai and Williams (26) carboxymethylated both methionines (Residues 65 and 80) in horse heart cytochrome c, obtaining a modified protein which had lost the hemochrome properties characteristic of native cytochrome c, as well as all of its activity in the succinate oxidase system. The methionine at position 65 is not essential as such, since it is replaced by phenylalanine in the Samia cynthia (45), screw worm fly (43) and Neurospora proteins (37). Utilizing the moth cytochrome c which carries a single methionine, that at Residue 80, Tsai and Williams (27) were able to show that it is the carboxymethylation of this particular methionine which is entirely responsible for the observed effects. A similar conclusion was reached by Ando et al. (28) who managed to carboxymethylate only the methionine at position 65 by running the reaction at pH 5-6, giving a derivative which had properties identical to those of the native protein, or alternatively obtained the dicarboxymethylated derivative at pH 3. Again it should be noted that residue 80 is the carboxyl-terminal end of the invariant sequence.

More recently, Harbury et al. (49) have shown that a variety of thioethers, including N-acetylmethionine, can coordinate with heme, an adduct of heme and glutathione or an 8 amino acid heme peptide of cytochrome c, to yield a compound having a typical hemochrome spectrum, both in the reduced and oxidized forms, and exhibiting low spin characteristics. They explain the results of Schejter and George (25), who found that carboxymethylation of the cyanide complex of cytochrome c with bromoacetate gives a product with grossly altered spectral characteristics, by indicating that the tertiary structure of the cyanide complex is so altered that the entering carboxymethyl group does in fact bind to methione 80, rather than to a histidyl residue, as commonly assumed for carboxymethylation reactions at neutral pH with bromoacetate.

Other interesting results of recent chemical substitution' work relate to the role of lysyl residues in hemochrome formation. Hettinger and Harbury (22,23) find that cytochrome c in which all of the lysines have been transformed to homoarginyl residues by guanidine is very similar to the native protein, both spectrally and enzymically, at neutral or acid pH values. Similarly, cytochrome c in which all the $\epsilon$-amino groups have been trifluoracetylated is spectrally identical to normal cytochrome c (20). Thus, it appears unlikely that $\epsilon$-amino groups are involved in hemochrome formation, though it should be noted that such experiments do not completely eliminate that possibility. Indeed, if one assumes that the hemochrome-forming groups differ in the ferrous and ferric forms, it is still possible that an $\epsilon$-amino function does coordinate with the heme iron in one of the two oxidation states, even though when it is prevented from doing so by chemical transformation the hemochrome spectrum can still be obtained in both oxidation states. If this is correct one would expect that oxido-reduction in a protein in which only one form of the hemochrome is possible would not show the numerous protein conformation effects attending changes of valency of the heme iron (30). This possibility has not yet been tested.

In conclusion, the evidence provided by carboxymethylation, by the coordination of thioethers to heme iron, by the absence of histidines 26 or 33 in various cytochromes c and by the absolute constancy of the polypeptide segment between residues 70 and 80, makes it probable that histidyl residue 18 and methionyl residue 80 afford the hemochrome-forming groups in at least one of the oxidation states, probably the reduced form. Whether the same groups are involved in both oxidation states is uncertain. In this connection it is interesting to note that the great difference in affinity of methionine for the ferrous and ferric forms of heme (49) is just what would be expected if changing valency brings about a concomitant substitution of one of the hemochrome-forming groups for another, thereby providing a mechanism for the shift in the conformation of the protein.

## IV.  Mutant Iso-1-cytochromes c of Bakers' Yeast

Perhaps the most direct way of studying structure-function relations in cytochrome c is to obtain variants of the protein in which different amino acids have been substituted for particular single residues in the polypeptide chain, without introducing any other changes.  This would indeed make it possible to localize accurately the origin of any observed effects and circumvent both the difficulties of interpretation inherent in comparisons of natural proteins from different species which contain a number of variant residues, and the experimental as well as the interpretive difficulties which arise with chemically produced protein derivatives (see Introduction).

There seem to be two ways of utilizing this approach. The first involves the chemical synthesis of the polypeptide chain, introducing at will residues different from the ones present in natural proteins.  Such a synthesis appears to be well within the capabilities of existing techniques.  Moreover, the recent work of Sano and Tanaka (50) has shown that it is possible to link the prosthetic group directly to the heme-free extended polypeptide chain, and recover a preparation which exhibits the enzymic properties of the original material.  It thus appears likely that such procedures will eventually yield all the information necessary to determine unequivocally the functional role of every amino acid residue in cytochrome c.

A relatively simpler course with more immediately attainable ends involves the use of artificially induced cytochrome c mutants showing primary structure variations.  This approach has been made possible by the recent identification of the $CY_1$ locus as the structural gene of iso-1-cytochrome c of bakers' yeast (51).  The method by which such proteins were prepared first selects nitrous acid-induced mutant strains which specifically lack the ability to make iso-1-cytochrome c while carrying normal amounts of iso-2-cytochrome c and of all the other cytochromes as well.  Twelve such cytochrome c-deficient mutant strains have been obtained to date, and the lesions in all of them map genetically within a very small region of the structural gene.  The second step has consisted of selecting from each mutant strain, following irradiation with ultraviolet light, revertant strains which now have the ability to synthesize iso-1-cytochrome c.  Such revertants can be readily selected on a medium containing lactate as the sole carbon source, since cells lacking their major cytochrome c will not be able to grow at all, or grow only very slowly on such a medium.  If the original mutation occurred at the structural locus and the reversion is not the exact reverse of the first step, then the revertant cytochrome c will show a change in primary structure.

This is likely to occur whether the reverse mutation is at the same genetic site as the original mutation or whether the reversion occurred through the appearance of a suppressor mutation. Both types of reversions have already been observed and indeed a number of revertant cytochromes c have been shown to have altered primary structures (51).

It should be emphasized that the above procedure can only lead to the selection of functionally acceptable cytochromes c. Thus, the study of a number of independently produced revertants of each mutant strain can readily be utilized to determine the whole spectrum of amino acid residues that can be located at one particular position and form cytochromes c which are functionally competent to varying degrees.

It is remarkable that all the variant residues observed so far by this procedure occur either between the heme-bonded cysteines or amino-terminal to them (51). Since the mutants lacking cytochrome c have so far been selected merely on the basis of their inability to produce a heme-containing protein, it is likely that the initial genetic event is the introduction of a "nonsense" or "missense" mutation, precluding the attachment of the prosthetic group to the polypeptide chain. The localization of the variant residues indicates that in bakers' yeast cytochrome c is laid down from the amino to the carboxyl-terminal end, as is the case for other proteins in a variety of systems (52-56). A by-product of this work has been the demonstration that the structural gene for cytochrome c is a normal chromosomal locus obeying Mendelian laws (51). Thus, even though mitochondria are self-duplicating organelles (57-62) and in bakers' yeast the synthesis of cytochromes a and b is under the control of a cytoplasmic factor (63) which appears to be carried by the mitochondria themselves (64), a typical intramitochondrial protein, cytochrome c, is coded for by a typical chromosomal gene.

Finally, there is no reason why a procedure could not be devised which would select mutant yeast strains containing variant cytochromes c which are partially or totally functionally deficient. Such cytochromes could be used to define the structural requirements and functional role of all critical residues in the polypeptide chain.

# References

1. Anson, M. L., and A. E. Mirsky. J. Physiol. (London), 60, 51 (1925).

2. Anson, M. L., and A. E. Mirsky. J. Physiol. (London), 60, 161 (1925).

3. Keilin, D. Proc. Roy. Soc., B100, 129 (1926).

4. Theorell, H., and R. J. Åkesson. J. Am. Chem. Soc., 63, 1804, 1812, 1818 (1941).

5. Theorell, H. J. Am. Chem. Soc., 63, 1820 (1941).

6. Ehrenberg, A., and H. Theorell. Nature, 176, 158 (1955).

7. Ehrenberg, A., and H. Theorell. Acta Chem. Scand., 9, 365 (1955).

8. Paleus, S., A. Ehrenberg, and H. Tuppy. Acta Chem. Scand., 9, 365 (1955).

9. Margoliash, E., N. Frohwirt, and E. Wiener. Biochem. J., 71, 559 (1959).

10. Harbury, H. A., and P. A. Loach. Proc. Natl. Acad. Sci. U. S., 45, 1344 (1959).

11. Harbury, H. A., and P. A. Loach. J. Biol. Chem., 235, 3640 (1960).

12. Harbury, H. A., and P. A. Loach. J. Biol. Chem., 235, 3646 (1960).

13. George, P., and A. Schejter. J. Biol. Chem., 239, 1504, (1964).

14. Westcott, W. L., and S. R. Dickman. J. Biol. Chem., 210, 499 (1954).

15. Ishikura, H., K. Takahashi, K. Titani, and S. Minakami. J. Biochem. (Tokyo), 46, 719 (1959).

16. Minakami, S., K. Titani, and H. Ishikura. J. Biochem. (Tokyo), 45, 341 (1958).

17. Takemori, S., K. Wada, K. Ando, M. Hosokawa, I. Sekuzu, and K. Okunuki. J. Biochem. (Tokyo), 52, 28 (1962).

18. Conrad-Davies, H., L. Smith, and A. R. Wasserman. Biochim. Biophys. Acta, 85, 238 (1964).

19. Okunuki, K., K. Wada, H. Matsubara, and S. Takemori. In Oxidases and Related Redox Systems (T. E. King, H. S. Mason, and M. Morrison, eds.), John Wiley and Sons, Inc., New York, 1965, p. 549.

20. Fanger, M. W., and H. A. Harbury. Biochemistry, 4, 2541 (1965).

21. Takahashi, K., K. Titani, K. Furuno, H. Ishikura, and S. Minakami. J. Biochem. (Tokyo), 45, 375 (1958).

22. Hettinger, T. P., and H. A. Harbury. Proc. Natl. Acad. Sci. U. S., 52, 1469 (1964).

23. Hettinger, T. P., and H. A. Harbury. Biochemistry, 4, 2585 (1965).

24. Nakatani, M. J. Biochem. (Tokyo), 48, 633 (1960).

25. Schejter, A., and P. George. Nature, 206, 1150 (1965).

26. Tsai, H. J., and G. R. Williams. Can. J. Biochem., 43, 1409 (1965).

27. Tsai, H. J., and G. R. Williams. Can. J. Biochem., 43, 1995 (1965).

28. Ando, K., H. Matsubara, and K. Okunuki. Proc. Japan Acad., 41, 79 (1965).

29. Horinishi, H., K. Kurihara, and K. Shibata. Arch. Biochem. Biophys., 111, 520 (1965).

30. Margoliash, E., and A. Schejter. Adv. Prot. Chem., 21, 113 (1966).

31. Jacobs, E. E., and D. R. Sanadi. J. Biol. Chem., 235, 531 (1960).

32. Smith, E. L., and E. Margoliash. Federation Proc., 23, 1243 (1964).

33. Margoliash, E., and E. L. Smith. In Evolving Genes and Proteins (V. Bryson and H.J. Vogel, eds.), Academic Press, Inc., New York, 1964, p. 221.

34. Barlow, G. H., and E. Margoliash. Abstr. 150th Am. Chem. Soc. Meeting, Atlantic City, 1966, p. 16C.

35. Barlow, G. H., and E. Margoliash. J. Biol. Chem., 241, 1473 (1966).

36. Stewart, J. W., E. Margoliash, and F. Sherman. Federation Proc., 25, 647 (1966).

37. Heller, J., and E. L. Smith. Proc. Natl. Acad. Sci. U. S., 54, 1621 (1965).

38. Kreil, G. Z. Physiol. Chem., 334, 154 (1963).

39. Kreil, G. Z. Physiol. Chem., 340, 86 (1965).

40. Nolan, C., and E. Margoliash. J. Biol. Chem., 241, 1049 (1966).

41. Chan, S.K., I. Tullose, and E. Margoliash. Biochemistry, in press.

42. Chan, S.K. and E. Margoliash. J. Biol. Chem., 241, 507 (1966).

43. Chan, S.K., I. Tullose, and E. Margoliash. Unpub. data.

44. Stewart, J. W. and E. Margoliash. Unpub. data.

45. Chan, S.K. and E. Margoliash. J. Biol. Chem., 241, 335 (1966).

46. Reichlin, M., S. Fogel, A. Nisonoff and E. Margoliash. J. Biol. Chem., 241, 251 (1966).

47. Reichlin, M., A. Nisonoff and E. Margoliash. Unpub. data.

48. Elliott, W.B. and E. Margoliash. Unpub. data.

49. Harbury, H.A., J.R. Cronin, M.W. Fanger, T.P. Hettinger, A.J. Murphy, Y.P. Myer, and S.N. Vinogradov, Proc. Natl. Acad. Sci. U.S., 54, 1658 (1965).

50. Sano, S. and K. Tanaka. J. Biol. Chem., 239, PC3109 (1964).

51. Sherman, F., J.W. Stewart, E. Margoliash, J. Parker, and W. Campbell. Proc. Natl. Acad. Sci. U.S., in press.

52. Bishop, J., J. Leahy and R. Schweet. Proc. Natl. Acad. Sci. U.S., 46, 1030 (1960).

53. Dintzis, H.M. Proc. Natl. Acad. Sci. U.S., 47, 247 (1961).

54. Naughton, M.A. and H.M. Dintzis. Proc. Natl. Acad. Sci., 48, 1822 (1962).

55. Yoshida, A. and T. Tobita. Biochim. Biophys. Acta, 37, 513 (1960).

56. Canfield, R.E. and C.B. Anfinsen. Biochemistry, 2, 1073 (1966).

57. Luck, D.J.L. Proc. Natl. Acad. Sci. U.S., 49, 233 (1963).

58. Luck, D.J.L. J. Cell Biol., 16, 483 (1963).

59. Garnjobst, L., J.F. Wilson and E.L. Tatum. J.Cell Biol., 26, 413 (1965).

60. Diacumakos, E.G., L. Garnjobst and E.L. Tatum. J. Cell Biol., 26, 427 (1965).

61. Gibor, A. and S. Granick. Science, 145, 890 (1964).

62. Wilkie, D. Science Progress, 52, 459 (1964).

63. Ephrussi, B. In Nucleo-Cytoplasmic Relations in Micro-Organisms, Clarendon Press, Oxford, 1953.

64. Tuppy, H. and G. Wildner. Biochem. Biophys. Res. Comm., 20, 733, 1965

65. Margoliash, E. and E.L. Smith. Nature, 192, 1121 (1961).

66. Kreil, G. and H. Tuppy. Nature, 192, 1123 (1961).

67. Margoliash, E., E.L. Smith, G. Kreil and H. Tuppy. Nature, 192, 1125 (1961).

68. Margoliash, E., J.R. Kimmel, R.L. Hill and W.R. Schmidt. J. Biol. Chem., 237, 2148 (1962).

69. Margoliash, E. and E.L. Smith. J. Biol. Chem., 237, 2151 (1962).

70. Margoliash, E. J. Biol. Chem., 237, 2161 (1962).

71. Tuppy, H. and G. Kreil. Monatsch. Chem., 92, 780 (1962).

72. Matsubara, H. and E.L. Smith. J. Biol. Chem., 238, 2732 (196

73. Stewart, J.W. and E. Margoliash. Can. J. Biochem., 43, 1187 (1965).

74. Narita, K., K. Titani, Y. Yaoi, and H. Murakami. Biochim. Biophys. Acta, 77, 688 (1963).

75. Yasunobu, K.T., T. Nakashima, H. Higa, H. Matsubara, and H. Benson. Biochim. Biophys. Acta, 78, 791 (1963).

76. Chan, S.K., S.B. Needleman, J.W. Stewart and E. Margoliash. Unpub. data (1964).

77. Rothfus, J.A. and E.L. Smith. J. Biol. Chem., 240, 4277 (196

78. Needleman, S.B. and E. Margoliash. J. Biol. Chem., 241, 853 (1966).

79. McDowall, M.A. and E.L. Smith. J. Biol. Chem., 240, 4635 (1965).

80. Bahl, O.P. and E.L. Smith. J. Biol. Chem., 240, 3585 (1965).

81. Narita, K. and K. Titani. Proc. Japan Acad., 41, 831 (1965)

82. Walasek, O.F. and E. Margoliash. Unpub. data.

83. Needleman, S.B. and E. Margoliash. Unpub. data.

84. Paleus, S. and H. Tuppy. Acta Chem. Scand., 13, 641 (1959).

85. Dus, K. and M. D. Kamen. Biochem. Z., 338, 364 (1963).

86. Dus, K., R.G. Bartsch and M.D. Kamen. J. Biol. Chem., 236, PC47 (1961).

87. Dus, K., R.G. Bartsch and M.D. Kamen. J. Biol. Chem., 237, 3083 (1962).

88. Kamen, M.D. Acta Chem. Scand., 17, S41 (1963).

89. Ambler, R.P. Biochem. J., 89, 341 (1963).

90. Ambler, R.P. Biochem. J., 89, 349 (1963).

CARBOXYMETHYL CYTOCHROME c

DISCUSSION

Harbury: As observed by Schejter and George (1), the reaction of horse heart ferricytochrome c with bromoacetate at pH 7 is without effect on the visible absorption spectrum, whereas reaction of the cyanide complex of the molecule, followed by removal of the cyanide, results in very major alterations. The product so obtained no longer remains a hemochrome in acid solution, and in the reduced form is partly in the high-spin state even at neutral pH. These results appeared consistent with the possibility that the cyanide displaces a coordinated imidazole group of the protein, which as a result becomes subject to alkylation, and once modified, cannot resume its ligand role when the cyanide is withdrawn (1). Upon comparison of the products of the reactions, we find, however, that the change in spectrum does not reflect a cyanide-dependent carboxymethylation of histidine. The only histidine residue alkylated is histidine-33, and modification of this residue occurs in the absence as well as in the presence of cyanide. If the experiment is carried out with tuna cytochrome c, which contains histidine residues only in positions 18 and 26, there is no carboxymethlyation of histidine. It turns out, rather, that the change in spectrum parallels, for tuna cytochrome c as for horse heart cytochrome c, the modification of a methionine residue; more specifically, the modification of methionine-80 (2,3).

Similar results hold for Pseudomonas cytochrome c (2,4). Here the residue in question is methionine-61. This is seen most clearly in experiments in which the amino groups are first blocked, so that there is no opportunity for such groups to assume a ligand role in the alkylated derivative. Trifluoroacetylation of all of the amino groups, followed by carboxymethylation of methionine-22, results in retention of the characterisitic hemochrome spectrum of the molecule. However, when the carboxymethylation is carried out in the presence of cyanide, not only methionine-22, but also methionine-61 is modified, and upon removal of the cyanide, spectra such as those shown in Fig. 1 are obtained. These curves resemble closely the spectra for the high-spin heme peptide systems which we have studied.

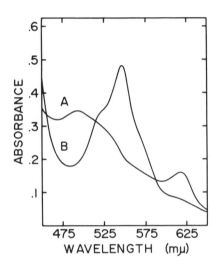

Figure 1. Spectra of Pseudomonas cytochrome c with all amino groups trifluoroacetylated and methionine residues 22 and 61 carboxymethylated. Phosphate buffer, pH 7.5. A. Oxidized form; B. Reduced form.

Pseudomonas cytochrome c has an amino acid sequence and composition very different from those of horse and tuna cytochromes c (5-7). Yet, for each of the three proteins worked with, the loss of hemochrome character accompanies the alkylation of a single methionine residue, which, under the conditions used, is modified only upon the addition of extrinsic ligand. One possible interpretation is that this methionine is bound to the heme group. Such binding would lead to structures in which, in Pseudomonas cytochrome c, the heme is linked to histidine-16 and methionine-61, and, in horse and tuna cytochromes c, to histidine-18 and methionine-80. Binding in this manner to two groups near the opposite ends of the single peptide chain could be a contributing factor to the compactness and unusual stability of these proteins. Furthermore, it may be worth noting, as mentioned before, that methionine-80 forms part of the most invariant segment of the amino acid sequences determined for what is by now a very substantial number of "mammalian-type" cytochromes c. Lastly, thioether coordination would pose some interesting possibilities in connection with electron-transfer mechanisms.

That methionine can form complexes with hemochrome-type spectra has been shown in studies with model heme peptides(2).

The complex formation in such systems is maintained to low pH, and is greatly favored when the metalloporphyrin is in the reduced form. These are attractive features in connection with some of the characteristic properties of the parent proteins.

At the risk of belaboring the obvious, let me emphasize, though, that none of the evidence I have cited demonstrates conclusively that heme-methionine binding does in fact occur in the cytochromes c. The results of the chemical modification studies show only that, under the conditions used, the binding of cyanide renders a specific methionine residue susceptible to carboxymethylation, and that once this modification has been effected, the initial hemochrome cannot be reformed. It is thus important to give careful consideration also to alternative interpretations.

Schejter: A hemoprotein with unusual properties can be obtained by reacting the cyanide ferri- complex of horse and beef cytochrome c with bromoacetate at neutral pH (1). Preliminary studies show that the only structural modification caused by this treatment and subsequent removal of cyanide by dialysis is the carboxymethylation of one histidine and one methionine residue. The latter is probably that located at position 80, at the end of the invariant sequence found in "mammalian-type" cytochrome c (2).

Carboxymethyl cytochrome c thus prepared shows three different spectroscopic types, depending on the pH of its solutions. A high-spin type is present up to pH 2.5; in less acid solutions, the spectrum is that of a high-spin - low-spin mixture, with peaks at 530 and 620 m$\mu$. This mixed-spin type is chromatographically and electrophoretically homogeneous, and its spectrum is not temperature dependent. A further change, to a purely low-spin type, occurs with a pH 4.7 at 20°. The transition from mixed to low spin type can be reversed, but upon acidification the spectrophotometric change is very slow, due to a large unfavorable entropy of activation. The low-spin type forms complexes with ionic ligands, including fluoride, indicating a much looser crevice structure than that of native protein. It cannot be reduced by $H_2$ in the presence of palladium black, nor by ascorbate.

Dithionite reduces the mixed-spin type readily, but the reduction of the low-spin type is slow and is catalyzed by imidazole. The spectrum of the reduced form has the typical $\alpha$ and $\beta$ bands of low-spin hemoproteins located at 550 and 520 m$\mu$, but their extinctions increase with increasing pH. This spectral change is not characteristic of a single ionization, since it proceeds over several pH units; addition of imidazole at any pH brings the spectrum to its maximal extinction in a typical association reaction. The closed crevice structure of reduced carboxymethyl cytochrome c̲ is also much looser than that of the native protein, as evidenced by the formation of complexes with cyanide, imidazole, n-butylamine, and CO at neutral pH. Very striking is the fact that by bubbling oxygen the spectrum obtained is similar to that of oxyhemoglobin. This "oxycytochrome c̲", at neutral pH and $pO_2$ = 150 torr, is stable for 10-15 minutes at room temperature, after which period it goes into the ferric state. An additional interesting fact is that in the presence of imidazole, the "oxy" form is not observed after air bubbling, and the conversion to the ferric state is immediate: similarly, addition of imidazole to "oxycytochrome c̲" changes it instantaneously into ferricytochrome c̲.

The absence of the 695 mμ band from the spectra of ferric carboxymethyl cytochrome c̲ in all its spectroscopic forms apparently indicates that its configuration is different from that of the native protein (3). In the succinic dehydrogenase system, the modified enzyme is entirely devoid of any catalytic properties; in the cytochrome c̲ - cytochrome oxidase system its activity cannot be tested because of the instability of carboxymethyl cytochrome c̲ in the presence of oxygen.

## References

1. Schejter, A. and P. George. Nature, 206, 1150 (1965).

2. Harbury, H. A., J. R. Cronin, M. W. Fanger, T. P. Hettinger, A. J. Murphy, Y.P. Myer, and S. N. Vinogradov. Proc. Natl. Sci. U.S., 54, 1658 (1965).

3. Harbury, H. A., Abstracts of the 151st National Meeting of The American Chemical Society, Pittsburgh, H30 (1966).

4. Hettinger, T. P., M. W. Fanger, S. N. Vinogradov, and H. A. Harbury. Federation Proc., 25, 648 (1966).

5. Ambler, R. P., Biochem. J., 89, 349 (1963).

6. Margoliash, E., E. L. Smith, G. Kreil, and H. Tuppy. Nature, 192, 1125 (1961).

7. Kreil, G. Z. Physiol. Chem., 334, 154 (1963).

8. Margoliash, E. and A. Schejter. Adv. Prot. Chem., 21, 113 (1966).

9. Schejter, A., and P. George. Biochemistry, 3, 1045 (1964).

# REACTION OF CYTOCHROME c OXIDASES OF BEEF HEART AND Micrococcus denitrificans WITH MAMMALIAN AND BACTERIAL CYTOCHROMES c*

Lucile Smith, Norma Newton and Peter Scholes

Biochemistry Department, Dartmouth Medical School, Hanover, New Hampshire

## Introduction

Evidence from several experimental approaches points to the involvement of electrostatic attractions in the interaction of soluble mammalian cytochrome c (isoelectric point around pH 10) with mammalian cytochrome c oxidase (1-6). The reaction is highly sensitive to the concentration of salts in the reaction medium, and polycations are strongly inhibitory. The polycations appear to compete with cytochrome c for a negatively charged site on the oxidase, the degree of inhibition depending upon the number of charged groups per particle size of the polycation and upon the ionic strength of the reaction medium. The electrostatic attraction between the cytochrome c and the oxidase might serve to bring oxidation-reduction groups into juxtapostion (2,5,6).

In contrast to the mammalian pigment, the cytochrome c isolated from Micrococcus denitrificans is reported to have an isoelectric point at acid pH (7). However, the oxidase of these bacteria will oxidize mammalian cytochrome c rapidly (7). We have made some further studies of the reactions of the oxidases from beef heart and M. denitrificans with the cytochromes c from beef heart and from these bacteria.

## Methods

Growth of bacteria. M. denitrificans, ATCC 13543, was cultured in a peptone-yeast medium either aerobically or anaerobically in the presence of nitrate as described elsewhere (8).

*This work was supported by USPHS Grant GM 06270.

Preparations. Membrane fragments of M. denitrificans bearing the respiratory chain system were isolated by treatment of the cells with lysozyme, subsequent osmotic lysis of the spheroplasts formed, then the insoluble membrane fragments collected by centrifugation at 30,000 x g for one hour (8). Anaerobic minus aerobic difference spectra of these membrane fragments show evidence of cytochromes $a + a_3$ and b- and c-type cytochromes (8). Fragments of beef heart mitochondrial membrane were prepared by a modification of the Keilin-Hartree method (9). In some experiments both the heart muscle particles and the bacterial membrane fragments were treated with deoxycholate by addition of 5 percent sodium deoxycholate to strong suspensions of the particles, incubating in the cold for about five minutes, then diluting with phosphate buffers of varying concentrations (9).

Soluble cytochrome c was isolated from the buffer washings of M. denitrificans which had been grown anaerobically for at least 48 hours by a method which will be described elsewhere (10). The properties of the bacterial cytochrome c are summarized in Table I. Beef heart cytochrome c was prepared by the methods of Keilin-Hartree (11) and Margoliash (12).

TABLE I

Comparison of absorption spectra of Micrococcus and

| Mammalian Cytochrome c | Cytochrome c | |
|---|---|---|
| Band Positions (mμ) | Micrococcus | Mammalian |
| α band reduced | 550.5 | 550 |
| β band reduced | 522 | 520.5 |
| γ band reduced | 415.5 | 416 |
| α band oxidized | 526 | 528 |
| γ band oxidized | 411 | 410 |
| δ band oxidized | 360 | 361 |
| | | |
| Band Ratios | | |
| α/β reduced | 1.64 | 1.65 |
| γ/α reduced | 4.74 | 4.58 |
| | | |
| $\dfrac{550 \text{ m}\mu \text{ reduced}}{280 \text{ m}\mu \text{ oxidized}}$ | 1.113 | 1.32 |

A soluble brown protein which showed feeble cytochrome $c$ oxidase activity was also isolated from the soluble portion of lysates of anaerobically grown cells by ammonium sulfate fractionation and chromatography on DEAE cellulose (13). This protein contained $a_2$ - and $c$-type cytochromes (13).

Assay methods. Cytochrome $c$ oxidase activity was assayed spectrophotometrically (14) at $25^{\circ}$ in 0.05 M phosphate buffer, pH 7.0. The cytochrome $a_3$ content of the preparations was calculated from the difference in optical density at 605-630 mμ in the reduced minus oxidized difference spectra obtained with a Cary Model 14 spectrophotometer (15), using a value of of 23 $mM^{-1}$ $cm^{-1}$ (16). Turnover rates of cytochrome $a_3$ were calculated as described previously (15).

Cytochrome $c$ concentrations were calculated from the optical density at 550 mμ of the preparation reduced with sodium dithionite, using the value of 27.6 as the millimolar coefficient (17). The same value was used in expressing the concentration of the bacterial and beef heart cytochromes.

Protein content of the particulate preparations was measured using the biuret method in the presence of 0.2 percent deoxycholate (18).

## Results

Oxidation of mammalian and bacterial cytochromes c by preparations from M. denitrificans. Particulate preparations as isolated from both aerobically and anaerobically grown bacteria show very high activity in oxidizing mammalian cytochrome $c$. Tables II and III compare the turnover rates of the cytochrome $a_3$ of some bacterial preparations with those of suspensions of fragments of heart mitochondrial membrane, either calculated to an infinitely high concentration of cytochrome $c$ or at a fixed low concentration of cytochrome $c$. The turnover rates were calculated on the assumption that the extinction coefficients of beef and bacterial cytochromes $a$ and $a_3$ are the same. Both on the basis of protein content and in terms of the content of cytochrome $a_3$, the bacterial preparations are more active in oxidizing beef cytochrome $c$ than the oxidase of the beef heart particles, and the preparations from anaerobically grown bacteria are more active than those from aerobically grown cells. There was little difference observed in the reactivity of the bacterial oxidase in oxidizing the beef and the bacterial cytochromes $c$.

TABLE II

Activity of particulate preparations from M. denitrificans and beef heart in oxidizing beef heart cytochrome c.

| Particle Preparation | Turnover rate of $a_3$ at infinitely high$[c]$ |
|---|---|
| Anaerobic Micrococcus | |
| Prep. 1 | 1100 |
| Prep. 2 | 750 |
| | |
| Aerobic Micrococcus | |
| Prep. 1 | 350 |
| Prep. 2 | 303 |
| Prep. 3 | 169 |
| Prep. 4 | 435 |
| | |
| Keilin Hartree Particle | |
| Prep. 1 | 81 |
| Prep. 2 | 122 |
| Prep. 3 | 71 |
| Prep. 4 | 224 |
| | |
| Beef Heart Mitochondria* | 124 |

*Data from Smith and Camerino (19)

TABLE III

Comparison of the oxidase activity of particulate preparations of beef heart and M. denitrificans in oxidizing beef heart and bacterial cytochrome c (cytochrome content 15 $\mu$M in all cases).

| | $\dfrac{k \ sec^{-1}}{mg \ protein}$ | Turnover rate |
|---|---|---|
| Beef heart cytochrome c: | | |
| M. denitrificans particles | 0.76 | 168 |
| Beef heart particles | 0.20 | 14 |
| | | |
| M. denitrificans cytochrome c: | | |
| M. denitrificans particles | 0.52 | 101 |
| Beef heart particles | 0.0011 | 0.8 |

As with preparations from beef heart, the oxidase activity of different preparations from bacteria was somewhat variable from preparation to preparation, and the activity was stimulated by treatment with detergents. Maximal stimulation was obtained on addition of 1 mg deoxycholate per 4 mg protein to strong suspensions of particles, then dilution with 0.015 M phosphate buffer (Table IV). With beef heart particles a higher ratio of detergent to protein (1 mg DOC/mg protein) is required for maximal increase in oxidase activity (9). The already high rate of the bacterial oxidase in oxidizing beef cytochrome $\underline{c}$ is increased by the detergent treatment to very high values (Table IV).

TABLE IV

Effect of treatment with deoxycholate on the oxidase activity
of particulate preparations from M. denitrificans

In each experiment 5 percent DOC was added to a strong (13.8 mg protein/ml) suspension of particles, the mixture incubated for 5 minutes in the cold, then diluted 50-fold with 0.015 M phosphate buffer.

14.7 μM beef heart cytochrome $\underline{c}$ was present in all assays.

|  | Turnover rate of cytochrome $\underline{a}_3$ sec$^{-1}$ |
| --- | --- |
| Untreated particles | 172 |
| Particles treated with 1 mg DOC/mg protein | 743 |
| "         "        "  2 mg DOC/mg protein | 634 |
| "         "        "  1 mg DOC/2 mg protein | 1440 |
| "         "        "  1 mg DOC/4 mg protein | 2370 |
| "         "        "  1 mg DOC/8 mg protein | 2080 |

The kinetics of the oxidation of mammalian cytochrome $\underline{c}$ by the oxidase of the bacterial particles are the same as those characteristic of the mammalian oxidase (1); the reaction is always first order with respect to the concentration of ferrocytochrome $\underline{c}$ and the rate constant decreases with increasing concentration of total cytochrome $\underline{c}$ in the reaction mixture. The oxidase of the bacterial particles is also very sensitive to the ionic strength of the reaction medium, and the optimal ionic strength is dependent upon the cytochrome $\underline{c}$ content (Fig. 1). Preparations from aerobically grown bacteria show maximal activity at lower ionic strength than those from anaerobically grown bacteria (Fig. 1). Also

like the mammalian oxidase (2), no sharp pH optimum is apparent
when the oxidase of the bacterial particles is tested in buffers
of constant ionic strength.

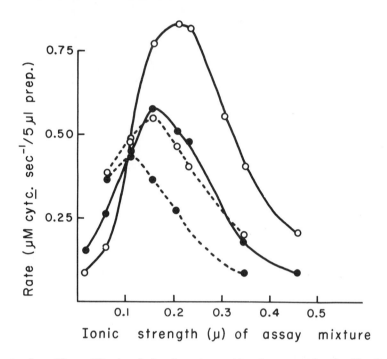

Figure 1. The effect of ionic strength at a constant pH of 7.0
on the cytochrome c oxidase activity of particles from aerobically and anaerobically grown M. denitrificans. Solid lines
represent particles from anaerobically grown cells; dashed
lines, preparations from aerobically grown cells; open circles
correspond to data obtained with 14 µM beef heart cytochrome c
and closed circles, with 52 µM beef heart cytochrome c.

    A soluble brown protein from anaerobically grown cells
of M. denitrificans containing $a_2$ and c-type cytochromes (13)
also oxidizes bacterial and mammalian cytochrome c. The
kinetics and the effects of ionic strength and pH are similar
to those observed with the particulate oxidase. However, the
turnover rates are very low (around 1 sec$^{-1}$ at 25° in 0.05 M
phosphate buffer, pH 7.0, and 16 µM bacterial cytochrome c).

The brown protein appears to be similar to one purified from anaerobically grown Pseudomonas aeruginosa by Yamanaka and Okunuki (19) and designated by them as a nitrite reductase and a cytochrome c oxidase. The turnover rate of their preparation in oxidizing bacterial cytochrome c with oxygen was reported to be 10 $sec^{-1}$ at 27° with 14 µM cytochrome c (20). This is somewhat higher than the rate observed with the brown protein from M. denitrificans but much lower than the rates obtained with the particulate oxidase of these bacteria.

Oxidation of bacterial cytochrome c by heart muscle particles. Untreated preparations of membrane fragments from heart muscle mitochondria shown very low activity in oxidizing bacterial cytochrome c (Table III). However, with one preparation treatment of the heart muscle fragments with deoxycholate increased the turnover rate over 10-fold. Due to a short supply of the bacterial cytochrome c, we have not yet ascertained whether varying the conditions of detergent treatment would increase the activity still further.

## Discussion

The turnover rates of the bacterial oxidase are calculated on the assumption that the bacterial cytochromes a and $a_3$ have the same extinction coefficients as the mammalian pigments and therefore may not be correct. However, the reaction rates of the mammalian and the bacterial oxidases in oxidizing beef heart cytochrome c must be of at least comparable magnitude, even though the bacterial and the beef cytochromes c have different charges at pH 7. Thus, the overall charge on the cytochrome c is not important, and electrostatic interactions between the oxidase and the cytochrome c must involve some localized charge on the cytochrome c.

The unusual oxidase kinetics and the sensitivity of the reaction to the ionic strength of the reaction medium are apparent in the interactions of different preparations of particulate oxidases and also in the slow reaction of the soluble brown protein from M. denitrificans with either beef or bacterial cytochrome c. These characteristics do not seem to be related to the insoluble lipoprotein structure of the particulate oxidases.

There are numerous indications of the importance of the structural arrangements within the oxidase complex in determining the extent to which the oxidase is accessible to interaction with soluble cytochrome c. Evidences of this in the present work are the variability of the reactivity among different preparations from bacteria, the differences in reactivity of preparations from aerobically grown cells as compared with anaerobically grown ones and the effects of detergent treatment on the oxidase activity. Differences in the membrane structure of the bacteria and heart muscle mitochondria are indicated by the different conditions of detergent treatment required to give maximal stimulation of the oxidase activity. There are indications that the beef heart oxidase will react rapidly with the bacterial cytochrome $c$ if proper conditions for treatment with detergent are found. This would mean that the species specificity in the oxidase-cytochrome $c$ reactions previously observed may at least in part be due to the lack of proper exposure of the membrane-bound oxidases for reaction with the soluble cytochrome $c$. The requirements for very rapid reaction of the oxidases with soluble cytochrome $c$ appear to be narrowed down to a properly placed charged group on the cytochrome $c$ and an oxidase treated in some manner (detergent, for example) to expose the reactive site on the oxidase.

## Acknowledgment

The skillful assistance of Mrs. Marjorie Krause Brown is greatly appreciated.

## References

1. Smith, L., and H. Conrad. Arch. Biochem. Biophys., 63, 403 (1956).

2. Davies, H. C., L. Smith, and A. R. Wasserman. Biochim. Biophys. Acta, 85, 238 (1964).

3. Person, P., and A. S. Fine. Arch. Biochem. Biophys., 94, 392 (1961).

4. Person, P., P. T. Mora, and A. S. Fine. J. Biol. Chem., 238, 4103 (1963).

5. Smith, L., and N. Newton. In Oxidases and Related Redox Systems (T. E. King, H. S. Mason and M. Morrison, eds.), Academic Press, Inc., New York, 1965, p. 745.

6. Smith, L., and K. Minnaert. Biochim. Biophys. Acta, 105, 1 (1965).

7. Kamen, M. D., and L. P. Vernon. Biochim. Biophys. Acta, 17, 10 (1955).

8. Scholes, P. B. In preparation.

9. Smith, L., and P. W. Camerino. Biochemistry, 2, 1432 (1963).

10. Scholes, P. B., and N. Newton. In preparation.

11. Keilin, D., and E. F. Hartee. Biochem. J., 39, 289 (1945).

12. Margoliash, E. Biochem. J. 56, 529, 535 (1954).

13. Newton, N., P. B. Scholes, and L. Smith. In preparation.

14. Smith, L. Arch. Biochem. Biophys., 50, 285 (1954).

15. Smith, L., and P. W. Camerino. Biochemistry, 2, 1432 (1963).

16. Chance, B. J. Biol. Chem., 202, 407 (1953).

17. Margoliash, E., and N. Frohwirt. Biochem. J., 71, 570 (1959).

18. Gornall, A., C. Bardawill, and M. David. J. Biol. Chem., 177, 751 (1949).

# ENZYMATIC AND SPECTRAL PROPERTIES OF VARIOUS TYPES OF CYTOCHROME c[*]

Ronald W. Estabrook[‡]

Johnson Research Foundation, University of Pennsylvania
Philadelphia, Pennsylvania

As our knowledge of the chemistry and structure of cytochrome c increases, it becomes more imperative to establish a means of assessing subtle alterations in the enzymatic activity of this hemoprotein. A number of various enzymatic assays have been employed, such as DPNH-cytochrome c reductase or cytochrome c oxidase. For these assays relatively high concentrations of cytochrome c are used, permitting the direct measurement of cytochrome reduction or oxidation. The inhibitory action of cytochrome c (for example in the interaction with cytochrome oxidase (1)) may complicate the interpretation of small changes in enzymatic activity. Therefore, a series of studies have been carried out employing the cytochrome c-deficient submitochondrial particles from liver. As first described by Schneider et al. (2), water lysis of liver mitochondria followed by salt extraction essentially removes (3) all the functional cytochrome c of mitochondria. Jacobs and Sanadi (4) demonstrated the stoichiometric reconstitution of the succinoxidase activity of such particles by the reincorporation of cytochrome c. The properties of cytochrome c interaction in the reconstituted particles have been examined in detail by Nicholls (5) and Jacobs et al. (6).

In the present report, experiments were carried out in an attempt to assess differences in the enzymatic activity of cytochrome c prepared by Margoliash from a variety of sources. Cytochrome c-deficient particles were prepared from liver mitochondria as described previously (3). Samples of purified cytochrome, obtained as a gift from E. Margoliash, were dialyzed to remove any salts required for crystallization, and concentrations were determined spectrophotometrically.

*Supported in part by a USPHS Research Grant GM 12202.

‡This study was carried out during the tenure of a USPHS Research Career Development Award GM-K3-4111.

Fig. 1 illustrates the polarographic measurements of oxygen utilization during the reconstitution of the succinoxidase activity of liver submitochondrial particles. Very low concentrations of cytochrome $c$ are seen to have an immediate response on the rate of oxygen uptake.

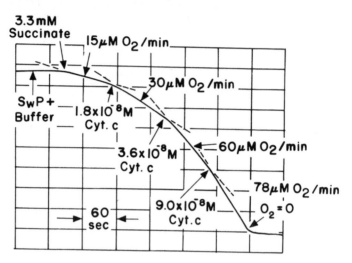

**Figure 1.** Effect of moth cytochrome $c$ on restoring the succinoxidase activity of cytochrome c-deficient submitochondrial particles of liver. A 0.1 ml aliquot of saline-washed, water-lysed liver mitochondria (3.2 mg protein) was diluted to 3.2 ml in 0.025 M phosphate buffer, pH 7.4. Sodium succinate and varying concentrations of moth cytochrome $c$ were added as indicated. The rate of oxygen utilization was determined from the slope of the linear portion of the tracing. Experiment 10/16/63.

When a series of experiments of the type illustrated in Fig. 1 are repeated, using a number of different types of cytochrome $c$, pronounced differences in the effectiveness of cytochrome $c$ to restore activity are apparent. Fig. 2 presents the data from one such series of experiments. It is seen that the cytochrome $c$ from moth is most effective in reconstituting activity with a half maximal restoration of oxygen uptake observed with $0.6 \times 10^{-10}$ moles of moth cytochrome $c$.

The next most active cytochrome $c$ is that prepared from horse heart with half-maximal restoration of oxygen uptake occurring when $1.3 \times 10^{-10}$ moles of cytochrome $c$ is added. Of interest is the observation that an identical titration curve

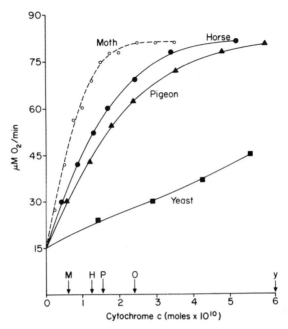

Figure 2. Effect of varying types of cytochrome c on the rate of oxygen uptake. Experiments of the type illustrated in Fig. 1 were carried out using dialyzed samples of purified moth (M), horse heart (H), pigeon breast (P) muscle and yeast (Y) cytochrome c. The concentrations of cytochrome c required for 50 percent restoration of maximal activity are indicated on the abscissa. The concentration of cytochrome c originally present in the mitochondria before salt extraction (2.2 x $10^{-10}$ moles/mg protein) is indicated on the abscissa by (0).

is obtained when cytochrome c preparations from hog kidney or hog liver are used in place of the horse heart cytochrome c. Of the cytochrome c's tested, that prepared from pigeon breast muscle was next in order of its effectiveness with half-maximal restoration of oxygen uptake occurring with 1.6 x $10^{-10}$ moles of cytochrome c. Least effective was yeast cytochrome c with greater than 6 x $10^{-10}$ moles of cytochrome c required to activate the succinoxidase oxidase system to 50 percent of its maximal capacity. This data illustrates the extreme sensitivity of the assay method for determining differences in the enzymatic activity of various types of cytochrome c with greater than a ten-fold range in activity observed with the few samples tested. Of interest is the ability to restore maximal activity with moth cytochrome $\underline{c}$ using less than stoichiometric concentrations relative to the concentration of cytochrome $\underline{c}$ originally present in the mitochondria before extraction $(2.2 \times 10^{-10}$ moles).

Having determined differences in the enzymatic activities of the various types of cytochrome $\underline{c}$, it was of interest to see if there was any physical parameter which was also modified. Previous studies (7) using low temperature spectrophotometry had demonstrated a difference between heart and yeast cytochrome $\underline{c}$ in the satellite band structure of the $\alpha$ band of the reduced pigment. A similar examination of the samples employed here for the enzymatic studies also revealed changes in the nature of the satellite absorption bands. As demonstrated by the tracings in Fig. 3, there is a progressive change in the magnitude of band splitting progressing from yeast cytochrome $\underline{c}$, where only $\underline{c}\alpha_1$ and $\underline{c}\alpha_3$ absorption bands are

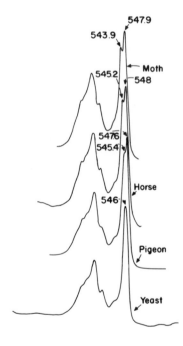

Figure 3. Low temperature spectra of reduced cytochrome c from various sources. Samples of cytochrome c were diluted in 0.1 $\overline{M}$ phosphate buffer, pH 7.4 and then diluted with an equal volume of glycerol and the spectra recorded as described previously (7).

observed to moth cytochrome $\underline{c}$ where a 4 m$\mu$ displacement of the $\underline{c}\,\alpha_2$ band from $\underline{c}\,\alpha_1$ is obtained. It may be fortuitous, but the order of displacement of the $\underline{c}\,\alpha_2$ satellite band from $\underline{c}\,\alpha_1$ corresponds with the ordered sequence of reactivation of suc-cinoxidase activity, as determined in the enzymatic assay.

## Summary

The present report has illustrated the use of an enzymatic assay for determining differences in activities of cytochrome $\underline{c}$ prepared from a variety of sources. In addition, low temperature spectra have been presented demonstrating differences in the satellite band structure of the $\alpha$ band of reduced cytochrome $\underline{c}$ from a number of sources.

## References

1. Smith, L., and Newton, N. In Oxidases and Related Redox Systems (T. E. King, H. S. Mason, and M. Morrison, eds.), Vol. II, John Wiley and Sons, New York, 1964, p. 745.

2. Schneider, W. C., A. Claude, and G. Hogeboom. J. Biol. Chem., 172, 451 (1948).

3. Estabrook, R. W., J. Biol. Chem., 230, 735 (1958).

4. Jacobs, E. E., and D. R. Sanadi. J. Biol. Chem., 235, 531 (1960).

5. Nicholls, P. In Oxidases and Related Redox Systems (T. E. King, H. S. Mason, and M. Morrison, eds.), Vol. II, John Wiley and Sons, New York, 1964, p. 784.

6. Jacobs, E. E., E. C. Andrews, and F. L. Crane. In Oxidases and Related Redox Systems (T. E. King, H. S. Mason, and M. Morrison, eds.), Vol. II, John Wiley and Sons, New York, 1964, p. 784.

7. Estabrook, R. W. In Haematin Enzymes (J. E. Falk, R. Lemberg, and R. K. Morton, eds.), Vol. II, Pergammon Press, New York, 1961, p. 436.

MULTIPLE MOLECULAR FORMS (ISOCYTOCHROMES)
OF BEEF HEART CYTOCHROME c

Torgeir Flatmark

Department of Biochemistry, Nobel Medical Institute
Stockholm, Sweden
Department of Chemistry, University of California San Diego
La Jolla, California

The occurrence of more than one molecular form of monomeric cytochrome c isolated from beef heart muscle has recently
been demonstrated. Thus, four subfractions of the hemoprotein
were quantitatively separated from one another by disc electrophoresis on polyacrylamide gel, and they were termed, in order
of their decreasing mobility towards the cathode, Cy I, Cy II,
Cy III, and Cy IV (1). The relative percentages of the three
main fractions (Cy I - Cy III) were approximately 90 : 9 : 1
in terms of absorbancy at $\lambda$ = 416 m$\mu$. The same pattern of
heterogeneity was found by chromatography on Duolite CS-101 (1)
by moving-boundary electrophoresis (2) and by isoelectric
fractionation by electrolysis in a natural pH-gradient (3).
The data so far obtained support the view that all fractions
occur in vivo. Thus, the pattern of heterogeneity is independent of the extraction procedure, and each of the four fractions is quite stable when subjected to the whole purification
procedure. Finally, tracer studies with $^{59}$Fe in rats have
shown a difference in and a change of the specific activity of
the iron in the different subfractions which is compatible with
a conversion of Cy I to the other fractions in vivo (4). Since
all forms can be isolated from a single organ (1) the term isocytochromes is proposed in analogy with the terminology of
multiple molecular forms of enzymes, i.e. isoenzymes (5).

The isocytochromes were separated from one another on the
basis of a difference in net charge, the main component (Cy I)
being the most positively charged (Table I). Thus, the difference in electrophoretic and chromatographic behavior of
Cy II and Cy I is explained by the presence of one more negatively charged group (carboxyl) in Cy II than in Cy I, since
the latter contains one amide group more than the former. The
difference in electrophoretic and chromatographic behavior of
Cy III and Cy I is similarly explained by the presence of two
more negatively charged groups (carboxyl) in Cy III than in Cy I.

TABLE I

Some Physico-Chemical Properties of
Isocytochromes Cy I - Cy III

| | Cy I | Cy II | Cy III | Ref. |
|---|---|---|---|---|
| Percentage distribution | 90 | 9 | 1 | (1) |
| Moving-boundary electrophoresis (0° C) | 10.80 | 10.60 | 10.32 | (2) |
| pI (ferrous form) | | | | |
| Isoelectric fractionation (4° C) | 10.80 | 10.58 | 10.38 | (3) |
| Difference in net charge [a] | ~ 1 | ~ 1 | | (2) |
| Amino acid composition | No difference | | | (2) |
| Amide-N/molecule | 8.40 | 7.51 | -- | (2) |
| $E_{m,7}$ (volts) [b] | 0.247 | 0.212 | 0.187 | (7) |
| Autoxidability (pH 7) | Cy I $<$ Cy II $<$ Cy III | | | (7) |
| Binding of CO (pH 7) | 0 | 0 | 0 | (2) |

a Calc. from the moving-boundary electrophoresis and the acid-base titration curve

b Oxidative titration

The light absorption spectra of Cy II and Cy III reveal certain differences from those of Cy I indicating a difference in conformation of the isocytochromes (2). Thus, in the ferric form the spectrum of Cy II and of Cy III is very similar to that obtained by exposing Cy I to different concentrations of a denaturing agent such as urea. The negative peaks at 290.5 m$\mu$ and 230.5 m$\mu$ of the difference spectrum are especially noteworthy, since the same peaks are seen in all types of difference spectra of Cy I where a conformational change does occur, i.e. in urea, in acid solution (6), and at high temperatures. In addition, the optical rotatory dispersion (ORD) spectrum of the ferric form indicates a difference in the conformation of isocytochromes Cy I – Cy III (7); the amplitude of the Soret Cotton effect is smaller and the dispersion at 380 m$\mu < \lambda <$ 260 m$\mu$ is more levorotatory in Cy II and Cy III than in Cy I. However, isocytochromes Cy II and Cy III do not combine with carbon monoxide at neutral pH, but are slowly oxidized by molecular oxygen (Cy III > Cy II > Cy I). Furthermore, the oxidation-reduction potential of Cy II and Cy III is lower than that of Cy I (Table I). Finally, the isocytochromes are reduced at a decreasing rate by ascorbate and by NADH$_2$ cytochrome c reductase (EC 1.6.2.1) in the order Cy I > Cy II > Cy III, which indicate that the physico-chemical differences concern an essential part of the hemoprotein structure, i.e. the isocytochromes are not biologically equivalent (7).

An interesting question about the isocytochromes concerns their biological significance. The fact that they represent irreversibly denaturated molecular forms may indicate that the deamidations of glutamine/asparagine residues are intermediary steps in the catabolism of the hemoprotein in vivo.

## References

1. Flatmark, T. Acta Chem. Scand., 18, 1656 (1964).

2. Flatmark, T. Acta Chem. Scand., in press.

3. Flatmark, T. and O. Vesterberg. Acta Chem. Scand., in press.

4. Flatmark, T. and K. Sletten. In preparation.

5. Markert, C. L. and F. Möller. Proc. Nat. Acad. Sci., 45, 753 (1959).

6. Flatmark, T. Acta Chem. Scand., in press.

7. Flatmark, T. In preparation.

413

## DISCUSSION

**Margoliash:** The sort of molecules that Dr. Flatmark has been speaking of should be distinguished from so-called "isozymes". Since the original definition was introduced, isozymes have been shown to be under independent biosynthetic genetic control and to have different primary structures. In this case, I understand that the cytochromes c are a series of deamidated products of the native protein, and whether they occur in vivo or are artifacts of the preparation is not particularly to the point. One cannot compare these with, for example, the iso-1 and iso-2 cytochromes of Baker's yeast, which have different polypeptide chains and are quite clearly under separate genetic control.

**Flatmark:** I have used the term "isocytochromes" for these four molecular forms of cytochrome c in analogy with the terminology of multiple molecular forms of enzymes, i.e., "isoenzymes" or "isozymes", terms which were introduced by Markert and Møller in 1959 (1). In this definition, it was not intended that there should be a difference in the primary structure of the isoenzyme.

### References

1. Markert, C. L., and F. Møller. Proc. Natl. Acad. Sci., 45, 753 (1959).

# OPTICAL ROTATORY DISPERSION STUDIES OF CYTOCHROME c[*]

Henry A. Harbury, Yash P. Myer, Alexander J. Murphy,[‡]
and Serge N. Vinogradov

Department of Biochemistry, Yale University
New Haven, Connecticut

Our studies of the optical rotatory dispersion (ORD)[**] of
the cytochromes c are still at an early stage, and the results
to be summarized are largely those of some initial, broad comparisons. We shall begin with the curves for the oxidized and
reduced forms of horse heart cytochrome c at neutral pH, proceed from there to data for related heme peptide systems, and
then, returning to the protein, shall touch briefly on effects
of change in solution conditions, modification of functional
groups, and species variation.

Fig. 1 shows the dispersion patterns for horse heart
ferri- and ferrocytochrome c in 0.1 M phosphate buffer of
pH 6.8. Particularly striking are the composite Cotton effects
in the Soret region, and the major changes introduced in this
part of the wavelength range upon change in the state of
oxidation of the molecule. Additional Cotton effects are
evident at other wavelengths, including those in the visible
range. A region of special interest is that from 270 to 300 mμ,
where the curve for the oxidized form exhibits two distinct
peaks, one of which gives way to a small shoulder upon reduction
of the system. The relationships reflected in this as in other
regions of the curves are highly complex, but it seems a
reasonable premise that transitions of the sidechain groups of
tyrosine and tryptophan are involved (1-4). These are very
marked effects for a molecule which contains just one tryptophan
and four tyrosine residues (5). Lastly, it may be noted that
the rotation for the reduced species at the negative extremum
near 231 mμ is somewhat greater than that for the oxidized form.
Although calculations of the helix content are attended by a

*This work was supported by USPHS GM-07317 and NSF GB-1556.

‡Predoctoral fellow of the National Institute of Health.

**Abbreviations: ORD, optical rotatory dispersion; [M], molar
rotation; [m], mean residue rotation.

number of difficulties (1,2,6), it may be that the conversion
of ferri- to ferrocytochrome c results in the appearance of
added helicity (3,4).

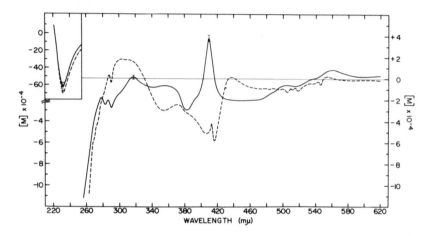

Figure 1. Optical rotatory dispersion curves for horse heart
cytochrome c (1,2).* Potassium phosphate buffer, 0.1 M, pH
6.8; temperature, 25°.
——————— Oxidized form   — — — Reduced form

Upon enzyme hydrolysis of horse heart cytochrome c, the
following heme octapeptide can be obtained (7,8):

┌─── Heme ──┐
│           │
Cys·Ala·Gln·Cys·His·Thr·Val·Glu

The only nitrogenous group of this peptide capable of intramolecular coordination is the imidazole group of the single
histidine residue. Addition of extrinsic imidazole or N-
acetylmethionine methyl ester results in the formation of
mixed ligand complexes with hemochrome-type spectra (8,9), and
Fig. 2 shows the ORD curves obtained at neutral pH. In the
Soret region, these curves exhibit the comparatively simple form
found for hemoglobin and myoglobin (10-14). More complicated
patterns, resembling somewhat more that exhibited by the parent ferricytochrome molecule, have been observed in the case
of the octapeptide only in the absence of extrinsic ligand,
and under conditions where aggregation is known to occur (2).

*Cf. also Urry and Doty (3) and Ulmer (4).

416

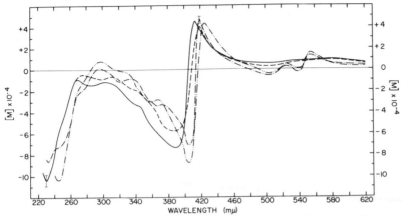

Figure 2. Optical rotatory dispersion curves for complexes of a heme octapeptide from horse heart cytochrome c (2). Potassium phosphate buffer, 0.1 M, pH 6.8; temperature, 25°.

――――――― ferri heme peptide + 0.05 M imidazole
― . ― ferro heme peptide + 0.05 M imidazole
― ― ― ferri heme peptide + 2.3 M N-acetyl-DL-methionine
― .. ― ferro heme peptide + 0.2 M N-acetyl-DL-methionine methyl ester

Reduction of the imidazole and methionine complexes results in a shift of the curves to longer wavelengths in the Soret region, the appearance of well-defined Cotton effects associated with the two hemochrome bands near 520 and 550 mμ, and extensive modification of the complicated pattern in the ultraviolet region. The rotations are oxidation-state dependent throughout the wavelength range studied. The differences in the region 270-300 mμ emphasize the complexity of the summation represented by the curves for the intact protein, in which, at these wavelengths, there is reflected also the optical activity presumed to be associated with transitions of the tyrosine and tryptophan side chains. A further feature meriting comment is the level of the rotation at the low-wavelength limit of the range covered with the peptide systems. The molar rotation of the oxidized form of the imidazole complex is, at the negative extremum, about one-sixth that of horse heart ferricytochrome c, although the number of amino acid residues is but one-thirteenth that of the protein. This rotation is not diminished by the addition of 8 M urea, but is reduced greatly upon protonation or photooxidation of the single histidine residue (2). The most straightforward interpretation is that there is no α-helix in this small peptide, and that the comparatively large levorotation is indicative of maintenance of binding between the histidine side chain and the heme.

The results obtained thus far with larger heme peptides suggest that appreciable helicity is attained only at rather long chain lengths (Fig. 3). There is no indication, under the conditions used, of helix formation in the case of the imidazole complex of a heme hexadecapeptide (oxidized form) comprising residues 11-26 of the protein from horse heart, or in the case of the corresponding complex of a heme peptide containing residues 1-38. On the other hand, the readings near 231 mμ for the imidazole complex of a segment containing residues 1-80, if interpreted on the basis of relationships applicable to simple polypeptides (15), do indicate the presence of α-helix. There is no change in the rotation at the negative extremum upon reduction of this 80-residue system.

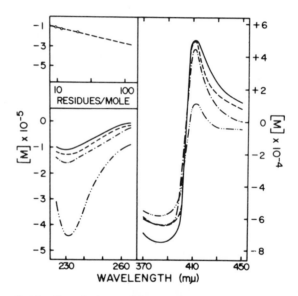

Figure 3. Optical rotatory dispersion curves for imidazole complexes of heme peptides of varied chain length. Potassium phosphate buffer, 0.1 M, pH 6.8; 0.05 M imidazole; temperature, 25°. All peptides from horse heart cytochrome c and in the oxidized form.

——————  heme peptide containing residues 14-21
— — — —  heme peptide containing residues 11-26
— ، —  heme peptide containing residues 1-38
— ،، —  heme peptide containing residues 1-80

Insert: Molar rotation at 231 mμ as a function of chain length.

It should be noted, though, that the important methionine-80
residue (9,16-18) is, as a result of use of the cyanogen bromide cleavage procedure in preparing the peptide, present in
modified form. It will be desirable to obtain data for some
heme peptides of chain lengths intermediate between 38 and 80
residues, and to examine also a longer peptide in which
methionine-80 is retained intact.

For all of the imidazole-heme peptide complexes studied,
the Soret Cotton effects are of simplified form, in keeping
with the fact that complex formation with extrinsic imidazole
results in comparable simplification of the curve for the parent ferricytochrome molecule (1). Indeed, to revert now to
the ORD of the protein, simplification of the complex pattern
shown in Fig. 1 can be obtained upon change in any of a number of variables, including that of pH, as illustrated in
Fig. 4. With increase in the pH, appreciable differences are
seen by the time a pH of 9 is attained, and it might be that
the underlying structural change is a factor in the pH-dependence of the oxidation-reduction potentials observed over this
range (19).*

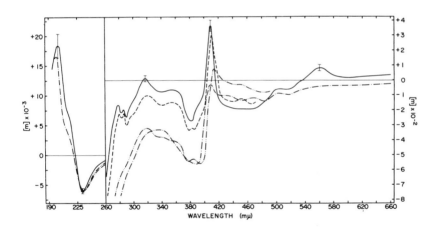

Figure 4. Optical rotatory dispersion curves for horse heart
ferricytochrome c as a function of pH (1)**. Protein dissolved
in 0.1 M potassium phosphate buffer, pH 6.8, and solutions
then adjusted with 6 M hydrochloric acid or 6 M potassium hydroxide to pH values indicated; temperature, 25°.

———— pH 6.8         — — — pH 8.8
— · — pH 1.5         — ·· — pH 11.4

*A similar conclusion has been drawn by G. P. Hess (private
communication).
**Cf. also Urry (6).         419

As the pH is increased still further, extensive alterations are obtained throughout the Soret, visible, and near-ultraviolet regions, and such changes are observed also upon adjustment of the solution to low pH. However, these alterations are, at the ionic strengths at which the curves of Fig. 4 were determined, essentially unattended by change at the negative extremum near 231 mμ. Major changes can thus be effected in the protein-heme interaction without apparent change in the helix content of the molecule.

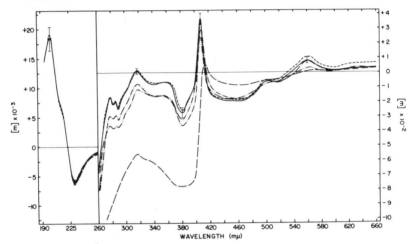

Figure 5. Optical rotatory dispersion curves for chemically modified forms of horse heart ferricytochrome c (1). Potassium phosphate buffer, 0.1 M, pH 6.8; temperature, 25°.

——————— unmodified
— — — lysine residues guanidinated
— · — lysine residues trifluoroacetylated
— ·· — lysine residues guanidinated and 2 moles O-acetyltyrosine per mole protein
—— —— carboxyl groups esterified.

Fig. 5 illustrates the dispersion patterns for some chemically modified forms of horse heart cytochrome c, all in 0.1 M phosphate buffer, pH 6.8. Guanidination of all of the lysine residues (20) has little or no effect on the ORD at neutral pH. Trifluoracetylation of all of the lysine residues (21) results in some alteration of the curve, but, in view of the major change in net charge that is introduced, the effect must be rated a very modest one. A greater change is seen upon partial acetylation of the tyrosine residues (22), but

easily the most extensive alteration is that obtained upon
modification of all the carboxyl groups of the molecule,
(A. J. Murphy and H. A. Harbury, in preparation). The curve
for the fully esterified derivative corresponds closely, at
wavelengths above 260 mμ, to the pattern for the nonesterified molecule in the presence of 8 M urea. Quite clearly, the
protein-heme interaction is markedly altered from that which
characterizes the native system. However, whereas in the case
of the nonesterified protein in 8 M urea the negative extremum
at the lower wavelengths shifts to 210 mμ, a change comparable
to that obtained upon helix-random coil transition in model
polypeptides, the esterified derivative in 0.1 M phosphate
buffer continues to yield a curve with a trough near 231 mμ,
and with about the same rotation at the extremum as is exhibited by the unmodified protein. The change in heme interaction attendant upon esterification is thus, under these
conditions, unaccompanied by an appreciable change in helix
content.

On the other hand, at sufficiently low ionic strengths,
curves are obtained which do indicate a loss of helicity by
the esterified derivative. This is illustrated in Fig. 6,
where the dispersion pattern of an unbuffered solution of
pH 6.8 is given for the region 200-250 mμ as a function of

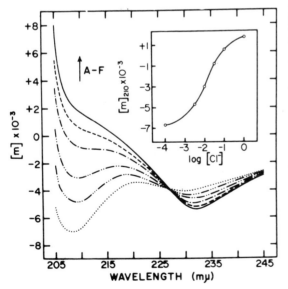

Figure 6. Optical
rotatory dispersion
curves for fully
esterified horse
heart ferricytochrome
c as a function of
potassium chloride
concentration. Un-
buffered solutions
of pH 6.8; tempera-
ture, 25°.
A. $10^{-4}$ M KCl
B. $3 \times 10^{-3}$ M KCl
C. $10^{-2}$ M KCl
D. $3 \times 10^{-2}$ M KCl
E. $10^{-1}$ M KCl
F. 1 M KCl

potassium chloride concentration. The midpoint of the transition occurs at $[Cl^-] \approx 0.01$ M. A similar change with ionic
strength can be observed with the nonesterified protein at
pH 1.5, but the loss of helix at this low pH is paralleled by
a change in coordination (23), and the situation becomes thus
a more complicated one. The potential usefulness of the
esterified system is that the helix-random coil transition can
be studied under conditions where there is minimal overlap
with change in the protein-heme binding. It should be noted
that diminution of the ionic strength is without effect on the
helix content of the nonesterified system at neutral pH, and
that extensive changes in the dispersion pattern below 250 m$\mu$
have been obtained only upon prior or accompanying introduction of structural alterations leading to simplification of the
curve at longer wavelengths.

The fact that esterification results in major modification
of the protein-prosthetic group interaction suggests that one
or more of the carboxylate groups of the molecule plays an
important role in maintenance of the native structure. Studies
are under way with partially esterified preparations in an
effort to establish which of the carboxylate groups are so
involved. An obvious possibility is that the propionate side
chains of the porphyrin are of major influence.

It is clear from the data for both the peptide and the
protein systems that the dispersion patterns sensitively reflect differences in the environment of the central coordination
complex. Similarity of the ORD curve exhibited by cytochromes
c from different source materials is thus likely to be indicative
of similarity of main structural features in the vicinity of the
heme group. Such correspondence has been found among preparations from horse, man, chicken, and tuna (1), and, as shown
in Fig. 7, can to varying degree be recognized also among
"mammalian-type" (24) cytochromes c from sources as diverse as
Ustilago sphaerogena, Neurospora crassa, and the moth, Samia
cynthia.* It should be emphasized that the curves shown are
based on single runs with single samples. Some of the
differences, particularly in terms of vertical displacement,
could be a consequence simply of differences in preparative
procedure or sample handling. The purpose here is but to
indicate the general similarity of the patterns.

Pseudomonas cytochrome c has an amino acid sequence very
different from those of the "mammalian-type" cytochromes c
(25,26). For example, the methionine involved in maintenance

*We are grateful to Dr. Emanuel Margoliash for a generous gift
of cytochrome c from Samia cynthia.

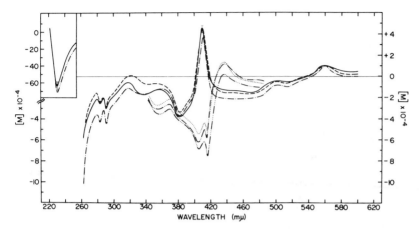

Figure 7. Optical rotatory dispersion curves for cytochromes
c. Potassium phosphate buffer, 0.1 M, pH 6.8; temperature, 25°.

|  | Ferricytochrome c: |  | Ferrocytochrome c: |
|---|---|---|---|
| ———— | Ustilago sphaerogena | — ·· — | Ustilago sphaerogena |
| — — — | Neurospora crassa | ·········· | Neurospora crassa |
| — · — | Samia Cynthia | — ··· — | Samia Cynthia |

of the hemochrome character of the molecule, methionine-61
(9,27), forms part of a segment in which, within a span of
six residues, four are prolines. It would thus not be surprising were the dispersion patterns to differ appreciably
from those for the "mammalian-type" cytochromes c at neutral
pH, and, as shown in Fig. 8, the curves obtained indeed are
of a different form. The Soret pattern for the oxidized state
bears little resemblance to that for the "mammalian-type"
ferricytochromes c and, grossly, conforms more nearly to the
Soret pattern for the "mammalian-type" ferrocytochromes c.
The curve for the reduced Pseudomonas protein resembles those
obtained with the reduced heme peptide complexes, and, in contrast to the case for the "mammalian-type" cytochromes c,
exhibits essentially the same rotation at the trough in the
ultraviolet as does the curve for the oxidized form.

An interesting property of Pseudomonas cytochrome c is
that the addition of urea to the oxidized form at neutral pH
results not only in a helix-random coil transition (Fig. 8),
but, in addition, a change in spectrum indicative of a low-
spin to high-spin conversion. This is evident also from the
shift to lower wavelengths of the Soret Cotton effect. When

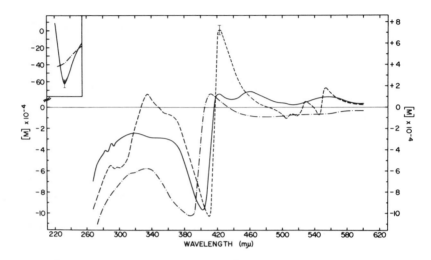

Figure 8. Optical rotatory dispersion curves for Pseudomonas cytochrome c. Potassium phosphate buffer, 0.1 M, pH 6.8; temperature, 25°.

——————— oxidized form
— — — reduced form
— · — oxidized form, 8 M urea

such urea-containing solutions are reduced, the spectrum again becomes typically that of the hemochrome, and the dispersion pattern below 250 mμ reverts to the form observed in the absence of urea. These would appear to be useful characteristics for the study of relationship between ligand binding and the helicity of the molecule.

In another respect, too, Pseudomonas cytochrome c would seem to be an attractive system for further studies. As in the case of the "mammalian-type" cytochromes c, the dispersion pattern in the region 270-300 mμ exhibits optical activity presumed to be associated with transitions of the tyrosine and/or tryptophan side chains. It is not known whether this results from direct interaction with the central coordination complex, but that would be a particularly interesting possibility. Since the protein from Pseudomonas contains but one tyrosine and two tryptophan residues, further analysis is likely to be more easily achieved than in the case of the more complex "mammalian-type" systems.

# References

1. Myer, Y. P., and H. A. Harbury. Proc. Natl. Acad. Sci. U. S., 54, 1391 (1965).

2. Myer, Y. P., and H. A. Harbury. J. Biol. Chem., in press.

3. Urry, D. W., and P. Doty. J. Am. Chem. Soc., 87, 2756 (1965).

4. Ulmer, D. D. Biochemistry, 4, 902 (1965).

5. Fasman, G. D., E. Bodenheimer, and C. Lindblow. Biochemistry, 3, 1665 (1964).

6. Urry, D. W. Proc. Natl. Acad. Sci. U. S., 54, 640 (1965).

7. Tuppy, H., and S. Paleus. Acta Chem. Scand., 9, 353 (1955).

8. Harbury, H. A., and P. A. Loach. J. Biol. Chem., 235, 3640 (1960).

9. Harbury, H. A., J. R. Cronin, M. W. Fanger, T. P. Hettinger, A. J. Murphy, Y. P. Myer, and S. N. Vinogradov. Proc. Natl. Acad. Sci. U. S., 54, 1658 (1965).

10. Beychok, S., and E. R. Blout. J. Mol. Biol., 3, 769 (1961).

11. Beychok, S. Biopolymers, 2, 575 (1964).

12. Samejima, T., and J. T. Yang. J. Mol. Biol., 8, 863 (1964).

13. Harrison, S. C., and E. R. Blout. J. Biol. Chem., 240, 299 (1965).

14. Breslow, E., S. Beychok, K. D. Hardman, and F. R. N. Gurd. J. Biol. Chem., 240, 304 (1965).

15. Simmons, N. S., C. Cohen, A. G. Szent-Gyorgyi, D. B. Wetlaufer and E. R. Blout. J. Am. Chem. Soc., 83, 4766 (1961).

16. Ando, K., H. Matsubara, and K. Okunuki. Proc. Japan Acad., 41, 79 (1965).

17. Tsai, H. J., and G. R. Williams. Can. J. Biochem., 43, 1409 (1965).

18. Harbury, H. A. Abstracts of the 151st National Meeting of the American Chemical Society, Pittsburgh, H30 (1966).

19. Rodkey, F. L., and E. G. Ball. J. Biol. Chem., 182, 17 (1950).

20. Hettinger, T. P., and H. A. Harbury. Proc. Natl. Acad. Sci. U. S., 52, 1469 (1964).

21. Fanger, M. W., and H. A. Harbury. Biochemistry $\underline{4}$, 2541 (1965).

22. Cronin, J. R., and H. A. Harbury. Biochem. Biophys. Res. Commun., $\underline{20}$, 503 (1965).

23. Boeri, E., A. Ehrenberg, K. G. Paul, and H. Theorell. Biochim. Biophys. Acta, $\underline{12}$, 273 (1953).

24. Margoliash, E. Brookhaven Symposia in Biology, $\underline{15}$, 266 (1962).

25. Ambler, R. P. Biochem. J., $\underline{89}$, 349 (1963).

26. Margoliash, E., and E. L. Smith. In Evolving Genes and Proteins (V. Bryson and H. J. Vogel, eds.), Academic Press, New York, 1965, p. 221.

27. Hettinger, T. P., M. W. Fanger, S. N. Vinogradov, and H. A. Harbury. Fed. Proc., $\underline{25}$, 648 (1966).

MAGNETO OPTICAL ROTATION SPECTRA OF CYTOCHROME C*

V. E. Shashoua

Department of Biology, Massachusetts Institute of Technology
Cambridge, Massachusetts

and

R. W. Estabrook

Johnson Research Foundation, School of Medicine
University of Pennsylvania
Philadelphia, Pennsylvania

We have made measurements of the magneto optical rotation (MOR) spectra (1) of cytochrome c samples from different species:  horse heart, pigeon breast, tuna and yeast cytochrome c provided by Dr. Margoliash.

The MOR spectrum of cytochrome c is very sensitive to the oxidation state of the molecule (2). As shown in Figs. 1 and 2, the specific magnetic rotation changes from about -8000 ($1.04 \times 10^6$ on a molar basis) for ferrocytochrome c to about -150 for ferricytochrome c at the $\alpha$ band region of the molecule. The figures show the induced rotations obtained by a 10,000 gauss magnetic field as defined by the following equation:

$$[\alpha]_{sp} = \frac{\theta}{lc}$$

where $\theta$ is the observed rotation in degrees, 1 is the path length in decimeters and c is the concentration in grams/ml. It is of interest to note that the MOR spectrum of ferrocytochrome c has three negative peaks for the $\alpha$ band similar to the vibrational structure of the absorption spectrum obtained at low temperature (3) and also three for the $\beta$ band region.

Fig. 3 compares the MOR results for yeast and pigon breast ferrocytochrome c. The data depict the measured rotations at pH 10 as a function of wavelength in the $\alpha$ and $\beta$ band absorption regions. The ORD measurements for this region are quite small.

*This work was supported by PHS GM 12202, USPHS Research Career Development Awardee GM-4111.

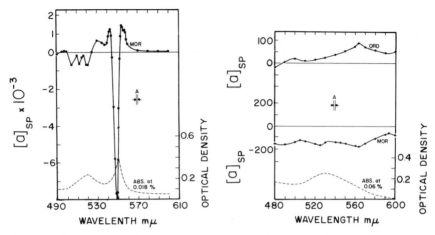

Figure 1. MOR spectrum of ferro-cytochrome c. pH 7 (0.05 M phosphate buffer), 23° C. Sample prepared by reduction of oxidized material from Dr. E. Margoliash with formamidine sulfinic acid.

Figure 2. MOR and ORD spectra of ferricytochrome c. pH 7.
A = monochromator band pass in both figures.

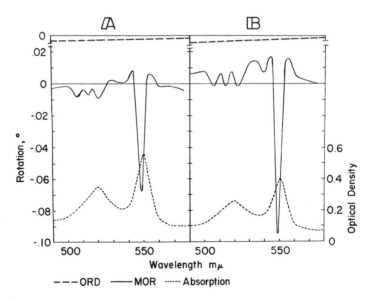

Figure 3. A comparison of ORD, MOR, and absorption spectra of pigeon breast (A) and yeast (B) ferrocytochrome c. pH 10, 10° C.

Table I presents an analysis of the results at pH 7 and
pH 10. All the samples were converted to the fully reduced
state with formamidine sulfinic acid (4). If we assume that
a ratio of 1.7 to 1.8 for the optical densities (2) at $\alpha$ and
$\beta$ bands represents the fully reduced state of the molecule,
then the magnetic rotation per optical density unit can be
used as an index (B in Table I) for comparison of the samples.
The values of B were obtained by dividing the total magnetic
rotation (i.e., the sum of the negative and positive components
at the $\alpha$ band) by the optical density of the sample used in the
measurement. As shown in Table I, there appears to be no difference in the magnitude of the magnetically induced ORD between the various samples when measured at pH 7: however, at
pH 10, the isoelectric point region, yeast cytochrome c has
over twice the magnetic rotation per optical density unit than
horse heart or pigeon breast. Also tuna cytochrome c shows
about a 50 percent increase in its B value at pH 10, above the
horse heart cytochrome c.

### TABLE I

MOR Data - Cytochrome c

| SOURCE | pH = 7 | | pH = 10 | |
|---|---|---|---|---|
| | A | B | A | B |
| YEAST | 1.77 | 0.22 | 1.70 | 0.37 |
| TUNA | 1.75 | 0.21 | 1.80 | 0.21 |
| HORSE H. | 1.79 | 0.23 | 1.71 | 0.15 |
| PIGEON B. | 1.75 | 0.23 | 1.71 | 0.15 |

$$A = (O.D.)\alpha / O.D.)\beta \qquad B = \Delta MOR / O.D.$$
$$\text{at } \alpha \text{ band}$$

There are a number of speculative proposals which may be
offered to explain these results. One possibility is that the
specific magnetic rotations reflect the magnitude of the ligand
fields of the substituents at the iron atom of the porphyrin
nucleus of the molecule. This would be similar to the MOR data
for hemoglobin presented earlier at this symposium (5), where
the magnetic rotation changed about two- to four-fold for the
$\alpha$ and $\beta$ bands in the substitution of water by carbon monoxide
as the ligand. For cytochrome c we can consider at least two
alternatives, namely, variable ligands for cytochrome c of
each species, or fixed ligands with a secondary influence on
their ligand fields provided by the amino acids in their immediate neighborhood. During this meeting Dr. Margoliash (6)

was kind enough to provide us with the amino acid sequences the four cytochromes used in this study. While it is not possible to predict which amino acids are actually in the immediate neighborhood of the ligands to the porphyrin nucleus until a complete X-ray analysis becomes available, we can nevertheless note two significant features of the amino acid sequence. The first is at the disulfide bridge region where yeast cytochrome c has one acidic amino acid (glutamic acid) replacing the neutral amino acid alanine of horse cytochrome c. The second feature which may be significant is observed at positions 86, 87, 88 near the methionine residue (Number 80). Here yeast cytochrome c has a glutamic acid replacing a lysine residue at position 88 of horse heart cytochrome c, again a change to an acidic amino acid.

If these changes in the magnetic rotations prove to be a valid method for studying changes in ligand fields of substituents at the porphyrin nucleus of cytochrome c, then MOR spectroscopy, in conjunction with a knowledge of the three dimensional structure of the molecule, may provide a useful tool for examining conformation changes during migration of various ligands into and out of the molecule.

## References

1. Shashoua, V. E., J. Am. Chem Soc., 86, 2.09 (1964).

2. Shashoua, V.E. Arch. Biochem. and Biophys., 111, 550 (1965).

3. Estabrook, R. W.  J. Biol. Chem., 223, 781 (1956).

4. Shashoua, V. E.  Biochemistry 3, 1719 (1964).

5. Shashoua, V. E.  This volume, p. 93

6. Margoliash, E.  This volume, p. 371.

# A COMPARISON OF THE MAGNETICALLY-INDUCED OPTICAL ROTATORY DISPERSION OF MAMMALIAN AND YEAST CYTOCHROME c *

M. Morrison and J. Duffield

Department of Biochemistry, City of Hope Medical Center
Duarte, California

The absorption spectrum of hemoproteins reflects the heme prosthetic group as well as the environment provided by the protein. The protein not only provides the actual ligands but also the conformational environment for the heme. Thus, destruction of the protein environment from its native form results in spectral changes. When the spectrum of the reduced form of cytochrome c is recorded at the temperature of liquid nitrogen, the absorption peaks are intensified five- to tenfold. The low temperature spectrum also contains a great deal of fine structure not present at higher temperatures. Estabrook has recorded the low temperature spectrum of a variety of hemoproteins. In these studies it was shown that the spectra reflect alterations in the protein structure and also that cytochrome c isolated from different sources had different low temperature spectra (1) from which one could conclude that the protein environment for the heme was different. For example, the spectra of yeast cytochrome c varied from horse cytochrome c at the low temperature although at room temperature there was little difference in the absorption spectrum.

A study of the magnetically-induced optical rotatory dispersion spectrum of cytochrome c provides a method not only of studying the protein ligands of the heme prosthetic group but also its configurational environment. In our earlier report on the magnetically-induced optical rotatory dispersion of cytochrome c (2) we noted the great intensification of the optical rotation induced by the magnetic field and the increased fine structure in the MORD spectrum. This led us to suggest that the MORD was reminiscent of the low temperature spectrum. Shashoua has subsequently made the same correlation (3). It was the object of the present investigation to compare the ORD and MORD spectra of yeast and horse heart cytochrome c.

*This work was supported in part by USPHS Research Grant GM 10214.

## Material and Methods

The horse heart cytochrome $c$, type III, was purchased from Sigma Chemical Co., and was purified by ion exchange in sephadex chromatography. Crystalline yeast cytochrome $c$ suspended in ammonium sulfate was kindly provided by the Sankyo Research Laboratories, Japan. The cytochrome $c$ was spun free of ammonium sulfate and the crystals were suspended in 0.1 M phosphate buffer, pH 7.4, and purified by passage through a Sephadex G-75 column in equilibrium with the buffer. The concentration of the cytochrome $c$ was determined spectrophotometrically at 550 mµ. The optical rotatory dispersion was recorded on a model 60 Cary spectropolarimeter and the magnetically-induced optical rotatory dispersion was recorded on a prototype instrument designed by P. Hooper and J. Duffield (4).

## Results and Discussion

Fig. 1 presents the MORD spectrum of horse heart cytochrome $c$. Our results do not vary significantly from the most recent reports of Shashoua on the MORD spectrum of cytochrome $c$ (3). Fig. 2 shows the MORD spectrum of yeast cytochrome $c$. The results show that the shape of the curves of the two preparations are comparable to that reported for mammalian cytochrome $c$ in the visible region and are very similar for both preparations of cytochrome $c$. However, our results in both preparations are at variance with those reported by Shashoua in the Soret region.

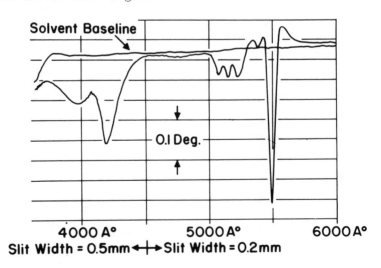

Figure 1. Magnetic optical rotation of ferrocytochrome $c$, 0.0007 mM, reduced with dithionite in pH 7.4, 0.05 M phosphate buffer, 5000 Gauss.

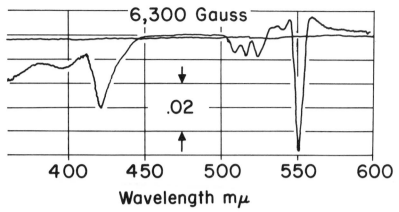

Figure 2. Baker's Yeast Cytochrome c, 0.133 μM. Phosphate buffer 0.05 M, pH 7.4.

In our spectra the rotation in the Soret region remains negative. Our spectra also contain evidence for two Cotton effects in this region -- one clearly identifiable with the major absorption peak at 415 mμ and the other at a lower wave length and the region just about 400 mμ. This second peak is not present in other reports. The magnitude of the trough of the Cotton effect in this region is lower than that in the visible region. This also contrasts sharply with Shashoua's data where the opposite appears to be the case. The reason for this discrepancy is not apparent.

The differences in absorption spectra at low temperature certainly must be due to differences between the mammalian and yeast cytochrome c in the region of the prosthetic group. A number of such differences can be picked out from the published data on the amino acid sequence of cytochrome c. To which of these differences can be attributed to change in low temperature spectrum is not clear. These differences, however, do not reflect themselves in the nature of the ORD or MORD spectra and hence are not primarily configurational but must be electronic in nature.

### References

1. Estabrook, R. W. In Haematin Enzymes (J. E. Falk, R. Lemberg, and R. K. Morton, eds.), Pergamon Press, New York 1961, p. 436.

2. Morrison, M. In Oxidases and Related Redox Systems (T. E. King, H. S. Mason, and M. Morrison, eds.), John Wiley and Sons, 1965, p. 414.

3. Shashoua, V. E., Nature, <u>203</u>, 972 (1964), Arch Biochem. Biophys., <u>111</u>, 550 (1965).

4. Hooper, P. and J. Duffield. Third Pacific Conference on Spectroscopy, Instrumentation and Chemistry, San Francisco, Oct., 1964, Abstracts, p. 11.

# EVIDENCE FOR HEME - HEME INTERACTIONS
# IN HEME PEPTIDE AGGREGATES[*]

Dan W. Urry

Institute for Biomedical Research
Education and Research Foundation
American Medical Association
Chicago, Illinois

We are currently using optical rotatory dispersion, circular dichroism and absorption measurements to study the heme undecapeptide of cytochrome c with emphasis on its aggregated state at pH 9 in 0.05 M sodium tetraborate. Our first objective is to determine, in this aggregate in which the heme moieties are necessarily in relatively close proximity, if it is possible to detect an excitation resonance interaction (exciton interaction) between the heme groups and if so to determine the relative orientation of these hemes. A means of detecting distances between heme moieties in mitochondria and the electron transport particle would seem to be an important step in arriving at a mechanism of electron transfer between these metalloporphyrins. Specifically a natural sequel to the study of aggregated heme peptide model systems would be to examine the optical rotation and absorption characteristics of cytochrome oxidase in various states to assess the relative orientation and proximity of hemes a and $a_3$. In addition such a study is relevant to the so-called heme-heme interaction in hemoglobin.

Because of the magnitude of its transition electric dipole moment, the doubly degenerate Soret band provides a useful spectral region to examine. However, it introduces the complication of having to establish whether the increased complexity in the optical rotatory dispersion and circular dichroism curves is due to a discernible removal of this degeneracy as appears to be the case in ferricytochrome c (1,2,3) or whether it is due to exciton interactions between Soret transitions of different heme groups in the aggregate. Dependence of the complex Soret Cotton effect on the

[*]This work was carried out while visiting Dr. Melvin Calvin's laboratory at the University of California, Berkeley.

aggregated state can be determined by the addition of ligands such as imidazole and lysine, the first mentioned of which is known to disperse the aggregate (4) (Fig. 1). A decrease in the complexity of the Cotton effect upon dilution as well as upon increasing the temperature also would demonstrate a dependence on the aggregated state of the Soret transition energy splitting. Another important criterion is the number of extrema observed in the circular dichroism curves. The presence of more than two extrema provides evidence that the energy level splittings are due to heme–heme interaction.

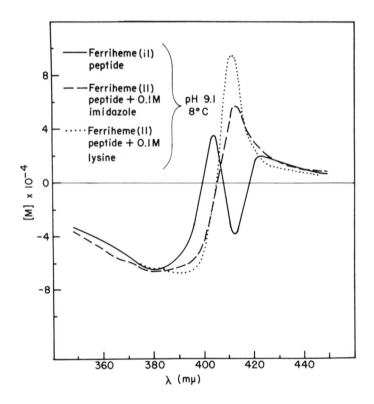

Figure 1. The optical rotatory dispersion curves of the ferri-heme undecapeptide in 0.05 M sodium tetraborate, pH = 9.1, 8° C. It may be noted that addition of either imidazole or lysine results in return to a relatively simple Soret Cotton effect.

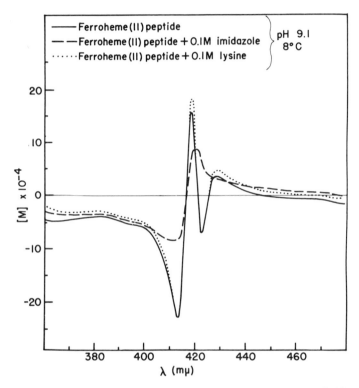

<u>Figure 2.</u>  The optical rotatory dispersion curves of the ferro-
heme undecapeptide (sodium dithionite reduced) in 0.05 M sodium
tetraborate at pH 9.1 and 8° C.  Under these conditions only
imidazole causes a return to a simple Cotton effect.

    The presence of the sought-after complex Soret Cotton
effect (5) for the aggregate may be seen in any of the accompanying figures.  This complexity is essentially removed in
the case of the ferriheme undecapeptide by addition of imidazole or lysine (see Fig. 1).  In Fig. 2, it is interesting to
note that only imidazole causes the simplification in the
reduced case.  The concentration effect is clearly seen for
the oxidized heme peptide in Fig. 3, and is also seen for the
reduced system in Fig. 4.

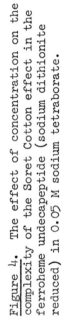

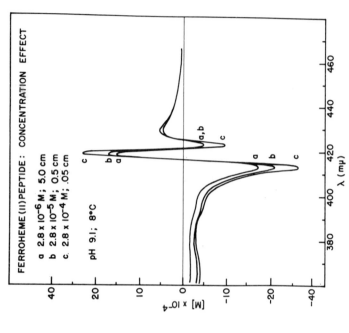

Figure 4. The effect of concentration on the complexity of the Soret Cotton effect in the ferroheme undecapeptide (sodium dithionite reduced) in 0.05 M sodium tetraborate.

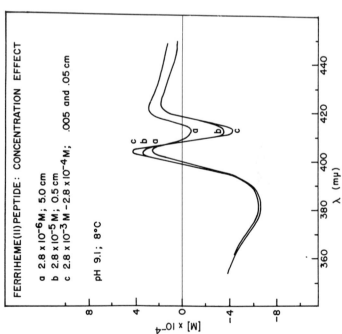

Figure 3. The effect of concentration upon the complexity of the Soret Cotton effect in the ferriheme undecapeptide in 0.05 M sodium tetraborate.

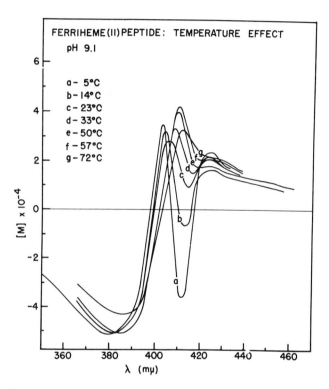

Figure 5. The effect of temperature on the complexity of the Soret Cotton effect in the ferriheme undecapeptide in 0.05 M sodium tetraborate at pH 9.1.

Increasing the temperature from $5^\circ$ C causes a return to a relatively simple Cotton effect as may be seen in Fig. 5 for the oxidized aggregate. The transition is almost complete by $33^\circ$ C with little effect of further increases in temperature until about $70^\circ$ C at which temperature the amplitude begins to decrease. The latter effect is not completely reversible.

The following is a listing of circular dichroism data for the heme peptides giving the wavelength of the extrema and their sign, positive or negative.

ferriheme peptide pH 9.1:

398 mμ  (+)      411 mμ (-)      420 mμ (+)
in the presence of imidazole, 403 mμ (+)

ferroheme peptide pH 9.1:

404 mμ (-)      416 mμ (+)      420 mμ (-)      425 mμ (+)
in the presence of imidazole, 418 mμ (+)

The circular dichroism curve of the oxidized aggregate in the presence of imidazole deviates from a gaussian curve only slightly on the long wavelength side. The reduced aggregate curve shows a larger deviation but still introduces no new extrema. This data is consistent with the sedimentation data of Ehrenberg and Theorell (4) which was interpreted by those authors to indicate that while the pentamer or hexamer was dispersed, the resulting system was not monodisperse. In this connection it might also be mentioned that at acid pH where the sedimentation data indicate a monodisperse monomeric species, the Cotton effect is of the simple form.

In addition, corresponding absorption data were obtained for each sample for which the rotatory dispersion curves are reported. Both the oxidized and reduced aggregates show a hyperchromism in the concentration and temperature studies; that is, the oscillator strengths per heme of the Soret transition increases upon aggregation. The ferriheme undecapeptide exhibits a small bathochromic shift (2-3 mμ) upon increasing the concentration while no band shift was noted for the ferroheme undecapeptide.

The preceding data are cumulatively taken to indicate that we are observing in the aggregates an excitation resonance interaction between the heme moieties in which case the sharp complex Cotton effects may be taken to indicate nearness of heme groups, or more correctly, the absence of such complex Cotton effects may, in general, be taken as evidence against close proximity of heme moieties. Furthermore, the data present an opportunity to attempt an unravelling of the relative orientations of the iron porphyrins. As iron binding ligands disperse the aggregate, ligand binding may be taken as the mode of polymerization, thereby placing some constraints and limits against which a geometrical interpretation may be compared.

Taking the heme plane directions to be more polarizable
than the direction perpendicular to the plane, the observed
hyperchromism indicates in the dipole-dipole approximation
either that the orientation of the heme planes is more nearly
head to tail than in card pack fashion (6,7,8) or that the
angle between the hemes is greater than $70^{\circ}$. The slight bathochromic shift of the absorption maximum for the ferriheme
peptide is consistent with the head to tail orientation (9).
The lack of a band shift in the ferroheme peptide raises the
possibility of an oblique (9) or alternate transitional (8)
arrangement for this aggregate. However, such a straightforward interpretation must be regarded with pessimism and should
be accepted or rejected upon comparison with additional data.

If the circular dichroism extrema could actually be taken
as corresponding to the transition frequencies, one could calculate maximal distances between hemes. In reality overlap-
ping positive and negative gaussian curves, for example, when
summed would result in exaggerated splitting energies and consequently in distances which are not maximal. However, if one
had several gaussian curves of equal amplitude and alternating
sign, then this effect would tend to cancel. For this reason
it is still instructive, particularly in the case of interest,
to take the extrema and calculate distances, for one can determine how well such distances compare with those values imposed
by the known structure of the monomer and the likely ligand
effecting the polymerization. Both aggregates would have maximal heme-heme distances of roughly $10\text{\AA}$. The maximal distance
corresponds to the head-to-tail alignment. If the arrangement
is other than head-to-tail then the correct distance is less.

In the case of the ferriheme undecapeptide the data are
in accord with the $\epsilon$ amino group of lysine as the ligand
effecting a polymerization in which the hemes are arranged in
a head-to-tail fashion with imidazole filling the fifth coordination position of its own heme iron and the $\epsilon$ amino group
binding at the sixth coordination position of the adjacent
heme iron. However, the data for the ferroheme undecapeptide
differs from the oxidized heme peptide in several important
respects. The amplitude of the complex Soret Cotton effect is
approximately five times greater for the reduced aggregate
suggesting closer proximity of the hemes in an arrangement
other than head to tail. The reduced heme peptide will form
the characteristic aggregate in the presence of a $10^4$-fold
excess of lysine, but under the conditions studied will not
aggregate in the presence of imidazole. Thus the $\epsilon$ amino
group would seem not to be involved in effecting polymerization of this aggregate. Furthermore, there is no discernible
band shift upon aggregation of the reduced species. One

explanation for these results is an oblique arrangement in which the heme planes are at an angle sufficient to give the observed hyperchromism. The prime candidate for effecting the bridging would be imidazole bridging between two hemes. Yet with imidazole as a bridging group one cannot achieve an angle greater than 70° which is required in the dipole-dipole approximation to get hyperchromism. However, the dipole-dipole approximation assumes that the dipole length is negligible with respect to the distances between dipoles. This is certainly not the case for the Soret band with a transition electric dipole moment of about $8 \times 10^{-18}$ esu cm, i.e.,

$$\frac{8 \times 10^{-18} \text{ esu cm}}{4.8 \times 10^{-10} \text{ esu}} = 1.7 \text{ Å when the distance is about 5-6 Å.}$$

The relevance to hemoglobin of the effect seen in the heme peptide aggregates may briefly be mentioned. The optical rotatory dispersion data of Frankel and Doty (R. Frankel and R. Doty, personal communication) on met-, deoxy-, and oxyhemoglobin disclose simple Soret Cotton effects in all three cases. Thus the effects which we interpret to be exciton interactions in the heme peptides are too small to be detected in hemoglobin. As the exciton interaction between identical transitions has an $R^{-3}$ distance dependence and is not detectable in hemoglobin, it is unlikely that there can be an appreciable van der Waals interaction which has an $R^{-6}$ distance dependence. The conclusion would seem to be that the so-called heme-heme interaction in hemoglobin is necessarily mediated by the protein.

## References

1. Ulmer, D. D. Biochemistry, 4, 902 (1965).

2. Urry, D. W., and P. Doty. J. Am. Chem. Soc., 87, 2756 (1965).

3. Myer, Y. P., and H. A. Harbury. Proc. Nat. Acad. Sci., 54, 1391 (1965).

4. Ehrenberg, A., and H. Theorell. Acta Chem. Scand., 9, 1193 (1955).

5. Urry, D. W. Proc. Nat. Acad. Sci., 54, 640 (1965).

6. Tinoco, Jr., I. J. Am. Chem. Soc., 81, 1540 (1959); J. Chem. Phys., 34, 1067 (1961).

7. Rhodes, W. J. Am. Chem. Soc., 83, 3609 (1961).

8. Kasha, M. Radiation Research, 20, 55 (1963).

9. Kasha, M., M. A. El-Bayoumi, and W. Rhodes. J. Chem. Phys., 58, 916 (1961).

ORD STUDIES OF CYTOCHROME c

DISCUSSION

Margoliash: May I make a guess as to which carboxyl groups are involved in the large ORD effects Dr. Harbury has shown us? There are only two positions in cytochrome c which have invariably held a glutamic or an aspartic acid, and we have liked to link this situation to the two positions in which arginines have also been invariant, thinking that there is, perhaps, some form of double bonding between them helping to hold the protein together. I would like to guess that the groups that affect very strongly Dr. Harbury's ORD spectra are the aspartic or glutamic acid in position 90 and/or the aspartic or glutamic acid in position 66. You will note that the second arginine is at position 91, and that the first arginine is in position 39, so that if there is to be any combination of this kind, the only possibility is that arginine-38 will be combined to acidic residues at position 90, and that arginine-91 will be combined to the residue at position 66.

Yamazaki: I would like to discuss one possiblity for heme-sulfur binding. In 1940, Theorell found paraperoxidase(1), which is a low-spin type peroxidase. This paraperoxidase is converted to a high-spin type peroxidase by the addition of 0.5 mole mercuric chloride of 1 mole PCMB per heme; this conversion is reversed by cysteine (2).

Estabrook: That does not mean, however, that the sulfur is a ligand to the heme, but only that a sulfhydryl is necessary for the conformation of the protein.

Lemberg: You will find, in Dr. Falk's book, a mention of hemochrome-like spectra obtained by reacting hemes with sulfur-containing substances such as mercapto-ethanol (3).

Urnes: May I ask Dr. Harbury whether any change in degree of intermolecular association occurs on reduction of cytochrome c? On analogy with his finding for the heme octapeptide, aggregation may favor the interaction of heme groups and produce complexity in the Soret Cotton effect. In addition, since the aggregation of helices of poly-L-glutamic acid is accompanied by rather large changes in optical rotation (4), one may ask whether the difference in rotatory power observed at low wavelength between oxidized and reduced cytochrome c might also reflect the presence of intermolecular complexes.

443

<u>Harbury</u>: In the case of the cytochrome <u>c</u> curves, we have worked over just a 50-fold range of concentrations. Within that range, we have seen no effects that we would attribute to aggregation.

<u>Urry</u>: We have examined about a $10^3$ difference in concentration using a 0.05 mm cell all the way up to a 10 mm cell. We see no reason to believe that there is any concentration effect.

<u>Margoliash</u>: We have looked over the sedimentation coefficients of cytochrome <u>c</u> over a wide range of concentrations, and there is no trace of aggregation if the preparation is originally monomeric and not strictly native.

<u>Mirsky</u>: We have studied the ORD spectra of horse heart cytochrome <u>c</u> monomer, dimer, and higher polymers to see whether changes in autoxidizibility and the loss of the 695 mμ band could be correlated with changes in the ORD spectra.

In the oxidized form, the main shape of the curve from 450 to 260 mμ remains the same in all three species, although the background rotation is more levorotatory as we go from monomer to dimer to higher polymers. The shoulder of the complex Cotton effect centered around the Soret absorption peak

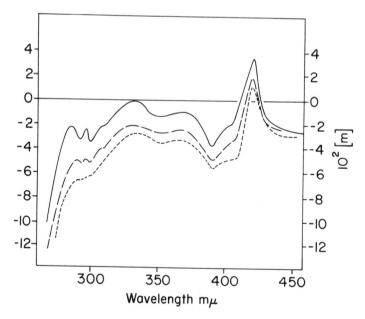

<u>Figure 1</u>. ORD spectra of oxidized horse heart cytochrome <u>c</u>. Monomer, ———— ; dimer, -------- ; higher polymers, ......

diminishes, and the Cotton effects at 287 mµ and 279 mµ are markedly less well-defined and more levorotatory in the dimer and higher polymers, as shown in Figure 1. The value of the 233 mµ trough remains the same in all three species. The ORD spectra of all three reduced forms are almost identical, with no shift to more levorotatory values. This behavior of the oxidized and reduced forms of the polymers is similar to the effects of pH variation on the ORD spectrum of monomeric cytochrome c, where the oxidized form varies widely over the pH range from 2 to 12, while the reduced form does not change. Since the disappearance of the shoulder centered at 388 mµ and of the peaks at 287 and 279 mµ seem to occur together, it seems likely that the difference in properties between the monomer and the dimer can be attributed to structural changes in the oxidized form. These may be a decreased interaction between the heme and a portion of the peptide chain involving the invariant tryptophan residue at position 59, and some of the tyrosine residues which probably give rise to the Cotton effects at 279 mµ.

King: Dr. Urry, have you calculated rotational strengths in the experiments you reported?

Urry: Actually, we have calculated rotational strengths and compared them with the rotational strength of denatured ferricytochrome. The ferriheme undecapeptide has about the same value. More useful for comparison with other cytochromes and other transitions in general is a quantity called the "anisotropy", which is the ratio of the rotational strength to the dipole strength, multiplied by a factor of 4. This ratio is low when compared to other optically active transitions.

King: What is the order of magnitude?

Urry: The rotational strength of the Soret band of ferriheme undecapeptide in 0.10 M imidazole and 0.05 M sodium tetraborate at pH 9 is about $8 \times 10^{-39}$, giving an anisotropy of about $5 \times 10^{-4}$.

## References

1. Theorell, H. Ark. Kemi Min. Geol., 14B, No. 20 (1940).

2. Yamazaki, I., R. Nakajma, and K. Yokota. Biochem. Biophys. Res. Commun., 23, 566 (1966).

3. Falk, J. E. In Haematin Enzymes (J. E. Falk, M. R. Lemberg, and R. K. Morton, eds.) Pergamon Press, London, 1961, p. 75.

4. Schuster, T. M. Biopolymers, 3, No. 6, 681 (1965).

# THE STRUCTURE AND REACTIVITY OF CYTOCHROME $\underline{b}_5$*

Phillip Strittmatter and Juris Ozols

Department of Biological Chemistry,
Washington University School of Medicine
Saint Louis, Missouri

The ultimate objective of studies on cytochrome $\underline{b}_5$ is to utilize information on the precise structure of this heme protein to understand the chemical basis of its specific spectral properties and catalytic activity. As a member of the $\underline{b}$ group of cytochromes this protein offers several experimental advantages. It is a low molecular weight protein containing a single tightly bound iron protoporphyrin IX group (1). The absorption spectra of the oxidized and reduced forms (Fig. 1) and the fact that the protein, in either oxidation state, does not react with the commonly used heme ligands (1) suggest that heme binding in cytochrome $\underline{b}_5$ involves interaction of both iron coordination positions with the protein. The $\alpha$ and $\beta$ bands of the reduced heme protein are not precisely symmetrical at 25°,

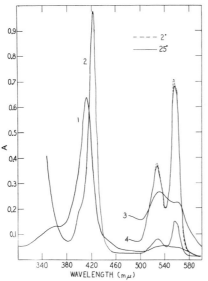

Figure 1. Absorption spectra of oxidized and reduced cytochrome b5 at pH 7.5. Curve 1. 5.4 x $10^{-6}$ M cytochrome b5 and Curve 2, reduced with sodium hydrosulfite. Curve 3. 3 x $10^{-5}$ M cytochrome b5 and Curve 4, reduced with sodium hydrosulfite.

*This work was supported by USPHS Research Grant H-5514.

and this is even more pronounced at $2°$. Similar asymmetry, particularly of the $\alpha$ band, has been observed by Shichi and Hackett (2) for cytochrome b-555 isolated from mung bean seed-lings, and Estabrook has presented low temperature spectra of cytochrome $b_5$ which show marked band splitting (3). Cytochrome $b_5$ reduction occurs readily with a number of the commonly used reducing agents for heme proteins (1), and the enzymatic reduc-tion by NADH cytochrome $b_5$ reductase is remarkably specific for this heme protein (4). To design experiments which might relate these spectral and catalytic properties to the protein struc-ture, the homogeneity of cytochrome $b_5$ preparations became a crucial question.

Homogeneity and structure of cytochrome $b_5$. Crude calf liver cytochrome $b_5$ (5, 6) (Fig. 2A) contains a major heme protein component (I), which accounts for 60-90 percent of the total heme protein content, and variable amounts of two others. (5-40 percent of II, and traces of III). Components I and II, the only forms present in significant quantities in any

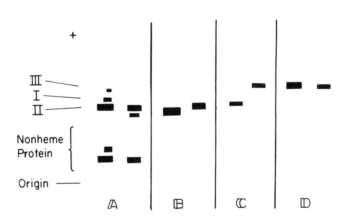

Figure 2. Diagram for electrophoresis of cytochrome $b_5$ prepara-tions and the heme peptides on cellulose acetate. A. Two dif-ferent crude cytochrome $b_5$ preparations. B. Left, cytochrome $b_5$ II; right, cytochrome $b_5$ I. C. Right, cytochrome $b_5$ I; left, I heme peptide. D. Left, I heme peptide; right, a mixture of I and II heme peptides. From (6).

preparations were separated and isolated by DEAE-Sephadex chromatography (Fig. 2B). Preliminary studies had already indicated that heme protein preparations containing both forms were relatively stable to proteolysis by trypsin and completely resistant to several other proteases. Thus, the spectrum of the heme protein is not altered by trypsin and there is a limited and small change in molecular weight. Following incubation of either cytochrome $\underline{b}_5$ I or II with trypsin, however, the heme peptides, which are distinguished by a higher net negative charge (C and D), were isolated by Sephadex gel filtration. The mobilities of the heme peptides derived from the two preparations are identical (D) suggesting that the original net charge difference resides in the peptide fragments resulting from tryptic cleavage.

The results of subsequent studies involving the isolation of all of the peptides produced by tryptic digestion of cytochrome $\underline{b}_5$ I and II, carboxyl and amino end group determinations and amino acid sequence studies on the small peptides are summarized in Fig. 3 (5, 6). End group analyses on the cytochrome indicated the cytochrome $\underline{b}_5$ is a single polypeptide chain. Both cytochrome components have the same amino-terminal tripeptide sequence and a core heme peptide of the same amino acid composition. Cytochrome $\underline{b}_5$ II apparently lacks only the carboxyl terminal glutamyl-serine sequence in the heptapeptide present in cytochrome $\underline{b}_5$ I. This single variation, resulting in a net charge difference of one, is consistent with the increased electrophoretic mobility of form I compared to that of form II.

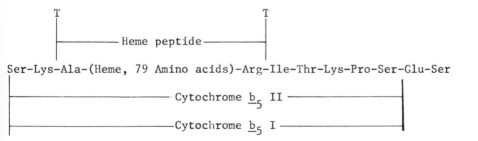

Figure 3. Cytochrome $\underline{b}_5$ structure. T. indicates sites of tryptic cleavage. From (6).

Before proceeding to the chemistry of the heme protein and core heme peptide, we should consider the possible origin of different forms of cytochrome $b_5$ in variable amounts in crude calf liver preparations. Either multiple forms normally exist in the endoplasmic reticulum or they are formed as a result of peptide bond cleavage during the isolation procedure. The former situation could arise either from biosynthetic multiplicity or from a population of the heme protein species reflecting the catabolic processes in the turnover of this cytochrome. In the latter case, the solubilization of the heme protein could involve exo- or endopeptidases associated with the crude microsomal suspensions or as a contaminant of the purified pancreatic lipase used to extract the heme protein. If the detectable variability in primary sequence, which lies outside of the heme peptide core and is restricted to a few carboxyl-terminal amino acids, is an isolation artifact, then the possibility arises that all isolated forms of cytochrome $b_5$ may represent heme peptide fragments which may be covalently bound to a structural protein or another enzymatic component of the endoplasmic reticulum. In this regard, the early discrepancy between the oxidation-reduction potentials of bound and soluble cytochrome $b_5$, as well as the fact that the rabbit liver heme protein preparations have a higher molecular weight, may be significant (7).

Because the distinctive spectral and catalytic properties of the two forms of cytochrome $b_5$ are identical and unaffected by tryptic digestion, the heme peptide can be used as the simplest unit for a more complete analysis of the heme binding and protein structure. The amino acid composition of cytochrome $b_5$ I and II and the heme peptide (5, 6) (Table I) show the amino acid losses resulting from proteolysis and emphasize the limited number of reactive amino acid residues present in this protein. The heme peptide of only 81 amino acids has a molecular weight of slightly less than 10,000 and the carboxyl terminal arginyl residue can in fact be cleaved with carboxypeptidase B without affecting the heme binding. This polypeptide contains no methionine or cysteine and only a single tryptophan residue. Although the amino acid sequence is still underway, it has been possible to examine several essential features of this structure by utilizing group specific reagents to modify amino acid residues and by a characterization of the heme binding.

Heme binding. Fig. 4 shows the spectrum of the apocytochrome and its recombination with heme to yield the original spectra of cytochrome $b_5$ (8). The presence of only a single tryptophan and three tyrosyl residues results in the low absorption at 280 mμ . By masking the tyrosyl residues by

TABLE I

Amino Acid Composition of Cytochrome $b_5$ I and II

and Heme Peptides

| Amino Acid | Moles amino acid/Mole heme | | | |
| | Cytochrome $\underline{b}_5$ I | Cytochrome $\underline{b}_5$ II | I Heme Peptide | II Heme Peptide |
| --- | --- | --- | --- | --- |
| Lysine | 8.20 | 8.24 | 5.95 | 5.85 |
| Histidine | 4.73 | 4.75 | 4.89 | 4.93 |
| Ammonia | 6.31 | 6.31 | 6.65 | 6.80 |
| Arginine | 2.90 | 3.00 | 2.95 | 3.00 |
| Aspartic Acid | 8.80 | 8.30 | 9.20 | 9.25 |
| Threonine | 6.68 | 6.63 | 5.80 | 6.20 |
| Serine | 6.92 | 6.10 | 4.20 | 3.94 |
| Glutamic Acid | 14.7 | 13.5 | 13.6 | 13.2 |
| Proline | 3.16 | 2.97 | 2.22 | 2.0 |
| Glycine | 6.05 | 5.85 | 6.01 | 6.30 |
| Alanine | 4.18 | 3.99 | 4.10 | 4.30 |
| Cystine (half) | 0.0 | 0.0 | 0.0 | 0.0 |
| Valine | 3.45 | 3.32 | 3.80 | 4.15 |
| Methionine | 0.0 | 0.0 | 0.0 | 0.0 |
| Isoleucine | 4.09 | 3.71 | 3.05 | 2.89 |
| Leucine | 8.00 | 7.70 | 7.73 | 8.00 |
| Tyrosine | 3.16 | 3.05 | 2.96 | 3.04 |
| Phenylalanine | 2.86 | 3.10 | 2.70 | 3.04 |

From (6)

iodination and the reactive amino groups with acetic anhydride, it was possible to titrate one histidyl residue with diazotized sulfanilic acid and block the heme binding completely (8). The most reactive of the five histidyl residues is thus essential for heme binding and the more direct interpretation is that it is involved in coordination with the heme iron.

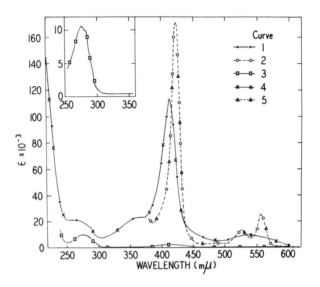

Figure 4. Absorption spectra of apocytochrome b5 and recombined cytochrome b5. Curve 1. Oxidized cytochrome b5; Curve 2, reduced b5; Curve 3, apocytochrome b5; Curve 4, apocytochrome b5 plus heme; Curve 5, reduced recombined cytochrome b5. From (8).

The structural requirements of the coenzyme in the heme-protein interactions were examined with various porphyrins and metalloporphyrins (9). Fig. 5 illustrates the fact that a number of iron porphyrins are bound by apocytochrome b5 to yield heme protein spectra similar to those of cytochrome b5, but with somewhat altered absorption bands. Protoporphyrin IX as well as other metal complexes with porphyrins are bound to the apoprotein in a one-to-one stoichiometry (Table II).

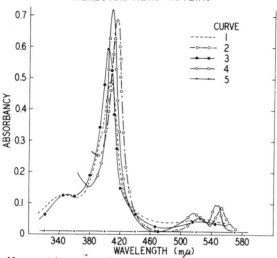

Figure 5. Absorption spectra of iron porphyrin-apocytochrome b5 complexes. Apocytochrome complex with hematoheme, oxidized (Curve 1) and reduced (Curve 2). Apocytochrome complex with mesoheme, oxidized (Curve 3) and reduced (Curve 4). Curve 5, apocytochrome b5. From (9).

All of the metalloporphyrin-protein complexes in which metal coordination with the protein is possible, with the exception of the hematoheme derivative, are quite stable and are not displaced from the protein by heme. Protoporphyrin IX and hematoheme are readily displaced by heme. Both the weak binding of free porphyrins and the absence of spectral changes in forming porphyrin-protein complexes point to a stable metal coordination with the apoprotein.

The tight binding of metalloporphyrins by apocytochrome b5 might be expected to affect both the structure and stability of the protein. The specificity of cytochrome b5 was used as one criterion of the similarity in the structures of the various metalloporphyrin-apoprotein complexes (9). All of the iron porphyrin-protein complexes are reduced rapidly by NADH cytochrome b5 reductase and the cobalt and manganese derivatives are competitive inhibitors of cytochrome b5 reduction. Furthermore, a comparison of the stabilities of the apocytochrome and metalloporphyrin-protein complexes to tryptic digestion, low pH and urea showed that binding of the metalloporphyrin protects that protein from destruction by any one of these methods (9).

Table II

Separation of Porphyrin-apocytochrome b₅ Complexes by
Gel Filtration on Sephadex Column

| Porphyrin derivative | Reaction mixtures* apocytochrome (mµ moles) | Effluent | |
|---|---|---|---|
| | | cytochrome complex (mµ moles) | porphyrin apocyto-chrome ratio |
| Protoporphyrin | 6.8 | 5.0 | 0.73 |
| Hematoporphyrin | 5.0 | 0 | 0 |
| Ni Protoporphyrin | 9.3 | 11.0 | 1.18 |
| Cu Protoporphyrin | 4.2 | 4.8 | 1.14 |
| Co Protoporphyrin | 3.6 | 3.0 | 0.83 |
| Mn Mesoporphyrin | 6.0 | 4.6 | 0.77 |
| Heme | 6.8 | 6.4 | 0.94 |
| Mesoheme | 3.6 | 3.4 | 0.94 |
| Deuteroheme | 4.2 | 4.2 | 1.00 |
| Pyrroheme | 4.8 | 5.0 | 1.04 |
| Hematoheme | 4.5 | 4.2 | 0.93 |

*The reaction mixtures contained the indicated amount of apo-cytochrome b₅, 100 to 200 µmole of Tris-acetate, pH 7.9, and a 3-to 6-fold excess of the porphyrin derivative. The Sepha-dex gel filtration was carried out at 0 to 4° to isolate the complexes. From (9).

The contrasting properties of the hematoheme-apocytochrome complex, in which the metalloporphyrin is readily displaced by heme, provide some information on the role of the metal and possible alteration in protein structure as a result of met-alloporphyrin binding (9). The weaker binding of hematoheme is reflected in a greater sensitivity of the complex with the apoprotein to urea (Fig. 6). Whereas heme binding is still complete in 6 M urea, hematoheme association is incompletely inhibited at a concentration of 6 M. The hematoheme complex is also sensitive to tryptic digestion under conditions which do not affect other metalloporphyrin-apocytochrome complexes (9). The effect of pH on iron porphyrin-apoprotein association and dissociation is particularly significant, because only the hematoheme complex undergoes a reversible association involving ionizable groups with an apparent pH of 5.5 to 6.0 (9) as shown in Fig. 7. The heme association reaction has a similar pH depen-dence, but the heme protein is now stable at pH values as low as 4.9.

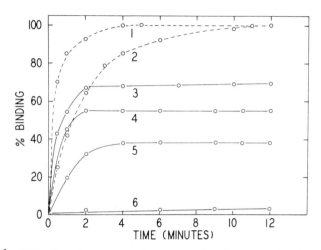

Figure 6. Effect of urea on iron porphyrin association with apocytochrome b5. Curves 1 and 2, heme association in 5 and 6 M urea, respectively. Curves 3,4,5, and 6, hematoheme association in 3,4,5, and 6 M urea, respectively. From (9).

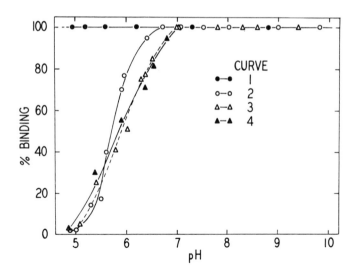

Figure 7. The effect of pH on iron porphyrin-apocytochrome b5 association and dissociation. Curve 1, cytochrome b5; Curve 2, heme-apocytochrome b5 association; Curve 3, hematoheme-apocytochrome b5 association; Curve 4, hematoheme-apocytochrome b5 dissociation. From (9).

These data are consistent with the assumption that in cytochrome $b_5$, as well as other stable metalloporphyrin-apo-cytochrome complexes, the peptide chain assumes a folded conformation which is stabilized, and perhaps determined, by the interaction with both perpendicular metal coordination positions. By this argument, the steric factors which lead to the more unstable complex with hematoheme might also exclude the normal protein-iron bonding. This appears to be the case because the reduced form of the hematoheme-apocytochrome will react with carbon monoxide and the oxidized form, with potassium cyanide. The cyanide complex is shown in Fig. 8 because in this case it is clear that the hematoheme is still bound to the protein. This complex, in which one coordination position of the metal is liganded to cyanide, still reacts with cytochrome $b_5$ reductase. The substitution of hydroxyl ethyl groups for the two vinyl groups in the porphyrin thus leads to sufficient distortion of the apoprotein complex to accommodate a small ligand rather than an amino acid residue of the protein without destroying the structural features essential for its catalytic activity.

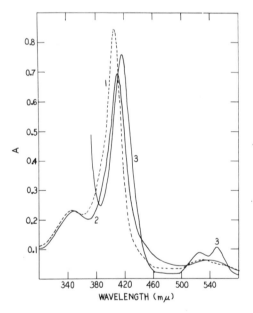

Figure 8. Hematoheme-apocytochrome $b_5$ reaction with cyanide. Curve 1, oxidized hematoheme-cytochrome $b_5$; Curve 2, oxidized complex in 0.02 M cyanide; Curve 3, reduced cyanide complex.

The effect of modification of the reactive amino acid
residues.  The alternative approach to the structure of cytochrome $b_5$ has utilized group-specific reagents to examine the
reactivity of various amino acid residues, and to examine the
effects of peptide alterations on the structure and stability
of the apoprotein and intact cytochrome.  In the early studies
which implicated an imidazole group in heme binding (8), it
became apparent that the three phenolic groups of the heme
protein are exposed and can react with iodine with no appreciable alteration of the spectral or catalytic properties.  More
recent efforts have centered on the single amino-terminal seryl
and the eight lysyl residues.

All of these amino acid groups are sufficiently exposed
to react with several group-specific reagents (5, 10).  The
specificity of trinitrobenzene sulfonate and the intense
absorption bands of the trinitrophenylated amino groups provide
a sensitive method for demonstrating that acetylation or
succinylation of the amino groups of cytochrome $b_5$ is complete.
Since the spectra of the oxidized and reduced forms of cytochrome $b_5$ are unaffected by complete acylation, the lysyl residues are apparently not involved in the heme binding.  This
conclusion was confirmed by the observation that apocytochrome,
which had been acetylated under conditions that result in
complete acylation of amino groups but no other amino acid residues, will recombine completely with heme to yield unaltered
cytochrome $b_5$ spectrum.

Although the $\epsilon$-amino groups are chemically reactive in
this heme protein, these amino acid residues clearly differ in
their reactivity toward trinitrobenzene sulfonate.  This is
obvious in the  pH sensitivity of the trinitrophenylation reaction (5, 10) (Fig. 9).  At pH 7.5 only three amino groups will
react even after a 24-hour incubation.  It is of interest in
considering subsequent experiments that the rate and extent of
reaction is not affected by the removal of the heme from the
protein.  The reactive amino groups at pH 7.5 are largely in
the heme peptide core with a very limited reaction of the
amino-terminal seryl residue (10) (Table III).  Each of the
two peptides cleaved by trypsin contains one of the eight lysyl
residues in the protein.  The lysyl residue in the dipeptide is
a site of tryptic attack on cytochrome $b_5$, whereas the prolyl-
lysyl bond in the heptapeptide of cytochrome $b_5$ I is resistant to trypsin.  It is surprising, therefore, to find that
neither of these residues, which occur near the amino and carboxyl ends of the protein and are presumably relatively exposed,
will not react with trinitrobenzene sulfonate at pH 7.5.

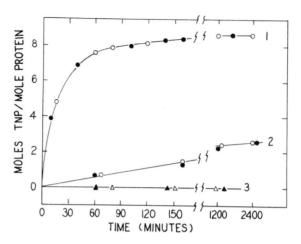

Figure 9. The effect of pH on the rate of trinitrophenylation of cytochrome $b_5$ derivatives at 0°. Curve 1, ●——●, cytochrome $b_5$, —o——o— apocytochrome $b_5$ at pH 10; Curve 2, ●——●, cytochrome $b_5$, —o——o—, apocytochrome $b_5$ at pH 7.5; Curve 3, ▲——▲, succinylated cytochrome $b_5$, —△——△—, acetylated apocytochrome $b_5$ at pH 7.5 or 10. From (10).

Conversely, the three lysyl residues of the heme peptide core which are chemically reactive, as well as the three which will only react with trinitrobenzene sulfonate at pH 10, are protected from tryptic cleavage.

TABLE III

Distribution of Trinitrophenyl Groups in Partially

Trinitrophenylated Cytochrome $b_5$

| Preparation | I Heme peptide | | Heptapeptide(I-2) | | Dipeptide(I-1) | |
|---|---|---|---|---|---|---|
| | Percent recovery | moles TNP / mole peptide | Percent yield | moles TNP / mole peptide | Percent yield | moles TNP / mole peptide |
| 2.7 TNP-Cytochrome $b_5$ | 100 | 2.4 | 100 | 0.0 | 97 | 0.2 |
| Cytochrome $b_5$ | 100 | --- | 93 | --- | 100 | --- |

From (9).

The complete acylation or trinitrophenylation of cytochrome $b_5$ results both in gross alteration in the charged groups in the protein and the introduction of a number of hydrophylic or hydrophobic groups. At pH 7.5 the heme protein contains from 19 to 25 negatively charged groups, depending upon the exact amide content, and 11 positively charged amino acid residues. Nine of the 11 positive charges are absent in the acetylated cytochrome and these have been replaced by negative charges in the succinylated preparation. Nevertheless, the spectra of the oxidized and reduced derivaties are unchanged, and the heme proteins can be reduced in the NADH cytochrome $b_5$ reductase system. This implies that these substitutions on the amino groups do not result in marked modification of the tertiary structure of the protein. However, the more subtle changes in the protein conformation are reflected in alterations in the stability of the heme protein. Fig. 10 (10) shows that heme dissociation from either acylated derivative occurs more rapidly in urea. The acetylated heme protein is also more sensitive to extensive tryptic digestion (9), and more preliminary experiments suggest that the rate of recombination of acetylated or succinylated apocytochrome $b_5$ with heme is decreased.

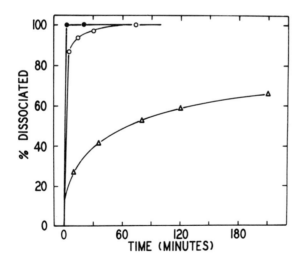

Figure 10. The rate of heme dissociation from cytochrome $b_5$ derivatives in 7 M urea. ●——●, succinylated cytochrome $b_5$; ○——○, acetylated cytochrome $b_5$; △——△, cytochrome $b_5$. From (10).

The modification of cytochrome $b_5$ with trinitrobenzene sulfonate involves the introduction of a relatively large and hydrophobic residue. In this case the reaction of more than three amino groups apparently yields structural changes in the protein that affect the heme binding (10) (Fig. 11) as shown by the decrease in the absorption at 413 mμ. In spite of an appreciable change in the spectrum of the derivative containing eight trinitrophenyl groups, enzymatic reduction still occurs. Trinitrophenylation in the absence of the coenzyme results in more extensive disruption of the protein structure. Even partial trinitrophenylation can be detected by altered heme binding. Complete reaction of the apoprotein apparently yields an equilibrium of protein conformations which bind heme very loosely to yield a heme-protein complex that is inert in the cytochrome $b_5$ reductase system. Its spectrum (10) bears little resemblance to cytochrome $b_5$ and it can only be reduced chemically.

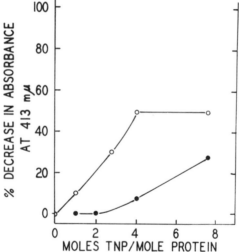

Figure 11. The effect of trinitrophenylation on the spectrum of cytochrome $b_5$ and recombined apocytochrome $b_5$ derivatives. ●——●, trinitrophenylated cytochrome $b_5$ ○——○ trinitrophenylated apocytochrome $b_5$ plus heme.

Conclusions. These results emphasize the crucial role of the bound metalloporphyrin in stabilizing a heme protein conformation in which a very significant portion of the amino acid residues is exposed to the medium and is chemically reactive. Thus, cytochrome $b_5$ can accomodate extensive charge and steric alterations at these sites without consequent loss of its characteristic spectral and catalytic properties. The observation that the apoprotein undergoes structural changes more readily during extensive reaction of the amino groups similarly draws attention to the importance of heme binding in maintaining the functional cytochrome structure. The present data implicate both iron coordination positions in this specific interaction, but the extent of porphyrin interaction remains obscure since only one heme analogue forms a measurably weaker complex with the apocytochrome. It is essential now to complete the determination of the primary structure and to utilize the physical methods available for characterizing the tertiary structure of the various modified cytochrome $b_5$ derivatives. Any interpretation of such data to describe the relation of heme binding to protein structure, however, must conform to the restrictions imposed by the present studies with heme analogues and group specific reagents.

## Acknowledgment

The technical assistance of Janice Van Buren is gratefully acknowledged.

## References

1. Strittmatter, P., and S. F. Velick. J. Biol. Chem., 221, 253 (1956).

2. Shichi, H., and D. P. Hackett. J. Biol. Chem., 237, 2955 (1962).

3. Estabrook, R. W. In Haematin Enzymes (J. E. Falk, R. Lemberg and R. K. Morton, eds.), Pergamon Press, Inc., New York, 1961, p. 436.

4. Strittmatter, P. In The Enzymes (P. D. Boyer, H. Lardy, and K. Myrbäck, eds.), Vol. VIII, Academic Press, Inc., New York, 1963, p. 113.

5. Ozols, J., and P. Strittmatter. Federation Proc., 24, 532 (1965).

6. Strittmatter, P., and J. Ozols. Submitted for publication.

7. Velick, S. F., and P. Strittmatter. J. Biol. Chem., 221, 265 (1956).

8. Strittmatter, P. J. Biol. Chem., 235, 2492 (1960).

9. Ozols, J., and P. Strittmatter. J. Biol. Chem., 239, 1018 (1964).

10. Ozols, J. and P. Strittmatter. Submitted for publication.

## DISCUSSION

Gibson:  In describing your binding studies, you have stressed the role of the metal in binding the porphyrin ring to the protein.  If this is what you really mean, obviously there is a marked difference between $b_5$ and globin in this respect; in globin the metal does not seem to matter at all.  Have you used any porphyrins without metals in them?  This might make a comparison possible.

Strittmatter:  The table (1) showed that protoporphyrin IX is bound but easily displaced by heme.

Ehrenberg:  In collaboration with Dr. Poltoratsky of Paris, we have studied the ESR spectra of cytochrome $b_5$, which may be of use in identifying $b_5$ in biological preparations.  At neutral pH, with 1-2 mM $b_5$, we obtained a low-spin compound with g-values at 3.03, 2.23, and 1.43.  At higher pH values (10 to 12) we found a change to another type of low-spin spectrum.  There is also a little high-spin form with g = 6 at this pH region.

Estabrook:  It is interesting that you do not see this type of ESR spectrum for $b_5$ in intact microsomes.

Ehrenberg:  One explanation might be that the spin-lattice relaxations are different when it is bound in the tissue from those in solution.

Bendall:  Some years ago, I measured the potential of $b_5$ in rat liver microsomes by titration in the presence of the ferric oxalate system, and obtained a value of approximately +25 mV (2).  This removes the discrepancy between the potential of cytochrome $b_5$ in the free state and that bound to the microsomes that Dr. Strittmatter mentioned.

Schonbaum:  We have recently investigated manganese myoglobin and manganese peroxidase, i.e., derivatives in which the prosthetic group, iron protoporphyrin, has been replaced by manganese protoporphyrin.  Could you describe the stabilities and spectroscopic properties of Mn(II), Mn(III), and Mn(IV) forms of cytochrome $b_5$?

<u>Strittmatter</u>: The data on the manganese complex are limited; it appears to be bound as Mn(III). We use all our solutions within two hours and then discard them, so I really cannot answer for the stabilities of the various manganese-porphyrin complexes.

## References

1. Strittmatter, P., and J. Ozols. This volume, p. 454.

2. Bendall, D. Ph.D. Thesis, University of Cambridge, 1957.

# VII.
Ligand Binding and Reaction Mechanisms of Oxidases
J. H. Wang, Chairman

# EFFECT OF FLUORIDE AND AZIDE ON THE ABSORPTION SPECTRUM
## OF CYTOCHROME c OXIDASE

A. O. Muijsers, B. F. van Gelder, and E. C. Slater

Laboratory of Biochemistry, University of Amsterdam
Amsterdam, The Netherlands

In 1939, Keilin and Hartree (1) observed that the reduction of cytochrome $a_3$ by the respiratory chain in heart-muscle preparation is prevented by the addition of cyanide, azide, sulphide, fluoride, hydroxylamine or ethyl hydrogen peroxide. They concluded that these compounds combine with the ferri form of cytochrome $a_3$, and pointed out the close analogy with the reactions of these ligands with methemoglobin, catalase and peroxidase.

A number of workers have shown that cyanide causes a shift of a few millimicrons towards the red of the Soret peak of oxidized cytochrome c oxidase preparations with little change of intensity of the band. No effects of other ligands on the absorption spectrum of ferricytochrome $a_3$ have been reported. In this paper we report some preliminary results on the effects of fluoride and azide.

As first demonstrated by van Gelder (2-5), cytochrome c oxidase preparations contain equal amounts of cyanide-reacting heme a (corresponding to cytochrome $a_3$ as defined by Keilin and Hartree (1)) and of heme a inert to cyanide (corresponding to cytochrome a). Similarly, one-half of the copper, present in amounts equimolar with the heme a (3-7), reacts with chelating agents and one-half does not. Cyanide and azide react with both the heme a and the copper, whereas EDTA and salicyl aldoxime react only with the copper, and fluoride only with the heme. Fluoride is, therefore, particularly suitable for the study of the effects on the heme.

Fluoride. The effects of fluoride on the titration of cytochrome c oxidase by NADH in the presence of phenazine methosulphate at 830 m$\mu$, 605 m$\mu$ and 445 m$\mu$ are shown in Fig. 1. It has little effect at 605 m$\mu$, causes a decline in the slope at 445 m$\mu$, and an increase at 830 m$\mu$. Furthermore, it doubles the ratio Cu(I):ferroheme a, measured during the course of

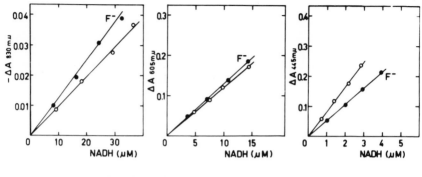

○──○ , Without Fluoride ;  ●──● ,With IOmM Fluoride

Figure 1. Titration of cytochrome c oxidase with NADH in the presence of phenazine methosulphate at 830 mμ, 605 mμ, and 445 mμ under anaerobic conditions. For procedure, see ref. (5).

TABLE I

Effect of Fluoride on Titration of Cytochrome c Oxidase by NADH in the Presence of Phenazine Methosulphate (5)

| $\Delta A$ : NADH (mM) | | |
|---|---|---|
| At 445 mμ: calculated* | -- | 52 |
| found | 82 | 54 |
| | | |
| At 605 mμ: calculated* | -- | 13.0 |
| found | 12.0 | 12.7 |
| | | |
| At 830 mμ: calculated* | -- | 1.28 |
| found | 0.96 | 1.38 |
| | | |
| Cu(I):Ferroheme a | | |
| calculated[+] | 1.0 | 2.0 |
| found | 0.98 | 1.92 |

*Calculation based on the following assumptions:
(i) The composition of cytochrome c oxidase is aa₃2Cu;
(ii) a₃ contributes 52 percent of the absorbance in the difference spectrum (reduced minus oxidized) at 445 mμ, 19 percent at 605 mμ, and none at 830 mμ. The values of 52 percent and 19 percent were obtained by determining the effect of cyanide on the difference spectrum measured with excess reducing agent;
(iii) fluoride prevents specifically the reduction of a₃.

+ Calculation based on assumptions (i) and (iii).

the titration (4,5). Table I shows that the effects observed
are close to those expected on the basis of the composition
($aa_3$, 2 Cu) for the cytochrome c oxidase, if the fluoride
specifically prevents the reduction of the heme of cytochrome $a_3$.

The effect of fluoride on the absorption spectrum of
cytochrome $aa_3$ is shown in Fig. 2. There is an increase of ab-'
sorption between 426 mμ and 550 mμ, between 560 mμ and 660 mμ,
and between 660 mμ and 950 mμ. In the difference spectrum (not
shown), peaks are found at 480 mμ, 600 mμ, 640 mμ and at about
800 mμ. The increased absorption at 480 mμ, 640 mμ, and around
800 mμ is characteristic for the formation of a compound with
increased high-spin content (8). The effect on the Soret band
is similar to that seen with other hemoproteins (9,10). The
effect in the infrared is of particular interest, since heme a
of cytochrome $a_3$ makes no contribution to the 830-mμ band in the
difference spectrum: oxidized minus reduced (4,5,11,12).

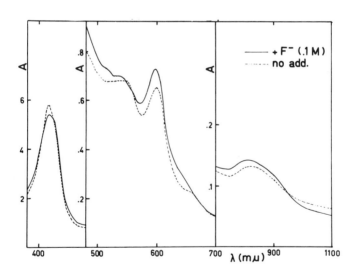

Figure 2. Effect of fluoride on absorption spectrum of cytochrome c oxidase in 0.1 M phosphate buffer (pH 7.4) containing
1 percent Emasol 4130. The spectra were measured after one
day, during which the solutions were kept at 4°, except during
measurement of the spectra when they were brought to 22°.
Fifty μM reducible heme a (calculated according to ref. (14))
present. The spectra were measured in cuvettes of different
light paths and converted to 1 cm.

The spectral effects shown in Fig. 2 were measured after no further changes in the spectrum were observed. A long incubation period (about 24 hours at 4°) was required to reach this stage. Orii and Okunuki (13) have reported the same experience with respect to combination of cyanide with cytochrome c oxidase. The rate of development of the effects on the Soret peak are shown in Fig. 3. Initially, there was an increase at 400 mμ and a decline at 432 mμ. On further standing, the decline at 415 mμ became more pronounced.

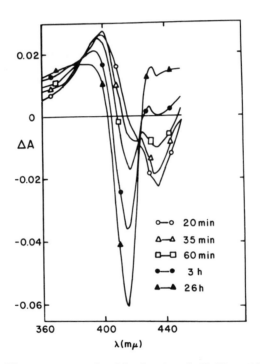

Figure 3. Time course of effect of o.1 M fluoride on absorption spectrum of cytochrome c oxidase in the region of the Soret band. The difference spectrum with fluoride minus without fluoride is plotted. The solutions were kept at 4°, except during measurement of the spectra, during which they were brought to 22°. Traces measured at indicated times after addition of fluoride. Cytochrome c oxidase containing 50 μM reducible heme a dissolved in 0.1 M phosphate buffer (pH 7.4) containing 1 percent Emasol 4130. Light path, 0.2 cm.

The dissociation constant of the fluoride complex was determined by measuring the effects of different concentrations of fluoride on $A_{450\ m\mu} - A_{415\ m\mu}$. This combination is written by the following equation (cf. ref. 13).

$$\underset{3}{a^{3+}} + \underline{n}F^- \ \rightleftharpoons \ \underset{3}{a^{3+}} - F^-_{\ n} \qquad (1)$$

$$K_D = \frac{\left[\underset{3}{a^{3+}}\right]\left[F^-\right]^{\underline{n}}}{\left[\underset{3}{a^{3+}} - F^-_{\ n}\right]} = \frac{(1-\alpha)\left[F^-\right]^{\underline{n}}}{\alpha} \qquad (2)$$

where $\alpha = \dfrac{\left[\underset{3}{a^{3+}} - F^-_{\ n}\right]}{\left[\underset{3}{a^{3+}} \ tot\right]}$ \qquad (3)

Fig. 4 shows a plot of $\log\dfrac{1-\alpha}{\alpha}$ against $-\log\left[F^-\right]$. The slope of the straight line equals $\underline{n}$, and the intercept on the ordinate equals $\log \underline{K}$.

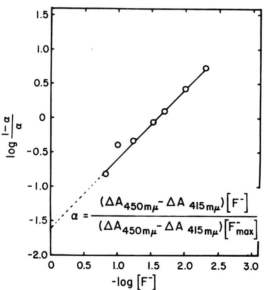

Figure 4. Determination of dissociation constant of the compound between fluoride and oxidized cytochrome c oxidase, $\alpha$ calculated from $\Delta A_{450 \ m\mu} - \Delta A_{415 \ m\mu}$ with different $[F^-]$.

Cytochrome c oxidase containing 10.2 $\mu M$ reducible heme a was dissolved in 0.05 M phosphate buffer (pH 7.4) containing 1 percent Emasol 4130. The concentration of uncombined fluoride was assumed to be equal to that of the total fluoride. The samples were kept for 3 days at $4^{\circ}$ and measured at $22^{\circ}$.

As was to be expected, $\underline{n}$ was found to be equal to 1. The value of $K_D$ was found to be 25 mM. This is fairly close to the $K_i$ (16 mM) determined from the inhibitory effect of fluoride on the rate of oxidation of ferrocytochrome $\underline{c}$ by the enzyme, determined spectrophotometrically (unpublished studies by I.R.M. Obbema). However, in view of the fact that, in the latter measurements, no account was taken of the slow equilibration of the enzyme with fluoride, the agreement may be coincidental. Surprisingly, only 10 mM fluoride was sufficient to eliminate cytochrome $\underline{a}_3$ from the titration in the experiment described in Fig. 1. Clearly, studies of the effect of preincubation of the enzyme with fluoride on the inhibition, and determinations of $K_D$ after short periods of reaction between enzyme and fluoride are required.

Azide. The effects of 50 mM azide on the absorption spectrum are shown in Fig. 5. In contrast to the effect of fluoride, there is a marked shift in the Soret peak (from 418 mμ to 428 mμ) and a considerable decline in intensity. Between 428 mμ and 640 mμ there was increased absorption (with peak at 600 mμ), but the band at about 640 mμ observed with fluoride was not obtained with azide. Instead, there was increased absorption between 660 mμ and 750 mμ (maximum 670-690 mμ). The red shift of the Soret peak is characteristic of an increase in low-spin content (8).

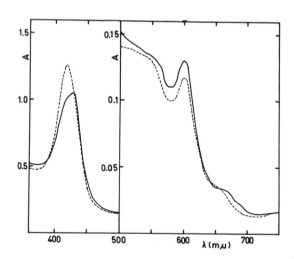

Figure 5. Effect of 50 mM azide on the absorption spectrum of cytochrome $\underline{c}$ oxidase (10.2 μM reducible heme $\underline{a}$), dissolved in 0.1 M phosphate buffer (pH 7.4), containing 1 percent Emasol 4130. Measurements were made at 22° after 3 days at 4°. Light path, 1 cm. ———, + azide (50 mM); - - - -, no addition.

Reaction with azide was also slow, being incomplete after 19 h at 4° (Fig. 6).

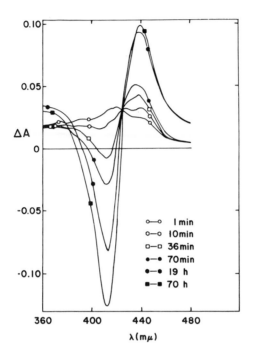

Figure 6. Time course of effect of 10 mM azide on the absorption spectrum of cytochrome c oxidase (10.6 μM reducible heme a) in the region of the Soret band. The difference spectrum with azide minus without azide is plotted. The solution was kept at 0°, except during measurement of the spectra, during which it was brought to 22°. Light path, 1 cm.

Determination of the binding constant of azide with the enzyme, determined in the same way as with fluoride, gave the surprising result that $\underline{n}$ = 0.5. The dissociation constant of the reaction:

$$N_3^- + 2\,\underline{a}_3^{3+} \rightleftharpoons 2\ \text{product}$$

i.e. $\qquad K = \dfrac{[N_3^-]\,[\underline{a}_3^{3+}]^2}{[\text{product}]^2}$

was found from the plot shown in Fig. 7 to equal 6.3 mM. It is not possible to compare this with the $K_i$, since no data are available for $\underline{n}$ in the inhibitory reaction.

Further work is necessary to elucidate the significance of this result.

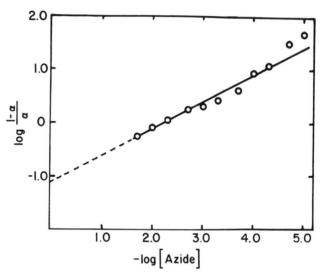

Figure 7. Determination of dissociation constant of the compound between azide and oxidized cytochrome $\underline{c}$ oxidase, calculated from $A_{437\ m\mu} - A_{414\ m\mu}$ with different concentrations of azide.

$$\alpha = \frac{\Delta A_{437\ m\mu} - \Delta A_{414\ m\mu}}{\left(\Delta A_{437\ m\mu} - \Delta A_{414\ m\mu}\right)[N_3^-] = 75\ mM} . \quad \text{Cytochrome } \underline{c} \text{ oxidase}$$

containing 10.2 µM reducible heme $\underline{a}$ was dissolved in 0.05 M phosphate buffer (pH 7.4) containing 1 percent Emasol 4130. Where necessary, the amount of bound azide was subtracted from the total azide concentration to give the full azide concentration. Measurements were made at $22^\circ$ after keeping 3 days at $4^\circ$.

## Summary

Preliminary observations on the effects of fluoride and azide of the absorption spectrum of cytochrome $\underline{c}$ oxidase suggest that ferricytochrome $\underline{a}_3$ is a thermal mixture of high-spin and low-spin forms, perhaps of the hydroxide. Combination with fluoride increases the high-spin content, whereas combination with azide increases the low-spin content.

## References

1. Keilin, D., and E. F. Hartree.  Proc. Roy. Soc. (London) B, 127, 167 (1939).

2. van Gelder, B. F., and E. C. Slater.  Biochim. Biophys. Acta, 73, 663 (1963).

3. van Gelder, B. F., and A. O. Muijsers.  Biochim. Biophys. Acta, 81, 405 (1964).

4. Slater, E. C., B. F. van Gelder, and K. Minnaert.  In Oxidases and Related Redox Systems (T. E. King, H. S. Mason, and M. Morrison, eds.), Vol. 2, John Wiley and Sons, New York, 1965, p. 667.

5. van Gelder, B. F., and A. O Muijsers.  Biochim. Biophys. Acta, 118, 47 (1966).

6. Takemori, S.  J. Biochem. (Tokyo), 47, 382 (1960).

7. Griffiths, D. E., and D. C. Wharton.  J. Biol. Chem., 236, 1850, 1857 (1961).

8. George, P., J. Beetlestone, and J. S. Griffith.  In Haematin Enzymes (J. E. Falk, R. Lemberg, and R. K. Morton, eds.), Vol. 1, Pergamon Press, Oxford, 1961, p. 105.

9. Keilin, D., and E. F. Hartree.  Biochem. J., 49, 88 (1961).

10. Morell, D. B.  Biochem. J., 56, 683 (1954).

11. Morrison, M.  In Oxidases and Related Redox Systems (T. E. King, H. S. Mason, and M. Morrison, eds.), Vol. 2, John Wiley and Sons, New York, 1965, p. 639.

12. Wharton, D. C.  Biochim. Biophys. Acta, 92, 607 (1964).

13. Orii, Y., and K. Okunuki.  J. Biochem. (Tokyo), 55, 37 (1964).

14. van Gelder, B. F.  Biochim. Biophys. Acta, 118, 36 (1966).

# THE "OXYGENATED" INTERMEDIATE OF CYTOCHROME c OXIDASE*

M. Rudolf Lemberg[‡]

Johnson Research Foundation, University of Pennsylvania
Philadelphia, Pennsylvania

If cytochrome oxidase is reduced by sodium dithionite
and then oxygenated, a compound with a Soret band at 426-428 mμ
is formed (1,2,3). Some of the published absorption curves
with a band at 424-425 might be interpreted as mixtures of
ferrous and ferric oxidase, as Chance (4) suggested. However,
in these instances, the spectrum of the ferrous enzyme obtained
by reduction reveals a partial destruction of the oxidase.

This can be avoided by the use of small amounts of dithionite (0.1 - 3 mM) in evacuated Thunberg tubes and excess oxygen, whether in the form $O_2$, air, or even nitrogen containing
about half a percent of oxygen. The curve (Fig. 1) then shows
a symmetrical peak at 428 mμ of a height equal to that of ferric oxidase at 418 mμ. The isosbestic point with ferrous oxidase lies at 435 mμ (5), like the isosbestic point of ferri-
and ferrocytochrome a, but the absorbance at the isosbestic
point of the 428 mμ compound is far higher. The wavelength
difference, 428-418 mμ, is useful for differentiation of conversion of the ferrous either to the ferric or to the 428 mμ
compound, since there would still be a considerable difference
for the oxidation of the ferrous to the ferric compound but
practically none for the conversion of the ferrous to the
428 mμ compound. Later I shall show a double-beam experiment
in which use is made of this.

In contrast to Orii and Okunuki (6), we find no distinct
evidence for a difference of the compound formed with oxygen
from that formed by the action of $H_2O_2$ on the _ferrous_ oxidase
(3). In contrast to Davison and Wainio (2) we can neither remove oxygen from the 428 mμ compound by evacuation, nor replace

*This work was supported by grants from NIH and the Nat. Health
and Med. Res. Council of Australia.

[‡]Permanent address: Institute of Medical Research, the Royal
North Shore Hospital, Sydney, Australia.

it by CO, nor expel it by ferricyanide. There is, however,
a slow spontaneous conversion to the ferric oxidase.

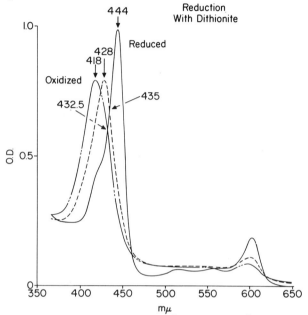

Figure 1. Ferrous, ferric, and "oxygenated" cytochrome oxidase spectra. Cytochrome oxidase 8.4 μM in sodium dithionite
0.12 mM. Oxygen 1.2 mM. ——··—— oxidized;
————— reduced; — — — "oxygenated".

Therefore, I do not believe that the compound is a reversibly oxygenated ferrous oxidase. I shall still speak of oxygenation, but shall call the 428 mμ compound here simply "the
compound". It should also be noted that there is no shoulder
at 444 mμ different from the Soret band of the CO-oxidase which
has a similar Soret band position (430 mμ) but shows a distinct
shoulder; thus no ferrocytochrome a is present in the "compound".
The decrease at 605 mμ by conversion of ferrous oxidase to the
"compound" is 70-80 percent, that at 444 mμ, 80-85 percent of
the difference between ferrous and ferric oxidase. In contrast
to the distinctly biphasic reduction of ferric cytochrome
oxidase by dithionite (half time of about 20 sec for cytochrome
a, but at least 15 times as long for cytochrome a$_3$) (Fig. 2),
that of the "compound" is monophasic, rather fast and first
order for the heme, but dependent on dithionite concentration.
Reduction restores ferrous oxidase of unaltered spectrum and
absorbance and oxygenation and re-reduction can be repeated
with the same result.

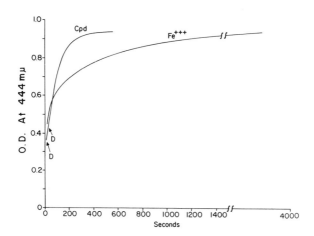

Figure 2. Biphasic reduction of ferric cytochrome a and a<sub>3</sub> $(Fe^{+++})$, and monophasic reduction of "oxygenated" compounds with dithionite. Cytochrome oxidase 8.4 μM. Sodium dithionite 0.12 mM. Reduction was done in a Thunberg cell.

This evidence indicates that the "compound" is a peroxidic one involving both cytochromes a and a$_3$. The shift of the Soret band from 418 to 428 mμ resembles that observed on conversion of horseradish peroxidase to Compound II or Compound III.

Dalziel and O'Brien (7) have observed formation of a peroxidic hemoglobin complex in the aeration of dithionite-reduced hemoglobin and have interpreted this as due to the formation of H$_2$O$_2$ by autoxidation of dithionite. Neither Okunuki, nor Wainio, nor we have been able to demonstrate formation of the "compound" on adding autoxidized dithionite to ferrous oxidase. More decisive, however, are the following experiments. The "compound" is formed from ferrous oxidase prepared by reduction with 16 mM formamidine-sulphinic acid (8), or by an equimolar amount of ferrocytochrome c which was certainly peroxide-free, since some of Yonetani's pure cytochrome c peroxidase from yeast had been added.

The autoxidation rate of ferrous cytochrome oxidase is rapid even in the presence of excess dithionite, with a half-time of 20-40 m sec (Fig. 3).

479

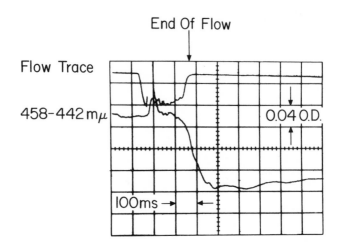

Figure 3. Rapid reaction of ferrocytochrome oxidase with oxygen.

In interpreting these results we start with the assumption that $\underline{a}_3$ $FeO_2$, the Warburg-Chance compound able to react reversibly with CO, reacts very rapidly with cytochrome $\underline{a}$ which is present in equimolar amounts (9). There are three such possibilities, considering only nominal iron valences:

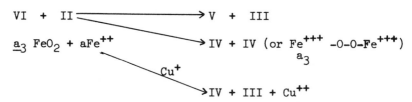

So far the monophasic reduction rate and the single Soret band in liquid nitrogen support the second assumption. This would necessitate a conformational change in cytochrome $\underline{a}$ on oxidation.

Objections have been raised against considering a relatively stable compound as an intermediate in the rapid enzymic reaction of cytochrome oxidase. This is not necessarily true, however, if such a compound can react rapidly with other participants of the respiratory chain, e.g., with cytochrome $\underline{c}$.

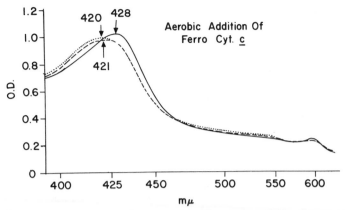

Figure 4. Conversion of "oxygenated" compound to ferric oxidase by cytochrome c. 8.2 µM cytochrome oxidase reduced with
160 µM sodium dithionite in a Thunberg cell, oxygenated with
240 µM oxygen. ———— "oxygenated" compound;
— — — plus 16.4 µM ferrocytochrome c. An equivalent amount
of ferricytochrome c was added to the reference cell.
· · · · · · · 10 minutes after the cytochrome c addition.


The compound reacts indeed rapidly with ferrocytochrome c as
Dr. Gilmour has shown in our Federation paper (10), and ferrocytochrome c reforms ferric cytochrome oxidase and, if in
excess, ferrous oxidase (Fig. 4). Further studies are, however, necessary to show that the compound formed during the
rapid autoxidation of ferrous oxidase is identical with our
428 mµ compound, and whether its reaction with ferrocytochrome
c is rapid enough to account for the rate of the enzymic
action. Fig. 5 shows how we can approach this problem.

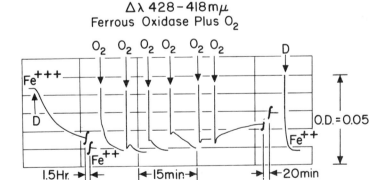

Figure 5. Formation of "oxygenated" compound observed in the
double beam spectrophotometer. 1.4 µM cytochrome oxidase
plus 5.8 mM sodium dithionite. $O_2$ was added by bubbling with
oxygen gas.

Setting the double-beam spectrophotometer at the wavelengths 428 and 418 mμ, we see first the biphasic slow reduction of the ferric enzyme which is complete in 30-45 min. Formation of the ferric compound on oxygenation should be accompanied by a return to the baseline, but in fact we observe only a small change as predicted from the absorption curves, and only a very slow rise at the completion of the oxygenation, due to the slow and partial formation of the ferric compound. The perpendicular lines indicate the switching off of the high voltage and its return. Finally reduction with a second amount of dithionite is fast and practically monophasic. It might be possible in this way to demonstrate whether or not the compound is formed in the rapid autoxidation of the oxidase, i.e., whether it is a true intermediate or a stabilization product of an intermediate. Our examination of this is still in progress.

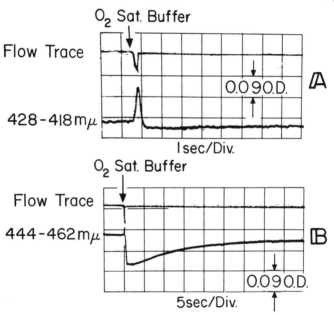

Figure 6. Formation of the "oxygenated" compound in the stopped-flow apparatus.

Fig. 6B shows that on oxygenation in the presence of excess dithionite in the stopped-flow apparatus, there is a rapid decrease at 444 mμ, using 462 mμ as reference wavelength, followed by a moderately fast increase; in contrast at 428 mμ, using 418 mμ as reference wavelength, (Fig. 6A) there is very little change upon oxygenation. If the product were ferric enzyme, the alteration should be about half of that at 444 mμ as Fig. 1 shows.

The reaction mechanism postulating direct interaction of the "compound" with ferrocytochrome c may, if it can be proved for the enzymic mechanism, remove three difficulties of the classical reaction scheme (Fig. 7): 1) this did not explain what happens to the three other electrons of molecular oxygen in the formation of ferric cytochrome $a_3$; 2) it postulated a rapid oxidation of ferrocytochrome a by ferricytochrome $a_3$ which is not found in purified oxidase preparations, whether cytochrome c is absent or present; 3) the effect of the presence of oxygen on the rate of oxidation of ferrocytochrome c by ferric oxidase which was already known to Keilin, could not be explained.

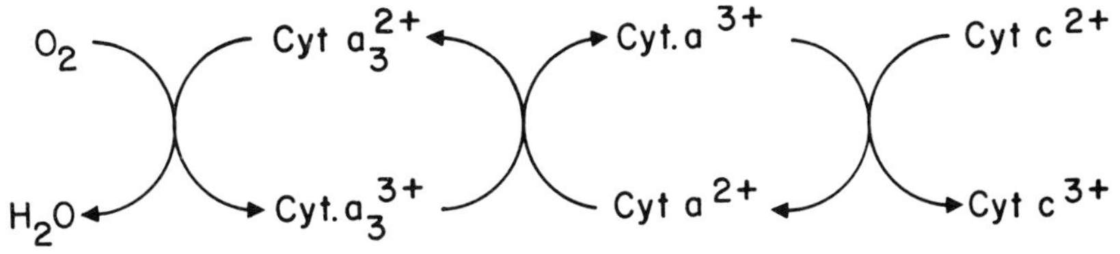

$$O_2 \quad \searrow \quad Cyt\ a_3^{2+} \quad \leftarrow \quad Cyt.a^{3+} \quad \searrow \quad Cyt\ c^{2+}$$

$$H_2O \quad \leftarrow \quad Cyt.a_3^{3+} \quad \searrow \quad Cyt\ a^{2+} \quad \leftarrow \quad Cyt\ c^{3+}$$

Figure 7. Classical scheme for cytochrome chain.

It will have to be seen whether the now postulated mechanism can overcome all these difficulties. If it can be confirmed, it will, on the one hand, show that in spite of the now well proved existence of two functionally different types of heme a-proteins represented by cytochromes a and $a_3$, they may act together in the oxidative function, thus supporting the "unitarian" concept of Okunuki and Wainio to that extent, while the reduction process, at least in the absence of such an electron carrier as phenazine methosulphate, reveals clearly two components. Secondly, even if the "compound" is a stabilization product of an intermediate, there is now revealed a closer relationship between cytochrome oxidase and peroxidases than had been hitherto recognized.

# References

1. Orii, Y., and K. Okunuki. J. Biochem. (Tokyo), 53, 489, (1963); 57, 45 (1965).

2. Davison, A. J., and W. W. Wainio. Federation Proc., 23, 1332 (1964).

3. Lemberg, R., and G. E. Mansley. Biochim. Biophys. Acta, 118, 19 (1966).

4. Chance, B. In Oxidases and Related Redox Systems (T. E. King, H. S. Mason, and M. Morrison, eds.), Vol. II, John Wiley and Sons, New York, 1965, p. 634.

5. Lemberg, R., and G. E. Mansley. Biochim. Biophys. Acta, 96, 187 (1965).

6. Orii, Y., and K. Okunuki. J. Biochem. (Tokyo), 54, 207 (1963).

7. Dalziel, K., and J. R. P. O'Brien. Biochem. J., 67, 119, 124 (1957).

8. Shashoua, V. E. Biochemistry, 3, 1719 (1964).

9. Mansley, G. E., J. T. Stanbury, and R. Lemberg. Biochim. Biophys. Acta, 113, 33 (1966).

10. Lemberg, R., M. V. Gilmour, and J. T. Stanbury. Federation Proc., 25, 2582 (1966).

# OPTICAL PROPERTIES OF PLANT CYTOCHROME OXIDASE[*]

D. S. Bendall and W. D. Bonner, Jr.

Johnson Research Foundation, University of Pennsylvania
Philadelphia, Pennsylvania

A consistent feature of low-temperature difference spectra of plant mitochondria is an extra component whose absorption lies between the 428 mμ b Soret-band and the 445 a₃ Soret-band (1). The absorption maximum of this extra component is in the region of 438 to 440 mμ. This extra component has been associated with the oxidases of plant mitochondria. In this brief communication we wish to show the absorption characteristics of cytochromes a and a₃ as determined in plant mitochondria; as shown below the 438 mμ band is provided by reduced cytochrome a.

Fig. 1 shows some low-temperature difference spectra in the Soret region of mung bean hypocotyl mitochondria. The top spectrum, No. 1, is that of the fully reduced mitochondria, using ascorbate and tetramethylparaphenylenediamine (TMPD) as substrate, compared to oxidized mitochondria. This shows a peak at 446 mμ with a shoulder at about 440 mμ. Spectrum 3 is that of the mitochondria reduced with ascorbate + TMPD in the presence of cyanide and maintained aerobic compared to an oxidized suspension of mitochondria. Under these conditions one gets essentially the spectrum of cytochrome a alone. A characteristic feature of this spectrum is the double-banded cytochrome a-Soret-band with peaks at 445 mμ and 438 mμ . If one compares an anaerobic suspension of mitochondria reduced with ascorbate + TMPD to an aerobic suspension reduced with ascorbate + TMPD in the presence of cyanide one obtains a difference spectrum of ferro and ferri cytochrome a₃ and here, curve 4, there is a single peak of absorption maximum at 445 mμ. Curves 3 and 4 when added together give curve 2 which is essentially the same as curve 1, the anaerobic minus aerobic difference spectrum. We would like to emphasize the essential similarity between the spectra of cytochrome oxidase in plant mitochondria, as illustrated in Fig. 1, and those obtained from animal systems. There is the convenient difference that in plant mitochondria the second band of cytochrome a is shifted

[*] This work was supported by a grant from the National Science Foundation.

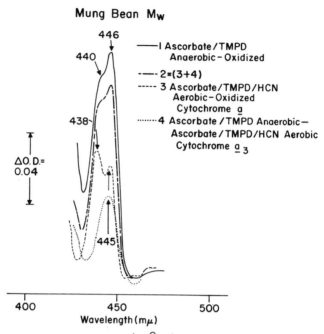

**Figure 1.** Low temperature ($77^{\circ}$ K) difference spectra of mung bean hypocotyl mitochondria. The conditions for obtaining the spectra are described in the figure. Final concentrations of reagents were: ascorbate, 10 mM; TMPD, 0.1 mM; KCN, 0.1 mM. Light path of cuvette was 2 mm, 10 mg mitochondrial protein.

a few m$\mu$ towards the ultraviolet which allows differentiation between cytochromes $\underline{a}$ and $\underline{a}_3$. This difference is not so marked in the animal mitochondrial oxidase.

Fig. 2 shows some spectra obtained with skunk cabbage mitochondria using essentially the same conditions as illustrated in Fig. 1 except that succinate has been used instead of ascorbate + TMPD. If one uses succinate as a substrate and adds cyanide to aerobic mitochondria, one can see the double band of cytochrome $\underline{a}$; but on reduction, following anaerobiosis, there is a very large increase in absorption which is accompanied by the appearance of a shoulder in the $\alpha$-band region at 590 m$\mu$ These relationships are made clear in Fig. 3 where anaerobic mitochondria reduced with succinate are compared to anaerobic mitochondria reduced with succinate in the presence of cyanide. This spectrum shows a trough at 588 m$\mu$ and a peak at 447. It is very similar to the difference spectrum of reduced

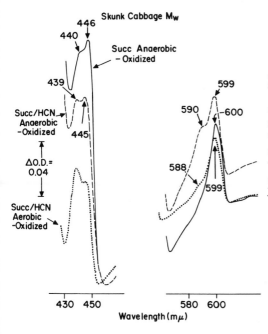

Figure 2. Low temperature (77° K) difference spectra of skunk cabbage spadix mitochondria. The conditions for obtaining the spectra are described in the figure. 6.8 mM succinate, 0.1 mM KCN, 2 mm light path.

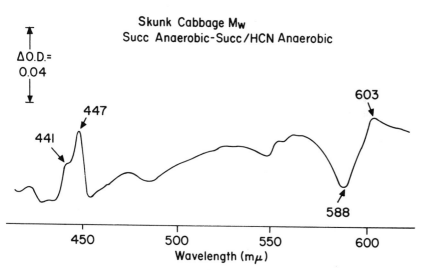

Figure 3. Low temperature (77° K) difference spectrum of skunk cabbage spadix mitochondria. 6.8 mM succinate, 0.1 mM KCN, 10 mg mitochondrial protein; light path, 2 mm.

cytochrome $a_3$ compared to reduced cytochrome $a_3$ cyanide which Yonetani (2) has described with purified cytochrome oxidase preparations. Therefore, under the conditions we have used, which is to allow a three minute period of reduction in the presence of cyanide, the $a_3$ cyanide complex in these mitochondria becomes reduced, a result which is rather contrary to what we expected.

Fig. 4 shows similar spectra using succinate-reduced skunk cabbage mitochondria but with azide replacing cyanide. Again, the sharp differentiation of $a$ and $a_3$ can be seen with the double-peaked Soret band of cytochrome $a$. Again one sees the increase in absorption on anaerobiosis which corresponds to the reduction of the azide $a_3$ compound complex. In the skunk cabbage mitochondria oxidizing succinate in the steady state in the presence of inhibitor, there is a more rapid turnover of $a_3$ azide than there is of $a_3$ cyanide.

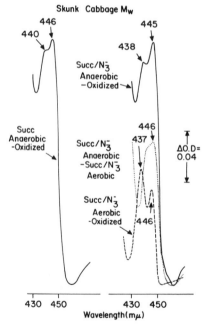

Figure 4. Low temperature (77° K) difference spectra of skunk cabbage spadix mitochondria. 6.8 mM succinate, 1.0 mM azide, 10 mg mitochondrial protein, 2mm light path.

## References

1. Bonner, W. D., Jr.  In Proceedings of the Fifth International Congress of Biochemistry, Vol. 2, 1963, p. 50.

2. Yonetani, T.  J. Biol. Chem., 235, 845 (1960).

## CYTOCHROME c OXIDASE

### DISCUSSION

**Lemberg**: With regard to the observations of Drs. Bonner and Bendall, I must admit that previously I have had reservations that one of the two bands seen may be due to ferrocytochrome $a_3$-CN. However, we have seen this same double-banded Soret band in solutions of cytochrome oxidase in which only very little $a_3$ had been reduced by freezing in the initial stages of dithionite reduction.

**Chance**: Professor Slater, can you calculate the $\Delta\epsilon$ for the fluoride compound, particularly at 640 mµ? Does this approach the value of 4-6 mM$^{-1}$ cm$^{-1}$ which might be expected for a typical ferrihemoprotein combining with fluoride? Perhaps only a small fraction of the cytochrome oxidase is binding these ligands.

My second point is to refer to Dr. Wilson's data (1) that the azide reaction in mitochondria requires only 60 µM for half maximal inhibition of respiration; this is remarkably different from the operational value of 6 mM which you gave.

**Slater**: According to a quick calculation, the $\Delta\epsilon$ at 640 mµ is equal to about 1.2 mM$^{-1}$ cm$^{-1}$ based on total reducible heme $a$, i.e., 2.4 mM$^{-1}$ cm$^{-1}$ based on reducible cytochrome $a_3$.

As I emphasized in my talk, further studies are required to elucidate the nature of the combination of azide with cytochrome $a_3$.

**Chance**: Professor Lemberg, I am better convinced by the clear spectra which you have shown, as compared with the data of others. The 2.5 mµ shift of the isosbestic point verifies the existence of the three compounds, the oxidized, the reduced, and some intermediate. I agree that the identification of the compound as an oxygen compound is far from assured, and certainly feel that a peroxide compound is more likely. But we must not forget that the ethyl hydrogen peroxide compound, at least in our hands, acts like an inhibitor of the overall activity (2).

<u>Lemberg</u>:  As I have stated in my paper, we cannot be sure, on our present evidence, whether the 428 mμ compound is an intermediate, or the stabilization product of an intermediate.  To decide this must be left to further experimentation, which I hope to carry out with Dr. Chance.

<u>Nicholls</u>:  When I was working in Dr. King's laboratory several years ago, I compared the spectroscopic effect of cyanide and the inhibitory effect of cyanide on an Okunuki-type preparation. I obtained about 90 μM as the $K_d$ for the spectroscopic effect and about 5 μM for the inhibitory effect.  I could not understand this result at all, so I did not report it anywhere; but more recently, Dr. Okunuki has reported about 92 μM for the spectroscopic effect (3), which is very similar to the value that I had calculated.  These differences in the apparent catalytic and spectroscopic affinities resemble those Dr. Slater had obtained for fluoride and azide; I think this is a complete and baffling mystery.

<u>Gibson</u>:  I have one main point.  Most cytochrome oxidase preparations are really terrible messes.  We know that there is not more than about two-thirds of native oxidase present in them.  It may even be that Slater's <u>n</u> in the Hill plot is an example of this.  As you recall, his last slide showed some points which lie around a somewhat inflected line; this is exactly what is obtained by superimposing two ordinary hyperbolic curves with different equilibrium constants, and then applying the Hill plot.  This may be evidence that his preparation is heterogeneous and is no reflection on him; everyone else's preparations are equally heterogeneous.

Similar considerations apply to Dr. Lemberg's presentation and permit an alternative explanation of his "oxygenated" complex.  On Slater's picture, I suggest that oxygen diffuses very rapidly into the unit, and that the rate of diffusion is the second order rate-limiting process described by $k_1$ in the following scheme:

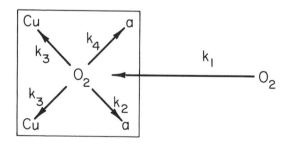

There is no change in spectrum associated with this. Once the $O_2$ molecule is in, it reacts successively in a way which, being no chemist, I will not pretend to define, first with $a_3$ with a rate constant $(k_2)$ of about $3 \times 10^4$ $sec^{-1}$, then with $\underline{Cu}$ $(k_3)$ at about $5 \times 10^3$ $sec^{-1}$, and lastly $(k_4)$ with $\underline{a}$ at $7 \times 10^2$ $sec^{-1}$. The products are water and oxidized enzyme $(Fe^{+++})$.

This is what the native enzyme does; a denatured preparation cannot do this. The Cu's are perhaps out of reach, and higher oxidation states of the iron are generated, forming the material which is commonly called the "oxygenated" complex. This may or may not be right, but at least it is my proposal.

One last point. Professor Lemberg said that his intermediate reacted slowly in the absence of cytochrome $\underline{c}$ but rapidly with it. The reaction of reduced oxidase with oxygen goes on splendidly with only 1 $\underline{c}$ to 100 $\underline{a}$; furthermore, the absorbance changes at 440 mμ during the first msec can be accounted for to within about 1 percent, using two spectrophotometric species, $\underline{a}_3$ and $\underline{a}$. You do not need another complex in the rapid reaction which follows mixing with oxygen.

Lemberg: I cannot agree that the cytochrome oxidase preparations obtained by the Yonetani method are "terribly messy". In fact, the results of a number of investigators using this preparation agree remarkably well, as Vanneste has recently confirmed (4). There is no detectable evidence for "denaturation", of which we have shown no less than three types; the only one which does not alter the CO-heme $\underline{a}$ ratio nor the ferrous oxidase spectrum is the shift from 418 mμ to 423 mμ of the ferric enzyme while the two other ones make all the heme able to react with CO. We have used the 418 mμ enzyme, as has Dr. Gibson (5). It is, of course, impossible to exclude any unobservable denaturation on enzyme isolation, but Dr. Gibson's kinetic results were, in fact, obtained with the same Yonetani preparation (6), and have been interpreted by him as showing a faster oxidation of cytochrome $\underline{a}_3$ than $\underline{a}$ with moderately high oxygen concentrations (5). Absorption alterations at only the two wavelengths 605 and 445 mμ were studied and therefore evidence for or against the absence of the 428 mμ compound could not be obtained, since the decrease at both wavelengths in terms of the percentage difference between ferrous and ferric iron is quite similar, as stated in my paper. One may even assume that the faster decrease of the 445 mμ than the 605 mμ band with moderately high oxygen concentrations is, at least partially, due to the formation of the 428 mμ compound. Finally, we can observe no abnormality in the behavior of the 830 mμ band ascribed to copper, although this does not necessarily disprove Gibson's speculation.

Slater:  I agree with Dr. Gibson that cytochrome $c$ oxidase preparations contain non-reducible cytochromes $a$ and $a_3$.  Contrary to his suggestion at the ISOX meeting that the non-reducible fraction consists entirely of cytochrome $a_3$ (7), van Gelder and Muisjers have shown that the non-reducible fraction, like the reducible, contains equal amounts of cytochrome $a$ and $a_3$ (8). We must still investigate whether the non-reducible cytochrome $a_3$ combines with azide or fluoride.  I do not place any significance on the points lying above the line in the Hill plot, since these lie in the part of the plot where experimental errors are magnified.

One comment on Dr. Lemberg's paper that is also relevant to Dr. Gibson's remarks:  The titration with NADH in the presence of phenazine methosulfate shows that, under these conditions, cytochromes $a$ and $a_3$ are reduced in collusion.  Non-reducible cytochromes $a$ and $a_3$ are completely inert in this titration.  They interfere no more than any other irrelevant protein that is present.

Gibson:  I should like to ask Dr. Lemberg about the CO-binding capacity of his preparation.  So far as I know, no one has reported CO-binding capacity, which accounts for more than a fraction of the total heme $a$ present, and I am afraid that I disagree entirely with the point about the reducibility of these materials.  One gets widely different difference spectra and quite different values for the extinction coefficients of $a$ and $a_3$ if one arranges to examine what is, hopefully, the undenatured material present in the preparation.  For example, at 444 m$\mu$ the normal partition of the extinction coefficients between $a$ and $a_3$ is of the order 1 : 1, i.e., about half the change is attributed to $a_3$ and half to $a$.  In rapid spectrophotometric measurements, the ratio is about 2.3 : 1 in favor of $a_3$, and I maintain that the reason for this is that the slowly determined static spectra take into account all the material in the preparation and not just the active material; I think that most of the spectra which have been published are substantially affected by this.  It is not a matter of the ratio of $a_3$ to $a$ in native materials, but of active $a_3$ to total $a$. We all agree that the ideal ratio would be 1 : 1, but Gibson, Palmer, and Wharton (9) do not agree that real preparations have one-half the total heme present as a reactive and functional heme $a_3$.  There is a smaller fraction present as functional $a_3$, and the total CO bound as a proportion of the total heme $a$ present is the relevant figure.  I have not seen Dr. Lemberg's data, but if he agrees with Vanneste (4), then he agrees with us, because Vanneste got just the same results as we did, i.e., about one-third the total heme $a$ in the preparation was capable of combining with CO.

<u>Lemberg</u>:  Data on the CO-binding properties of my preparation have been fully published (10).  Like the figures of Vanneste (4), they give ratios of CO bound to total heme, in my case, ranging from 0.48 to 0.53.  I therefore disagree emphatically with Dr. Gibson's interpretation.

To the point of reducibility, the ratio 420 : 444 mµ--and it is at 420 rather than 424 mµ that we find the maximum of the bulge which is interpreted by Drs. Gibson and Slater as an ir-reducible heme <u>a</u> compound--has, in our earlier preparations (11) been found quite as variable as those found by van Gelder (12); these preparations, however, did not give as good a 428 mµ com-pound as the preparations used in our recent experiments here at the Johnson Foundation, the spectra of which were shown in Fig. 1 of my paper (13).  From this it will be seen that the 424 : 444 mµ ratio was 0.47, while that of the 420 : 444 mµ was 0.43.  This is as low as in the van Gelder preparation which contained the smallest amount of "irreducible oxidase". It can be readily calculated that the bulge corresponds to about 5 percent of the ferric maximum at 420 mµ.  This is within the experimental error for the height of the $\alpha$-band of the ferrous oxidase from which the heme <u>a</u> concentration is calculated.  It cannot seriously influence the ratio of CO bound to total heme, which has been found by us (10) to vary between 0.485 and 0.53, using $\epsilon_{605}$ = 23 mM$^{-1}$ cm$^{-1}$ or $\epsilon_{605}$ = 21 mM$^{-1}$ cm$^{-1}$, respectively.

I should not call the simultaneous reduction of <u>a</u> and <u>a</u>$_3$ by NADH in the presence of phenazine methosulfate "reduction in collusion" but rather would term it an electron carrier-catalyzed acceleration of the reduction of ferricytochrome <u>a</u>$_3$ by ferrocytochrome <u>a</u>.

Finally, we have no definite evidence with regard to the contribution of cytochrome <u>a</u> to the Soret band ( $\Delta$ferrous-ferric). Our preliminary results, based on kinetic studies of the reac-tion, agree better with a ratio of 0.33 than with Dr. Slater's figure of 0.5 for the contributions of cytochrome <u>a</u> to the $\Delta\epsilon_{445}$, but further investigation is required.

<u>Chance</u>:  We all want to use the most "native" cytochrome oxi-dase preparation, and all criteria by which we judge this are useful.  Submitochondrial particles are useful for this pur-pose; there a large part of the absorption at 444 mµ is due to <u>a</u>$_3$.  There seems to have been a discrepancy with a number of purified oxidase preparations ever since Dr. Lucile Smith and I have worked with the purified oxidase preparations.

Wang:  To have the most "native" oxidase is to leave it in the
mitochondria and not to extract it at all.  Since this is im-
practical, perhaps we should study each other's preparations
for comparison.

King:  Let us first study Professor Slater's scheme without
Professor Gibson's modification.  Professor Slater put azide
and fluoride at the same level and loci of the reactions as
cyanide.  I suppose Slater has oversimplified the reactions
for the convenience of his presentation.  However, it may be
worthwhile to keep the record straight even by belaboring the
details a little.  The action of cyanide on cytochrome oxidase
certainly differs from that of azide; I do not have much personal experience with fluoride.  However, I should suppose
cyanide also differs dramatically from fluoride in action.
The cyanide inhibition of cytochrome oxidase, even from as
little as 30 μM cyanide, is not readily reversible insofar as
spectra and enzymatic activity are concerned.  This "not-ready-
reversibility" was missed, so to speak, by Warburg and Keilin
who concluded, in their classical experiments, that cyanide
inhibition was readily reversible.  This was probably due to
technique; Warburg used the Warburg apparatus and Keilin the
Barcroft manometer, for they did not have the Chance machine
with a sophisticated servo mechanism at that time.  On the
other hand, azide inhibition, under the conditions used for
the cyanide experiment, can be immediately reversed, as we
have found.  This difference between azide and cyanide has
also been shown in Dr. Wilson's work from the Johnson Foundation (1) on the azide reaction in mitochondria.  One thing is
certain:  that cyanide action on cytochrome oxidase, either
in the particulate or in the soluble form, is much more complicated than azide action.  With respect to "ready reversibility",
I wonder how fluoride, indeed, behaves experimentally?

Finally, I should point out that some years ago, Dr.
Wainio found some "mysterious" cyanide reaction for cytochrome
oxidase (14).  That reaction might have some relation with the
one which I just mentioned and reported in detail elsewhere (15).

Slater:  We have not yet checked whether the combination with
fluoride after prolonged incubation is readily reversible.

King:  I should like now to make a comment on Professor Gibson's
modified scheme, which I am inclined to agree is very attractive and appealing.  However, I am not certain about one essential feature; I wonder whether the geometry or the distances
involved really allows Dr. Gibson to put an oxygen molecule in
the center of a square with, at the four corners, $\underline{a}$ and $\underline{a}_3$ and

two Cu atoms, like an elegant Victorian tea set, with the reactions proceeding as smoothly as the chalk lines he drew and the electrons being collected as simply as pouring tea back into the oxygen "pot".

My last point pertains to soluble cytochrome oxidase. I am in agreement with Professor Lemberg. I think some people have used "bad" cytochrome oxidase as Dr. Gibson has depicted, i.e., soluble preparations aged for various lengths of time, and therefore some "strange" or "different" results have been reported. We have found a very simple test method: fresh oxidase preparations show the Soret maximum at 418-419 mμ in the oxidized form. Upon aging at $0°$, or by lyophilization, this maximum gradually shifts to as high as 424 mμ with practically no change of the reduced maximum at 444-445 mμ. I would like to point out that our soluble cytochrome oxidase can be prepared within 24 hours from the Keilin and Hartree preparation. The specific activity is more than twice as high as the highest value reported in the literature; it has a first order constant of about 16 per second per mg of protein in a 3-ml assay system at the optimal pH of approximately 5.7. The complete method of preparation has not been published.

In this connection, I would like to acknowledge Dr. Lucile Smith. Her suggestions for cytochrome oxidase assay are very helpful. At one time, using her method, the assay suddenly did not come out in the expected first order manner, but rather resembled almost (of course, not quite) a second order reaction. Although we were using crystalline c of the Margoliash type, the trouble was that the solution was too old!

Gibson: Professor King, my source of information on the location of the active groups is the same as yours--a personal communication from Maxwell's demon. Seriously, however, it is not really necessary that the groups should be in extremely close relation. One may have intermediates of quite finite lifetimes inside the box I drew, and I do not feel that a and a₃ must be right up against one another. All I postulate is that radical intermediates are contained within the black box and normally, with the native enzyme, these radicals do not escape into the solution.

Has anyone any comments on the initiation of sulfite oxidation by cytochrome oxidase, which might be correlated with the presence of denatured material in the preparation as well?

King: I am happy to hear Professor Gibson mention some radical intermediates in the cytochrome oxidase reaction. However,

I am still not quite sure whether I should take it. One of my objections is that according to the proposal, cytochrome $\underline{a}$ (just like $\underline{a}_3$) is "auto-oxidizable", although I am aware of the reacting species in Professor Gibson's mind may not be the free molecular oxygen but is an oxygen radical of some sort. If it is true, his interesting idea may be confirmed experimentally without too many complications. The next point is that if the distance is immaterial, then this oxygen radical of some sort must be able to move quite freely in the black box (i.e., in the protein milieu) but at the same time the radical does not escape into the solution. It is a bit difficult to visualize that these two conditions can exist simultaneously.

Lemberg: One may assume that the initiation of the sulfite oxidation is due to the conversion of the initial $Fe(II)O_2$ form of cytochrome $\underline{a}_3$ into $Fe(III)O_2^-$, as Handler suggested (16) and to its partial escape from Dr. Gibson's black box before it had time to interact with ferrous cytochrome $\underline{a}$ to form the 428 m$\mu$ compound.

Morrison: I must say that I believe the problem of the ratio of cytochrome $\underline{a}$ to $\underline{a}_3$ was more or less resolved at the ISOX Symposium (17). At that time there was general agreement that the differences in the ratios observed in several laboratories were not due to experimental technique but could be attributed to differences in the preparations. This is apparent in the degree of scatter we obtained with different preparations and in the studies of Professor Gibson which showed that only in the intact mitochondria does the ratio of $\underline{a}$ to $a_3$ approach unity. In all purified preparations, the amount of CO bound per mole of heme present increases with the age and treatment of the preparation. For most purified preparations, three or more moles of heme $\underline{a}$ are present for each mole of CO bound (18).

I do have a point about Professor Lemberg's spectrum, and I wonder if this might not explain his data. I noticed, Professor Lemberg, that the entire spectrum of your peroxide complex has a higher extinction than either the reduced or oxidized form of cytochrome oxidase. The basis of your argument is that the extinction coefficient at 428 m$\mu$ is too high to account for a mixture of partially reduced, partially oxidized cytochrome oxidase. Now, if there were some turbidity in a partially reduced, partially oxidized preparation, it would shift the entire spectrum to higher extinction and also change the position of the isosbestic point. This would also be consistent with your observation that the changes in the $\alpha$ and $\gamma$ maxima are identical to those observed for reduced and oxidized forms.

Lemberg: Our solution was crystal clear and had no detectable absorption in the 650-700 mµ region; turbidity cannot, therefore, explain the spectrum. In my paper (13) I have also shown that the 428 mµ compound behaves quite differently from the cytochrome a-a_3 mixture on reduction with dithionite. Finally, our difference spectrum (ferrous-ferric) for cytochrome a, which we obtained by partial reduction of the oxidase, has its α-maximum at 605 rather than 600 mµ.

Slater: I would not like to leave people with the impression that there is complete disagreement about the composition of cytochrome oxidase preparations. Since there is no time for a proper discussion, let me in 30 seconds express my position, in which I believe very firmly. Even "good" cytochrome c oxidase preparations contain only roughly 70 percent of reducible, functionally active oxidase; the remaining 30 percent is functionally non-active oxidase. This functionally non-active oxidase also contains equal amounts of a and a_3. Thus, the CO-binding heme a is less than one-half the total heme a, but does equal one-half the reducible heme a. And, in agreement with Dr. Gibson, I do believe that Dr. Lemberg has got some non-reducible cytochrome oxidase in his preparation. In his spectrum of reduced cytochrome c oxidase, one can see the band of oxidized cytochrome oxidase, exactly as Dr. Gibson pointed out, at the ISOX meeting (7) was present in our preparations as well.

Lemberg: I still disagree with the amount of "irreducible" oxidase which Dr. Slater assumes to be present in our preparation. If this were 30 percent, the CO:total heme a ratio would be 0.35, and not 0.5 as we find it.

Wainio: I feel obliged to comment briefly on our studies of the "oxygenated" intermediate. Although the work was completed in 1964 with Dr. Allan Davison (19), it is still in thesis form. Because the suggestion had been made that this form might be a mixture of the oxidized and reduced forms, Dr. Davison mixed oxidized and reduced cytochrome oxidase, and very clearly got a double peak. In the so-called "oxygenated" form, there was very clearly a single peak.

I also want to object to the statement that the differentiation of this form was inconclusive. The isosbestic point of this form was different from that of the oxidized and reduced mixture, as shown in the curves we published in the ISOX volume (20).

Many reductants produce this effect, as Dr. Lemberg has already stated. We went back to some of our very old work and found that, in fact, we had obtained the same spectrum with ferrocyanide (21).

Furthermore, the reduced character of the 605 mμ peak and the loss at 445 mμ do not always parallel one another. In some preparations, the remaining 605 mμ absorption is about 25 percent of the difference between the oxidized and reduced forms, and in other cases it is as much as 40 percent (21).

What Maxwell's demon has suggested to explain the difference when you introduce oxygen and shift the entire absorption is that with oxygen you involve both hemes, and with CO you involve only one heme.

A warning to those who are working with the most purified preparations of cytochrome oxidase. It would appear possible to have a second-order reaction with respect to cytochrome c̲. Thus, if anyone is working with the kinetics of purified preparations, they should be careful to analyze the order of the reaction, and make sure that they do not have second order kinetics. With some of our preparations, Grebner and I have found that for the first 25 seconds we get a perfect second-order reaction, which then changes into the expected first-order reaction (D. Grebner and W. W. Wainio, unpublished results). (See Figure 1 below)

Gibson: Where, in the scheme for $O_2$ and CO you drew, did the a̲3 go?

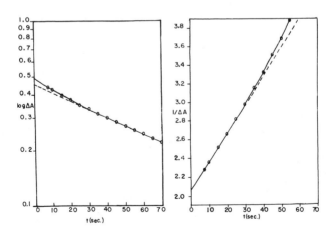

Figure 1. (Wainio) Oxidation of ferrocytochrome c̲ by a soluble cytochrome oxidase. The reaction is second order ($1/\Delta A$ is linear) for 30 sec.

<u>Wainio:</u>  In my scheme for cytochrome oxidase there is no $a_3$.
The point being made is that when you add oxygen, you shift all
the 445 mμ absorption to about 428 mμ,* whereas when you add
CO, there is only a partial shift of the 445 mμ band to 430 mμ.
In this scheme, the oxygen of CO is going to react with one of
the hemes (obviously, the carbon cannot), whereas in the $O_2$,
both O atoms react with the two hemes.

<u>Morrison:</u>  We have continued to study the conditions required
for the preparation of cytochrome <u>a</u> free of cytochrome $a_3$ (23,
24).  In Fig. 2 is shown the spectrum of a cytochrome <u>c</u> oxidase preparation treated with borohydride under special conditions.  The preparation, after treatment, is nearly all reduced

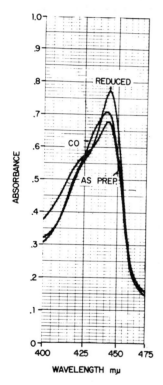
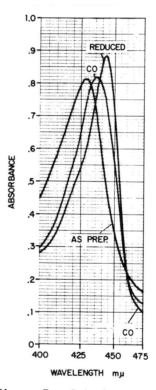

Figure 2.  Cytochrome <u>c</u>
oxidase treated $BH_4^-$.

Figure 3.  Cytochrome <u>c</u>
treated $BH_4^- K_3Fe(CN)_6$; passed through Sephadex G25.

*Editors' note:  This statement does not apply to measurements
made at short times with the rapid flow apparatus, see this
discussion, page 492 , or T. Yonetani in the Proceedings of
the Vth Congress of Biochemistry (22).

and is not very auto-oxidizable. This preparation in the reduced form has its maxima in the same region as would be expected for cytochrome $\underline{a}$ (24,25). Saturation with carbon monoxide does not shift the peak, although there is a small amount of material present which obviously does combine with carbon monoxide as the change in spectrum shows.

If this preparation is oxidized with ferricyanide and then passed down a Sephadex column to remove the ferricyanide, the spectral properties are completely changed. As shown in Fig. 3, the spectrum is now similar to the original cytochrome $\underline{c}$ oxidase and the preparation now combines with carbon monoxide to give the shift usually obtained with cytochrome $\underline{c}$ oxidase. There is an increase in enzyme activity on treatment with ferricyanide, but the specific activity remains very low--only about 15 percent of the original preparation--even though the spectrum has returned.

Our present interpretation of the data is that we have affected two different properties of the cytochrome $\underline{c}$ oxidase required for enzyme activity. One of these involves the ability of cytochrome $a_3$ to combine with carbon monoxide. This might well be due to groups such as disulfide bonds which hold the proteins open, allowing carbon monoxide access to the cytochrome $\underline{a}_3$ prosthetic group. Thus, when the disulfide is reduced the protein prevents access to the heme and no carbon monoxide is formed. When the sulfhydryl groups are oxidized by ferricyanide treatment, the protein configuration allows access to the prosthetic group of cytochrome $\underline{a}_3$ and again the cytochrome will combine with carbon monoxide. A second group also appears to be involved in these reactions. It does not contribute to the spectral properties of the enzyme, but is important for enzyme activity. We are now working on the explanation of these phenomena.

From our work with cytochrome $\underline{c}$ oxidase, in which we converted the formyl group of cytochrome $a_3$ to an alcohol (23), you will recall that this preparation was still quite active and yet the CO which did combine with the prosthetic group only combined with the heme prosthetic group whose formyl group had been changed. Thus it would appear that the heme prosthetic groups are not equivalent, and so the possibility suggested by Dr. Wainio has already been excluded.

Kamen: I should, for the sake of completeness, remark in connection with the cross-reaction between bacterial or mammalian-type cytochromes and bacterial or cow-heart oxidases, that these have also been studied in great detail by T. Yamanaka (26).

He has attempted to make an evolutionary correlation based on the relative velocity of the reactions exhibited by these various combinations. He had 38 crystalline purified cytochromes from a variety of sources, which he tested against the Pseudomonas oxidase (cytochrome cd) and the cow-heart oxidase. (For more on the subject of the reaction between mammalian cytochromes and bacterial oxidases, see Dr. Lucile Smith's contribution to this symposium (27).)

## References

1. Wilson, D. Federation Proc., 25, Abstract No. 1915 (1966).

2. Chance, B. Nature, 169, 215 (1952).

3. Orii, Y., and K. Okunuki. J. Biochem., 55, 37 (1964).

4. Vanneste, W. H. Biochemistry, 5, 838 (1966).

5. Gibson, Q. H., and C. Greenwood. Biochem. J., 86, 541 (1963).

6. Yonetani, T. J. Biol. Chem., 236, 1680 (1961).

7. Gibson, Q. H. In Oxidases and Related Redox Systems (T. E. King, H. S. Mason, and M. Morrison, eds.), John Wiley and Sons, New York, 1965, p. 603.

8. van Gelder, B. F., and A. O. Muisjers. Biochim. Biophys. Acta, 118, 36 (1966).

9. Gibson, Q. H., G. Palmer, and D. C. Wharton. J. Biol. Chem., 240, 915 (1965).

10. Mansley, G. E., J. T. Stanberg, and R. Lemberg. Biochim. Biophys. Acta, 113, 33 (1966).

11. Lemberg, R., and G. E. Mansley. Biochim. Biophys. Acta, 118, 19 (1966).

12. van Gelder, B. F. Biochim. Biophys. Acta, 118, 36 (1966).

13. Lemberg, R. This volume, p. 478

14. Wainio, W. W. Arch. Biochem. Biophys., 90, 18 (1960).

15. Caminio, P. W., and T. E. King. J. Biol. Chem., 241, 970 (1966).

16. Handler, P. In Oxidases and Related Redox Systems (T. E. King, H. S. Mason, and M. Morrison, eds.), John Wiley and Sons, New York, 1965, p. 809.

17. Oxidases and Related Redox Systems (T. E. King, H. S. Mason, and M. Morrison, eds.), John Wiley and Sons, New York, 1965.

18. Morrison, M., and S. Horie.  J. Biol. Chem., 240, 1359 (1965).

19. Davison, A. J., and W. W. Wainio.  Federation Proc., 23, 323 (1964).

20. Wainio, W. W.  In Oxidases and Related Redox Systems (T. E. King, H. S. Mason, and M. Morrison, eds.), John Wiley and Sons, New York, 1965, p. 622.

21. Wainio, W. W.  J. Biol. Chem., 212, 723 (1955).

22. Yonetani, T.  In Proceedings of the Vth International Congress of Biochemistry, V, Pergamon Press, Oxford, 1963, p. 396.

23. Morrison, M., and S. Horie.  J. Biol. Chem., 239, 1432 (1964).

24. Horie, S., and M. Morrison.  J. Biol. Chem., 239, 1438 (1964).

25. Horie, S., and M. Morrison.  J. Biol. Chem., 238, 2859 (1963).

26. Yamanaka, T.  Science, in press.

27. Smith, L., N. Newton, and Peter Scholes.  This volume, p. 395.

MOR AND ORD OF CYTOCHROME OXIDASE

DISCUSSION


Shashoua:  I should like to present some spectral studies which
Dr. Estabrook and I carried out on cytochrome oxidase.  Fig. 1
shows a comparison of the optical rotatory dispersion (ORD) and
magneto-optical rotation (MOR) with the absorption spectra of
samples of oxidized and reduced cytochrome oxidase.  Both the
MOR and ORD data show changes with the oxidation state of the
molecule.  The largest differences are observed in the ORD data.
The reduced state shows two positive Cotton effects centered
about 595 and 540 mμ, while the oxidized molecules show a positive Cotton effect at about 510 mμ.

Morrison:  I would also like to report some preliminary work on
the optical rotatory dispersion of cytochrome c oxidase.  Fig.
2 shows the ORD of the reduced, oxidized and CO-derivative of
cytochrome c oxidase in the Soret region of the spectrum.  You
will note that the Cotton effects obtained with this hemoprotein
are not greatly different from those obtained with other hemoproteins.  There are positive Cotton effects for all three
forms of the preparation, corresponding to absorption maxima
at 444 mμ for the reduced, 430 mμ for the CO-derivative, and
424 mμ for the oxidized form of the cytochrome c oxidase.  Like
cytochrome c, the preparation shows negative rotation and this
is not affected by the solubilizing agent; the same results are
obtained in Tween 80 or cholate.

A single Cotton effect is present for all three forms of
the preparation.  Since the absorption maxima for the reduced
and oxidized forms of cytochromes a and $a_3$ are nearly identical, it was not unexpected that a single Cotton effect would be
obtained with these forms of the cytochromes.  CO, however,
forms a derivative only with cytochrome $a_3$, and the maximum is
shifted from the reduced position by about 14 mμ.  If cytochrome
a remained unaffected by CO, we should have found evidence for
a double Cotton effect--one due to cytochrome a and the other
to $a_3$:CO.  However, only a single Cotton effect was observed
for the CO compound of cytochrome c oxidase.  One possible
explanation is that the protein containing the cytochrome a
is disoriented and does not contribute an asymmetric center;

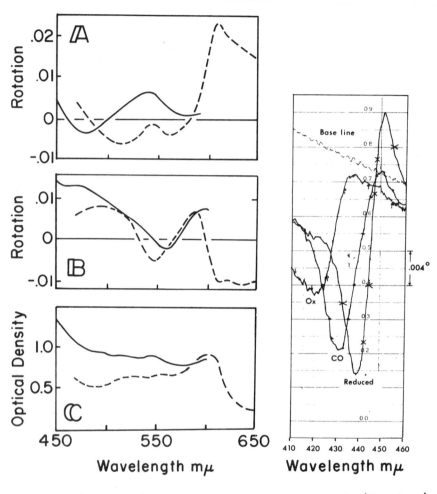

Figure 1. (Shashoua) A comparison of A) ORD, B) MOR, and C) absorption spectra of cytochrome oxidase.

————— oxidized
--------- reduced

Figure 2. (Morrison) Comparison of ORD spectra of reduced, oxidized, and CO-derivative of cytochrome oxidase.

that is, the cytochrome a is on a disoriented portion of the peptide chain and is analogous to the situation found with denatured hemoproteins, where the Cotton effect of the heme chromatophore is completely lost.

King: I also would like to make some comments on ORD of cytochrome oxidase. In collaboration with Dr. J. A. Schellman,
a molecular spectroscopist, we have made an investigation of
the ORD behavior of the reduced and oxidized forms of cytochrome oxidase (1).

Fig. 3 represents a replotting of the experimental rotations in terms of mole heme a per liter. Reduced cytochrome
oxidase shows a Cotton effect with an amplitude of 220,000°
centered at 446 mμ, close to the absorption maximum at 444-445
mμ. Upon oxidation, the center of the Cotton effect is shifted
to 426 mμ, and its amplitude is 150,000°.

In addition, a small anomaly which may arise from one or
several Cotton effects at about 400 mμ is also observed; it is
much less pronounced in the reduced form. This second Cotton
effect may be of considerable significance in the dispute concerning a vs. a₃. I do not think that time will permit me to
elaborate further here. However, I should add that the rotatory strength is 0.47 Debye magneton in the oxidized form and
0.35 in the reduced form, in spite of the fact that the amplitude of the latter is more than 30 percent greater than that

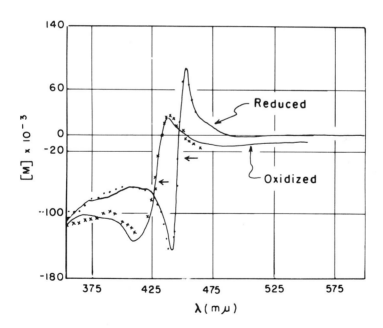

Figure 3. (King) Molar rotation of cytochrome oxidase showing heme Cotton effects.

505

of the oxidized form. Equally important, the order of magnitude of the rotatory strength is unusually high in both forms, clearly indicating the great perturbation of the asymmetrical environment (the protein) executed on the heme moiety. The huge amplitude of the Cotton effect may also be due to the fact that the heme a, when attached to the protein is monomeric, so to speak, and thus shows optical asymmetry by itself, in contrast to the optical inactivity found experimentally for heme a in solution.

The dots and crosses on Fig. 3 are the calculated values. You can see that there is some deviation from the experimental values. This deviation might be due to the fact that even our computation is not refined enough to separate the extrinsic Cotton effects from rotations associated with the structural conformation. Actually, it is not too surprising because of the huge Cotton effect of heme a. However, the deviation may also be caused by (a) the Cotton effects not being gaussian, (b) more than one minor Cotton effect being involved, and/or (c) the Schecter-Blout formalism not being adequate. At any rate, the effect of the oxidation state influences not only the heme Cotton effects but also the peptide backbone rotation. This observation is attested by a displacement of the entire ORD curve to a more negative rotation. As shown in Fig. 3, the displacement in the Soret region amounts to nearly 50,000°, and the displacement in the UV region is equally distinct.

In conclusion, not only the interactions between the heme and the apoprotein differ, but also the conformation of the backbone (as determined by the Schecter-Blout method) changes with the oxidation state of the enzyme.

Urry: The absence in the Soret region of a complex Cotton effect of the sort found in the hemepeptide aggregates may reasonably be taken to indicate that the heme moieties in the preparations of cytochrome oxidase are at distance greater than 10-15 Å.

## References

1. King, T. E., and J. A. Schellman. Federation Proc., 25, 1251 (1966).

# ANALYSIS OF ORD DATA OF HEMOPROTEINS[*]

John A. Schellman
University of Oregon, Eugene

Tsoo E. King
Oregon State University, Corvallis

We should like to comment on the analysis of ORD data of hemoproteins, using the following phenomenological equations for computing the helical content on the basis of linear models:

$$[M]_\lambda = \frac{A'_{193}(193)^2}{\lambda^2 - (193)^2} + \frac{A'_{225}(225)^2}{\lambda^2 - (225)^2} + \sum_i F\,(\lambda_i, \Delta_i, A_i) \quad (1)$$

Here $[M]$ is the experimental rotation in terms of mole heme $\underline{a}$ per liter at an operational wave length $\lambda$; $A'_{193}$ and $A'_{225}$ are Shecter-Blout parameters on the molar basis; $\Delta_i$; $A_i$, and $\lambda_i$ are the band-width, strength parameter, and the center, respectively, of Cotton effect; and:

$$F = \frac{A_i \lambda_i}{\Delta_i} \left[ e^{-x^2} \int_o^x e^{t^2}\, dt - \frac{\Delta_i}{2(\lambda + \lambda_i)} \right] \quad (1a)$$

$$\text{and } X = \frac{\lambda - \lambda_i}{\Delta_i}$$

When measurements are made at $|\lambda - \lambda_i| > 4\Delta_i$, the formula (Eq. 1) is representable by a sum of Drude terms, i.e.:

$$[M] = \frac{A'_{193}(193)^2}{\lambda^2 - (193)^2} + \frac{A'_{225}(225)^2}{\lambda^2 - (225)^2} + \frac{A_i \lambda_i^2}{\lambda^2 - \lambda_i^2}$$

*This work was supported in part by grants from the National Institutes of Health, the National Science Foundation, and the Life Insurance Medical Research Fund.

As shown in these equations, we have endeavored to separate extrinsic Cotton effects from those due to structural conformation. In hemoproteins, there are not only Cotton effects due to disulfide, tyrosine, other aromatic amino acids, etc., but also large Cotton effects of heme itself. These equations have been used in the analysis of ORD data of cytochrome oxidase and we have taken pain in computing. As you can see, Eq. 2 is a combination of the Shecter-Blout formalism (1) for the rotation of the peptide backbone combined with the Kuhn-Moscowitz procedure (2,3) for representing separate Cotton effects. However, the last term in Eq. 1, $F(\lambda_i, \Delta_i, A_i)$ plays a great role in analyzing any protein other than linear models in general, and hemoproteins in particular. If the curve is Gaussian, the F term becomes that indicated in Eq. la.

Now back to cytochrome oxidase, $A_{225}$ and $A_{193}$ parameters have been computed. Preliminary data are summarized in Table I.

TABLE I

"A" parameters and effective
helical content of cytochrome oxidase

| Form | $A^*_{225}$ | $H_{225}$ | $A^*_{193}$ | $H_{193}$ | $H_{mean}$ |
|------|------|------|------|------|------|
|  | deg. | % | deg. | % | % |
| Reduced | -990 | 46 | 1320 | 54 | 50 |
| Oxidized | -820 | 38 | 1020 | 48 | 43 |
| Oxidized + 8 M urea | -430 | 18 | 210 | 21 | 20 |

*$A_{225}$ and $A_{193}$ are the Shecter-Blout parameters on the residue basis (1); they are converted from $A'_{225}$ and $A'_{139}$ as shown in Eq. 1 by taking the mean residual weight of 110 and the experimental value of grams of protein per mole of heme a, i.e. $10^5$. $H_{193}$ and $H_{225}$ are per cent of helicity computed from $A_{193}$ and $A_{225}$.

It may be noted that in Shecter and Blout's original report for synthetic polyamino acids and some simple proteins, helical contents computed from $A_{193}$ and $A_{225}$ values agree well (1). However, it is not true for at least half a dozen proteins, such as apomyoglobin and re-natured apomyoglobin (4), ovalbumin and conalbumin (5), and malate dehydrogenase under various conditions (6). The deviations are in about the same order as shown here. The helicity calculated from $A_{193}$ is always larger than that from $A_{225}$.

Mention may be made that the effective helicity computed from A parameters does not conform to the negative rotation at 233 mµ trough from our preliminary data of cytochrome oxidase. This disparity at the present time cannot be settled without further experimentation.

At any rate, we are gratified to see that Dr. Urry has also warned against the inordinate interpretation of ORD data for hemoproteins (7). We have used these equations for computation and have paid special attention to rotatory strength. Rotatory strength is a scalar product of the magnetic and electric moments of the transition. The electric dipole can be computed from absorption spectra but the evaluation of the magnetic moment and its orientation constitutes the central problem of optical rotation theory.

## Acknowledgement

We acknowledge Dr. Paul Carver who kindly sent us the computing program which with minor alterations was the basis of this work. We thank Dr. Irving Listowsky for Dr. Cassman's data.

## References

1.  Shecter, E., and E. R. Blout. Proc. Natl. Acad. Sci., 51, 695 (1964).

2.  Kuhn, W., and E. Braun. Z. Physik. Chem., B8, 445 (1930); Kuhn, W., Amn. Rev. Phys. Chem., 9, 417 (1958).

3.  Moscowitz, A. In Optical Rotatory Dispersion (C. Djerassi, ed.), McGraw-Hill Book Co., New York, 1960, p. 150.

4.  Harrison, S. C., and E. R. Blout. J. Biol. Chem., 240, 299 (1965).

5.  Tomimatsu, Y., and W. Garfield. Biopolymers, 3, 509 (1965).

6.  Cassman, M. Thesis, Albert Einstein Medical College, New York, 1966.

7.  Urry, D. W. Proc. Natl. Acad. Sci., 54, 640 (1965).

# EFFECT OF SUBSTRATES ON MICROSOMAL CYTOCHROME P-450[*]

R. W. Estabrook[‡], J. B. Schenkman, W. Cammer
D. Y. Cooper[‡], S. Narasimhulu, and O. Rosenthal

Johnson Research Foundation and Harrison Department
of Surgical Research, University of Pennsylvania
Philadelphia, Pennsylvania

After hearing the discussion (1,2) on reactions of cytochrome oxidase, particularly the influence of ligands modifying its spectral properties, it is appropriate to describe
briefly some recent experiments with a second type of hemoprotein oxidase (3) present in many mammalian cells. This
hemoprotein is cytochrome P-450--a pigment with protoheme as
its prosthetic group (4). Cytochrome P-450 is generally found
associated with the endoplasmic reticulum where it serves (3)
as the "oxygen activating enzyme" for a number of mixed function oxidations involved in the oxidative metabolism of drugs,
steroids, carcinogenic compounds, and insecticides. The general equation for these reactions is as follows:

$$H^+ + AH_2 + TPNH + O_2 \longrightarrow AHOH + TPN^+ + H_2O$$

Concomitant with the oxidation of one mole of TPNH, one atom
of atmospheric oxygen is incorporated into the substrate $AH_2$
to give the hydroxylated product AHOH. Previous studies (5,6,
7) have demonstrated that many reactions of this type are inhibited by CO and that the CO-inhibited reaction is reversed
by light. Using the photochemical action spectrum technique
developed by Warburg (8), cytochrome P-450 has been identified
(5,6) as the terminal oxidase for this type of reaction.

Recently our attention has turned to an investigation of
the influence of various substrates ($AH_2$) on the optical and
magnetometric properties of cytochrome P-450. Narasimhulu et
al. (9,10) had demonstrated reversible spectral changes occurring upon the addition of 17-hydroxyprogesterone to adrenal

[*]These studies were carried out during tenures of Public Health
Service Research Career Development Awards HE 25132 to D. Y.
Cooper and GM K3-4111 to R. W. Estabrook.

[‡]This work supported in part by U.S. PHS Grants AM 07217, AM
04484, GM 27706, and GM 12202 and NSF Grant GB 2451.

cortex microsomes. As illustrated in Fig. 1, addition of 17-hydroxyprogesterone causes the loss of absorbance at 419 mµ with an associated increase in absorbance at about 385 mµ. The magnitude of absorbance change observed (10) was dependent on the concentration of 17-hydroxyprogesterone added as well as the concentration of microsomal protein.

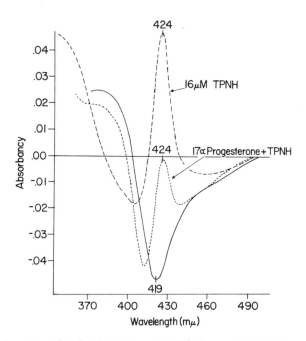

Figure 1. Spectral changes on addition of 17-hydroxyprogesterone and TPNH to beef adrenal cortex microsomes. An aliquot of adrenal cortex microsomes was diluted in glycylglycine buffer, pH 7.4, containing bovine serum albumin. The sample was divided equally in two cuvettes and a baseline of equal light absorbance recorded with a wavelength scanning spectrophotometer. An aliquot of 17-hydroxyprogesterone was added to one cuvette and the difference spectrum (solid line) recorded. TPNH was then added to the same cuvette and the pigments reduced during the steady state of steroid hydroxylation determined (short dashes). After conversion of 17-hydroxyprogesterone to 17,21-dihydroxyprogesterone, the spectral contribution of cytochrome $b_5$ (long dashes) was recorded.

A number of spectral titration curves are plotted in Fig. 2
Of interest is the observation that very low concentrations of
17-hydroxyprogesterone are required to cause these spectral
modifications--the half maximal spectral change is observed
with only 2 mμ moles of 17-hydroxyprogesterone per milligram
of microsomal protein. This concentration of 17-hydroxy-
progesterone is not much greater than the concentration of
cytochrome P-450 in adrenal cortex microsomes (about 1 mμ
mole per milligram of protein).

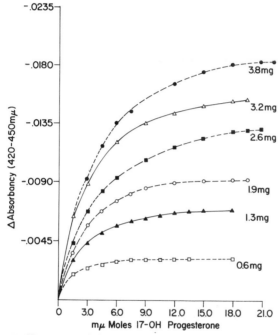

Figure 2. Influence of 17-hydroxyprogesterone on the extent
of absorbance decrease at 420 mμ relative to 450 mμ using
varying concentrations of adrenal cortex microsomes. The
change in absorbance was determined with the Aminco-Chance
dual wavelength spectrophotometer. Reprinted from (2).

A second point of interest, observed with the adrenal
steroid hydroxylation reactions, is the reversibility of the
substrate-induced spectral changes which can be obtained on
addition of the reductant TPNH. A series of spectral transitions observed on addition of limiting concentrations of 17-
hydroxyprogesterone and TPNH to aerobic adrenal cortex microsomes is presented in Fig. 3. As 17-hydroxyprogesterone is
hydroxylated to form the product, 17,21-dihydroxyprogesterone
(cortexolone), the decrease in absorbance at 420 mμ is reversed, returning to its initial absorbance level. Some

interference, due to the concomitant reduction of cytochrome $b_5$ (cf. Fig. 1), is also observed on addition of TPNH; but subsequent oxidation of reduced cytochrome $b_5$ as the TPNH concentration reaches zero confirms (10) the loss of the steroid-induced spectral change at 420 mμ.

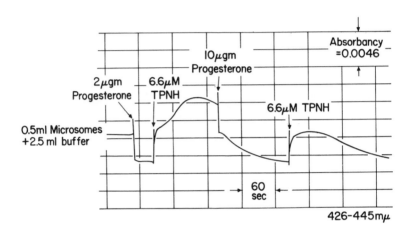

Figure 3. The kinetics of spectal changes occurring on addition of 17-hydroxyprogesterone and TPNH to adrenal cortex microsomes.

Since cytochrome P-450 is the predominant pigment present in liver microsomes, where it also functions in the hydroxylation of a number of compounds such as barbiturates, polycyclic hydrocarbons, aromatic amines, etc., a series of spectral studies with liver microsomes have recently been undertaken. These studies revealed (11,12) that two classes of spectral changes are obtained on addition of a number of various types of substrates to aerobic liver microsomes. As illustrated in Fig. 4, the addition of hexobarbital causes a loss in absorbance at 420 mμ with an associated increase in absorbance at 385 mμ--a type of spectral change (termed Type I) directly analogous to that observed by Narasimhulu et al. (9) for the interaction of steroids with adrenal cortex microsomes. With liver microsomes, however, a second type of spectral change (Fig. 5) was also observed on addition of substrates such as aniline, pyridine, nicotinamide, etc. This type of spectral change (termed Type II) is characterized by an increase in absorbance at 430 mμ, with a decrease at about 390 mμ.

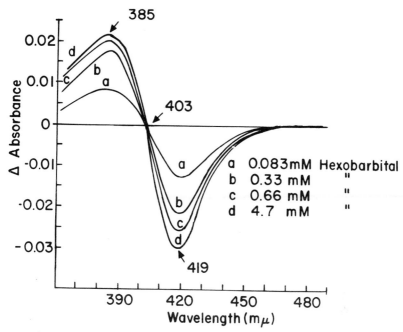

Figure 4.  "Type I" spectral changes occurring on addition of varying concentrations of hexobarbital to rat liver microsomes(12).

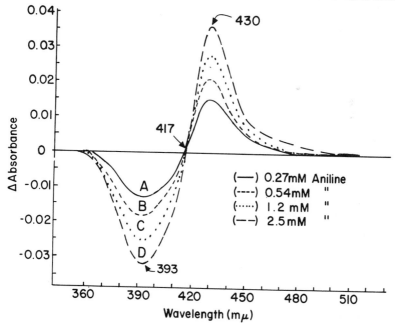

Figure 5.  "Type II" spectral changes occurring addition of varying concentrations of aniline to rat liver microsomes (12).

As in the above described studies of the 17-hydroxyprogesterone interaction with adrenal microsomes, the two types of spectral changes observed with liver microsomes were dependent on the concentration of substrate added and the concentration of microsomal protein employed. However, with liver microsomes, the concentrations of substrates required were considerably higher per milligram of protein than that observed for steroids reacting with adrenal microsomes. Concentrations from 0.05 mM to nearly 1 mM were required, depending on the compounds used, to obtain a half-maximal spectral change.

In a number of instances (11,12) the relationship between the substrate concentration required to cause a half-maximal spectral change has been compared with the affinity of the liver microsomal mixed function oxidase for substrate hydroxylation. As demonstrated in Fig. 6 for aminopyrine (which is hydroxylated to form formaldehyde and aminoantipyrine), there is a similarity between the enzymatically determined $K_m$ and the optically determined "spectral dissociation constant."

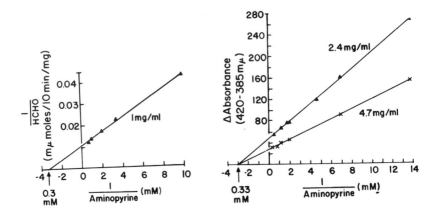

Figure 6. Correlation of the "spectral dissociation constant" with the enzymatically determined $K_m$ for aminopyrine. The figure on the right presents plots of the reciprocal of aminopyrine concentration versus the reciprocal of the change in absorbance at 420-385 mμ. Absorbance change was determined at two different protein concentrations as indicated. The figure on the left presents a reciprocal plot of the influence of aminopyrine concentration on the over-all rate of the mixed function oxidase reaction as determined by measuring the rate of formaldehyde formation.

These observations have led to the hypothesis that substrates
are interacting with a microsomal hemoprotein (cytochrome P-450),
forming an enzyme-substrate complex prerequisite to the interaction with oxygen during the reactions of substrate hydroxylation. This hypothesis has been strengthened by recent
electron paramagnetic resonance measurements of the microsomal
component FeX described by Mason and his colleagues (14,15).

Liver microsomes, adrenal cortex microsomes, and adrenal
cortex mitochondria all contain cytochrome P-450 as well as
the low spin hemoprotein component FeX (16). Addition of substrates to microsomes causes a modification of the EPR spectra
of this low spin hemoprotein. As shown in Fig. 7, addition of
aniline to liver microsomes modifies the position of the $g_1$
and $g_3$ contributions of the first derivative EPR spectrum indicative of substrate modification of ligand interaction with

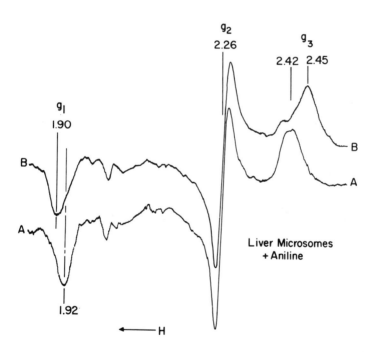

Figure 7. The effect of aniline on the EPR characteristics
of the low-spin hemoprotein (FeX) of rat liver microsomes.
The upper curve shows the first derivative spectrum obtained
with the untreated preparation, while the lower curve shows
the influence of 5 mM aniline. Reprinted from (16).

the heme. Those components which give the Type I optical spectral change on addition to microsomes (for example, hexobarbital addition to liver microsomes or 17-hydroxyprogesterone addition to adrenal cortex microsomes) also modify the EPR spectrum of FeX, but in a manner different from that observed with the other class of compounds such as aniline. As seen in Fig. 8, the $g_1$ and $g_3$ components move in just the opposite direction from that seen with aniline. It is suggested that these differences observed in the EPR spectra are a reflection of two different types of substrate interactions with the microsomal hemoprotein cytochrome P-450. This hypothesis that, as a prerequisite to the hydroxylation reaction, the substrate interacts with the microsomal hemoprotein, cytochrome P-450, to form a type of complex modifying ligand interaction with the heme now affords a unique demonstration of a physiologically important ligand interaction with a hemoprotein.

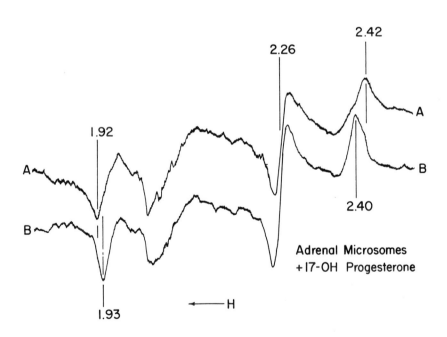

Figure 8. The influence of 17-hyroxyprogesterone on the EPR characteristics of the low-spin hemoprotein present in beef adrenal cortex microsomes. Curve A is the first derivative spectrum of untreated microsomes, while curve B is a comparable sample pretreated with 17-hydroxyprogesterone.

## References

1. Muijers, A. O., B. F. van Gelder, and E. C. Slater, this volume, p. 467.

2. Lemberg, M. R., this volume, p. 477.

3. Omura, T., R. Sato, D. Y. Cooper, O. Rosenthal, and R. W. Estabrook. Fed. Proc., 24, 1181 (1965).

4. Omura, T., and R. Sato. J. Biol. Chem., 239, 2370 (1964).

5. Estabrook, R. W., D. Y. Cooper, and O. Rosenthal. Biochem. Z., 338, 741 (1963).

6. Cooper, D. Y., S. Narasimhulu, O. Rosenthal, and R. W. Estabrook. Science, 147, 400 (1965).

7. Orrenius, S., G. Dallner, and L. Ernster. Biochem. Biophys. Res. Commun., 14, 329 (1964).

8. Warburg, O. In Heavy Metal Prosthetic Groups and Enzyme Action, Oxford, 1949.

9. Narasimhulu, S., D. Y. Cooper, and O. Rosenthal. Life Science, 4, 2101 (1965).

10. Cooper, D. Y., S. Narasimhulu, O. Rosenthal, and R. W. Estabrook. In Oxidases and Related Redox Systems (T. King, H. S. Mason, and M. Morrison, eds.), John Wiley and Sons, New York, 1965, p. 838.

11. Remmer, H., J. B., Schenkman, R. W. Estabrook, H. Sasame, J. Gillette, D. Y. Cooper, S. Narasimhulu, and O. Rosenthal. Mol. Pharmacol., 2, 187 (1966).

12. Schenkman, J. B., H. Remmer, and R. W. Estabrook, in press.

13. Imai, Y., and R. Sato. Biochem. Biophys. Res. Commun., 23, 5 (1966).

14. Mason, H. S., T. Yamano, J. C. North, Y. Hashimoto, and P. Sakagishi. In Oxidases and Related Redox Systems (T. King, H. S. Mason, and M. Morrison, eds.), John Wiley and Sons, New York, 1965, p. 838.

15. Mason, H. S., J. C. North, and M. Vanneste. Fed. Proc., 24, 1172 (1965).

16. Cammer, W., J. B. Schenkman, and R. W. Estabrook. Biochem. Biophys. Res. Commun., 23, 264 (1966).

# LIGAND BINDING REACTIONS OF CYTOCHROME cc'[*]

Martin D. Kamen

Department of Chemistry, University of California
San Diego, California

Cytochromes cc' (also known as "RHP") are heme proteins of a new class in which covalent binding of the prosthetic heme group occurs, as in cytochrome c, together with unsaturation in the extraplanar positions, as in the hemoglobins (1). These features, together with apparently restricted access (2) to all ligands except small, uncharged molecules (CO, NO), present new possibilities in correlation of structure with reactivity in heme proteins. Data in elaboration of these properteis have been presented in the literature (1-4, 11,12). Certain salient features of ligand binding exhibited by cytochrome cc' will be reviewed here briefly.

Reactions with CO. Detailed studies have been made with two proteins, one derived from Rhodospirillum rubrum (R-cyto cc') and the other from Chromatium, strain D (C-cyto cc'). Equilibrium determinations (3) show that the dissociation constants for these two proteins differ by three orders of magnitude. Thus, for R-cyto cc', $K_{diss} = 4 \times 10^{-4}$ M and for C-cyto cc', $K_{diss} = 2 \times 10^{-7}$ M. Yet both proteins show comparable rates of reaction with CO. Kinetic studies, using stopped flow and flash techniques (3), have revealed that the difference in binding results from a great increase in association rate, rather than from any marked disparities in the rates of dissociation. It is necessary to suppose that a simple one-step process of the usual type (i.e., Heme $\cdot$ CO $\longrightarrow$ Heme + CO) is not an adequate representation of the process involved. Instead, one must assume a process which involves at least two partial sequential equilibria, viz:

$$\text{Heme} \cdot \text{CO} \underset{k_2}{\overset{k_1}{\rightleftharpoons}} [\text{Heme}...\text{CO}] \underset{k_4}{\overset{k_3}{\rightleftharpoons}} \text{Heme} + \text{CO}$$

$$\text{I} \qquad\qquad \text{II} \qquad\qquad \text{III}$$

[*]This work supported by NIH Grant HD-01262, NSF Grant GB-2892, and a Kettering Research Award from the C.F. Kettering Foundation.

Thus, there are two equilibria with constants $K_{I \to II} = \dfrac{K_1}{K_2}$ and $K_{II \to III} = \dfrac{K_3}{K_4}$ ; the over-all $K_{diss}$ is given by the product

$$K_{KK \to III} \quad K_{I \to II} = \dfrac{K_1 K_3}{K_2 K_4}$$

Tentative values for these partial equilibria, together with some rate constants, are given in Table I.

TABLE I

Rate Constants for CO-binding Equilibria of Cytochrome cc' (3)

| | R-cytochrome cc' | | C-cytochrome cc' | |
|---|---|---|---|---|
| $K_1$ (a) | $9 \times 10^{-3}$ | $\dfrac{K_1}{K_2} = 6 \times 10^{-1}$ | $1 \times 10^{-3}$ | $\dfrac{K_1}{K_2} = 1.6 \times 10^{-6}$ |
| $K_2$ (a) | $1.5 \times 10^{-2}$ | | $6 \times 10^{2}$ | |
| $K_3$ (a) | | $\dfrac{K_3}{K_4} = 7 \times 10^{-4} M$ | $60$ | $\dfrac{K_3}{K_4} = 2.3 \times 10^{-1}$ |
| $K_4$ (b) | | | $2.6 \times 10^{2}$ | |

(a) in $sec^{-1}$

(b) in $M^{-1} sec^{-1}$

The nature of the intermediate (II) is not known. A hypothesis which explains adequately the mechanism postulated envisions the heme groups of the protein as "caged", so that access to the reactive iron centers in hindered; that is the equilibrium II→III may be a hindered diffusion.

In one set of experiments (3), R-cyto cc' -CO was exposed to flash illumination in the presence of oxygenated buffer. The expected loss in photosensitivity, as usually noted on repeated flashing with "open"heme proteins like hemoglobin, catalase and cytochrome oxidase, was not observed to occur with R-cyto cc' despite its demonstrated low affinity for CO. Instead, the CO dissociated in its flash was observed to recombine rapidly even in the presence of oxygen at a concentration many orders of magnitude greater. This experiment was repeated using C-cyto cc' -CO, with similar results. These observations show that CO dissociated from the heme groups retains its association with the heme, rather than being lost into the medium and being displaced by the oxygen.

The simplest explanation is that the CO dissociation involves limited movement of the CO away from the heme, so that it retains a preferred position in subsequent recombination, compared to oxygen in the medium outside the protein. It is planned to extend these observations to test this hypothesis further. Obvious experiments include the effect of temperature, ionic strength, change in dielectric, etc.

Interesting consequences of the two-step equilibrium system proposed are: (1) Changes in characteristic spectroscopic properties (absorbancy) are not directly correlated with the over-all dissociation governed by $K_{diss}$, as is usually the case. Instead, the typical absorbancy change noted when CO is dissociated is correlated with the primary equilibrium process $(K_{I\rightarrow II})$. (2) Saturation cannot be obtained spectroscopically, even at infinite CO concentration. To see this, one may note that if X, Y, and Z represent mole fractions of I, II and III in the reaction scheme (A), then:

$$\frac{1}{X} = 1 + \left(\frac{K_1}{K_2}\right)\left[1 + \frac{K_3}{K_4\,(CO)}\right]$$

It is seen that X cannot become 1, even at infinite CO concentration, unless

$$\frac{K_1}{K_2} \longrightarrow 0.$$

From Table I, this condition can be seen to hold rather well, but not completely, for C-cyto cc', and not at all for R-cyto cc'. It has been noted (4) that the molar extinction coefficient for R-cyto cc' · CO is $480 \times 10^3$ $M^{-1}cm^{-1}$ at the Soret maximum, whereas for C-cyto cc' · CO it is $564 \times 10^3$ $M^{-1} cm^{-1}$. This discrepancy, which lies outside estimated error in molecular weight determinations, may be ascribed to incomplete saturation of R-cyto cc', because even at atmospheric CO only ~ 70 percent saturation is achieved (2,3).

Reactions with NO. These have been exhaustively studied with R-ctyo cc' (2). For our present purposes, it is sufficient to state the conclusion that NO proves to be much more weakly bound than CO and to act not solely as a ligand but as a reagent which causes oxidative alterations either in the porphyrin moiety, or in the immediate peptide environment of the central iron. The lowered affinity for NO compared to CO is in marked contrast to the behavior of other heme proteins.

The Problem of the Relation of Cytochrome cc' to Cytochrome "o". Although early researches pointed to the possibility that cytochrome cc' might function as an oxidase and could be identified with the CO-binding pigment ubiquitiously present as an oxidase in bacteria and named "cytochrome o" (5), recent experience strongly contraindicates such an identification. Thus, three separate groups of experimenters have isolated CO-binding pigments with oxidase activity and the spectroscopic properties of cytochrome o. The bacteria include representative strains of staphylococci (6), R. rubrum (7), and a colorless mutant of a blue-green alga (8). In all cases the prosthetic group can be dissociated with acid-acetone as protoheme. Since the prosthetic group of cytochrome cc' characteristically resists such treatment and requires the splitting of a covalent bond to produce mesoheme (hematoheme) as in cytochrome c, there appears to be no basis for a close relationship to the oxidase. Kinetic studies in whole R. rubrum cells, in which the reactions of the oxidase (corresponding to the CO-binding pigment) with CO and oxygen have been examined, reveal no trace of a pigment like cytochrome cc' with comparable kinetic behavior (9). Finally, Chromatium--a bacterium with no appreciable oxidase activity--possesses only mesoheme proteins, including cytochrome cc' (10).

The function of cytochrome cc' remains to be elucidated.

## References

1. Kamen, M. D. Acta Chem. Scand., 17, 541 (1963).

2. Taniguchi, S., and M. D. Kamen. Biochim. Biophys. Acta, 74, 438 (1962).

3. Gibson, Q., and M. D. Kamen. J. Biol. Chem., in press.

4. Bartsch, R. G. In Bacterial Photosynthesis (H. Gest, et al., eds.), Antioch Press, Yellow Springs, 1963, p. 475 et seq.

5. Castor, L. A., and B. Chance, J. Biol. Chem., 217, 453 (1955).

6. Taber, H., and M. Morrison. Arch. Biochem. Biophys., 105, 407 (1964).

7. Taniguchi, S., and M. D. Kamen. Biochim. Biophys. Acta, 96, 395 (1965).

8. Webster, D., and D. P. Hackett. J. Biol. Chem., in press.

9. Chance, B., T. Horio, M. D. Kamen, and S. Taniguchi. Biochim. Biophys. Acta, 112, 1 (1966).

10. Cusanovich, M. Private communication (1966).

DISCUSSION

Chance:  This is a very interesting result.  Do you presume
that CO interacts without bonding?

Kamen:  Our previous notion was that it was a hindered diffusion which can be tested experimentally.  The reason I am
talking about CO as being able to produce an effect at a distance is that I think of the CO as forcing its way through
the protein to the ligand site, so that a change in conformation takes place in this protein before the final arrival
of the CO.  I should say this protein has a 28,000 molecular
weight and two hemes in most of the specimens looked at.

Chance:  Would you go so far as to postulate a nonspectro-
photometrically operative bonding to one of the hemes?

Kamen:  We are assuming in this mechanism that the complete
dissociation of the CO from the heme is not unequivocally
associated with the change in absorption.  To clarify, there
is a binding of CO to heme in this mechanism that does not
show up spectroscopically.  Let me say what I mean by that
so that there should be absolutely no misunderstanding of
Dr. Gibson's and my notion about this.  We believe that if
the heme-CO linkage is lengthened so that the bond distances
are two or three times greater than the equilibrium distance,
then the transition moment for this situation is quite different from that in the equilibrium situation.  What we are
saying in this mechanism is that the initial partial dissociation $(K_1)$ is the one related to the change.  The following
step $(K_3)$ has no spectroscopic result.

Lemberg:  Dr. Kamen, how was the CO-compound of the cytochromes
cc' produced?  Was excess reductant present and in what concentration, and what is the affinity ratio for the cytochromes
cc' for CO and oxygen?

Kamen:  You have asked a question which opens up a large area
of discussion.  We reduced with ascorbate and with dithionite,
but we had to be very careful.  If we used excess ascorbate, we
ran into some interesting kinetic effects which we could not
reproduce.  We had to titrate accurately the reduced form, and

work with the freshly reduced form.  The oxidation kinetics changed by a factor of $10^3$ if we let this stuff sit with dithionite for two or three hours.  That is one of the bases for saying the oxygen reaction depends on the formation of an intermediate which mediates electron transfer to the protein.

# VIII.

## Kinetics of Electron Transfer Reactions in Cytochrome c
### T. Yonetani, Chairman

# NMR STUDIES OF METAL ION INTERACTIONS IN MODEL SYSTEMS OF CYTOCHROME c*

Arthur Kowalsky[‡]

Johnson Research Foundation, University of Pennsylvania
Philadelphia, Pennsylvania

The proton magnetic spectra of small molecular weight heme proteins consist not only of absorptions in the usual carbon-hydrogen region but also of absorptions which are characterized by the unusually large shifts (1) far from the normal region of carbon-hydrogen resonances. These anomalously shifted resonances may offer clues to the electronic relationships and interactions between metal, porphyrin and protein.

A proton magnetic resonance spectrum of ferricytochrome c in $D_2O$ is shown in Fig. 1. The prominent absorption in the center extending from about 0 to about $15\tau$ is the normal proton absorption of the protein; $0-10\tau$ is the normal region for carbon-hydrogen resonances. The anomalous resonances with which we are concerned are the small ones seen at about $-20\tau$ and about $+35\tau$.

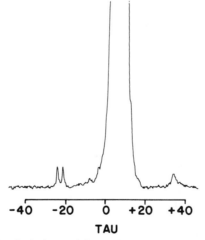

**TAU**

Figure 1. Contact interactions in cytochrome c.

*This work was supported by U. S. PHS Grants GM-12446, AM-06940.
‡U. S. PHS Research Career Development Awardee GM-6212.

Two reasons may be advanced for the abnormally large shifts of these resonances: a hyperfine contact interaction (2) or a pseudocontact interaction (3).

In the first, the hyperfine contact interaction, the unpaired electron of the low spin ferric iron is delocalized over the ligand carbon skeleton. This results in non-zero spin on carbon atoms of the ligand. This unpaired spin is transmitted then through the sigma bond to the adjacent hydrogen. The effect of this unpaired spin acting directly at the nucleus is to shift the nuclear resonance far from its normal position to either high or low field according to whether the spin density is negative or positive. A pseudocontact interaction is a dipolar type of interaction between metal ion and proton, dependent on the distance between them, which is not averaged to zero by the tumbling of the molecule (because of anisotrophy in the electronic g-value of the complex). Again shifts can be to either high or low fields.

It is difficult to distinguish between these two mechanisms and for proteins almost impossible. Because of the simplicity of the contact spectra, a hyperfine interaction involving delocalization of the odd electron is favored for the case of cytochrome c. The question of the identity of the protons of the protein responsible for these shifts has remained unanswered. Studies with an eleven-membered and an eight-membered peptide obtained from a proteolytic digestion of cytochrome c have shown that these also exhibit contact shifts, but also that these contact shifts may not be the same as those observed in cytochrome c itself (1).

There has been much interest in the suggestion that methionine in cytochrome c might complex with the heme group (4). If methionine is indeed the sixth ligand in cytochrome c, then its S-methyl protons might be responsible for the anomalous shifts. Complexes of methionine with metals have been studied before, but mostly by titration studies which would not pick up any interaction with the thio-ether linkage. For this reason we have been studying the interaction of methionine and methionine derivaties with paramagnetic metal ions and heme peptides by nuclear magnetic resonance. A few preliminary observations are presented briefly here.

The metals used were cobalt and nickel, because contact interactions have been observed in complexes of these metals (5,6); copper, because specific interactions with peptides and this metal have been observed (7); and iron, because of its involvement in the heme system. The approach adopted was extremely simple. The spectra of mixtures of the metal and methionine or its derivativewere observed at various pH's.

The results have been, in the case of nickel and iron, so far disappointing -- no specific or contact interaction was observed. In the case of cobalt, the results are puzzling and not understood. It is known that cobalt complexes of histidine exhibit contact interactions. Yet we have not yet been able to detect them in the systems cobalt-methionine or cobalt-acetyl-methionine. However, a crystalline cobalt complex of methionine has been isolated. Here the cobalt is apparently still in the +2 state. The elementary analysis for cobalt, carbon, hydrogen, and nitrogen agrees with that calculated for one cobalt and 2 methionines only. There are no other anions in the complex, and the visual absorption spectrum indicates octahedral co-ordination. Thus, the fifth and sixth coordination positions are probably occupied by the sulfur. The NMR spectra do indicate that at a pH of 6-7, considerable complex formation occurs. The complex incidentally only very slowly reacts with oxygen in solution and not at all in the dry state.

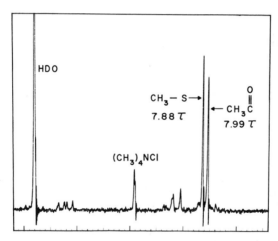

Figure 2.  NMR spectrum of N-acetylmethionine.

It was with copper that a specific interaction with the sulfur was first seen. Fig. 2 shows the spectrum of N-acetyl-methionine in $D_2O$. The acetyl methyl peak occurs at $7.99\tau$ and the S-methyl resonance at $7.88\tau$. These assignments are known with certainty from studies on other compounds, e.g., acetylalanine, acetone, and thioethers. Tetramethylammonium chloride was used as a reference for position and width deter-minations.

The spectrum of N-acetylmethionine in $D_2O$ in the presence of a small amount of copper, Fig. 3, shows marked modifications. Where there were two sharp methyl proton resonances, there is now only one and the remaining resonance is in the position of the acetyl methyl group. The S-methyl proton resonance has disappeared. There have been no fortuitous shifts in the presence of copper since, if one titrates with small amounts of copper, successive dimunitions in the S-methyl resonance can be seen with no shift, and the acetyl methyl proton resonance remains in the same position.

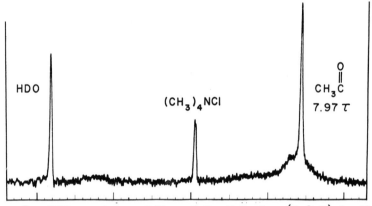

Figure 3. NMR spectrum of N-acetylmethionine (0.2 M) in the presence of a small amount of copper (2 x $10^{-4}$ M $CuCl_2$).

The system, N-acetylmethionine and heme octapeptide, which was studied so successfully by Harbury was then investigated. Fig. 4 shows the spectrum of this system. The acetylmethionine is in excess and is the only compound visible in the spectrum except for the reference and HDO.

Here again a specific interaction with the S-methyl protons can be seen. In the absence of heme peptide, the acetyl methyl proton resonance is approximately the same width as the S-methyl proton resonance, about 0.5 cps. The S-methyl proton resonance in the presence of heme peptide is three times as broad as the acetyl proton resonance, the widths being about 6 and 2 cps, respectively. The positions are the same as in the spectrum of the uncomplexed N-acetyl methionine. The width of the reference has only increased by a factor of about 1.5.

The temperature variation of this interaction was also observed and is shown in Fig. 5. The temperatures given are good to about ± 3°. The effect of increasing temperature is to narrow the resonance with no apparent change in position. This

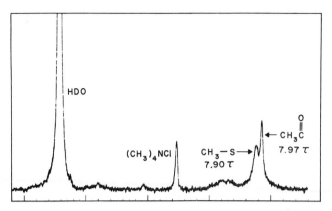

Figure 4. NMR spectrum of N-acetylmethionine in the presence of heme octapeptide.

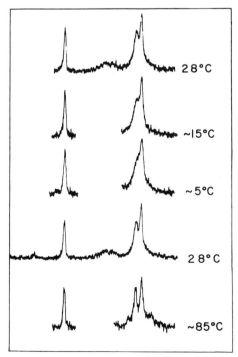

Figure 5. NMR spectra of N-acetylmethionine in the presence of heme octapeptide at different temperatures. The peak on the left is the reference, tetramethylammonium ion. The horizontal scale is the same in all cases.

behavior is consistent with a hyperfine contact interaction and a slow exchange between free and complexed species. However, a slow exchange implies that two resonances should be observed -- one in the normal position, broadened as is shown in the figure, and one shifted resonance. A search has been made for this second resonance, but as yet it has not been observed. This does not mean it does not exist. It may be that the right conditions did not exist.

In another phase of this work, a search was made for the interaction between acetylmethionine or poly-DL-methionine and protohemin. The solvents used were aqueous alkali, dimethyl sulfoxide, and a mixture of chloroform and trifluoroacetic acid. To eliminate possible rate effects which might obscure the phenomena, temperatures from $95^\circ$ to $5^\circ$ ($20^\circ$ in the case of dimethyl sulfoxide) were covered.

No specific interaction was observed in any case in contrast to the observation of Harbury (4). Each of these solvents suffers from obvious disadvantages -- in alkali hematin formation occurs, dimethyl sulfoxide is a weak complexing agent, and trifluoroacetic acid is a very strong acid. Yet specific interaction between the heme peptide and N-acetylmethionine occurred in one of these solvents, aqueous alkali. It may be argued that aggregation of the heme is preventing reaction. Yet the heme peptide at the concentration of these experiments is certainly also aggregated. It may be that, as Dr. Caughey suggested, substituents on the porphyrin ring, the alkyl groups or the peptide chain, profoundly affect the reactivity of the central metal.

## References

1. Kowalsky, A.  Biochem., 4, 2832 (1965).

2. Fermi, E.  A. Physik., 60, 320 (1930).

3. McConnell, H. M., and R. E. Robertson.  J. Chem. Phys., 29, 1361 (1958).

4. Harbury, H. A., J. R. Cronin, M. W. Fanger, T. P. Hettinger, A. J. Murphy, Y. P. Meyer, and J. N. Vinogradov.  Proc. Nat. Acad. Sci., 54, 1658 (1965).

5. McDonald, C. C., and W. D. Phillips.  J. Am. Chem. Soc., 85, 3736 (1963).

6. Milner, R. S., and C. Pratt.  Disc. Faraday Soc., 34, 88 (1962).

7. Li, N., R. Scruggs, and E. Becker.  J. Am. Chem. Soc., 84, 4650 (1962).

DISCUSSION

Caughey: Dr. Kowalsky, are the widely split protons quantitatively in accord with s-methyl group protons?

Kowalsky: In this experiment, we could not take areas, since the concentrations were such that only an estimated 10 percent would be in a complex form and our integration is not good to 10 percent.

Caughey: Would you expect multiple peaks if you had a single methyl group?

Kowalsky: No, I would not. I think there are a number of different groups contributing to these contact shifts, and I was looking to see if one particular group could be a source.

# ELECTRON TRANSFER TUNNELING TIMES[*]

## D. DeVault

Johnson Research Foundation, University of Pennsylvania
Philadelphia, Pennsylvania

The work which I am reporting here was done in collaboration with Dr. Chance who suggested the problem and the methods. We have studied photosynthesis induced in Chromatium with a pulsed ruby laser (1-11). Fig. 1 shows the general layout of our apparatus (12). At the left is the laser which gives a half-joule pulse of light of 694 nm wavelength, lasting about 10 nsec. The beam is attenuated about 1000 times with negative lens and neutral density filters. It hits the mirror at the right and is reflected into the cuvette. The spectrophotometric measurements are made with a beam of light from the monochromator which passes through the cuvette to a photomultiplier tube.

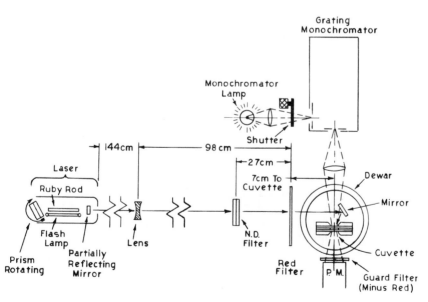

Figure 1. Apparatus for photosynthesis with pulsed ruby laser.

*This work was supported by PHS GM 12202.

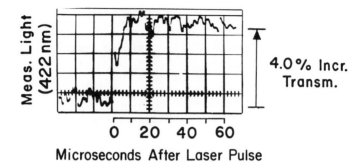

Figure 2. Response of Chromatium at 422 nm to laser flash at room temperature.

Fig. 2 shows a typical Chromatium response at room temperature with measuring light of 422 nm. The left hand part of the trace shows the level of transmission before the laser flash. At the time marked "0" the laser flashed. The peak shown half-way up is laser artifact, after recovery from which one can follow the course of an increase in transmission ending at a new level which is 4 percent more than the original level. From the time scale one can see that the half-time for this process was in the neighborhood of 3 μsec.

Fig. 3 shows a typical response at 35°K. Here the half-time is seen to be about 2 or 3 msec. At room temperature the bacteria recover in a few minutes and are ready for another shot, while at the low temperature there is no recovery. If the experiment is repeated at various measuring wavelengths the spectrum that results is typical of cytochrome oxidation.

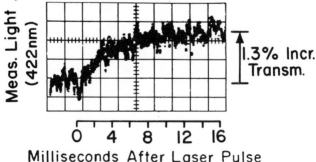

Figure 3. Response of Chromatium at 422 nm to laser flash at 35° K.

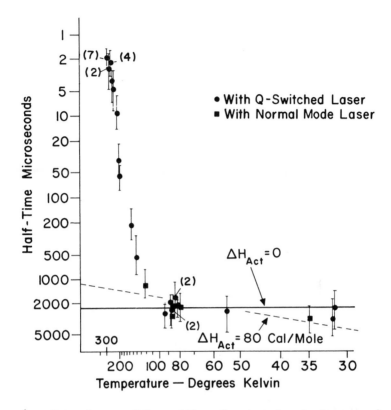

Figure 4. Dependence of logarithm of rate of cytochrome oxidation upon reciprocal absolute temperature. Numbers beside some points indicate the number of observations averaged into one point.

Fig. 4 shows the temperature dependence of the rate of the cytochrome oxidation. The half-time of the reaction is plotted on a logarithmic scale against the reciprocal of the absolute temperature. We see that there is a temperature-dependent portion from room temperature down to about 120°K. Between 100° and 30°K, however, it is plain that the reaction is essentially temperature-independent. To investigate the temperature-dependent portion we next subtract the temperature-independent part, and plot the remainder as shown in Fig. 5 We obtain a reasonably straight line corresponding to an activation energy of 3.3 kcal per mole.

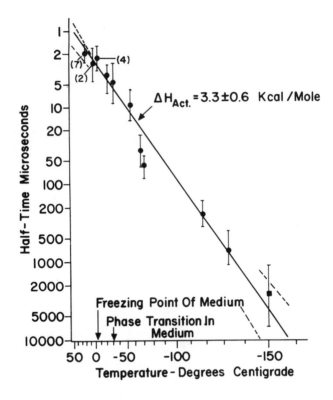

Figure 5. Temperature-dependent portion of cytochrome reaction. Logarithm of remainder after subtracting temperature independent portion from the data of Fig. 4 is plotted against reciprocal of absolute temperature.

Going back to the temperature-independent portion of the reaction we note that it is so slow (2.3 msec half time) that there must be some barrier in the way of the electron leaving the cytochrome. However, the lack of activation energy would indicate that the electron must be "tunneling" (13-16) through the barrier. The situation would seem to be about as pictured in Fig. 6. We have roughly plotted here the electronic energy levels on the vertical scale against different regions of the photosynthetic apparatus on the horizontal scale. On the right we represent the heme of the cytochrome with its sigma valence electrons at the bottom, above them the pi valence electrons, and at the top the empty electronic levels. At the left is a bacteria-chlorophyll with a similar electronic structure. In between we represent barrier material such as protein, lipid, water or even free space. We suppose the pi structure to be

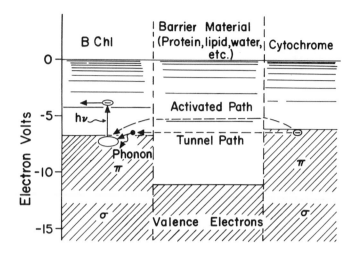

<u>Figure 6</u>. Electron transfer paths from cytochrome to chloro-phyll in Chromatium.

absent from the barrier. A photon absorbed in the bacteria-chlorophyll raises it to an excited level, leaving a hole in the pi shell. This hole can then be filled by an electron from the cytochrome. The temperature-independent pathway is represented by the direct tunneling path shown. Since the electron does not go back to the cytochrome, we have postulated that the energy in the chlorophyll is a little lower and that a phonon is emitted in the process.

The temperature-dependent portion is represented by the activated path shown. The activated path might be a semi-conductor mechanism (17,18) by way of electronic states avail-able in the barrier material as suggested in this figure. The semiconductor energy gap normally measured in proteins, lipids, etc. is 1 or 2 electron volts (19) but this would be with res-pect to the valence shell of the barrier material and would not apply to the present case where the electron starts and ends at a higher level in a different material.

As an alternative it may be that a vibrational or rota-tional mechanism is operating as suggested in Fig. 7. This elaborates on a scheme suggested by Chance and Williams (20).

While the vibration could be either linear or rotary we have pictured the latter since it is more economical of space. The zero-point vibration of amplitude is pictured. The non-activated tunneling at low temperatures would be over the

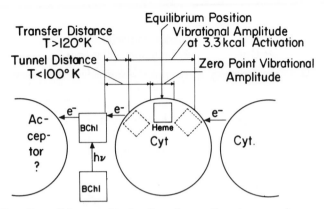

Figure 7. Possible mechanical scheme for temperature-dependent cytochrome oxidation.

distance from the zero-point amplitude to the bacteria chlorophyll. The amplitude of the vibration when the energy of vibration is 3.3 kcal is also pictured.

If, for simplicity, we assume a rectangular barrier, the half-time for penetration by tunneling is given by the formula (21):

$$t_{1/2} = \frac{0.693}{16f} \left(2 + \frac{V - E}{E} + \frac{E}{V - E}\right) \exp\left(\frac{a}{\hbar} \sqrt{8m(V - E)}\right)$$

where $f$ is the frequency with which a suitable electron approaches the barrier; $V$ is the energy the electron would have if it were at the top of the barrier; $E$ is the actual electron energy outside of the barrier; $(V - E)$ is, therefore, the height of the barrier; $\hbar$ is Planck's constant over $2\pi$; $m$ is the mass of the electron; and $a$ is the width of the barrier. The exponential dominates the expression so it does not make much difference what one assumes for the quantities outside of it. If we take $f = 10^{15}$ sec$^{-1}$, $(V - E)/E - 1$ and $t_{1/2} = 2.3$ msec, then a barrier height of 1 ev gives a width of 30 A and a height of 0.14 ev ( = 3.3 kcal/mole) gives a width of 80 A. These are certainly reasonable as orders of magnitude and so we conclude that the tunneling explanation of the temperature-independent reaction is highly likely.

For the temperature-dependent reaction we present in Table I some parameters consistent with the mechanically vibrating scheme pictured in Fig. 7. The vibrational frequencies, amplitudes, and Hook's law constants do not seem out of line with what might be expected for vibration of this type. However, other explanations such as the semiconductor type already mentioned also appear equally likely.

TABLE I

Some Parameters which Fit the Temperature-Dependent

Reaction Using Mechanical Vibration with Arrhenius Activation

| Parameter | Notes | Value | | | | Units |
|---|---|---|---|---|---|---|
| Activation energy | a | 3.3 | | | | kcal/mole |
| Wt. of vibrating mass | b | $10^3$ | | $10^5$ | | at. wt. units. |
| Radius | c,d | 6.4 | | 30 | | Å |
| Vibrational frequency | b | 20 | 2 | 0.5 | 0.05 | $cm^{-1}$ |
| Linear amplitude for activation | c,e | 0.4 | 4 | 1.7 | 17 | Å |
| Angular amplitude for activation | c,f | 0.11 | 1.1 | 0.09 | 0.9 | radians |
| Linear Hook's law const. | c,g | 20 | 0.2 | 1.5 | 0.015 | $Nt\ m^{-1}\ (Kg\ sec^{-2})$ |
| Angular Hook's law const. | c,h | 4 | 0.04 | 5 | 0.05 | $10^{-18} Nt\ m$ $radian^{-1}$ |

(a) Experimental data
(b) Assumed
(c) Calculated
(d) Assumed sphere of density 1.5 gm $cm^{-3}$
(e) If the vibration is torsional this would be measured at the "equivalent radius" which is $\sqrt{2/5}$ of the actual radius if the shape of the body is a solid sphere.
(f) If vibration is torsional.
(g) Measured at "equivalent radius" if torsional. Note that Hook's law constant for stretching vibration of $Br_2$ (e.g.) is 246 Nt $m^{-1}$.
(h) If torsional. Note that the angular Hook's law constant for hindered rotation about C - C single bonds may be estimated as 9/2 of the energy of the barrier height or about 1 x $10^{-19}$ Nt m $radian^{-1}$.

# References

1. Chance, B., and M. Nishimura. Proc. Nat. Acad. Sci., 46, 19 (1960).

2. Olson, J. M., and B. Chance. Arch. Biochem. Biophys., 88, 26 (1960).

3. Olson, J. M., and B. Chance. Arch. Biochem. Biophys., 88, 40 (1960).

4. Vredenberg, W. J., and L. N. M. Duysens. Biochim. Biophys. Acta, 79, 456 (1964).

5. Chance, B., and J. M. Olson, Arch. Biochem. Biophys., 88, 54 (1960).

6. Morita, S., M. Edwards, and J. Gibson. Biochim. Biophys. Acta., 109, 45 (1965).

7. Chance, B., H. Schleyer, and V. Legallais. In Studies on Microalgae and Photosynthetic Bacteria (Japanese Society of Plant Physiologists, eds.), University of Tokyo Press, 1963, p. 337.

8. Chance, B., and B. Schoener. Biophysical Society 8th Annual Meeting, Abstr. FD 9, 1964.

9. Chance, B., and D. DeVault. Ber Busengesellschaft phys. Chemie, 68, 722 (1964).

10. Chance, B., and D. DeVault. Biophysical Society 9th Annual Meeting, Abstr. WH5, 1965.

11. DeVault, D., and B. Chance. Biophysical Society 10th Annual Meeting, Abstr. WC4, 1966.

12. DeVault, D. In Rapid Mixing and Sampling Techniques in Biochemistry (B. Chance, Q. H. Gibson, R. Eisenhardt, and K. K. Lonberg-Holm, eds.), Academic Press, New York, 1964, p. 165.

13. Nordheim, L. Z. Phys., 46, 833 (1927).

14. Oppenheimer, J. R. Phys. Rev., 31, 66 (1928).

15. Gamow, G. Z. Phys., 51, 204 (1928).

16. Gurney and E. U. Condon. Nature, 122, 439 (1928).

17. Wilson, A. H. Proc. Roy. Soc., A136, 487 (1932).

18. Szent-Györgyi, A. Science, 93, 609 (1941).

19. Cardew, M. H., and D. D. Eley. Discussions of the Faraday Society, 27, 115 (1959).

20. Chance, B., and G. R. Williams. In Advances in Enzymology
(F. F. Nord, ed.), Vol. XVII, Interscience Publishers,
Inc., New York, 1956, p. 65.

21. See, for example, Bohm, D., Quantum Theory, New York,
Prentice-Hall, Inc., 1951, p. 239.

## DISCUSSION

Kamen: The question of the laser experiments and tunneling of
electrons is very interesting to me because of the continually
evolving nature of the concept that the primary photochemical
process in photosynthesis involves photo-oxidation of the cytochrome. I believe that not many of us have upheld this concept.
Most people want to talk of a reduction reaction being primary
in photosynthetic systems; that is, an oxidation of chlorophyll
with a concomitant reduction of a nucleotide, but some of us
have maintained for a long time that a photo-oxidation of cytochrome precedes this. In this most recent work, we see a process which probably takes place in the order of nanoseconds.
I am interested in this because, when the concept was originally introduced, we were looking at reactions in which we found
a photo-oxidation with a half-time of seconds or even minutes;
then, as Dr. Chance and his colleagues elaborated the use of
dynamic spectrophotometry for these reactions, we heard of
half-times in Chromatium on the order of milliseconds. And
now, with the laser, we find half-times on the order of nanoseconds. These are all, presumably, photo-oxidations of cytochromes, so the question arises, what cytochrome is being oxidized, and what percentage of it participates in all these
different reactions? I would like especially to know what
percentage of the cytochrome has been oxidized in this very
fast reaction, and how this compared with the percentage oxidized in the slower reaction. There is a limit, because there
is only so much cytochrome in the Chromatium; we must make
some kind of quantitative comparison.

DeVault: First, a correction on the time scale: the oxidation
in Chromatium at room temperature is about 2 μsec. The amplitude of the oxidation induced with the Q-switched laser is
about 1/5 or 1/6 the total cytochrome oxidation observed with
steady state light, so it is probable that we are only looking
at one of the several different cytochromes that are present.

Chance: It was very recently proposed that in the oxidized-
reduced state of cytochrome c there would be a switch from

histidine to methionine (1). This idea seems ruled out by the electron transfer reaction which DeVault mentioned to occur at 34° K in a couple of msec in Chromatium cells.

## References

1. Verbal discussion following paper by T. P. Hettinger, M. W. Fanger, S. N. Vinogradov, and H. A. Harbury. Federation Proc., 25, 648 (1966).

# KINETIC INVESTIGATIONS OF THE ELECTRON-TRANSFER PROCESSES OF CYTOCHROME c

G. P. Hess*, K. G. Brandt**, P. E. Parks+ and G. Czerlinski

Johnson Research Foundation, University of Pennsylvania
Philadelphia, Pennsylvania

Previous experiments have shown that the redox potential of cytochrome c is pH-dependent (1-4). The reason for this is obscure, although this pH dependence has been investigated under equilibrium conditions in a number of laboratories. We have now begun to investigate the kinetics of the oxidation-reduction reactions mediated by this protein.

The investigations to be described include chemical relaxation and stopped-flow experiments in the pH region 7 to 9.5 of the redox couple ferri-ferrocytochrome c - ferro-ferricyanide, the latter having a redox potential independent of pH in the region investigated (5).

Previously reported kinetic experiments on the reduction and oxidation of cytochrome c have indicated the order of magnitude of the rate constants. Chance (6) and Beetlestone (7) reported the rate constant of oxidation of ferrocytochrome c by the hydrogen peroxide complex of yeast cytochrome c peroxidase to be greater than $10^8$ $M^{-1}sec^{-1}$. Sutin and Christman (8) reported a bimolecular rate constant of $1.6 \times 10^7$ $M^{-1}sec^{-1}$ for the oxidation of ferrocytochrome c by ferrihexacyanide at pH 6.0, and Havsteen (9), for the same reaction at pH 7.0, reported a bimolecular rate constant of $1.2 \times 10^7$ $M^{-1}sec^{-1}$. Kinetic experiments of Greenwood and Palmer (10) on the reduction of ferricytochrome c by ascorbate gave a rate constant of $7.5 \times 10^2$ $M^{-1}sec^{-1}$ at pH 7.0, and

*Present address: Department of Chemistry, Cornell University, Ithaca, New York.

**National Science Foundation Postdoctoral Fellow, Department of Chemistry, Cornell University, Ithaca, New York.

+National Institutes of Health Postdoctoral Fellow.

indicated the existence of two functionally distinct forms of ferricytochrome c at alkaline pH.[*]

The chemical relaxation experiments were performed on the temperature-jump apparatus of Czerlinski (11), a coaxial modification of the original apparatus of Czerlinski and Eigen (12). A special small-volume stopped-flow apparatus designed by Chance and Legallais (13) was also used for rate measurements.

Mixtures of buffer (phosphate at pH's 7 and 8.4, glycine at pH 9.0, and glycyl glycine at pH's 9.4 and 9.5), sodium ferrocyanide (initial concentration at $8 \times 10^{-3}$ M in all experiments), sodium sulfate (to ionic strength of $\mu = 0.18$), and ferricytochrome c (initial concentrations from $5 \times 10^{-6}$ to $1.6 \times 10^{-4}$ M) were prepared for the experiments. Temperature-jump and stopped-flow experiments were followed at 550 mμ, where there is a strong absorption peak in ferrocytochrome c, and spectrophotometric measurements of the equilibrium system were recorded between 450 and 600 mμ to allow determination of the overall equilibrium constant.

The reaction for the electron transfer between horse-heart ferricytochrome c and ferrohexacyanide may be written:

$$\text{Cyt-C}^{III} + \text{Fe}^{II} \underset{k(ox)}{\overset{k(red)}{\rightleftharpoons}} \text{Cyto-C}^{II} + \text{Fe}^{III} \qquad (1)$$

where $\text{Cyt-C}^{III}$ is ferricytochrome c, $\text{Cyto-C}^{II}$ is ferrocytochrome c, $\text{Fe}^{II}$ is ferrohexacyanide, and $\text{Fe}^{III}$ is ferrihexacyanide. The relationship between the relaxation time, $\tau$, and the equilibrium concentrations of the components of the system is given by (14):

$$\tau^{-1} = k(red)\ [\overline{\text{Cyt-C}}^{III} + \overline{\text{Fe}}^{II}] + k(ox)[\overline{\text{Cyt-C}}^{II} + \overline{\text{Fe}}^{III}] \quad (2)$$

(A bar over the symbols denotes equilibrium concentration.) Under the conditions of the experiments, $\text{Fe}_0^{II} \gg \text{Cyt-C}_0^{III}$, where the subscript zero denotes initial concentration; since $\text{Cyt-C}_0^{II} = \text{Fe}_0^{III}$, it follows that $\text{Cyt-C}^{II} = \text{Fe}^{III}$. Thus Equation 2 becomes, under the conditions of the experiment:

$$\tau^{-1} = k(red)\ \text{Fe}_0^{II} + 2\ k(ox)\ \overline{\text{Cyt-C}}^{II} \qquad (3)$$

Since the initial concentration of ferrocyanide is known, and the equilibrium concentration of ferrocytochrome c can be

[*]The crystalline, monomeric horse-heart cytochrome c used in these experiments was a generous gift of Dr. Emanuel Margoliash, Abbott Laboratories, North Chicago, Illinois.

determined spectrophotometrically from aliquots of the solutions used in the temperature-jump experiments, k(ox) and k(red) can be determined from the intercept and slope of plots of the data according to:

$$\tau^{-1} [Fe_o^{II}]^{-1} = k(red) + 2\, k(ox)\, \overline{Cyt\text{-}C}^{II} [Fe_o^{III}]^{-1} \qquad (4)$$

Typical data, obtained at pH's 7.0 and 9.4 and plotted according to Equation 4, are shown in Fig. 1. The solid lines through the points were computed from the data by linear regression analysis.

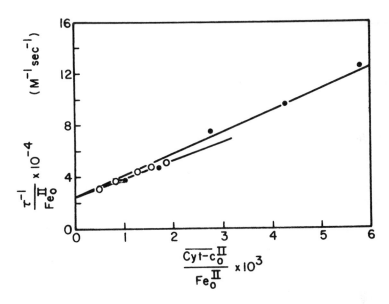

Figure 1. Results of temperature-jump experiments. Temperature ~22°. For details of solution composition, see Table I. ●, pH 7.0; phosphate buffer; initial sodium ferrocyanide concentration, 8 x 10⁻³ M; initial ferricytochrome c concentration, 1.1 - 16.5 x 10⁻⁵ M. O, pH 9.4; glycine buffer; initial sodium ferrocyanide concentration, 8 x 10⁻³ M; initial ferricytochrome c concentration, 1.0 - 7.2 x 10⁻⁵ M.

A summary of the rate constants obtained from the temperature-jump experiments are given in Table I. All values were obtained by linear regression analysis of the data. It is to be noticed that both the oxidation and reduction rate constants for the system are independent of hydrogen ion concentration in the pH region 7.0 to 9.4.

TABLE I

The $K_{eq}$ Values Obtained from a Number of Experiments
in the pH Region 7.0 to 9.4

| pH | $k(ox)$ $(M^{-1}sec^{-1})$ | $k(red)$ $(M^{-1}sec^{-1})$ | $k(ox)/k(red)$ | $k_{eq}$ (spectrophoto-metric) |
|---|---|---|---|---|
| 7.0 | $0.8 \times 10^7$ | $2.6 \times 10^4$ | 310 | 450 |
| 8.4 | $0.99 \times 10^7$ | $2.5 \times 10^4$ | 395 | 490 |
| 9.0 | $0.81 \times 10^7$ | $2.1 \times 10^4$ | 385 | 820 |
| 9.4 | $0.75 \times 10^7$ | $2.4 \times 10^4$ | 295 | 1800 |

For the system investigated, the overall equilibrium constant may be defined by:

$$K_{eq} = \frac{\overline{cyt\text{-}C}^{III} \cdot \overline{Fe}^{II}}{\overline{cyt\text{-}C}^{II} \cdot \overline{Fe}^{III}} \qquad (5)$$

Under the conditions of the experiments, in which initially excess ferrocyanide is mixed with ferricytochrome c, and with substitution of $\Delta D_{550}$ $(\Delta\epsilon_{M\ 550})^{-1}$ for the equilibrium concentration of ferrocytochrome c, Equation 5 becomes:

$$K = \left[ Cyt\text{-}C_o^{III} \left( -\frac{\Delta D_{550}}{\Delta\epsilon_{M\ 550}} \right) \right] Fe_o^{II} \left[ \frac{\Delta D_{550}}{\Delta\epsilon_{M\ 550}} \right]^{-2} \qquad (6)$$

When Equation 6 is written in the form:

$$\frac{\Delta D_{550}}{Fe^{II}_{o}} = \left[ \frac{Cyt\text{-}C^{III}_{o}}{\Delta D_{550}} \frac{(\Delta\epsilon_{M\ 550})^2}{K_{eq}} \right] - \frac{\Delta\epsilon_{M\ 550}}{K_{eq}} \quad (7)$$

$K_{eq}$ can be obtained from either the intercept or the slope. Typical plots of the data at pH's 7.0 and 9.4 according to Equation 7 are shown in Fig. 2. A value for $\Delta\epsilon_{M\ 550}$ of 2.1 x $10^4$ was used.

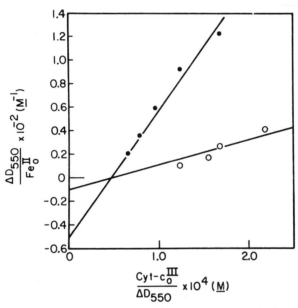

Figure 2. Spectrophotometrically measured equilibrium data. Temperature ~22°. Wavelength 550 mμ. Initial sodium ferrocyanide and ferricytochrome c concentrations as in Fig. 1. ● , pH 7.0.  O , pH 9.4.

The difference between $K_{eq}$, determined from spectrophotometric experiments, and the quotient of the rate constants, k(ox)/k(red), was thought to be due to an isomerization of ferricytochrome c which is slow compared to the observed relaxation processes. To investigate this possibility, stopped flow experiments were performed in which cytochrome c at pH 7 was mixed with ferrocyanide buffered so that the final pH after mixing would be 9.5. As shown in Fig. 3, there was an initial rapid decrease in transmittance at 550 mμ--too fast to be observed--corresponding to a rapid reduction of cytochrome c by the ferrocyanide, followed by a slow increase in trans-mittance requiring about 30 seconds for completion. Thus an apparent slow reconversion of reduced cytochrome c to ferri-cytochrome c is observed. The transmittance reading at 550 mμ made at the end of the experiment (t =∞) was taken to be a measurement of the equilibrium concentration of ferrocyto-chrome c. The zero transmittance reading (t = 0) was obtained by extrapolation of the slow transmittance change to zero time.

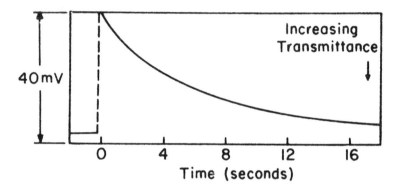

Figure 3. Typical stopped-flow trace of millivolts vs. time at 550 mμ. Temperature ~22°. A solution $9.2 \times 10^{-5}$ M in ferricytochrome c and $2 \times 10^{-3}$ M in ethylene diamine tetra-acetic acid at an ionic strength of 0.2 with $Na_2SO_4$ and adjus-ted to pH 7.0 with dilute NaOH, was mixed with a solution $1.6 \times 10^{-4}$ M in sodium ferrocyanide and $4 \times 10^{-2}$ M in glycine at an ionic strength of 0.2 and containing sufficient NaOH to produce a pH of 9.5 after mixing.

The data presented in Table I show that in the pH region 7 to 9.4, k(ox) and k(red), and hence their quotient, are pH-independent, while the overall equilibrium constant $K_{eq}$ in-creases with pH in this region, in agreement with the known redox potential. At pH 7 the quotient of the rate constants is approximately equal to $K_{eq}$, but at pH 9.4, $K_{eq}$ is much larger than k(ox)/k(red). The stopped-flow experiments show that this difference at high pH is due to a slow process re-sulting in loss of ferrocytochrome c.

The data obtained in the stopped-flow experiments at pH 9.5 are shown, plotted according to Equation 7, in Fig. 4. The "$K_{eq}$" obtained from the data at t = 0 is about 740; this value (obtained at pH 9.5) is in reasonable agreement with the value obtained at pH 7.0 by the spectrophotometric method (see Table I). The $K_{eq}$ value obtained from the stopped-flow measurements at t = $\infty$ is about 2000, in close agreement with the value obtained from spectrophotometric experiments at pH 9.4.

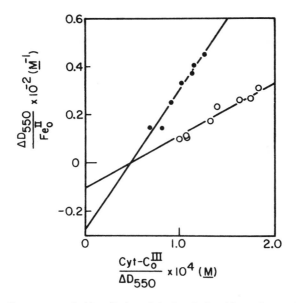

Figure 4. Summary of the data obtained in the stopped-flow experiments illustrated in Fig. 3. The results obtained at t = 0 (●) and t = ∞ (○) were converted to $\Delta D_{550}$ values and plotted according to Equation 7. The slopes of the lines are inversely proportional to $K_{eq}$.

Available experimental evidence suggests that this slow process is due to a pH-dependent equilibrium between at least two forms of ferricytochrome c having considerably different redox potentials. The existence of two functionally distinct forms of ferricytochrome c at alkaline pH is indicated by studies of its reduction with ascorbate (10). Furthermore, the optical rotary dispersion parameters of ferricytochrome c are strongly pH-dependent (15) in the pH region investigated, while those of ferrocytochrome c are pH-independent (16).

It thus appears that the effect of pH on the redox potential of cytochrome $\underline{c}$ is due not to an effect on the electron transfer reaction per se, but to the effect of pH on a slow isomerization of ferricytochrome $\underline{c}$ which results in conversion of part of the ferricytochrome $\underline{c}$ to a form incapable of participation in the electron transfer process with ferro-ferricyanide.

## References

1. Rodkey, F. L., and E. G. Ball. J. Biol. Chem., 182, 17 (1950).

2. Paul, K. G. Arch. Biochem. Biophys., 12, 441 (1947).

3. Green, D. E. Proc. Roy. Soc. London, Series B, 114, 423 (1934).

4. Coolidge, T. B. J. Biol. Chem., 98, 755 (1932).

5. Kolthoff, I. M., and W. J. Tomsicek. J. Phys. Chem., 39, 945 (1935).

6. Chance, B. In Enzymes and Enzyme Systems (J. T. Edsall, ed.), Harvard University Press, Cambridge, Mass., 1951, p. 95.

7. Beetlestone, J. Arch. Biochem. Biophys., 89, 35 (1960).

8. Sutin, N., and D. R. Christman. J. Am. Chem. Soc., 83, 1773 (1961).

9. Havsteen, B. H. Acta Chem. Scandinavica, 19, 1227 (1965).

10. Greenwood, C., and G. Palmer. J. Biol. Chem., 240, 3660 (1965).

11. Czerlinski, G. Rev. Sci. Instr., 33, 1184 (1963).

12. Czerlinski, G., and M. Eigen. A. Elektrochem., 63, 652 (1959).

13. Chance, B., and V. Legallais. Rev. Sci. Instr., 22, 627 (1951).

14. Eigen, M., and L. deMaeyer. In Technique of Organic Chemistry, Vol. VIII, Part 2 (A. Weissberger, ed.), Interscience Publishers, New York, 1963, p. 895.

15. Myer, Y. P., and H. A. Harbury. Proc. Natl. Acad. Sci. U. S., 54, 1391 (1965).

16. Mirsky, R., and P. George. Abstracts of the Biophysical Society Meeting, Boston, 1966, p. 97.

# THEORETICAL INTERPRETATIONS

# SOME THEORETICAL PROBLEMS CONCERNING IRON PORPHYRINS

R. J. P. Williams

Inorganic Chemistry Laboratory and Wadham College
Oxford University
Oxford, England

Recently we have had cause to look again at a number of theoretical problems associated with the chemistry of heme. The problems with which I am concerned are not those of structure--this realm belongs to the X-ray crystallographer or the electron microscopist. I shall be concerned rather with thermodynamic and kinetic problems, but I shall invoke the aid of spectroscopic methods generally.

Optical spectra. In the 1955 Faraday Society Meeting (1) I proposed that a close correlation existed between the spectral and magnetic properties of hemoproteins. Theorell pointed out to me that, in 1942 (and unknown to me) he had proposed a similar relationship (1). At the same meeting George stated that no such relationship existed. Subsequently Beetlestone, George and Griffith (2) proved that there is an exact relationship of this kind for the hydroxide complexes, though they did not give an exact account of the history of their ideas. In the absence of a theory of the spectra of the compounds the correlation remains of relatively slight use. This can be seen from Table I, which gives the data on magnetic moments and a reference to the spectra in the visible and near infrared. The g-values obtained from ESR data are also given. There is little doubt that the $CN^-$ and $N_3^-$ are either entirely or very largely low-spin. The low temperature ESR spectrum of the azide shows no marked change from that at higher temperatures and it shows little or no signal at $g = 6.0$ typical of the high-spin form. However, the azide shows considerable visible and infra-red absorption in the regions thought to be diagnostic for high spin. In fact we find that, while the "known" high-spin forms have intense absorption bands in the range $\lambda_{max} = 600 - 2000$ m$\mu$, even the low-spin cyanide still has some absorption in this region and the azide has a lot. The reasons for the spectral bands in the near infra-red, which can have very different origins, and for the differences in intensity of the spectra are not hard to find once the nature of the problem is recognized.

TABLE I

Magnetic Parameters

Myoglobin derivatives;  Iron(III)

| Compound | Magnetic Moment (B. M.) | g values | Conclusion on spin state |
|---|---|---|---|
| $F^-$ | 5.9 | 6.0 (2.0?) | high |
| $H_2O$ | 5.8 | 6.0 (2.0?) | high (mainly?) |
| $OH^-$ | 3.5 | 2.8, 2.2, 1.7 | mixed |
| $N_3^-$ | 2.3 | 2.8, 2.2, 1.7 | low (mainly?) |
| $CN^-$ | 2.2 | similar to above? | low |

The above magnetic data are discussed in references 3 and 4, and details of long-wave spectra are given in our article, "Structure and Properties of Biomolecules and Biological Systems" (5).

In the first instance we now know that in the $N_3^-$ and $H_2O$ complexes of myoglobin (i.e., both magnetic forms) the iron is out of the heme plane. This automatically invalidates, at least in part, the previous reasoning about spectra, ESR, etc. based on the iron being in-plane. (The fact that both magnetic forms are present in some compounds, e.g., the hydroxide, in thermal equilibrium makes it probable that the X-ray data on such compounds will not be very well-defined.) We shall next consider two symmetries and analyze the possible electronic transitions: $D_{4h}$ (planar iron-heme) and $C_{4v}$ (square-pyramidal iron-heme) for both high and low-spin systems. The allowed and forbidden transitions predicted are listed in Table II (6). The predicted polarizations of these transitions are also given. We see that·the out-of-plane character of the iron, no matter whether the iron is high or low-spin, is a decisive factor for the intensity of some bands. Fig. 1 and Table II give the polarization of the bands from our own single-crystal measurement.* All observed transitions are polarized xy, i.e. in the plane of the heme, much as expected.

*Single crystals of methoxide heme were kindly supplied by Prof. W. S. Caughey and of myoglobin fluoride and hydroxide by Prof. B. Chance.                558

TABLE II

Transitions of Fe(III)(Porphyrin)

| Chromophore | $\lambda$ (m$\mu$) | polarization |
|---|---|---|
| Porphyrin$^{--}$ alone ($D_{4h}$) | | |
| $A_1$  E | 400 and 500<br>? triplets<br>$\sim 1,000$ m$\mu$ | xy (predicted) |
| Metal alone high spin<br>$D_{4h}$ | | |
| $^6A_1$  $^4E$, $^4T$, $^4A$.<br>(all d---d) | expected around<br>600 - 1,000 m$\mu$ | xy (predicted)<br>(forbidden) |
| Complex (high spin) | | |
| $A_1$  E | 400, 500 and<br>600-650 (mixed<br>charge-transfer<br>ligand)<br>(4 bands)<br>similar in $C_{4v}$<br>and $D_{4h}$ | xy (predicted)<br>xy (observed)*<br><br>(allowed) |
| $A_1$ (ligand)<br>  $A_1$ (metal) | charge transfer<br>to $d_z2$ | z (predicted)<br>(not seen) |
| $A_1$ (metal)<br>  $T_1$ (metal) | d---d 900?<br>(mixed with<br> charge transfer)<br>intensity higher in<br>$C_{4v}$ than in $D_{4h}$. | xy (predicted)<br>xy (observed)* |

LOW SPIN  (1) d---d bands will be at high energy and of high
        intensity in $C_{4v}$,

        (2) If xz and yz occupied charge transfer to E
        excluded

        (3) However, if xy lower than either xz or yz then
        charge transfer mixing again possible but at
        higher energy.

*Observed in the methoxide of mesoporphyrin Fe(III) and in the
fluoride and hydroxide of myoglobin.

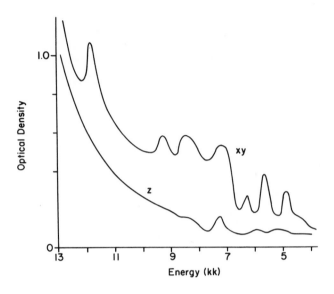

Figure 1. Polarized single crystal spectra of the methoxide of mesoporphyrin iron (III). From long wavelengths the probable assignments are vibration overtones, triplet, d-d, and charge transfer singlets (mixed), which are just seen on left.

In the case of the high-spin ions the very high long-wave intense bands are attributed to mixed charge-transfer ligand transitions and will be expected to persist even when the metal atom is in-plane. The d-d bands are spin-forbidden but are allowed in $C_{4v}$ but not in $D_{4h}$. They will also be mixed with charge-transfer character. It is possible that the band at 800 m$\mu$ in the high-spin heme methoxide ($C_{4v}$) is such a d-d band. For low-spin systems the presence of charge-transfer bands depends on the occupation of $d_{xy}$, $d_{xz}$ and $d_{yz}$, respectively. Assuming the latter to be the lower, then charge transfer is not possible in $D_{4h}$ or $C_{4v}$ with xy polarization. This is likely to be the case in most circumstances. (However, if xy is lower than either xz or yz, then charge transfer is again allowed. The order could depend on the planarity of the system and on the nature of the Z-axis ligand. Thus there is no clear-cut spectroscopic distinction between spin-states.) As for high spin in $C_{4v}$, the d-d transitions should be very strong (not in $D_{4h}$) for low spin and are spin-allowed. They could give rise to a moderately strong band in the infra-red ($\epsilon \gtrsim 100$) even for an

in-plane iron complex. There is a danger then in the interpretation of these spectra without full polarization data and magnetic moments. Again no reference has been made to ligand
triplet states which will occur in the near infra-red, Fig. 1.

Another danger, which applies forcibly to Mössbauer spectroscopy too, is the change of ionic equilibria as opposed to
spin state equilibria with temperature. Keilin and Hartree
reported that on cooling the hydroxides of hemoglobins and
myoglobins they revert to the acid form (high long-wave length
absorption). Beetlestone, George and Griffith (2) report that
on dropping the temperature, the change is to the low-spin form
(very little long-wave absorption). The question is not just
how to interpret the facts at one temperature, but what are the
facts about the spectra at different temperatures. The ESR
measurements at liquid nitrogen suggest that the hydroxide is,
at least in major part, low spin. The Mössbauer data are confusing as yet--see later.

The magnetic moments available are not very satisfactory
either. It seems to me to be essential to get good new measurements of many of the physical parameters over a wide range
of temperature if the electron distribution in these compounds
is to be understood.

A second problem to which I wish to draw attention is
that the ligand bound to the iron on the Z-axis may introduce
a lowering of symmetry. Both $C_{4v}$ and $D_{4h}$, the symmetries above,
have the four-fold axis of the parent metal porphyrin retained.
The introduction of a linear ligand lying across the porphyrin
breaks this symmetry. The result should be 1) a separation
of the $\alpha\beta$ and Soret band regions, 2) a gain in intensity of
the $\alpha\beta$ system relative to the Soret system and 3) possibly a
splitting of the Soret system. It should also produce splittings in the d-d bands. It is very interesting to note that
the spectra of $N_3^-$ complexes of heme-compounds, Fe(III), where
the $N_3^-$ is now known to lie across the heme, have always been
somewhat anomalous. The intensity of the 625 mμ band is invariably too high for the magnetic moment, giving the impression that the azide is more high-spin than was consistent with
magnetic data.

A third spectroscopic problem concerns the intensity of
the $\alpha\beta$ band system compared with the Soret ($\gamma$) system generally. The ratio of these intensities is a consequence of the
strength of configurational interaction. This is very sensitive to small changes in the energies of states with the same
symmetry. An example shows this. The spectrum of Co(III)
mesoporphyrin in different solvents is given in Fig. 2 (7). It

shows that there is a five-fold change in intensity of the band system. It is interesting to inquire if comparable changes occur in iron porphyrins? Looking at the data for various cytochromes there seems to be strikingly little change in the ratio $\beta/\gamma$ for one oxidation state (in one spin state), but change of cation or oxidation state does affect the ratio considerably. It is possible that the ratio will be sensitive to Z-axis ligands too. It could be that the loss of intensity of the $\alpha\beta$ system in high-spin Fe(III) is partly due to changes in configurational interaction. We shall return to this problem when we come to discuss the intermediates in the reactions of heme iron compounds and oxygen and hydrogen peroxide.

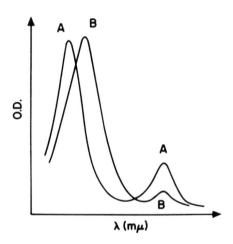

Figure 2. Changes in the absorption spectrum of Co(III) mesoporphyrin on change of solvent. (A) is chloroform and (B) is methanol solution.

## Mössbauer Spectra

Divalent iron. The Mössbauer spectra of divalent iron compounds of the heme-type is, as yet, grossly confusing. Values are known for HbCO, $HbO_2$, $HbH_2O$ (Table III). The parameters of the spectra may be compared with those of a series of model compounds, Fig. 3. In the models which are most closely related to heme-Fe we find a good relationship between the isomer shift and the quadrupole splitting, Fig. 3. This

relationship is observed in very different series of compounds: metal carbonyl, metal glyoxime, metal phthalocyanine
and metal cyanide derivatives, but fails for hemoglobin compounds. Why? The most obvious guess is that the uptake of
ligands by hemoglobins alters the geometry around the iron more
grossly than elsewhere. The oxygen compound has a most unusual
spectrum. We have no model $Fe(II)O_2$ complexes but it would be
good to look at Wang's polymer. Is this again a case of the
ligand breaking the Z-axis symmetry?

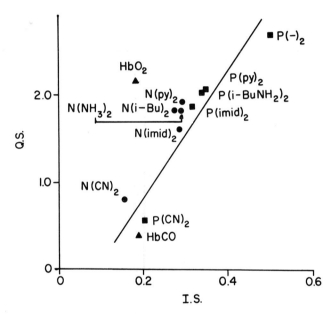

Figure 3. The correlation between the isomer shift and the
quadrupole splitting for a large number of tetragonal Fe(II)
complexes. The values for some hemoglobin compounds are shown.
(■), Phthalocyanines; (●) bis-glyoximes; (▲) Hemiglobins.

The next problem is to ask if a Mössbauer spectrum can
distinguish spin states of Fe(II). The results show that in
two series of compounds it can (Table III). However, for a
ligand which cannot relax its geometry, e.g. a porphyrin, the
answer may be less clear-cut. Thus some low-spin Fe compounds
of this type have very high quadrupole splittings, e.g. $HbO_2$,
and compare $Fe(DMG)_2(NH_3)_2$. Again some high spin (or spin = 1)
Fe(II) compounds have very low isomer shifts, e.g. Fe(II)
phthalocyanine. Thus a spectrum must be completely and very
clearly analyzed before a satisfactory degree of certainty

about spin states of the compound can be achieved. The situation is improved if experiments are done in a magnetic field at low temperatures. However, if the ground state of the high spin system becomes $S_z = 0$ once again the results are not definitive except after a long series of experiments. This is the case for ferrous phthalocyanine, which we shall publish shortly.

## TABLE III

### Mössbauer Data on Fe(II) Complexes

#### Hemoglobin (Rat)

| Ligand | Spin State | Isomer shift, $\delta$ | Q.S. |
|---|---|---|---|
| $H_2O$ (?) | high | 9.90 | 2.40 |
| CO | low | 0.18 | 0.36 |
| $O_2$ | low | 0.24 | 1.9* |

*Strongly temperature dependent

#### Other Compounds

| Complex | Spin State | Isomer shift, $\delta$ | Q.S. |
|---|---|---|---|
| $Fe(phen)_2(NCS)_2$ | high | 0.98 | 2.67** |
| " | low | 0.37 | 0.34** |
| $Fe(phen)_3$ | low | 0.45 | 0.30 |
| $Fe(Cp^-)_2$ | low | 0.7 | 2.4 |
| $Fe(py)_2$heme | low | 0.05 | 0.6 – 1.2 |
| phthalocyanine Fe | high? | 0.51 | 2.69 |
| "  $Fe(py)_2$ | low | 0.33 | 1.97 |
| "  $Fe(NH_3)_2$ | low | 0.32 | 1.94 |
| $Fe_3(CO)_{12}$  (a) | low | 0.2 | 0.0 |
| (b) | low | 0.3 | 1.2 |

$Fe(2(2\text{-pyridine})\text{-imidazole})_3SO_4$ is of intermediate magnetic moment and gives rise to two different Mössbauer signals.

**See reference (9).

Trivalent iron (10). The problems of the Mössbauer spectra of trivalent iron are no less severe. Thus we have measured a series of hemoglobin complexes over a wide range of temperature and magnetic field (Table IV). Firstly, the isomer shifts are not very sensitive to spin state. Secondly, the quadrupole splittings can be surprisingly large for S = 5/2 states. Thirdly, at low temperature and in a magnetic field $S_z$ = 1/2 (for S = 5/2) may lie lowest so that a low-spin or a high-spin state may give rise to a very similar six-line spectrum. Thus once more only a complete analysis of the spectrum, which is difficult except on single crystals, will yield definitive results and a satisfactory insight into the nature of the electron distribution.

TABLE IV

Mössbauer Data on Fe(III) Complexes

Hemoglobins (Rat)

| Ligand | Spin State | Isomer Shift (±0.02) | Q.S. (±0.05) | Temp. |
|---|---|---|---|---|
| $F^-$ | high | +0.4 | 1.0 | estimated |
| $H_2O$ | ? high(mostly) | +0.18 | 2.05 | 190°K |
| $OH^-$ | mixed | +0.17 | 1.65 | 190°K* |
| $N_3^-$ | ? low(mostly) | +0.15 | 2.30 | 190°K |
| CN | low | +0.15 | 1.50 | 190°K |

*Broad spectrum at liquid nitrogen. Data on the $CNO^-$ complex provide evidence that it is mixed spin.

Other Systems

| Complex | Spin State | Isomer Shift | Q.S. | Temp. |
|---|---|---|---|---|
| Hemin | high | 0.10 | 0.85 | high °K |
| $FeCl_4^-$ | high | 0.48 | small | high °K |
| $Fe(H_2O)_6^{+++}$ | high | 0.55 | small | high °K |
| $Fe(CN)_6^{---}$ | low | 0.0 | 0.1 | high °K |

See reference (10).

TABLE V

Mossbauer Spectra of Fe(III) Hemoglobin (Rat) Complexes

Magnetic Field Effects

| Derivative | 4.2° K | | | 83° K | | High Temperature |
|---|---|---|---|---|---|---|
| | No field | 1 KG | 30 KG | No field | 30 KG | No field |
| F⁻ | diffuse | inter-mediate (many lines) | 6 lines | broad | (broad?) | broad and diffuse |
| H₂O | sharp (many lines) | sharp 6 lines | no further effect | rather broad | S.Q.* | S.Q. |
| OH⁻ | diffuse | sharp 4 lines apparently | no further effect | broad | broader | S.Q. |
| N₃⁻ | sharp (many lines) | sharp 4 lines apparently | no further effect | broad | S.Q. | S.Q. |
| CN⁻ | sharp (many lines) | sharp 6 lines | no further effect | S.Q. | no further effect | S.Q. |
| CNO⁻ | sharp (many lines) | sharp 4 lines | no further effect | broad | S.Q.? | S.Q.? |
| Hemin | S.Q. | inter-mediate | sharp 6 lines | | | S.Q. |

*simple quadrupole

The recognition of mixtures of spin states should be relatively easy in the absence of spin lattice relaxation effects. However, there appear to be only two as yet rather poor examples of Mössbauer spectra which indicate a mixture of high and low spin states--HbOH$^-$ and HbCNO$^-$. Agreement with ESR measurement is good on this point. We feel that we still have no clear-cut Mössbauer evidence for thermal mixtures of spin states in other systems. Clearly the states of lower or higher spin are not far from the ground state in all these systems, so that kinetic problems (relaxation effects) may be under the control of excited electronic states.

The above discussion shows that, as yet, it is extremely dangerous to draw conclusions about spin states from Mössbauer spectra. A typical case is that of the cytochromes from Rhodospirillum rubrum (Moss). The Mössbauer spectrum for two cytochromes (oxidized) shows only a simple quadrupole spectrum, yet optical spectroscopy reveals two different heme-systems. This means that the Mössbauer study has failed to reveal any thing of significance about this system and, insofar as there are some who might use Mössbauer information as superior to other sorts of information, ground has been lost. It could be that in this case relaxation is so fast as to reveal only one "average" spectrum.

One very interesting result which we have observed during the course of Mössbauer studies is that the magnetic splittings in the spectrum are very differently sensitive to magnetic fields for the several derivatives. Curiously, the fluoride of hemoglobin behaves like hemin while the hydroxide, cyanide, azide and aquo complex behave differently. This relaxation is dependent upon either spin-spin interaction (unlikely here except for hemin) or spin-lattice relaxation due to coupling through orbital angular moment. The aquo complex is supposed to be of spin 5/2, yet it behaves like the low-spin complexes and unlike the fluoride (see Table V and Fig. 4), so that a simple connection with S states is apparently excluded.

At higher temperatures the effect of the magnetic field is expected to be to reduce the broadness due to magnetic splittings, leaving a more or less simple quadrupole spectrum. This is true for the azide, cyanide, and aquo-complexes, but there is remarkably little effect on the fluoride. More marked still is the effect on the hydroxide and especially the cyanate which show a broadened spectrum in the magnetic field. These two are the cases where a thermal equilibrium is thought to be present. The oddities seen in the hydrate may be due to the second proton on the oxygen of the bound $H_2O$.

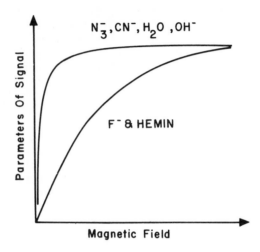

Figure 4. The qualitative effect of magnetic field on the Mössbauer spectra of hemoglobin derivatives. Note that if fluoride and hemin are used to define how an S state should behave, then the aquo-complex is decidedly odd. Other parameters of the Mössbauer spectra also show this distinction.

Optical rotatory dispersion and circular dichroism (11). The curious observations which have been made on cytochrome c (oxidized compared with reduced) circular dichroism spectra can be compared with results on vitamin $B_{12a}$ compounds. To appreciate the significance of these observations we shall use the extensive model experiments of Jackson, Hill, Pratt and Williams on vitamin $B_{12}$ complexes. They took the Co(III) derivatives of formulae Co(III), (Corrin)XY and, with X constant (benzimidazole), varied Y in the sequence

$$H_2O, \ NH_3, \ py, \ CNO^-, \ OH^-, \ CNS^-, \ CNSe^-, \ CH_3, \ C_2H_5^-, \ CN^-$$

The circular dichroism in the $\gamma$-band region and between 400–500 m$\mu$ inverts along the series (Fig. 5). Moreover, it has been shown that complete inversion can occur on changing temperature using just one of these compounds. The changes in ring conformation from one to another for some of the above compounds are known from the crystallography of Hodgkin and coworkers (12). The changes are small but significant, though the metal ion remains in-plane. It is a matter of conjecture

568

then whether the inversion in CD is caused by the changes of electron density on the cobalt due to the Z-axis ligand (relayed into the ring) or whether there is a regular shift in conformation along the series. The former seems the more likely on ligand change, but it seems probable too that the changes in circular dichroism with temperature are due to changes in conformation. On changing from Co(III) to Co(II) there is a complete change in the circular dichroism, and, as in the case of cytochrome c, the change is not similar in different regions of the spectrum. There are similar changes on change of temperature for some of the B$_{12}$ derivaties.

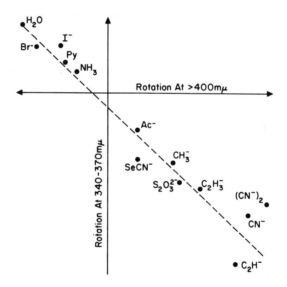

Figure 5. The strengths of the rotation in two wavelength regions for a series of vitamin B$_{12}$ derivatives. It would appear that electronic and conformational changes are involved.

Returning to the cytochromes we see that inversion could readily arise from 1) changes in electron interaction between the metal and all its ligands, or 2) a definitive change in conformation. The concomitant changes in the circular dichroism of the aromatic groups of the protein of cytochrome c suggest that oxidation causes a change in geometry. So far the required series of experiments, changing Z-axis ligand and temperature, have not been done with heme compounds.

## Electron Transfer

Recently we have made a series of studies on electron transfer in rigid matrices--usually single crystals. Table VI shows our results. In only one case, $Tl_3[Fe(CN)_6]$, is the activation energy low. Again in all cases the energy of the electron-transfer spectral absorption-band between the separate oxidizing and reducing species is large -- much larger than the thermal energy for conduction.

TABLE VI

### Electron Transfer in Iron Complexes

| Complex | $E_a$ Kcals | Charge-transfer band energy Kcals | $E_a$ solu-tion Kcals |
|---|---|---|---|
| Fe(III)(CN)$_6$/ Fe(II)(CN)$_6$ | 12.5 | not seen | 4.7 |
| $Tl^{++}/Tl^+$ | 6.5 | ? | |
| Fe(III)(CN)$_6$/Fe(II) | 10.0 | 50 | |
| Co(III)(CN)$_6$/Fe(II) | 15.0 | 70 | |
| Fe(III)/Fe(II) in asbestos | 16.0 | 50 | 10.0 in $H_2O$ |
| Cu(II)Cl$_5$/Cu(I)Cl$_4$ | 17.0 | 50 | very low |
| Fe(II) phthalocyanine | 30.0 | not seen | very low |
| [IrCl$_6$]$^{--}$/ [Fe (phenan)$_3$]$^{++}$ | not measurable | not seen | very low |

$E_a$ is the measured activation energy of conduction or of reaction. It is about 5-10 Kcal in the cytochrome chain. Note that in biological systems the geometry around a metal is often dictated by proteins and may well not suit particular valence states of metals. This incompatibility could lead to a very low relaxation energy and easy electron transfer.

Where a comparable reaction has been examined in solution we find that the rate of electron transfer is often very fast and that the activation energy for electron transfer is relatively low. All these facts indicate that the main energy-restricting electron-transfer is that associated with the unrelaxed atmosphere in the solid which surrounds the electron immediately after the electron has been transferred. Thus reactions in solution are of low activation energy compared with reactions in a solid just because the matrix, e.g., water, is not essentially rigid. Its ability to relax creates the possibility of rapid electron transfer. It could well be that electron transfer is even further facilitated in protein systems which are clearly more open to easy deformation. A study of electron transfer in different solvents would be of great value. It is interesting to ask whether it would be easier for electron transfer to occur in an organic or an aqueous phase, for the solvation energy is much more rigid in the latter. Some explanation is certainly needed for the high electron transfer rates in biological systems ($\sim 10^7$), e.g., in the cytochrome chain or even in chloroplasts after light absorption.

There is also the problem of exactly what is transferred from one redox center to another. The two candidates which are often postulated are the electron and the hydrogen atom. Now it is not altogether clear that these two entities are different. In water the equilibrium

$$H^{\cdot} \rightleftharpoons H^+ + e$$

has a value of $10^{-9}$. As the rate constant $H^+ + e$ is likely to be $10^{10}$, the forward reaction rate constant cannot be faster than $10^1$. Now electron transfer reactions in the cytochrome chain are not free solution reactions. Each cytochrome is not more than 10 Å from its nearest neighbor. In a molar solution in ice, electron transfer centers are, on average, 5-10 water molecules apart, i.e., $\sim 20$ Å, and the exchange rate is about $10^3$ extrapolated to $25^{\circ}$ C. Considering the fact that low-spin ions have much greater exchange rates, electron transfer in the cytochrome chain is not a specially facilitated transfer from the point of view of the distance apart of electron exchange centers. However, this exchange is clearly far faster than the reaction $H^{\cdot} \rightarrow e + H^+$ and is only slower than $e + H^+ \rightarrow H^{\cdot}$ at about pH 3.0. Thus $H^{\cdot}$, if it is the electron transfer reactant in the cytochrome chain, reacts faster than it could dissociate to $H^+ + e$ and only at very high $H^+$ is $e + H^+$ comparable in rate with electron transfer. Electron transfer and hydrogen atom transfer may not go readily over into one another. This could be a very important point in the cytochrome chain, see below.

The next point is that the absorption spectrum of the cy-tochrome chain as yet* shows no evidence of charge transfer, i.e., electron transfer  spectra from metal to metal ion or from the metal complex to some near neighbor ligand.  It is worth noting that such charge transfer bands are not easily seen in <u>outer</u> sphere systems.  Thus $[Fe(phenanthroline)_3]^{++}$ - $[IrCl_6]^{--}$ has no observable band.  This may be due to the low intensity of these bands, e.g., in $[Cu(I)Cl_4]$---$[Cu(II)Cl_5]$--- the intensity of the charge transfer band is only 5 x $10^2$, measured in a single crystal.  However, $[FeCl_4]^{--}$ and $PO^{++}$ (paraquat, PQ, is the inhibitor of photo-synthesis, bis N-methyl 4.4' dipyridyl) also give a <u>white</u> solid $PQ^{++}$ $[FeCl_4]^{--}$, no charge transfer band, which reacts rapidly to give blue $PQ^+[FeCl_4]^-$. Thus it appears that electron transfer can be fast (thermally) when charge transfer excitation by light is associated with an activation energy of  $\overline{>}3ev$.

In addition, the thermal charge transfer in the cytochrome chain has also to be coupled with condensation reactions, bring-ing about phosphorylation and with it cation accumulation.  The total reaction is one which can best be visualized as one phos-phorylation for a redox potential drop of about 0.15 volts by two electrons, i.e., some 7 Kcals.  The lack of understanding of oxidative phosphorylation (or cation transport) is closely linked with the failure to understand electron transfer in organized systems which are not single crystals.

<u>Comment on Electron Transfer Chains</u>.  The steps which <u>initiate</u> electron transfer are different at each end of the electron transfer chain.  DPNH oxidation by a flavoprotein must generate $H^+$.  (Any earlier oxidation of DPNH must also generate $H^+$ if there is an earlier step.)  At the other end of the electron transfer chain, initial oxidation removes an <u>electron</u> $(Fe^{++})cyt\ \underline{a}_3 \rightarrow (Fe^{+++})cyt\ \underline{a}_3$.  There is undoubtedly also a series of one-electron transfers down the chain of cytochromes. How do these occur?  If a semiconductor band model is postulated it seems impossible to connect electron transfer and the <u>above chemical</u> changes with which it is in communication.  Thus it is in a steady state relationship with $M^{++}$ and $M^+$ ion balances and with phosphorylation.  Moreover both of these changes can be connected with pH changes.  We must look for a hopping electron transfer involving chemical species.  Such a mechanism is open to inhibition by chemical species (as is observed) in a quite obvious way, which is not a feature of a band model.  Apparently, too, each step has a similar temperature dependence and a similar

---

*But see discussion of cytochrome <u>c</u> spectra, Hochstrasser and Williams, p.

solvent effect. What is the simplest system for such electron hops which can be connected both to $\underline{ion}$ movements and to condensation reactions? In my opinion, it is the generation of $H^+$ in the membrane at various redox steps. This will drive phosphorylation by removing water of condensation. (The suggestions of Mitchell (compare Williams 1960 and 1961) of a left-right attack by $OH^-$ and $H^+$ to give ATP from $P_i$ and ADP could be made equivalent to the earlier treatment of high $H^+(OH^-)$ concentrations assymetrically generated in a membrane.) Alteration of the $H^+$ concentration will be in steady-state communication with $M^+$ and $M^{++}$ balances, for it is an effective way of altering membrane mobilities. The problem of the specific way in which oxidation is linked to $H^+$ generation is obvious enough at the DPNH $\rightarrow$ DPN + $H^+$ stage and it is also clear that the oxidation of flavins can be written in steps involving $H^+$ generation. This cannot be done for cytochrome complexes. Thus it is essential to look for other linked redox systems which are $H^+$ dependent. Three are obvious:

$$2H^+ + \underset{\underset{RS}{\overset{|}{\phantom{R}}}}{RS} \xrightarrow{\phantom{xx}2e\phantom{xx}} RSH + RSH \qquad (1)$$

$$O{=}\!\!\left\langle\phantom{xx}\right\rangle\!\!{=}O \;+\; 2H^+ \xrightarrow{\phantom{xx}2e\phantom{xx}} HO{-}\!\!\left\langle\phantom{xx}\right\rangle\!\!{-}OH \qquad (2)$$

$$OH \;+\; H^+ \xrightarrow{\phantom{xx}e\phantom{xx}} H_2O \qquad (3)$$

The first may well be involved in ferredoxin type reactions and the second in the oxidation of para-phenols (well recognized in biology) and the third could also be part of the electron transport chain. If this mechanism is operative, it is important that the equilibrium $H \rightleftharpoons H^+ + e$ is not achieved. The $H^+$ (charged) should be generated in a specific part of space so as to link closely with phosphorylation.

I should like to summarize my views on electron transfer in the cytochrome chain in the following way:

1. Electron transfer must be fast, although the low-spin complexes involved are far apart. This is now not unknown in model systems but not at a sufficiently high rate except in liquid media. Thus, assuming that the membrane in which electron transfer takes place is more like a liquid than a solid phase, there is nothing particularly odd about electron transfer per se. Rotating cytochromes are not yet a necessary postulate.

2. Electron transfer could be by either the electron or by the hydrogen atom. Reasons have been given for keeping

the two ideas distinct.

3.   It is essential that any theory of electron transfer can be connected with compulsory movement of other charges, e.g., of the potassium and calcium ion, and with oxidative phosphorylation and hence with metabolism.  The mechanism must link with condensation reactions.

4.   Each of the major steps in the chain has much in common with all the others, e.g., phosphorylation, reversibility and effect of temperature and solvent, despite the different effects of inhibitors and the fact that some of the steps obviously require hydrogen atom transfer, while others seem only to require electron transfer.

5.   The only transfer system which seems to have the ability to generate all the required properties at all the different sites is the oxidation of hydrogen atoms between the sites.

6.   Such a system must set up certain ion concentration gradients, but it would be wrong to assume that specific chemicals are not involved in the hydrogen atom transfer.  Thus it is not necessary to think of two conflicting views about oxidative phosphorylation, i.e., the chemical view and the charge gradient view, for these are not essentially separate.

As there is a requirement for an intact membrane in both the theories of oxidative phosphorylation it might be of use to add a word or two about membranes.

Asymmetric membranes (13).  Physical chemistry deals with membranes which are homogenous.  The composition on the inside, in the center, and on the outside are identical.  Such membranes can generate many asymmetric properties provided that chemicals are supplied asymmetrically to the two sides of the membrane. The exact properties are dependent on the mobility of a variety of ions and molecules in the membrane material.  These properties are controlled by the chemical character of the membrane relative to the bathing solutions.  Based on this model is the concept of the "unit" membrane of Danielli and many others. Biological properties such as permeability are then treated by traditional physical chemistry.  In my opinion, biological membranes are not like this.  They contain an asymmetric array of molecules, e.g., proteins, so that the inside, outside and middle are distinct.  The consequences of this asymmetry would not be so dramatic but for the fact that the different large molecules which accumulate in the two surfaces and middle of the membrane catalyse different reactions. It is this property which causes many of the various features of "membranes" of biology. Some cases of asymmetric membranes are 1) light receptors, 2) chloroplasts, 3) mitochondria, 4) nerve endings. It is not an accident that in each case redox processes are associated with ion movements, though given these asymmetric membranes it is not clear that special carrier mechanisms for ions are required. This stresses the importance of discovering the exact location of the cytochromes.

$O_2$ carrying ability. The very attractive hypothesis of Wang that the $O_2$ carrying ability of hemoglobin or myoglobin is due to the environment-- the inability of water to reach the heme unit -- seems to me to require further experimental demonstration. There are now several reports from Caughey, Busch, Fallab and ourselves that this is not necessarily the case. At present, however, most of these experiments lack the quantitative proof of the presence of an oxygen carrier (in solution) which must be a pre-requisite of acceptance.

The magnitude of the cooperative effect in the uptake of oxygen by hemoglobin also has defied explanation so far. The simplest explanation, that the change of spin state of the iron alters the Fe(II) protein bondlengths sufficiently and that this is relayed to more distant parts of the molecule through hydrogen bonds, awaits a check. Now that it is known that high-spin iron sits out of plane, we need to know if low-spin Fe(II) sits in or out of plane, for then changes in the degree of out-of-planarity could cause long-range effects.

Hydrogen peroxide Complex I. The point was made earlier that spectroscopic changes can be used in a diagnostic manner. Brill and I did this in the case of Complex I of peroxidase and catalase. I now wish to modify the argument slightly. As was pointed out in the introduction, breaking the symmetry of the porphyrin ring will cause certain changes in spectrum. It is worth noting that apart from azide heme Fe(III) complexes, these same changes are apparent to a greater or lesser degree in 1) some hemin complexes, 2) RHP cytochromes at low pH, 3) peroxidase, 4) catalase inhibited with azetolamide. All these complexes are high-spin Fe(III). Thus it looks as if some high-spin Fe(III) compounds introduce a distortion of the four-fold axis of the porphyrin ring. However, the degree of distortion as shown by spectra is much greater in some proteins than in others, and in turn this suggests that the Z-axis ligands or other protein groups are crowded close to the heme, destroying its symmetry. (These are most likely to be anions.) The Complexes I of catalase and peroxidase have the spectrum which indicates such a gross distortion that they are almost the same as the spectra of molecules such as glaucobilin, in which the symmetry is broken by saturating one methene bridge. Thus hydrogen peroxide has introduced a greater distortion in the heme than any other ligand, including azide. The obvious conclusion is that the $H_2O_2$ has chemically attached the porphyrin, as Brill and I supposed, but it is possible that combination with another group has introduced gross steric modification of the ring. The second possibility is made improbable by the large change of magnetic moment.

## Acknowledgment

This paper is intended to be no more than a laboratory report of a wide range of activities. It is therefore essential that full recognition be accorded to my co-workers (see references 6-8, 10,11). In particular, the Mössbauer work is very largely due to Dr. C. Johnson of AERE (Harwell).

## References

1. Williams, R. J. P.  Disc. Faraday Soc., 20 290 (1955) and see Theorell, H.  Arkiv. Kemi., Min. Geol., 16A, No. 3, 1.

2. George, P., J. Beetlestone, and J. S. Griffith.  In Haematin Enzymes (J. E. Falk, R. Lemberg, and R. K. Morton, eds.) Pergamon Press, London, 1961, pp. 41, 105.

3. Ehrenberg, A.  Arkiv. Kemi., 19, 119 (1962).

4. Morita, Y., and H. S. Mason.  J. Biol. Chem, 240, 2654 (1965).

5. Braterman, P. S., R. C. Davies, and R. J. P. Williams.  In Advances in Chemical Physics, Vol. VIII (J. Duchesne, ed.), Interscience Publishers, New York, 1964, p. 359.

6. Studies with Mr. D. E. Smith and Dr. P. Day.

7. Studies with Mr. R. E. Collis and Dr. H. A. O. Hill.

8. Studies with Mr. B. Dale, Mr. P. Edwards, Dr. C. Johnson (AERE, Harwell), and Mr. B. Newman (Radcliffe Hospital).

9. König, E., and K. Madeja.  Chem. Comm. (London), 61 (1961).

10. In part this work is a continuation of work at AERE, Harwell by G. Lang and W. Marshall, and has been done by Mr. P. Edwards, Mr. M. Winter, Mr. B. Newman (Radcliffe Hospital), Dr. C. Johnson (Aere, Harwell) and myself.

11. Jackson, B., H.A.O. Hill, J.M. Pratt, and R.J.P. Williams. Royal Society Meeting on Optical Rotation, in press.

12. Hodgkin, D. C.  Nobel Prize Lecture (1964), The Nobel Foundation, 1965.

13. Compare Mitchell, P.  Nature, 191, 144 (1961) and Williams, R. J. P.  J. Theoret. Biol., 1, 1 (1961) and 3, 209 (1962).

# KINETICS OF THE AUTOXIDATION OF HEMES[*]

Irwin A. Cohen[**] and Winslow S. Caughey[‡]

Department of Physiological Chemistry
The Johns Hopkins University School of Medicine
Baltimore, Maryland

Reactions of molecular oxygen with iron (II) porphyrins are of particular interest as models for reactions of heme-proteins with oxygen (1). The kinetic aspects of these reactions in simple model systems have not been extensively studied. Here we report on the kinetics of autoxidation for two dipyridine iron (II) porphyrins in nonaqueous media.

Recently, Kao and Wang examined rates of autoxidation of dipyridineprotoheme which was prepared in situ (2). Most of their work dealt with aqueous solutions even though they pointed out that a nonaqueous solvent like benzene or benzene ethanol is a more appropriate model for the heme environment in a protein. In aqueous solution they found a two-term rate law which indicated that the autoxidation mechanistically involves formation of the superoxide ion by both an inner and an outer sphere electron transfer path. Kao and Wang also reported some kinetic results carried out in benzene-ethanol systems, but they did not report the effect of changes of the oxygen or pyridine concentration upon the rate although this is imperative for the determination of a rate law.

Our reactions were followed spectrophotometrically in the visible region in benzene or benzene-ethanol solution containing pyridine and oxygen at concentrations at least ten times greater than the heme. The two substrates examined were dipyridine protoporphyrin IX dimethyl ester iron (II) and dipyridine 2,4-diacetyldeuteroporphyrin IX dimethyl ester iron (II). In both cases it was possible to use pure solid hemes as substrates and thereby avoid complications of in

[*]This work was supported by U. S. PHS Research Grant HE-06079.

[**]National Institutes of Health, Post-doctoral Fellow.

[‡]Lederle Medical Faculty Award Scholar.

situ preparations. That our system is kinetically equivalent to that used by Kao and Wang was shown upon duplication of their conditions with the protoporphyrin derivative (50 percent ethanol-50 percent benzene, pyridine = .47 M, solvent saturated with 50 percent $N_2$ - 50 percent $O_2$) where good agreement with their results was found $k_1$ (Kao and Wang)= 8.4 x $10^{-3}$ and $k_1$ (this work = 9.2 x $10^{-3}$ sec$^{-1}$. Under these specific conditions the rate was clearly first order; however, a rate first order in heme is only observed at high oxygen concentrations.

Using benzene as solvent and varying the pyridine concentrations between 1 and 20 mM, the oxygen concentrations between 1.5 and 7.0 mM and the heme concentrations between $10^{-4}$ and $10^{-5}$ M, we found kinetics which can be summarized as follows. At low and intermediate oxygen levels both hemes were oxidized at rates which possessed both a first and a second order rate component. Statistical resolution of the rate terms indicated that a low $O_2$ levels the major term was second order in heme. Varying the pyridine and oxygen concentrations indicated the overall rate law at low $O_2$ levels was

$$\text{Rate} = \frac{k_{II}[O_2]}{[\text{pyridine}]^2} \, [\text{heme}]^2$$

and at 25° C

$k_{II}$(protoheme dimethyl ester) = 30 x $10^{-2}$ sec$^{-1}$, and

$k_{II}$(2,4-diacetyldeuteroheme dimethyl ester) = 7.6 x $10^{-2}$ sec$^{-1}$.

On the other hand at high $O_2$ levels the first order rate term becomes more important and the reaction becomes first order in heme and approaches a limit which is independent of both $O_2$ and pyridine concentration. At high $O_2$ the rate law was observed to be simply

$$\text{Rate} = \kappa_1 \, [\text{heme}]$$

A simple mechanism which can explain the results over the entire range is shown in Eqn. 1, 2 and 3 with py = pyridine and Fe = heme.

$$\text{py-Fe-py} \underset{k_2}{\overset{k_1}{\rightleftharpoons}} [\text{py} - \text{Fe}] + \text{py} \qquad (1)$$

$$2 \, [\text{py-Fe}] + O_2 \xrightarrow{k_3} [\text{py-Fe-}O_2\text{-Fe-py}] \qquad (2)$$

$$[\text{py-Fe-}O_2\text{-Fe-py}] + 2 \, H_2O \longrightarrow 2 \, \text{Fe(III)OH} + H_2O_2 + 2 \, \text{py} \qquad (3)$$

The peroxide formed in the last step would rapidly react with two more hemes in accordance with the overall stoichiometry of the reaction. Because the py-$\overset{\vee}{\underset{\wedge}{Fe}}$-py is low spin we cannot assume $k_1$ is fast but can apply a steady state approach with the statement in Eqn. 4:

$$0 = k_1 \; [\text{py-}\overset{\vee}{\underset{\wedge}{Fe}}\text{-py}] - k_2 \; [\overset{\vee}{\underset{\wedge}{Fe}}\text{-py}] \; [\text{py}] - k_3 \; [\overset{\vee}{\underset{\wedge}{Fe}}\text{-py}]^2 [O_2] \qquad (4)$$

When $[O_2] > [\text{py}]$, Eqn. 4 simplifies and yields a rate law as in Eqn. 5:

$$\text{Rate} = k_1 \; [\text{py-}\overset{\vee}{\underset{\wedge}{Fe}}\text{-py}] \qquad (5)$$

When $[\text{py}] > [O_2]$, Eqn. 4 simplifies and the final rate law becomes Eqn. 6:

$$\frac{k_1^2 \, k_3}{k_2^2} \quad \frac{[O_2][\text{py-}\overset{\vee}{\underset{\wedge}{Fe}}\text{-py}]^2}{[\text{py}]^2} \qquad (6)$$

This mechanism, in summary, involves: 1) inner sphere electron transfer between Fe(II) and $O_2$; 2) one-electron transfer from each of two iron atoms with no oxidation states of iron greater than (III) or superoxide ion formed; 3) the ability to proceed by a rate law which is overall either first or second order in heme.

## References

1. Caughey, W. S., J. O. Alben, and C. A. Beadreau. In Oxidases and Related Redox Systems (T. E. King, H. S. Mason, and M. Morrison, eds.), John Wiley and Sons, Inc., New York, 1965, p. 97.

2. Kao, O. H., and J. H. Wang. Biochemistry, 4, 342 (1965).

# SPECTRA OF SINGLE CRYSTALS OF FERRICYTOCHROME c

William A. Eaton[‡] and Robin M. Hochstrasser[#]

Department of Chemistry, and Laboratory for Research
on the Structure of Matter, University of Pennsylvania
Philadelphia, Pennsylvania

The comparison of the visible and near ultraviolet absorption spectra of hemoproteins with those of the corresponding parent porphyrin compounds clearly indicates that the main contributions to the intensity of absorption derives from electronic transitions involving the porphyrin $\pi$-electron orbitals. Since each of these orbitals has a node in the molecular plane, the corresponding transitions are expected to be polarized parallel to the molecular plane. A qualitative, yet strong, theoretical argument (see for example (1) predicts these transitions in the plane of the porphyrin. This result implies that measurement of optical absorption in light having known polarization with respect to the crystal axes can provide information regarding the relative orientation of the heme group and the unit cell axes. These notions have been used and confirmed in hemoproteins of known structure (2,3).

In this discussion our interest is centered on the polarized spectra of single crystals* of horse heart ferricytochrome c, especially in the region of the weak band at 6950 Å. The visible spectrum is rather typical of a low spin ferric porphyrin complex, and we shall use the polarization results from that region only as an indicator for obtaining the polarization of the 6950 Å band. The 6950 Å band is present in the native protein in aqueous solution at neutral pH. The importance of the band lies in the fact that it appears to be diagnostic of the native protein (4). For example, the band is absent in complexes of the hemoprotein with anionic ligands such as $CN^-$ and $N_3^-$; disappears at extremes of pH (i.e., 2.5 > pH > 9.0); the

‡Pennsylvania Plan Scholar.

#Alfred P. Sloan Foundation Fellow.

*The crystals were a kind gift from Dr. E. Margoliash of the Abbott Laboratories.

581

band is absent in the dimer and polymers of cytochrome c; denaturing agents such as urea cause the band to disappear; and
the intensity of the 6950 Å band is reduced as the temperature
is increased (4). It was therefore clear that an investigation
of the electronic states associated with this transition might
help in the elucidation of the structural environment of the
heme-group in native cytochrome c, and more particularly it
could contribute to our understanding of the detailed differences between the interactions of the heme with the native protein environment at different temperatures.

Crystals of horse-heart ferricytochrome c belong to the
tetragonal space group $P4_1$ (5), and there are four molecules in
the unit cell. The tetrad axis, parallel to the c-axis, determines the relative dispositions of these four molecules; thus
the $x(N_1-N_3)$, y or z (out-of-plane) directions in the four heme
groups make the same angle with the crystallographic c-axis.

The visible bands, and long wavelength edge of the Soret
region, are polarized considerably more strongly along the c-
axis than in the ab-plane. According to our earlier discussion
this implies that the plane of the porphyrin ring is considerably inclined towards the c-axis. A consequence of this inclin-
ation is that the z-axis of the heme is inclined away from the
c-axis towards the ab plane by more than 45°. It follows that
transitions polarized perpendicular to the porphyrin plane
should show a stronger absorption along a or b, than along c.

The spectrum of the 6950 Å region is shown in Fig. 1. On
the basis of the foregoing discussion the transition responsible
for this absorption is concluded to be <u>polarized approximately</u>
<u>perpendicular to the porphyrin ring plane</u>. In one sense this
is a fortunate result, since there are relatively few sources
of out-of-plane intensity in the heme complex (<u>vide</u> <u>infra</u>).
The polarization ratio at 6950 Å was found to be 2.6:1 ($O.D._{ab}$:
$O.D._c$). From the known thickness of the crystals, and the

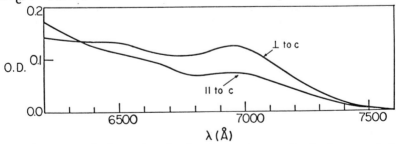

Figure 1. Near infrared polarized spectrum of single crystal
of horse heart ferricytochrome c at 295° K.

known intensity of the 6950 Å band, we estimate that the direction normal to the porphyrin plane makes an angle of ~70° with the c-axis of the crystal. A more precise measurement of this angle is in progress.

There are two obvious transition mechanisms whereby the 6950 Å band could appear as z-polarized: (1) A transition involving the promotion of an electron from a non-porphyrin ligand orbital into an iron-porphyrin orbital. This would be a charge-transfer transition polarized perpendicular to the plane if the orbitals in question are chosen to satisfy the experimental symmetry restriction. The relatively low energy of the transition would hint that either the ligand be very loosely bound, or that it contains other loosely bound electron pairs (e.g., a sulfur atom). (2) A transition involving the promotion of a porphyrin $\pi$-electron into a vacant iron orbital. The highest occupied $\pi$-orbital is noncentrosymmetric but symmetric to rotations about the z-axis of the porphyrin ring (i.e., it is of $\alpha_{2u}$ type). The only appropriate vacant iron orbital is a totally symmetric one ($d_z2$). The transfer of an electron between these orbitals, with retention of the doublet spin character, would give rise to a z-polarized transition. The energy of such a transition would be sensitive to small changes of the electronic structure of a sixth ligand, since the basicity of the complexing group would be modified.

It does appear likely that the temperature dependence of the 6950 Å band intensity is caused by the changing equilibrium between two ligand (or nearby group) heme configurations. At present we are hopeful that further optical experiments, and comparisons of the experiments with theoretical predictions will permit us to distinguish between the many possibilities which arise from the two mechanisms proposed.

## References

1. Gouterman, M. J. Mol. Spec., 6, 138 (1961).

2. Perutz, M. F. Acta Cryst., 6, 859 (1953).

3. Kendrew, J. C., and R. G. Parrish. Proc. Roy. Soc. A., 238, p. 305 (part III) (1956).

4. Schejter, A., and P. George. Biochem., 3, 1045 (1964).

5. Dickerson, R. E., this volume, p. 365.

# REACTIVITY AT THE IRON-HEME CENTER

R. J. P. Williams

Inorganic Chemistry Laboratory and Wadham College
Oxford University
Oxford, England

I wish to use this last session to introduce the general problem of reactivity in the protein region closely surrounding the iron porphyrin unit. Several different situations are conceivable. The iron can be high or low spin; the porphyrin can be bent or flat; the neighboring groups can be protective in two ways--producing steric hindrance or an unfavorable solvation sphere; the neighboring groups can be reactive. Two types of neighbors are present, proximal and distal. The final factor is the nature of the attacking group. Let us consider first one electron addition or removal.

The simplest case is that of low-spin iron bound to two Z-axis ligands, as we now presume it to be, in a cytochrome such as cytochrome c. If the ligands are fixed in one oxidation state, then electron transfer occurs, for that oxidation state, without change of ligand position (Franck-Condon). (Changes of ligand can occur subsequently. I do not wish to discuss the changes of geometry at first.) Thus, if electron transfer occurs it does so to (or from) a given environment, which is that seen spectroscopically. There is also the distinct possibility that the group which donates the electron to the iron must lie very close to it. This would help fast electron transfer. Thus, we might expect charge-transfer spectra from the group, which must be strongly reducing, to the Fe(III). The electron-transfer group is not a proximal ligand, I believe. The probable groups in the coordination position: imidazole, methionine, amino-groups, are poor reducing agents. It is very possibly a distal phenolate or $RS^-$ which could lie in the XZ or YZ planes close to the heme. In such a case we should see an intra-molecular charge-transfer band. (For example, it could well be the band seen at 695 m$\mu$ in cytochrome c--see (1) and discussion below.) The model for electron transfer then becomes very like that proposed by Williams (2). The sensitivity of the band to all manner of changes of environment are in line with this interpretation. Subsequent to electron transfer the protein will relax.

The radical generated may or may not be loosely bound to the heme at this stage. In all events, a rapid electron exchange between the "protected" free radical and the Fe(II) cytochrome could give rise to the very broad ESR spectrum of cytochrome c, i.e. still the Fe(III) form, adding both radical and Fe(II) together.

Now this model also brings out the point in my manuscript (3) of the difference between crystal (regular lattices) and protein electron transfer. The insertion of the phenolate group close to the iron atom in the XZ plane is an unlikely event in regular solids, but very possible in a solution collision or in a protein. If you like to say so, the iron is moving towards seven-coordination.

These observations are also supported by the changes in optical spectra in the tyrosine region in many cytochromes, which are well documented in the circular dichroism work at this meeting. However, they were already seen and discussed by Kamen (4) and by Williams (2) from the spectroscopic point of view.

With such a model in mind we can now turn attention to the peroxidase and catalases. I have stated in my manuscript (3) that high spin porphyrin Fe(III) systems appear open to porphyrin ring distortion in proteins. (The peroxide and oxygen reacting proteins are high spin.) Forcing a phenolate ligand in close in this case should lead to just the changes in spectrum I have noted in my manuscript. The redox mechanism is then obvious enough and the structures to be postulated for catalase I and peroxidase I will not be fundamentally very different from the cytochrome states. The exact spectrum and ESR pattern seen (associated with heme iron, radical "phenolate" or what you will) then depends on the tightness of the interaction between the phenolate, the heme moiety and, in this case, the oxidizing agent. We must expect a range of properties which also depend on the steric constraints due to the protein. In my opinion this is already seen in the beautiful work of Yonetani (5). I wish to suggest that a series of "compound I" and "compound II" spectra will be found in different peroxidases. Extreme cases could be catalase compound I and the cytochrome c peroxidase ES complex (which, by the way, is not exactly like complex II of catalase).

Oxygen is not a very different ligand from hydrogen peroxide. When it binds to myoglobin, we observe a spectrum with three typical regions: Soret, $\alpha\beta$, and 1000 m$\mu$. (Undoubtedly low-spin Fe(III) $O_2^-$ could have a very similar spectrum, the band at 1000 m$\mu$ corresponding to the cytochrome c 695 m$\mu$ band

in many ways.) Several structural possibilities exist before
$O_2$ addition, depending upon the strength of the other Z-axis
ligands, the exact heme involved, and the steric constraints
imposed by the protein. For myoglobin the latter are not such
as to produce a spectrum which indicates that the heme is
grossly distorted. With RHP cytochrome much greater distortion
is seen, and perhaps this steric hindrance is also responsible
for the observation that $O_2$ cannot reach the Fe(II) except at
long range (6). Once again the $O_2$ (radical) could attack the
ring initially through the (distorted) methene bridge (compare
$H_2O_2$ attack of Brill and Williams (7)). This could also explain the kinetic data of Kamen (compare to ref. 2). Cytochrome $a_3$ may not be so very different, and in Chemical Reviews, 1956 (8), I pointed out that oxygen attack need not be
at the iron atom in this case. It is very interesting too
that the spectrum of cytochrome a shows a split Soret band
and that azide reactions with $a_3$ produce quite strong 650 m$\mu$
bands (9). The heme may be in strain. In such distorted environments electron transfer can be particularly fast, so that
diffusion of the anions $O_2^-$, $O_2^{--}$ from the cations generated
by redox reactions may be much slower than electron transfer.
[This will aid the dislocation of reactions. The subsequent
removal of all four electrons from the cytochrome oxidase, in
its new geometry, will generate steric strain, energy-rich intermediates or locally high $H^+$ concentrations, and, as we
know, oxidative phosphorylation occurs. It is possible to
link oxidation-reduction to mechanical strain and thence to
ATP formation--the reverse of muscle reactions.] Thus, the
exact property of the heme-iron is under a variety of con-
straints--electronic (Z-axis proximal ligands and distal
groups), charge environment (distal groups), steric (Z-axis
and distal groups producing heme distortion), and steric (restricted access to iron). Lastly, properties will depend upon
the organization of the protein with other proteins and this
clearly differentiates cytochromes from many other heme proteins.

It is undoubtedly true that the same problems of steric
constraint (imposed by the protein), of reducing groups near
to oxidizing cations, generate in a variety of other iron and
copper proteins (e.g., ferredoxins and hemerythrin and blue
proteins and hemocyanin) the same confusion of physical and
chemical properties. It is this conjunction of chemical
effects which causes biological systems to react rapidly and
specifically.

## References

1. Hochstrasser, R. M. This volume, p. 581.

2. Williams, R. J. P.  J. Theoret. Biol., $\underline{3}$, 209 (1962).

3. Williams, R. J. P.  This volume, p. 557

4. Horio, T., and M. Kamen.  Biochim. Biophys. Acta, $\underline{48}$, 266 (1961).

5. Yonetani, T., H. Schleyer, and B. Chance. This volume, p.

6. Kamen, M.  This volume, p. 524

7. Brill, A. S., and R. J. P. Williams.  Biochem. J., $\underline{78}$, 253 (1961).

8. Williams, R. J. P.  Chem. Rev., $\underline{56}$, 299 (1956).

9. Muijsers, A. O., B. F. van Gelder, and E. C. Slater. This volume, p.

# EXTENDED HÜCKEL CALCULATIONS ON IRON PORPHYRIN COMPLEXES[*]

Martin Gouterman    and Michael Zerner

Conant Chemical Laboratory, Harvard University
Cambridge, Massachusetts

This paper reports some recent theoretical results obtained on the electronic structure of iron porphyrins. We work with the LCAO-MO (linear combination of atomic orbitals-molecular orbital) model. That is, we describe the electrons as existing in molecular orbitals $\Phi_j$. The latter are expanded as a linear combination of atomic orbitals $\chi_p$

$$\Phi_j = \sum_p \chi_p c_{pj}$$

The problem is to determine the expansion coefficients $c_{pj}$ and the orbital energies $w_j$. Most theory on such aromatic systems has been further restricted to considering the pi orbitals only. For heme this would limit the $\chi_p$ to carbon and nitrogen $2p_z$ orbitals, where z is the axis perpendicular to the aromatic plane. The most sophisticated pi electron theory has recently been applied to porphyrins (1) and establishes that the top filled pi orbitals are $a_{2u}$ ($\pi$) and $a_{1u}$ ($\pi$), and the lowest empty pi orbitals are a degenerate pair $e_g$ ($\pi$). (We here use the symmetry labels of the $D_{4h}$ point group to designate orbitals.) The transitions

$$a_{2u}(\pi) \qquad e_g(\pi)$$
$$a_{1u}(\pi) \qquad e_g(\pi)$$

are intimately mixed and give rise to the visible $\alpha, \beta$ bands and the near UV Soret bands in porphyrins. There is general agreement between the predictions of pi electron theory and experimental data. Although some discrepancies remain, the general features are well understood.

*This work was supported by PHS Research Grant GM-10833.

However, for the problems of heme porphyrins, other electrons are more important than the pi. Recently, the "Extended Hückel" model has been developed for considering these other electrons. Although less sophisticated than the most advanced pi electron theory, it has given many interesting results (see, for example, ref. 2). We have applied this model to various transition metal porphyrin systems (3), and have recently completed an extensive study of iron porphyrin with various ligands (4).

Our model uses for the basis orbitals $X_p$ all the valence orbitals of the iron, porphyrin, and ligand: for H, 1s; for C, N, and O, 2s and 2p; for Fe, 3d, 4s, and 4p. The orbital coefficients $c_{pj}$ and energies $w_j$ are determined by standard methods from the overlap integrals $\int dv X_p X_q = S_{pq}$ and the effective Hamiltonian integrals $\int dv X_p H_{eff} X_q = H_{pq}$. The overlap integrals are fairly straightforward for calculations and can be done readily. The nature of the model is to supply a simple approximation for the effective Hamiltonian integrals. The values $H_{pp}$ are determined from atomic data and correspond to the atomic ionization potential for an electron in orbital p. When $p \neq q$ we set

$$H_{pq} = 1/2 \ K S_{pq} (H_{pp} + H_{qq}).$$

In this equation, $K$ is a pure parameter calibrated so that the energy gaps between the top filled and lowest empty pi orbitals fit the observed absorption and emission data. The value of the model, of course, is subject to debate. Our own view is that the model gives $c_{pj}$ sufficiently close to the "best possible," which are well defined theoretical quantities, and gives energies of sufficient predictive value to be worth pursuing.

We here report a few results that appear most germane to the present conference. In the following discussion FePorp represents heme porphyrin and Fe·H₂O·Porp or Fe·CO·Porp represents the water or carbon-monoxide complexes. Iron in these three electrically neutral complexes is considered ferrous, and it might seem that a calculation for ferric could proceed by removing one electron from the system. However, we were reluctant to carry out calculations on a system with a net charge, in view of the fact that the calibration parameters were based on neutral atoms. For ferric, we calculated systems such as Fe·OH·Porp or Fe·CN·Porp. The latter two cases resulted in an electron assignment $d^5$, which we shall call "ferric". The cases FePorp, Fe·H₂O·Porp, Fe·CO·Porp resulted in an electron assignment $d^6$, which we shall call "ferrous".

One interesting result is that the net charge on the iron atom calculated by a Mülliken (5) population analysis is nearly the same for ferrous and ferric in the cases cited, with ferric more positive by about 0.1 electron.

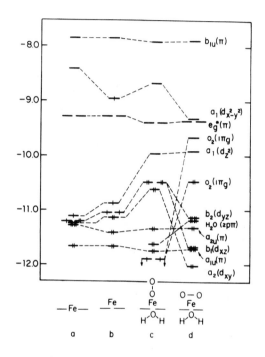

Figure 1.  (a)  FePorp planar
           (b)  FePorp, iron atom 0.492 Å out of plane;
           (c)  Co-axial Fe·O₂·H₂O·Porp, Fe out of plane toward O₂
           (d)  Coplanar Fe·O₂·H₂O·Porp, Fe out of plane toward O₂.

The obvious first calculation is FePorp with the iron in plane, even though such a species as a monomer may never be experimentally obtainable. The top filled and lowest empty orbital energies are shown in Fig. 1a. Five orbitals predominantly $d$ in character appear in this region. It is seen that $d_{xy}$, $d_{xz}$, $d_{yz}$, $d_{z2}$ are relatively close in energy while $d_{x2-y2}$ is at much higher energy. This is not surprising as

591

the latter orbital points directly at the four central nitrogen atoms. There are six electrons to be assigned among these
five d orbitals. Exchange interactions favor electron assignment with spin parallel; and hence the Pauli principle would
force the electrons into different spatial orbitals. However,
if the orbitals in question have different energy, a lower
energy state state may arise by the assignment of two electrons
with spins antiparallel to a low energy orbital. We have
calculated these competing effects based on the orbital energies
$w_j$ given by the model and exchange energies taken from atomic
values. For FePorp, with the iron atom in plane, we calculate
that $d_{x^2 - y^2}$ will be empty. Thus, there are two unpaired
electrons with total spin S = 1, intermediate between the high
spin case (S = 2) and the low spin case (S = 0). The weak
ligand, $H_2O$, in the fifth position causes the orbital $d_{z^2}$ to
rise in energy sufficiently to change the system to low spin,
but just barely. With any stronger ligand the system is
definitely calculated as low spin. There is no way that we
can put any ligand into our calculations to make for high spin,
either in ferrous or ferric, with iron in the plane.

Based on the X-ray results for myoglobin and the iron
porphyrin geometry found by Hoard and coworkers (6) we tried
calculations with iron 0.455 Å (ferric) and 0.492 Å (ferrous)
out of plane. The resulting energy levels for ferrous are
shown in Fig. 1b. The system is now calculated to be high spin,
and with $H_2O$ as fifth and/or sixth ligands it remains so. However, stronger ligands, such as CO or CN, ferrous and ferric,
respectively, bring about low spin with non-planar iron.

Another result of interest concerns the $O_2$ complex. A
variety of geometries have been suggested for this case;
unfortunately, or fortunately, our computer programs demand
two planes of symmetry. (This built-in constraint reduced
computer time by a factor of about six; as it is, each different
porphyrin system took about fifteen minutes on the IBM-7094).
We are therefore limited to two oxygen geometries: parallel or
perpendicular to the main porphyrin axis. This is a constraint
on our program, not on nature. In these calculations we included a water molecule, whose effect on the orbital coefficients and energies proved negligible.

The interesting results are given in Fig. 1c and 1d. With
$O_2$ parallel to the porphyrin axis, the orbital energy diagram
suggests immediate oxidation of ferrous iron to ferric. The
low-lying half filled orbitals should receive an electron from
the iron d orbitals. In the case with $O_2$ perpendicular to the
porphyrin axis, a stable orbital energy pattern results and a
low spin complex. Moreover, a very interesting thing has

happened. The orbital $d_{xz}$, where x is defined as parallel to the $O_2$ axis, is very strongly mixed with one of the $O_2$ pi orbitals, as shown in Fig. 2. (The other $O_2$ pi orbital parallel to the porphyrin plane interacts much less with the iron $d_{xy}$ orbital and is doubly occupied.)

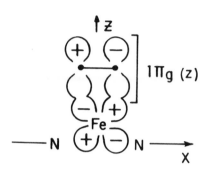

Figure 2. Iron $d_{xz}$, oxygen $\pi_g$ interaction.

The result is a strong delocalization of the electrons, nominally $d_{xz}$, into the $O_2$ part of the complex and onto the porphyrin moiety. In the final population analysis the iron atom in this case has a higher positive charge than in any other iron porphyrin complex we have calculated, either ferrous or ferric. These calculations, therefore, suggest that the interaction of heme and oxygen is strongly dependent on the geometry of the complex. This dependence may be very important for their special biological roles.

## References

1. Weiss, C., H. Kobayashi, and M. Gouterman. J. Mole. Spectry., 16, 415 (1965).

2. Hoffmann, R. J. Chem. Phys., 39, 1937 (1963).

3. Zerner, M., and M. Gouterman. Theoret. Chim. Acta., 4, 44 (1966).

4. Zerner, M., and M. Gouterman, in preparation; M. Zerner, PhD Thesis, Dept. of Chemistry, Harvard University, 1966.

5. Mulliken, R. S.  J. Chem. Phys., $\underline{23}$, 1833 (1955).

6. Hoard, J. L., M. J. Hamor, T. A. Hamor, and W. S. Caughey. J. Am. Chem. Soc., $\underline{87}$, 2312 (1965).

GENERAL DISCUSSION


Williams: Dr. Hochstrasser, in my text I have a possible assignment for bands in the 695 mμ region    . There are, in
fact, several alternative ways of getting bands polarized in
the z-direction. However, charge transfer from a group external to the coordination sphere of the metal to iron is possible,
and its polarization could be largely z, though it would also
be expected to have some xy character.

    I would like to make a general request of those who are
doing crystal spectra: I wonder if they could make measurements out to longer wave-lengths than are now conventional.
If you make measurements out beyond about 700 mμ, the chances
are that you will pick up extra possible absorption bands such
as d-d transitions. These might be very sensitive to small
changes in environment. Two crystal spectra which demonstrate
the type of spectra you can get in this region are shown in
Fig. 1. This figure illustrates that the polarizations of the
crystal spectra are parallel and perpendicular to the b-axis

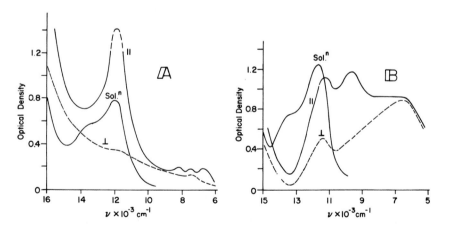

Figure 1. A comparison between single crystal spectra of
myoglobin hydroxide and its solution spectrum (A), and between single crystal spectra of myoglobin fluoride and its
solution spectrum (B).

which is very close to that of the heme plane. The exact correspondence between the spectra in (A) argue for an exactly
similar environment for the porphyrin in the solid and in solution. The big differences in the fluoride (B) could arise from
incomplete formation of the fluoride derivative when the peak
at 10,000 $cm^{-1}$ would be due to the aquo compound. Many more
experiments of this kind are desirable. (The compounds were
supplied by Dr. Chance.)

Gouterman: I also would like to stress the importance of establishing the assignments of infra-red bands by work such as
that presented by Dr. Williams and Dr. Hochstrasser. In our
calculations, we have a parameter $K$ that is calibrated from
the $\pi \rightarrow \pi^*$ transitions. Our predictions for charge transfer or
$\underline{d} \rightarrow \underline{d}$ transitions may have systematic errors. We need more information, particularly in the region 700-2,000 mμ, with which
to identify calculated transitions. Then we will know exactly
where our model stands. I want to stress how important this
is; unfortunately, when we look through the literature, the
biochemical work often does not go beyond 650 or 700 mμ.

Hanania: Dr. Cameron and I have published detailed absorption
spectra for sperm whale ferrimyoglobin derivatives (acid and
conjugate base, as well as the fluoride and cyanide complexes)
covering the wavelength range 200-2,000 mμ (1).

Cameron: May I also add that I have made a similar study of
the spectrum of human oxyhemoglobin, and that the 1,500 mμ
band which appears in ferrimyoglobin is present in this compound as well.

Maricic: Dr. Gouterman, I understand from your discussion that
you cannot yet treat quantitatively the asymmetric end-on
orientation of oxygen to heme because of the limitations of
your computer. Now, as Dr. Traylor suggested yesterday, our
data would also be consistent with such a configuration if
there were a rapid "flip-flop" exchange mechanism. We must
still do the temperature study, but I would like your opinion
on how probable such a mechanism is.

Williams: Is this included in your model, Dr. Gouterman? I
do not see how it could be.

Gouterman: Indeed we could not calculate the rate or effect
of such a flip-flop motion. But such a motion strikes me as
very unlikely.

Chance: The reaction you describe forms a stable bond; however, in the case of cytochrome oxidase, there is no evidence for the existence of a short-lived oxygen intermediate and perhaps an end-on reaction, in which electron transfer occurs on contact with no stable intermediate, occurs.

Williams: I have been drawing some models in my notebook and was thinking that, as you alter the angles and positions of the groups--Fe, $O_2$, other ligands, heme--around one another, you are, in fact, also altering the possible electron transfer reactions. I am sure that this is one of the things that you must consider, but I do not believe that the theoretician is yet in a position to say anything in detail about a problem of that sort.

George: I echo Dr. Williams' sentiments with respect to the limited value of just writing electron transport assignments in which, for example, the iron can be formally assigned different oxidation states, e.g., in the oxygen complex, $Fe(II)O_2$, $Fe(III)O_2^-$, $Fe(IV)O_2^{--}$, etc. However, if theoretical calculations can be made, the electron densities on particular atoms are, of course, of great interest for correlation with the known chemical reactivity. But in the case of the compounds formed with peroxides and other strong oxidizing agents, there is a very crucial question that must be answered first--and by experiment--namely, how many oxidation equivalents are associated with a particular compound in relation to a parent compound whose oxidation status is well authenticated.

Of all the compounds formed when peroxides and other strong oxidizing agents react with ferrihemoproteins, most is known about the red compound formed by ferrimyoglobin. From the point of view of the oxidation-reduction behavior of the iron-porphyrin prosthetic group, this compound is one, and not two, oxidation equivalents above the ferric oxidation state. This is not a matter of writing alternative oxidation state structures and electron assignments on paper, but an essential chemical fact about the structure that immediately puts certain limits on the kind of detailed molecular structure that is acceptable.

In addition to this kind of chemical observation, a knowledge of the participation of hydrogen ion in an oxidation-reduction reaction, in which the parent compound with the well authenticated oxidation status is involved, is not only valuable but essential, because it sets further limits to the kind of molecular structure that is acceptable.

On the basis of such considerations, Irvine and I have proposed the ferryl ion structure, or one of its isomers, for the red compound formed by ferrimyoglobin (2).

## References

1. Hanania, G., B. F. Cameron, and A. Yeghiayan. Biochem. J., 98, 185 (1966).

2. George, P., and D. H. Irvine. Biochem. J., 52, 511 (1952).

# A POSTSCRIPT:  THE FORGOTTEN CELL

## D. L. Drabkin

Department of Biochemistry, Division of Graduate Medicine
School of Medicine, University of Pennsylvania
Philadelphia, Pennsylvania

I was delighted to be an invited guest at this splendid colloquium, and happy to see again many who were present at an earlier international symposium at Canberra, convened by Professor Lemberg (1), who deserves richly to be honored on this occasion.

Now that the dizzying spin and orbital (as well as oral) dislocation have settled down to a more quiescent steady state, perhaps some sobering second thoughts may be in order.  I think it is remarkable that such an impressive armamentarium of modern weaponry--most revealing X-ray crystallography, EMR or ESR, IR, NMR, ORD, plus the penetrating Laser, plus a few more sophisticated probes, to say nothing of imaginative potentiality--has been deployed upon the field in both a frontal, flank and guerrilla-tactic attack upon my old friends, hemoglobin, myoglobin and cytochrome $\underline{c}$.  Am I wrong in the impression that each armor-bearer was at least as much concerned with logistics, propaganda for his own chosen weapon in comparison to the others, as with its role in the overall strategy?  These molecules have yielded ground in this merciless assault, but several important and ancient problems remain to be solved. Is it not fair to say that, despite the helpful protective crevice or hydrophobic pocket, we still do not know why the iron of hemoglobin does not rust in the presence of water and oxygen?  On the other hand, this I do know.  Oxyferrohemoglobin in solution is not readily changed to ferrihemoglobin, nor are suspensions of crystalline oxyferrohemoglobin.  But, if you allow air to enter a vessel containing lyophilized ferrohemoglobin, thinly spread and dried on its sides, the ferrohemoglobin is "explosively" and quantitatively oxidized to ferrihemoglobin (2).  As a biologist, I see no compelling reason to believe that the study of hemin proteins in the crystalline state (3) need have less validity than that of the isolated hemin proteins in solution. Each may be valid or invalid, with regard to their functional behavior in the structurally oriented or disoriented cellular state (see below).

I am convinced that whatever the orientation or structure of the difficult oxygen molecule may be with regard to the un-ruffled or ruffled plane of porphyrin and to the tetragonally (or pyramidally) positioned iron atom, hemoglobin within the red cell has functioned effectively for a number of years, and, barring the vitiation of our external and internal environments through human perversity or imbecility, will continue to do so. Of course, as scientists, we want to understand this very knotty problem of the oxygenation-deoxygenation of hemoglobin, but the red cell and its hemoglobin do know how to get this job done. If the red cell could only speak, and have presented its case at this conference! Mitochondria and microsomes did sneak in an appearance, but cells--the functional units of life--were not included in the agenda of this symposium.

Out of nostalgia, if nothing else, may I put in a plea for the absent cells? It is indeed pertinent to ask: "How well or how believably can we put the cellular fragments (mitochondria, microsomes, ribosomes and polyribosomes) together again, and reconstruct a valid picture of cells in tissues, and their per-formance in the light of the functional capacities of the whole body?" I addressed myself to this question recently (4).

Information derived from cells has relevance to a number of the problems which have occupied the concern of participants at these meetings:

(a) Molecular population of hemin proteins in cells (5,6). Some time before the age of molecular biology was formally ushered in, I pointed out that hemoglobin is present in the red cell at virtually a saturating concentration level of ~34 gm/100 ml of cells, equivalent to ~3 x $10^8$ molecules per cell (5). Interestingly enough, in the rat liver cell the molecular popu-lation of cytochrome $\underline{c}$ is rather similar, ~4 x $10^7$ molecules per cell (6). Of course, it was recognized that these relation-ships are inherent in expressing concentrations in molar terms (5). By appropriate techniques, using very thin cuvettes, we demonstrated that the absorption spectrum curves of hemoglobin and its derivatives within the red cells were quantitatively indistinguishable from those obtained in solution (7). I later found (unpublished observations) that most of the effect of scattering by the suspended cells was related to the difference in refractive index between the red cells and their suspension medium. Thus, in spectral regions (as the red) the low specific absorption owing to hemoglobin could be effectively determined by suspending the cells in ~30 percent plasma albumin solution.

(b) <u>Solubility and crystallizability of hemoglobins</u>.
Despite their close structural similarity, the oxyferrohemo-
globins of different species appear to have quite markedly
different solubility characteristics. Lower solubility in
general appears to go with ease of crystallization. The hemoglobins of dog and horse crystallize "spontaneously" from
washed red cells, hemolyzed by the addition of 9 volumes of
water, whereas the very soluble human oxyhemoglobin can be
effectively crystallized only from very concentrated solutions
(2,8,9) which have been referred to as the "Drabkin hemolystate"
(10). By my method of crystallization, now most frequently and
extensively used, human hemoglobin crystallizes in the unusual
(for hemoglobins) tetragonal system of symmetry. Such crystals
have been called "Drabkin crystals", I must say rather invi-
diously in the sense that there was something wrong with them,
perhaps they were pseudo-tetragonal (H. M. Jope and J. R. P.
O'Brien (cf. 11)). However, the "Drabkin crystals" were later
confirmed by Perutz and colleagues to be truly tetragonal (12).
This is an illustration that in this case the goodness of the
methodology of crystallization of the hemin proteins was rather
more important than the tools applied to the characterization
of the crystalline product. My discovery of the tetragonal
configuration was made by the lowly petrographic microscope
and brush patterns. The tetragonal human blood pigment is more
complicated than horse methemoglobin. This system of crystallization has internal symmetry, with 4 molecules per unit cell
(not 2), and with an asymmetric molecular weight unit of 34,000
(12). I believe that human hemoglobin still remains over-compli-
cated to study by X-ray crystallography.

It is of relevant interest that human oxyhemoglobin crystals, despite cries of "impossible", can be prepared by solution in water to attain homogeneous preparations, optically
clear, and at the extraordinary concentration of up to 38.2
mM (per 1 Fe atom), or 63.8 gm/100 ml. Such "solutions"
quickly gel, and can be regarded as in a metastable state (2).
Still more interesting is the case of rat oxyhemoglobin. This
is relatively insoluble even in moderately dilute solutions,
whereas deoxygenated rat hemoglobin is quite soluble--a situation which is the exact opposite of that associated with the
abnormal HbS. Rat oxyhemoglobin crystallizes readily within
the red cells, and is apparently present in these cells in a
metastable state of incipient crystallization (5,13). The
crystalline habit of rat hemoglobin is such that it fails to
deform the cell, in contrast with the situation in sickle
cells.

(c) <u>Molecular heterogeneity of hemoglobin</u> (10,14). What is the source of pure, isolated hemoglobin, and how "pure" is pure? I believe we can say with some assurance that the oxy-hemoglobin, isolated from its natural habitat and crystallized appears to contain less than 0.5 percent of methemoglobin (cf. 2,8,9) and retains fully its main functional characteristic of oxygenation-deoxygenation. On the other hand, we are on less safe ground if we assert that the crystallized hemoglobin is completely identical with that present in the red cell. In the first place it is no longer in its original environment. Actually, it is normally a mixture (in the case of man) of hemoglobins A and $A_2$. It was obtained from a mixed age population of red blood cells. In the body, most of the methemoglobin may be confined to the old or obsolescent red cells, since I have some experimental evidence that the ferrihemoglobin reductase system is relatively inactive in the cell fraction containing the old cells. (Such enzymic degeneracy may be among the stigmata of cellular aging.) Furthermore, in the red cells normally there may be a little carbonyl hemoglobin-- aside from that owing to smoking or air pollution, but from endogenous (metabolic) CO production (cf. 10,15).

The possible presence <u>in vivo</u> of monomeric, dimeric and tetrameric forms of hemoglobin should be considered. The creation of a crystalline hybrid of rat and dog hemoglobin at physiological pH suggests that hemoglobin is in a dynamic state (13). Two species, such as HbA and HbS present together in each red cell, could interchange their polypeptide chains. Such interchange could apply also to the normal species HbA and $AbA_2$. In this connection it is relevant to recall a presumably generally overlooked early paper by Ferry and Green (16) in which they reported an essentially hyperbolic curve for the oxygen dissociation of oxyferrohemoglobin at pH 8-9, i.e., a behavior essentially similar to that of monomeric myoglobin. As a shot in the dark, it would be interesting to know whether, with hemoglobin at mildly alkaline pH, Joan Keilin might succeed in demonstrating twin hemochromogen formation.

(d) <u>"Fixity" in the cellular structure and cellular turn-over</u>. Our problems become vastly more complicated for hemo-proteins, like cytochrome <u>c</u> and its oxidase, which are "fixed" in the cellular structure. Not only does such structural orientation have importance in the dynamics of function, but it is further complicated by the finite life-spans of the cells themselves. Some years ago I proposed that, not only the erythrocytes, but also tissue cells (liver, etc.) have a cellular turnover, i.e., cellular death is a concomitant of cellular life (17). One of the major differences between living systems and their isolated counterparts is that the latter are essentially closed systems. In the living flow state, synthesis and degradation go hand in hand (4).

F. J. W. Roughton regarded the blood pigment as a lovely but demanding mistress. I subscribed to this view, but found her to be, besides a colorful, mysteriously dimpled lady (apologies to Perutz and George), most elusive in disclosing her innermost secrets, and thereby worthy of the chase (10). I therefore found somewhat shocking what appeared to be adolescent boasting by the pursuers of the hard-to-catch-and-hold lady, cytochrome oxidase (or is she "no lady"?), who described her as "slippery," messy and impure. Taste and tastes do change. In words perhaps more fitting for the present state of the oxidase, a review (describing Alban Berg's early string quartet) wrote: "a kind of superb sticky chromatic morass but you have to enjoy wallowing in it; if you try to swim, you're finished."

May I close upon the same note which concluded my paper on "the oxygenation and oxidation functions, " at the Barcroft Memorial Conference (10). I referred to the loss of biological activity of isolated preparations of cytochrome $c$, and wondered whether we may miss something in regard to the activity of the living cellular structure by undue insistence on working with highly pure systems. Barcroft himself, referring to the splendid classical achievements by David Keilin, before cytochrome $c$ was isolated, or its structure known, had this to say: "I will at once concede to the organic chemist of the purist school that such a material is less satisfactory than if it had been isolated, but I claim for those who are prepared to study "life as a whole" that man places an undue limitation on his intellect if he is not prepared to look at living things as they are, but will merely study artifacts about which he can obtain more precise information." I am confident that this wise and witty Irishman was not compromising his experimental morals by a casual and tawdry acceptance of cytochrome $c$ in her yet impure state, but was thinking of information as to function at the higher and more complex level of the living cellular structure, which biologists should not forget is their eventual goal.

## References

1. Haematin Enzymes. (J. E. Falk, R. Lemberg, and R. K. Morton, eds.), Pergamon Press, Inc., London, 1961.

2. Drabkin, D. L. J. Biol. Chem., 164 703 (1946).

3. Chance, B., Ravilly, A., and Rumen, N. J. Mol. Biol., 17 525 (1966).

4. Drabkin, D. L At Ciba Discussion Evening. London. Sept 15, 1964, in preparation.

5. Drabkin, D. L. Science, 101, 445 (1945).

6. Drabkin, D. L. Federation Proc., 7, 483 (1948).

7. Drabkin, D. L. and R. B. Singer. J. Biol. Chem., 129, 739 (1939).

8. Drabkin, D. L. Arch. Biochem., 21, 224 (1949).

9. Drabkin, D. L. J. Biol. Chem., 185, 231 (1950).

10. Drabkin, D. L. Federation Proc., 16, 740 (1957).

11. Roughton, F. J. W. and J. C. Kendrew. Haemoglobin (Sir Joseph Barcroft Memorial Conference), Butterworths Scientific Publications, London, 1949, p. 269.

12. Perutz, M. F., A. M. Liquori and F. Eirich. Nature, 167, 929 (1951).

13. Drabkin, D. L. and C. D. Wise. J. Biol. Chem., 237, PC 263 (1962).

14. Drabkin, D. L. Symposium of Standardization, Documentation and Normal Values in Haematology, Xth Congress, International Society of Haemotology, Stockholm, S. Karger, New York and Basel, 1965, p. 33.

15. Wise, C. D. and D. L. Drabkin. Federation Proc., 23, 223 (1964); 24, 222 (1965).

16. Ferry, R. M. and A. A. Green. J. Biol. Chem., 81, 175 (1929).

17. Drabkin, D. L. In Porphyrin Biosynthesis and Metabolism (Ciba Foundation Symposium) (G. E. W. Wolstenholme and E. C. P. Millar, eds.), J. and A. Churchill, Ltd., London, 1955, p. 96.

# INDEX

*The following abbreviations have been used in preparing this Index:

CCP = cytochrome c peroxidase
CCP-ES = Complex ES of CCP
ESR = electron spin (paramagnetic)
  resonance
Hb = hemoglobin
HRP = horseradish peroxidase

Mb = myoglobin
metHb = met (ferri) hemoglobin
metMb = met (ferri) myoglobin
MOR = magneto optical rotation
NMR = nuclear magnetic resonance
ORD = optical rotatory dispersion

# INDEX